CW00350117

The Encyclopedia of Military Jets

GENERAL EDITOR: THOMAS NEWDICK

This edition first published in 2007 for Grange Books
An imprint of Grange Books Ltd
The Grange
Kingsnorth Industrial Estate
Hoo, nr Rochester
Kent ME3 9ND
www.grangebooks.co.uk

ISBN 978-1-84013-648-7

Produced by
Amber Books Ltd
Bradley's Close
74–77 White Lion Street
London N1 9PF
www.amberbooks.co.uk

Project Editor: Sarah Uttridge
Design: Hawes Design
Picture Credits: All © Aerospace Publishing Ltd except the following:
pages 5, 7, 134, 135: US Department of Defense; p6: Eurofighter; pages 235bl, 241t, 245bl: Lockheed Martin; pages 239bl, 243tl & tr, 273b, 407t: USAF; pages 275tr, 283t: Boeing; p282t and b: US Navy.

Printed in China

Contents

Above: A US Navy F-14B Tomcat launches off the Nimitz-class aircraft carrier **Harry S. Truman** *during a training exercise.*

Above:* *Operating out of the Spanish Air Force Base in Moron, a single seat Eurofighter IPA 4 flies over southern Spain.

Introduction

When, on 27 August 1939, Flugkapitän Erich Warsitz took off from Marienehe, near Rostock, in the diminutive Heinkel He 178 experimental aircraft, the era of the jet aircraft had arrived. The He 178 – the world's first aircraft to fly solely on turbojet power – appeared at an opportune time: its maiden flight occurred just a week before the outbreak of World War II, and warplane development had by now been refined to a point where stressed-metal construction, retractable undercarriage and cannon armament were fast becoming the norm. In addition, the swept wing was just around the corner and, although the He 178 was never intended to see operational service, this vitally important feature appeared on the Messerschmitt Me 262, the first jet fighter to enter combat and the most advanced aircraft of World War II.

A B-2 Spirit drops 32 inert Joint Direct Attack Munitions at the Hill Air Force Base Testing and Training Range in Utah.

The post-war years

In the immediate post-war years, and driven by the deteriorating political relations between the former Allied powers on either side of the Iron Curtain, aeronautical development drew heavily upon advanced wartime German ideas to produce a first generation of truly operational jet-powered fighters and bombers. The search for speed remained a priority for both defensive and offensive applications, especially in light of the Korean War experience (1950–1953). Over the disputed Korean peninsula, the swept-wing North American F-86 Sabre and Mikoyan-Gurevich MiG-15 demonstrated their prowess over earlier straight-wing jets, which in turn began to be relegated to fighter-bomber duties. The swept wing was clearly here to stay, and the jet entered the transonic era. Before long, the first jet-powered military transports – initially relatively straightforward adaptations of existing civil jetliners – were entering service, although it would not be until the Vietnam War that the first purpose-designed military jet-lifters became available.

While the aftermath of the Korean War had seen a further push towards high-speed jet fighters and bombers – culminating in the 'Century Series' (North American F-100 Super Sabre to F-106 Delta Dart) of high-performance fighters in the US, and the best-selling Mikoyan-Gurevich MiG-21 in the Soviet Union – the lessons of the Vietnam War would have very different implications. By this stage, counter-air fighters were typically 'heavyweights': routinely armed with powerful search and tracking radars, computerised fire control systems and sophisticated air-to-air missile armament – in some cases, gun armament was deleted altogether as all efforts were put into highly automated beyond visual range engagements. Vietnam, together with successive wars in the Middle East, showed that, in addition to sophisticated multi-role fighters, there was still a need for lighter, more agile warplanes, capable of operations from poorly prepared airstrips and with limited support and maintenance. At the same time, NATO was shifting from a mindset of nuclear strike towards one of 'Flexible Response', with tactical warplanes primarily tasked to carry conventional weapons.

By the mid-1970s, the lessons of the previous decade were being absorbed during the development of the next generation of more flexible warplanes. First expressed immediately after the end of World War II, the need for the strategic jet bomber remained – for the major superpowers at least – but, with the development of ever more capable air defence radars and surface-to-air missiles, free-fall offensive armament had now given way to stand-off cruise missiles with autonomous guidance. From now on, jet-powered fighters and airlifters would also be very different. Long-reaching air-to-air and air-to-surface missile armament, extreme levels of manoeuvrability and powerful radar-based fire control systems are all features of the modern fighter that were introduced in the 1970s, when a new level of fighter capability was represented by the arrival of the General Dynamics F-16 Fighting Falcon and the McDonnell Douglas F-15 Eagle. The mid-1970s also saw the first steps in the development of the McDonnell Douglas C-17 Globemaster III, the first heavy jetlifter with a true rough-field performance and global reach.

More recently, the concerns of the post-Cold War planner have brought low observables and 'netcentric' operations to the forefront in military jet operations. The former, pioneered in the closing years of the superpower stand-off, is better known as 'stealth' and this – albeit at a great cost – has provided an elite group of jet warplanes that are capable of avoiding radar detection to penetrate enemy defences; this ability was most famously put to the test by the formerly highly classified Lockheed F-117 Nighthawk during the 1991 Gulf War. While true 'stealth' jets remain the preserve of the US, low observable characteristics are now a fixture of the latest wave of fighter development: the so-called 'fifth generation'.

21st century combat aircraft

'Netcentric' operations, meanwhile, involve a new level of integration between the complex and various sensors that now routinely equip 21st century combat aircraft. At the same time, the pilot is provided with a single battlespace picture, through a process known as 'sensor fusion', and their aircraft is able to 'talk' with other platforms, exchanging vital information between them, be they other aircraft, warships or land systems. As we move into the 21st century, it is likely to be these avionics-based facets of military jet development that take centre stage. However, the age of 'netcentric' operations is also the age of the UAV (unmanned aerial vehicle), and commentators have long been predicting that the rise of the latter will eventually signal the end for manned combat aircraft. While this may eventually prove the case for certain strike and reconnaissance aircraft, the inherent flexibility of the manned warplane – not to mention the manned transport – means that there will remain a place for piloted military jets in the 21st century.

Aeritalia G.91

NATO's fighter

Winner of NATO's quest for a universal fighter for Europe's air forces, Fiat's (later Aeritalia's) G.91 did not reach unilateral European service, but was operated in significant numbers by Italy, West Germany and Portugal, seeing combat with the latter.

The last of Italy's G.91s were retired in August 1995, ending nearly four decades of service with the AMI. The aircraft's successor is the AMX, which operates primarily in the ground-attack role.

The Fiat G.91, affectionately known as the 'Gina', fulfilled a vital role at the height of the Cold War, and it built up an enviable combat record in Africa while in Portuguese service.

The Fiat G.91 originated in a NATO multinational requirement for a light tactical fighter and ground-attack aircraft to replace a disparate fleet of aircraft then in use with the French, West German, Italian, Greek, Turkish and Austrian air forces.

Of eight designs submitted in response to a December 1953 specification, it was the G.91 proposal that was chosen as the most promising, and three prototypes were ordered for evaluation. Any chances of a huge production run and NATO-wide adoption ended with Britain's commitment to the Hawker Hunter, and the fact that France would only have been willing to abide by the results of the competition had a French design been selected.

Although France proceeded with the Etendard, Italy had already ordered a pre-production batch of 27 G.91s for evaluation and service with the Aeronautica Militare Italiana (AMI).

The first G.91 prototype made its maiden flight on 9 August 1956 and was followed by three further prototypes. The pre-production G.91s were powered by Orpheus 801 engines and were armed with four 0.5-in (12.7-mm) machine-guns, although the armament bays on the sides of the nose were intended to allow for the optional fitting of two 20- or 30-mm cannon. After evaluation and tactical trials, most were converted to G.91PAN standards for service with the Frecce Tricolori aerobatic team.

Into service

The pre-production aircraft were followed by the production standard G.91R, which featured a new nose containing three cameras. The Italian air force G.91R/1 had the same armament as the basic G.91, as did the G.91R/1A, though the latter aircraft did introduce the same Doppler and navigation equipment as the G.91R/3.

Initial plans called for the production of 22 G.91R/1s and 25 G.91R/1As for Italy, 48 G.91R/2s for France (cancelled soon after the order was placed), 50 G.91R/3s for West Germany, 50 G.91R/4s to be divided between Greece and Turkey, and 14 G.91Rs for Austria. In the event, Austrian interest was only tentative, and the G.91R/4s were delivered to West Germany after rejection by Greece.

West Germany was one of the original G.91 customers, and immediately obtained twice as many aircraft as it had originally required when it took over the 50 G.91R/4s built for Greece and Turkey. West German G.91R/3s were delivered from the start with two 30-mm cannon, and also featured a four-pylon wing,

With the updating of existing machines and the influx of surplus aircraft from Germany, Portugal kept its G.91R fleet operational until 1993.

G.91Y

13° Gruppo of 32° Stormo replaced its G.91Rs with the far superior twin-engined G.91Y, transferred from 8° Stormo, from August 1973. All three of 13° Gruppo's *squadriglie* were re-equipped by September 1974 and were declared combat-ready in 1975.

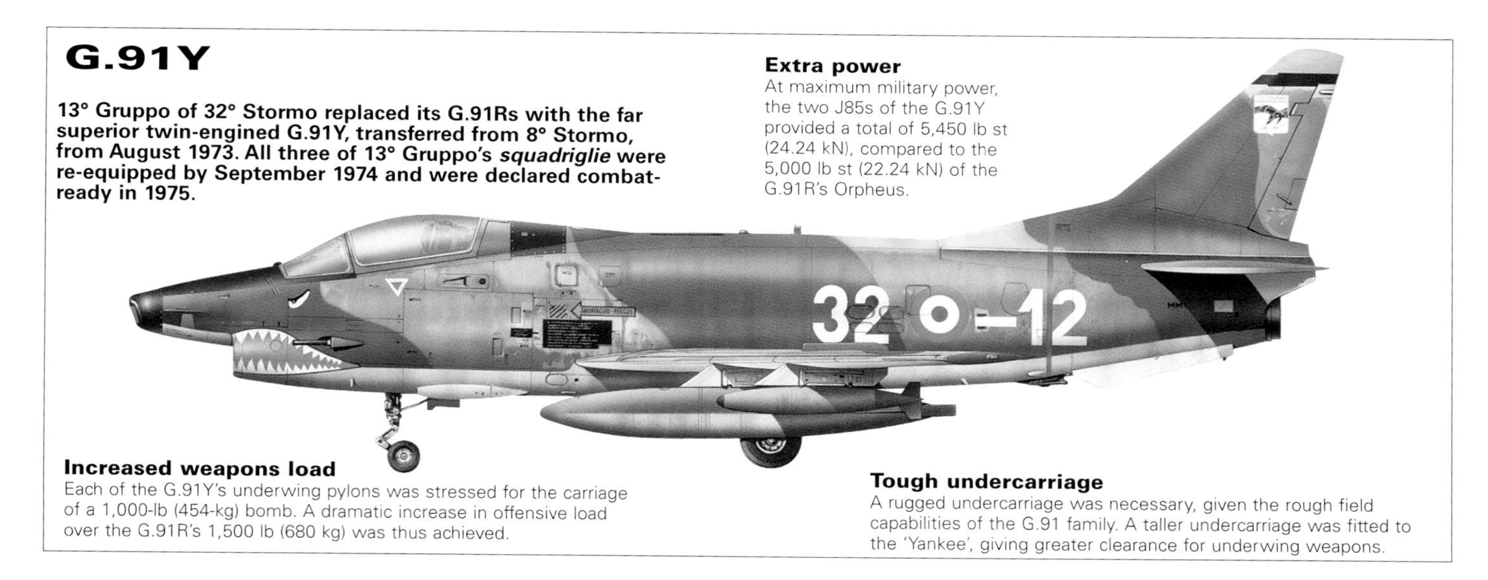

Extra power
At maximum military power, the two J85s of the G.91Y provided a total of 5,450 lb st (24.24 kN), compared to the 5,000 lb st (22.24 kN) of the G.91R's Orpheus.

Increased weapons load
Each of the G.91Y's underwing pylons was stressed for the carriage of a 1,000-lb (454-kg) bomb. A dramatic increase in offensive load over the G.91R's 1,500 lb (680 kg) was thus achieved.

Tough undercarriage
A rugged undercarriage was necessary, given the rough field capabilities of the G.91 family. A taller undercarriage was fitted to the 'Yankee', giving greater clearance for underwing weapons.

while the G.91R/4 was a hybrid, with the fuselage of the G.91R/1A mated to the wing of the G.91R/3. Italy also received 50 G.91R/1Bs with some reinforced structure, and with modified undercarriage. At one time, these aircraft were known as G.91R/6s.

West Germany used the G.91R/4s for training until 1966, when 40 of the aircraft were passed on to Portugal, but liked the type so much that it contracted to build a further 295 G.91R/3s under licence, and also acquired 44 Fiat-built G.91T/3 two-seat trainers. Over the years, West Germany passed on a total of 70 G.91R/3s and 26 G.91T/3s to Portugal.

Portuguese G.91Rs were used in Portuguese Guinea, Angola and Mozambique. The aircraft saw active service against insurgents and guerrillas, and some were lost to hostile fire. In 1989 the Portuguese G.91Rs underwent an upgrade, with new navaids, ejection seats, passive ECM and AIM-9 Sidewinder capability. The aircraft were finally retired in June 1993.

Italy had retired the last of its single-engined, single-seat G.91Rs in April 1992, though the single-engined G.91 remained in use in its two-seat guise.

G.91Ts and 'Yankees'

The G.91T/1 had been developed as an operational conversion and weapons trainer, and the first prototype made its maiden flight on 31 May 1960. Two prototypes were followed by 100 production two-seaters for the AMI. Originally due to retire during the mid-1980s, the G.91Ts were finally replaced by AMXs and MB.339s in 1994–95.

The Portuguese and Italian G.91Rs were outlived by the twin-engined G.91Y. Some 67 of these aircraft were eventually built, giving the AMI a G.91 with enhanced range, payload and survivability. Powered by two General Electric J85 engines, the G.91Y prototype first flew on 27 December 1966, and went on to equip the 101° Gruppo of the 8° Stormo, and the 13° Gruppo of the 32° Stormo. Post-Cold War CFE treaty limits on aircraft numbers saw the final G.91Y unit, 101° Gruppo, disband on 26 November 1994.

German service

The G.91 demonstration at Brétigny in 1957 and NATO's subsequent decision to select the G.91 as its Lightweight Fighter (LWF) convinced the Luftwaffe to purchase the Fiat aircraft for itself. In 1959, an agreement was signed that witnessed both the purchase of 50 G.91R/3 reconnaissance aircraft and the fighter's manufacturing licence.

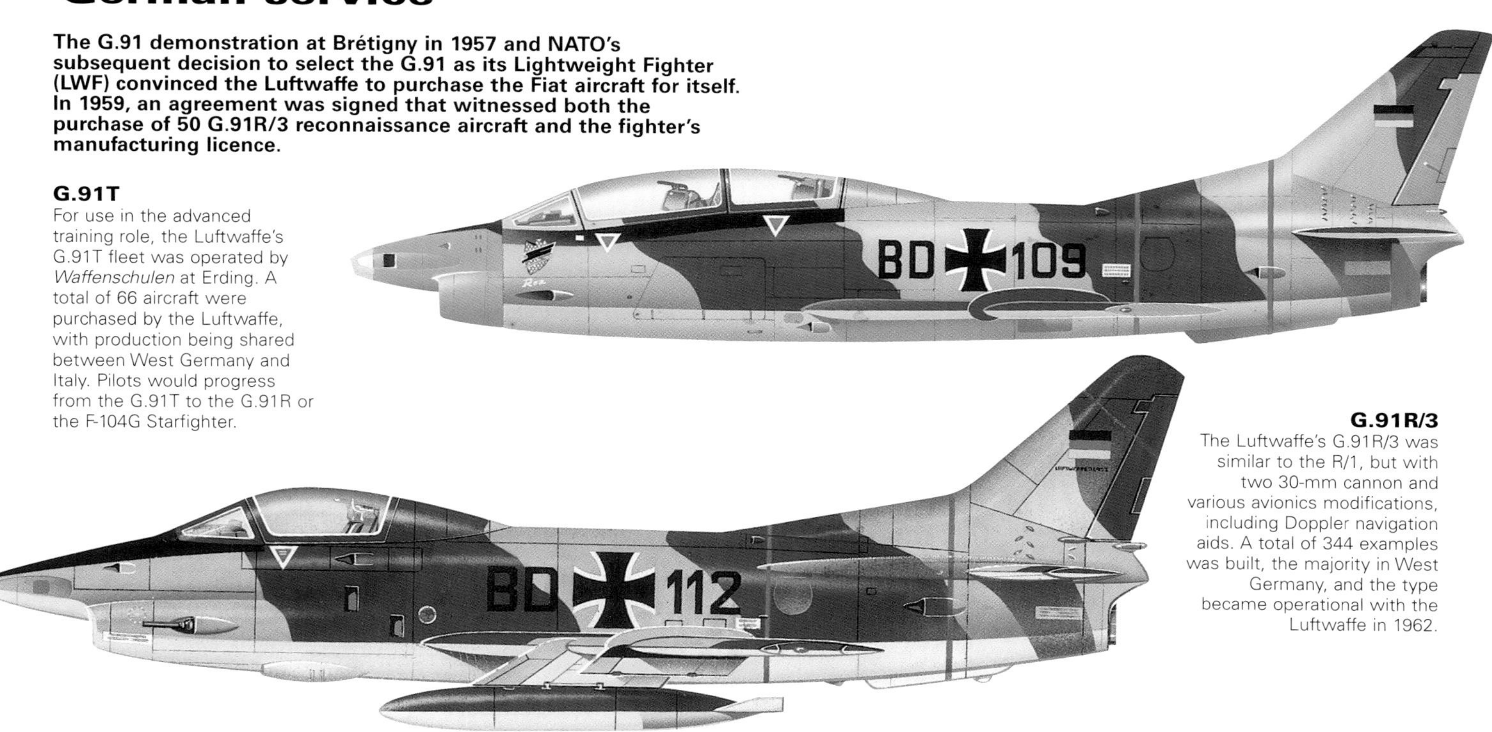

G.91T
For use in the advanced training role, the Luftwaffe's G.91T fleet was operated by *Waffenschulen* at Erding. A total of 66 aircraft were purchased by the Luftwaffe, with production being shared between West Germany and Italy. Pilots would progress from the G.91T to the G.91R or the F-104G Starfighter.

G.91R/3
The Luftwaffe's G.91R/3 was similar to the R/1, but with two 30-mm cannon and various avionics modifications, including Doppler navigation aids. A total of 344 examples was built, the majority in West Germany, and the type became operational with the Luftwaffe in 1962.

Aermacchi MB-326/-339

Trainers with teeth

Although not as glamorous as the front-line fast jets to which their pilots graduate, Aermacchi's MB-326 and MB-339 have proved to be highly capable in both the training and attack roles.

A docile instructional machine which can be quickly converted into a potent counter-insurgency (COIN) weapon, the MB-326 was one of the first of a still small number of two-seat trainers to spawn a single-seat derivative optimised for attack. The first of two prototype MB-326s flew at Milan on 10 December 1957 and, almost three years later (on 5 October 1960), the first order for 15 examples was placed by the Aeronautica Militare Italiana (AMI) for its military basic flying school at Lecce. Entering service in 1962, the first course to utilise the MB-326 commenced on 22 March that year. The aircraft now benefited from the increased thrust made available by the installation of the Rolls-Royce Viper Mk 22 turbojet.

Limited attrition

The MB-326 proved to be extremely popular with the AMI, returning an accident rate of only 0.8 per 10,000 hours. This meant that the purchase of attrition replacements was on a smaller scale than previously planned. Later deliveries to the AMI included 10 armed MB-326Es for weapons training, featuring a wing strengthened for the mounting of pylons.

The other principal operator of the unarmed trainer was Australia,

Above: Good handling characteristics are essential if a trainer is to prove successful, and the export success of the MB-326 is ample testimony to its qualities. Retired in 2005 pending full introduction of the BAE Systems Hawk, SAAF Impalas were still giving sterling service in the training role 40 years after entering service.

Above: The close resemblance between the training variant and its single-seat attack derivative is evident in this view of Aermacchi's demonstrator and an AMI two-seat trainer. For training purposes, AMI MB-326s adopted a vivid overall orange colour scheme.

Below: Argentina acquired a mixed fleet of Aermacchi MB-326GBs and EMBRAER-built EMB-326GB Xavantes. This example, an EMB-326GB, is seen in the colours of the Argentine Naval Aviation Command, which uses the type for and training.

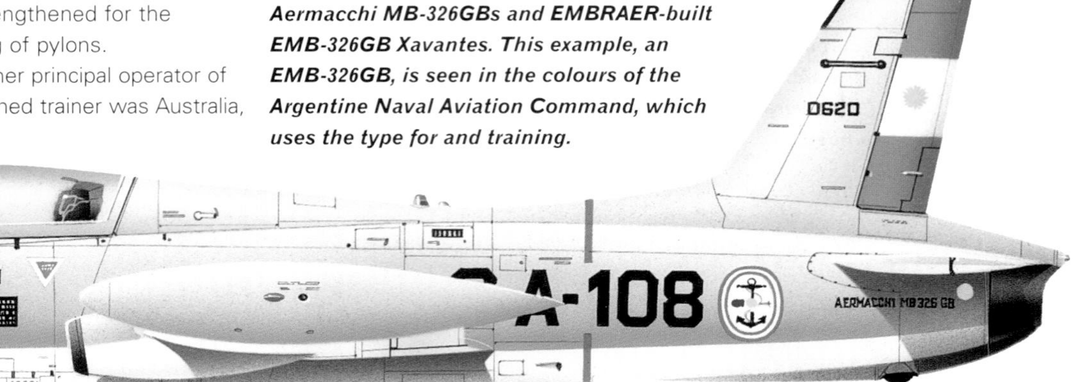

The MB-326 boasts a surprising payload for its size, as evidenced by this MB-326K close-support variant. The aircraft's useful attack capability saw the single-seat version win orders from the air forces of Dubai (MB-326KD), Ghana (KG), Zaire (KB) and Tunisia (KT).

SAAF's Impala Mk 2s were heavily utilised in the country's 'bush wars'. During one attack mission against SWAPO guerrillas, an Impala was hit by an SA-9 'Gaskin' SAM, but its warhead failed to explode and the aircraft returned to base.

which received 97 MB-326Hs for service with its air force and navy. Most of these were fitted with indigenous equipment which resulted in the aircraft being locally produced by the Commonwealth Aircraft Corporation as the CA-30. The 10 navy aircraft were transferred back to the RAAF in 1983, and the final examples were retired by No. 79 Squadron at Pearce, New South Wales, in March 2001.

Ground-attack models

The success of the MB-326 in the training role gave Aermacchi the incentive for the development of a specialised ground-attack variant. Designated the MB-326G, the aircraft featured a strengthened airframe and increased wingspan, enabling it to carry up to 4,325 lb (1962 kg) of stores.

Brazil's requirement was sufficient enough to justify local production by EMBRAER. Known as the EMB-326GB, or AT-26 Xavante in Brazilian service, the aircraft plays an important COIN role in combat squadrons, and is also used as an armed pilot trainer. A total of 166 examples was delivered from early 1972. Such was the demand for the MB-326 that EMBRAER later produced examples for Paraguay (10) and Togo (six).

EMBRAER's aircraft completed MB-326 production in all its forms, at what was officially the 761st aircraft, of which Aermacchi had built about 321.

Initial manufacture in South Africa related to the Atlas Impala Mk 1, otherwise known as the MB-326M. Similar to the initial armed trainer model with its shorter wingspan, the Impala Mk 1 had the uprated Viper Mk 540 engine of the MB-326G. First deliveries, from Italian-supplied kits, were made in June 1966, two years after a production licence had been obtained.

After the 151 Impala Mk 1s, Atlas produced at least 90, and almost certainly 100, examples of the Impala Mk 2 version of the MB-326K. A drastic departure from earlier models, the MB-326K was a single-seat attack aircraft based on the MB-326GB, but with a Viper 632-43 turbojet and an increased internal fuel capacity, which included wingtip tanks.

Latterly used in the training and light-attack roles, South Africa's last remaining Impalas were operated by No. 85 Combat Flying School until late 2005. They were replaced in service by the Hawk Mk 120, the first of which was delivered in November 2003.

While the MB-326 design was reaching the limits of its design capability, Aermacchi was already embarking on its replacement, known as the MB-339. It differed mainly in having a new and deeper forward fuselage section, which rectified the MB-326's limited visibility from the rear seat by enabling the seat to be raised. Aermacchi beat off competition from other aircraft manufacturers to win an initial order for two MB-339X prototypes. The first prototype flew on 12 August 1976 and was quickly followed by the second example on 20 May 1977. Compared to the earlier MB-326, the MB-339 has a more comprehensive avionics fit, including TACAN (tactical aid to navigation), IFF, VHF and UHF radio, and permanent externally mounted wingtip tanks.

Flight testing of the two prototypes preceded the delivery of 100 MB-339A production aircraft to the AMI, with which the type entered service in August 1979. Nineteen MB-339As were delivered in MB-339PAN form for service from 1982 with the *Frecce Tricolori*, the Italian national aerobatic team. The high-profile nature of the MB-339 with the display team resulted in a succession of orders and, more significantly, allowed Aermacchi to embark on a series of upgraded aircraft that ensure that the MB-339 offers far greater performance than its predecessor.

Nigeria ordered 12 MB-339As for delivery in mid-1984, as part of an ambitious re-equipment plan for its air force. The aircraft were primarily used for advanced training duties. Of the original number delivered, two were lost in accidents, and spares shortages soon resulted in the remaining 10 aircraft being grounded.

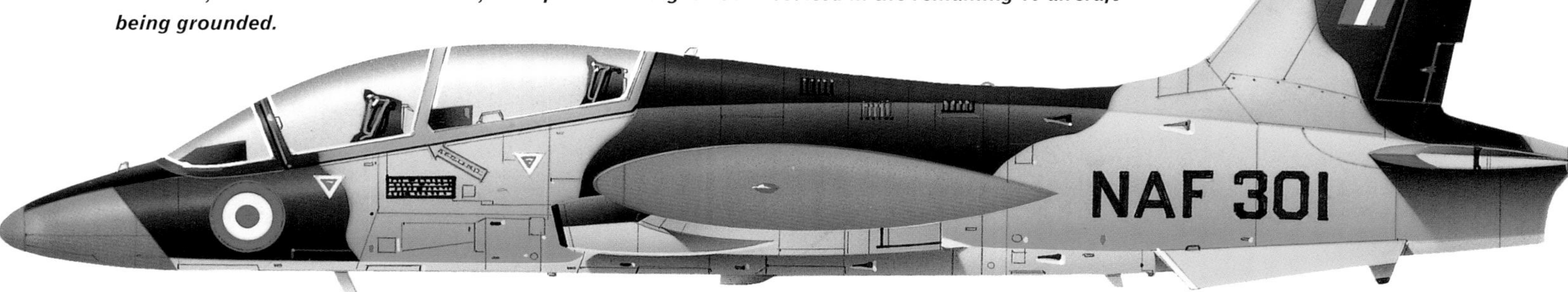

Aero L-39 Albatros

Wings for the WarPac

One of the few non-Soviet aircraft to enjoy major sales success in communist states, Aero's L-39 is a capable trainer and, although inferior to several Western types, remains in service with many air forces.

With production having exceeded 2,900 – and still continuing in the case of the advanced L-159 variant – the Czech Albatros is the machine behind one of the most successful aircraft production programmes in the world.

There was once some suspicion that the Aero L-39 owed its success to politics, in that it was selected as the standard Warsaw Pact trainer purely as a convenient *quid pro quo* to make up for the imposition of Soviet-built front-line aircraft types. Only Poland (with its own proud aircraft industry) selected an alternative.

Once it had been chosen by the USSR and other Warsaw Pact nations, the L-39 was certain to enjoy a huge production total, and orders from nations like Afghanistan, Cuba, Libya, Syria and Vietnam were hardly unexpected. But even before the Cold War had ended, the L-39 had started to gain something of a reputation for its superb handling, good performance, and low cost of ownership, and began to be selected, on merit, by a wide range of operators across the globe.

In fairness, the Albatros is technically no match for advanced trainers and light-attack aircraft like the BAE Systems Hawk, but it can compete head on with cheaper, lighter trainers, and has even snatched orders from under the nose of Dassault (for example, in Egypt). Although more economical turboprop basic trainers have become popular (with student pilots transitioning to jets only for advanced and tactical/weapons training), the L-39 and its derivatives offer the realistic prospect of straight-through all-jet basic, advanced and weapons training on a single aircraft type. A steady development programme has resulted in a stream of improved Albatros variants, keeping the basic aircraft thoroughly competitive.

The Albatros's predecessor in Warsaw Pact service was Aero's L-29 Delfin. This had itself been selected on merit after evaluation against the PZL TS-11 Iskra and the Yakovlev Yak-30, with some 1,943 being built by Aero. The L-39 used a similar configuration to the L-29, albeit with the wing dropped to the bottom of the fuselage, and the intakes moved above it, and with the T-tail replaced by a more conventional tail unit. The aircraft retained a single engine (albeit a turbofan rather than a turbojet, and producing roughly twice the power) and featured a simple, unswept tapering wing. Under the skin, the L-39's airframe was of modular construction, simplifying maintenance, overhaul and repair.

Above: OK-32, the first flying prototype Aero L-39, made its maiden flight on 4 November 1968. The aircraft is a generation older than aircraft like the Aermacchi MB-339 and BAE Systems Hawk.

Top: Following the division of Czechoslovakia, the Slovaks retained a total of 21 L-39s in C, MS, V and ZA variants. The remainder are used in the training role, with the exception of the V and MS versions, which were withdrawn in 1994 and 1998 respectively.

One of the roles of the L-39 is that of target-towing. This East German L-39V towed a KT-04 target from the centreline, with a winch in the rear cockpit.

Before its partition, Czechoslovakia operated 73 of the indigenous L-39, the majority being divided between L-39C and L-39ZA variants. Training took place at the Kosice air force training school.

These Aero L-39s formed an unnamed aerobatic display team for the Soviet-era DOSAAF paramilitary youth flying organisation.

The L-39 also followed contemporary fashion and design practice in having stepped tandem cockpits, giving the back-seater a reasonably good view forward over the long, slender nose. The first flying prototype made its maiden flight on 4 November 1968, and production began in 1972.

Upgrading the Albatros

Major variants of the L-39 are the baseline L-39C trainer, and the L-39ZO weapons trainer with underwing hardpoints. The first operationally capable Albatros was the L-39ZA, which combined the four-pylon L-39ZO wing with provision for an underfuselage gun pod and some structural strengthening.

The basic L-39ZA has been offered with some Western avionics (HUD, mission computer, navigation systems and displays) as the L-39ZA/MP. Thailand's aircraft are to this standard, with Israeli systems, but are officially designated as the L-39ZA/ART. Another variant with Western avionics was the L-139, with a 4,080-lb st (18.36-kN) Allied Signal engine in place of the standard 3,792-lb st (17.06-kN) Progress AI-25. A prototype flew on 8 May 1993, but no orders were received.

Although still in front-line service, the first-generation L-39 has also become a popular jet warbird. Production of the basic L-39 and improved L-59 has now ended, in favour of the L-159.

L-39C Albatros

This L-39C caused a major stir when it visited the Battle of Britain Salute in June 1990, the first time the type had visited the UK. It gave several spirited displays and wore a non-standard two-tone camouflage. The fact that it was a company aircraft meant that it also wore colourful nose bands and the Czech lion insignia.

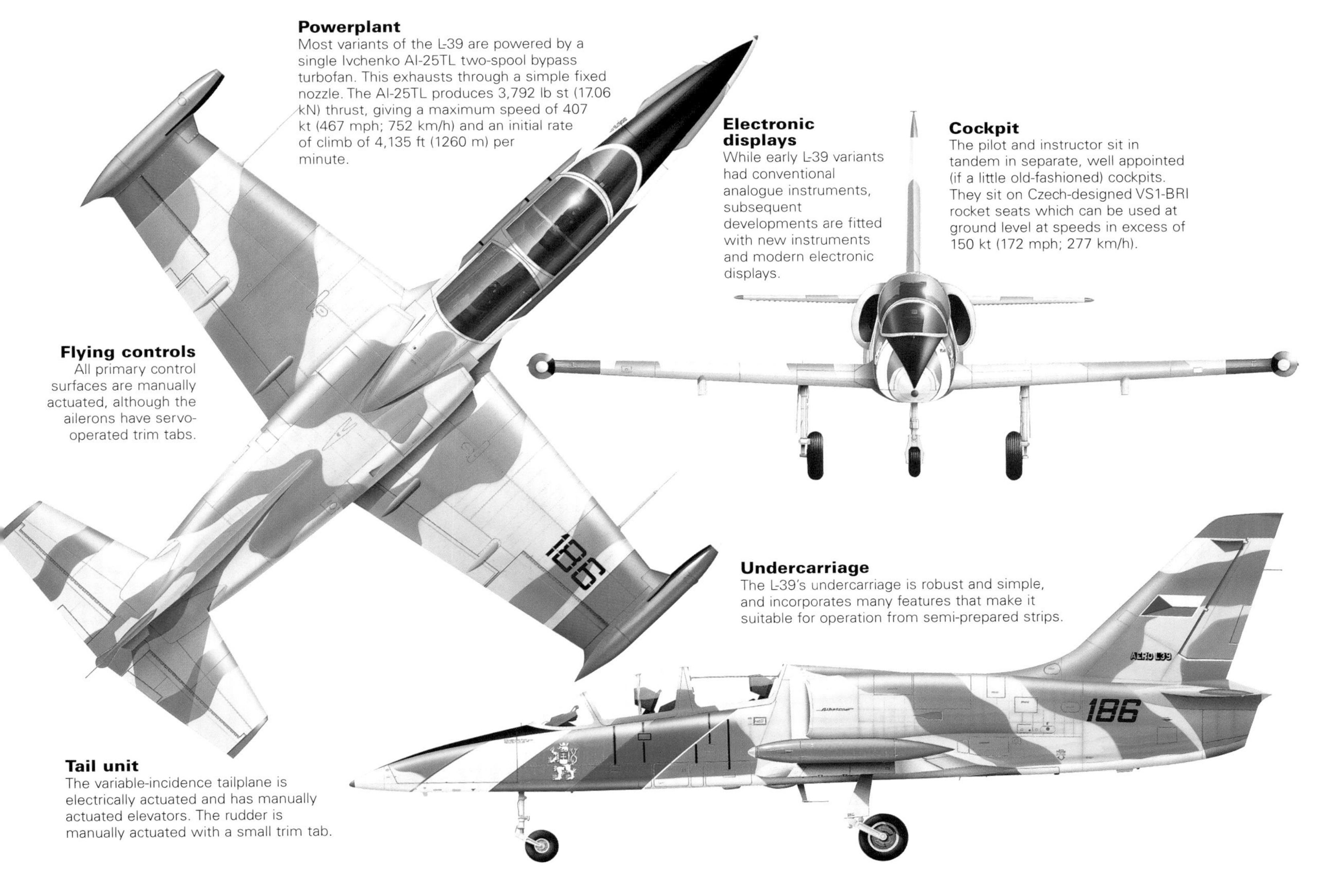

AMX International AMX

Lightweight warrior

Although the AMX has not achieved any export orders, it is an effective light-attack aircraft whose precision attack capabilities have led it to be compared to larger, more expensive interdictors.

Dubbed by some as a 'pocket Tornado', the joint Italian/Brazilian AMX is the only modern aircraft that has been solely designed with the attack mission in mind, a mission Italian AMXs performed with aplomb over the Balkans from 1995.

During NATO operations against Serb targets in Operation Allied Force, the Italian air force quietly flew 1,100 sorties, dropping 517 Mk 82 bombs and 79 Paveway II laser-guided bombs (LGBs). Almost a quarter of the total (252 sorties) was flown (with even less fanfare) by the AMX, which also introduced the Elbit Opher imaging infra-red guided bomb, 39 of which were dropped. This was perhaps appropriate, since the Italo-Brazilian AMX has always been a profoundly unglamorous aircraft, which nevertheless performs a vital role with quiet efficiency.

The AMX was originally designed to meet an Italian requirement for an advanced multi-role attack and reconnaissance aircraft to replace F-104G Starfighters and Aeritalia G.91s. In 1978 Aermacchi and Aeritalia pooled resources to design the aircraft, which represented a programme of vital importance to Italy's aircraft industry, not least as one of the few opportunities for local industry to provide an indigenous solution to an AMI requirement.

Brazilian involvement

Brazil (with a near-identical requirement) joined the programme in 1980, and the joint procurement of 272 aircraft (six prototypes, 79 aircraft for Brazil and 187 for Italy) was agreed in 1981. This gave programme shares of 46.5 per cent for Aeritalia (later Alenia), 23.8 per cent for Aermacchi and 29.7 per cent for Brazil's EMBRAER.

Despite its conventional appearance, the AMX had some cutting-edge features, including virtually full-span leading-edge and trailing-edge high-lift devices which confer superb short-field performance. The aircraft also has a state-of-the-art cockpit, with a head-up display (HUD), head-down display (HDD), 'hands on throttle and stick' (HOTAS) controls and advanced avionics.

The first AMX prototype made its maiden flight at Turin on 15 May 1984, with a Brazilian prototype following in October 1985. Despite the loss of the first prototype, development progressed relatively smoothly, using seven single-seat prototypes, and a first production AMX flew in May 1988.

Defence cuts following the end of the Cold War brought a premature end to production for the AMI, after 136 aircraft (including 26 AMX-T two-seaters). Aermacchi built 36 of the single-seat aircraft and nine two-seaters, while Alenia built 74 and 17. These aircraft equipped six *Gruppi*, though two of

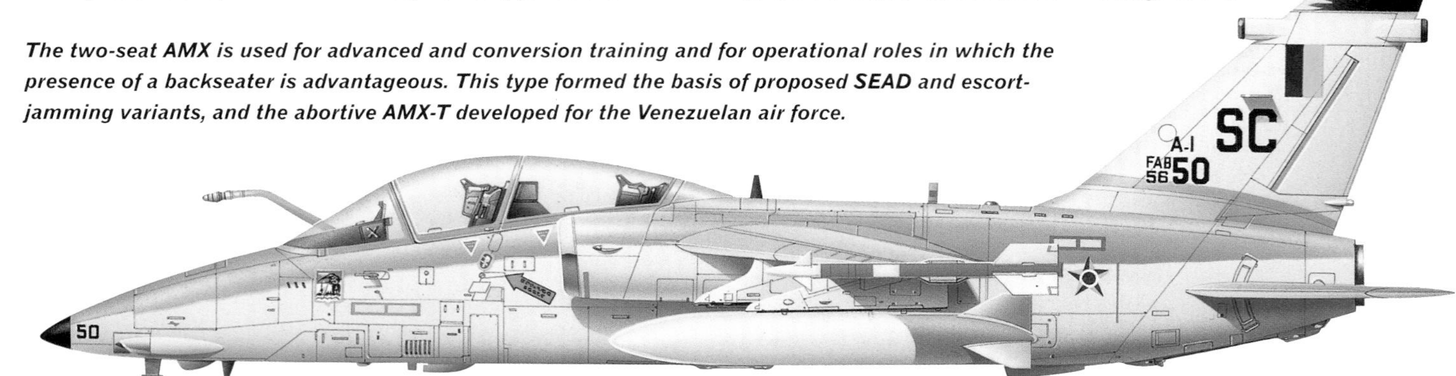

The two-seat AMX is used for advanced and conversion training and for operational roles in which the presence of a backseater is advantageous. This type formed the basis of proposed SEAD and escort-jamming variants, and the abortive AMX-T developed for the Venezuelan air force.

An aerial refuelling capability was considered desirable by the Força Aérea Brasileira. AMX prototype 006 therefore conducted trials with a FAB KC-130H (illustrated) and, later, a KC-137, at heights from 4,000–30,000 ft (1219–9144 m).

these have since disbanded, and all surviving Batch 1 aircraft have since been placed in reserve.

This left a force of 94 aircraft in service, all Batch 3 aircraft, or Batch 2 aircraft modified to the same FOC (Full Operational Capability) configuration. The AMXs of 3° Stormo have a reconnaissance capability, using Orpheus reconnaissance pods. The AMX fleet also uses Thomson CDLP laser designator pods, allowing the aircraft to 'self-designate' when delivering Paveway LGBs.

Close air support

In Brazil, the AMX replaced EMBRAER EMB-326Gs (AT-26s) in the CAS/reconnaissance roles, to equip two *Grupos*. The Força Aérea Brasileira ordered 56 aircraft (including 11 two-seater AMX-Ts), all built by EMBRAER, with options on 23 more single-seaters. The Brazilian AMXs and AMX-Ts (known as A-1A, and A-1B or TA-1 in service) differ from Italian aircraft in their avionics fit, and also feature twin DEFA 554 30-mm cannon in place of the Italian aircraft's single M61A1 20-mm weapon. The aircraft also carry indigenous MAA-1 Piranha AAMs on their wingtip launch rails, while AMI aircraft generally use the AIM-9 Sidewinder.The Brazilian aircraft also routinely carry a fixed 'bolt-on' inflight refuelling probe, following an extensive series of inflight refuelling trials using prototype 006.

In the air-to-ground role, Brazil's AMX operators are 1° Esquadrão 16° Grupo 'Esquadrão Adelphi' at Base Aérea de Santa Cruz, and 3° Esquadrão 10° Grupo 'Esquadrão Centauro', operating from Base Aérea de Santa Maria. The AMX also replaced the reconnaissance-configured RT-26s of 1° Esquadrão 10° Grupo 'Esquadrão Poker', also located at Santa Maria. When configured for the reconnaissance role, the Brazilian AMX carries the local designation RA-1 (or RA-1B for the two-seat reconnaissance version).

AMX

The 51- nosecode and cat-and-mouse fin badge identify this aircraft as one of those delivered to the first operational AMX unit, the 103° Gruppo, 51° Stormo at Istrana-Treviso. The squadron was previously equipped with the G.91R. The aircraft depicted wears an overall grey colour scheme, and has current-style roundels with a thin white central band for reduced conspicuity.

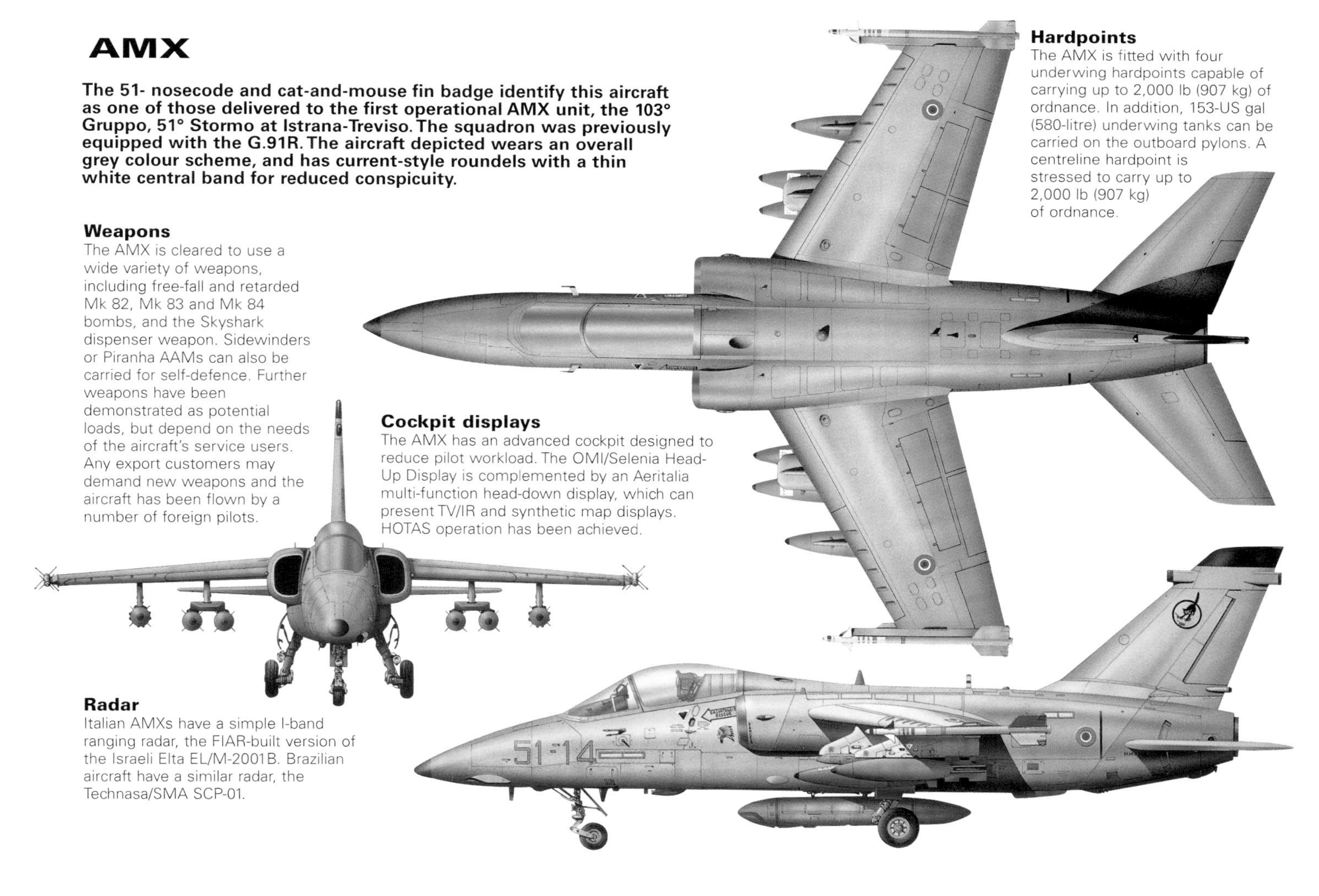

Hardpoints
The AMX is fitted with four underwing hardpoints capable of carrying up to 2,000 lb (907 kg) of ordnance. In addition, 153-US gal (580-litre) underwing tanks can be carried on the outboard pylons. A centreline hardpoint is stressed to carry up to 2,000 lb (907 kg) of ordnance.

Weapons
The AMX is cleared to use a wide variety of weapons, including free-fall and retarded Mk 82, Mk 83 and Mk 84 bombs, and the Skyshark dispenser weapon. Sidewinders or Piranha AAMs can also be carried for self-defence. Further weapons have been demonstrated as potential loads, but depend on the needs of the aircraft's service users. Any export customers may demand new weapons and the aircraft has been flown by a number of foreign pilots.

Cockpit displays
The AMX has an advanced cockpit designed to reduce pilot workload. The OMI/Selenia Head-Up Display is complemented by an Aeritalia multi-function head-down display, which can present TV/IR and synthetic map displays. HOTAS operation has been achieved.

Radar
Italian AMXs have a simple I-band ranging radar, the FIAR-built version of the Israeli Elta EL/M-2001B. Brazilian aircraft have a similar radar, the Technasa/SMA SCP-01.

The Ching-Kuo was designed with BVR capability in an effort to counter the vast numbers of air defence fighters fielded by Taiwan's great rival, the People's Republic of China.

AIDC Ching-Kuo

Taiwan's fighter

Beset by economic problems and the premature cessation of its production run, the Ching-Kuo has gained a reputation for being inferior to contemporary products. In fact, it represents an indigenous Taiwanese fighter with capabilities comparable with those of Sweden's JAS 39 Gripen.

Even when the Cold War was at its height, any thawing in relations between the People's Republic of China and the US was felt in Taiwan in the form of delivery restrictions affecting the latest weaponry. In 1974, the US began withdrawing its forces from Taiwan and, by 1979, relations with the People's Republic had reached the point where US–Taiwanese relations were broken off completely. Taiwan was left with a fighter force consisting of F-5 Tiger IIs and F-104 Starfighters, with no options for their replacement and all the headaches of supporting a US fleet without access to American spares resources. Nevertheless, Northrop designed the F-20 Tigershark aimed at the Taiwanese requirement but, in the event, the US government excluded Taiwan from the list of countries eligible for Tigershark exports, as it had with the list of potential Fighting Falcon and Hornet customers.

Indigenous solution

Luckily for Taiwan, the American restrictions on arms supply were ambiguous. Any form of technical assistance was allowed and the country took the brave decision to go it alone with a new fighter design, relying heavily on US help.

Taiwan's AIDC had already collaborated with Northrop on production of the AT-3 trainer and this experience, allied with that gained in building F-5s for the Republic of China Air Force (RoCAF), was the basis on which the Indigenous Defence Fighter (IDF) was to be built.

Initial studies began in 1980, with programme launch in 1982. The aim was to produce a lightweight fighter which was highly capable in both the air-to-air and air-to-ground roles. The codename An Hsiang (Safe Flight) was allocated to the programme as a whole, while Ying Yang (Soaring Eagle) covered the airframe, Yun Han (Cloud Man) the engine, Tien Lei (Sky Thunder) the avionics, and Tien Chien (Sky Sword) the missile armament. At an early stage, the concept of a true lightweight fighter was abandoned and US personnel were drafted in to assist the AIDC design team.

General Dynamics Fort Worth was deeply involved in the airframe development programme, supplying specifications and drawings from the F-16. It is therefore no surprise that the IDF bears some resemblance to the F-16, albeit in a twin-engined layout. The airframe is almost entirely of aluminium alloy and the cockpit features a wide-angle HUD, HOTAS controls and a Martin-Baker Mk 12 ejection seat.

Engine and avionics

Allied Signal/Garrett took most of the responsibility for the IDF's twin TFE1042 turbofan powerplant. In its final form, the ITEC (AlliedSignal/AIDC) TFE1042-70 offers 6,025 lb st (26.80 kN) dry and 9,460 lb st (42.08 kN) with reheat. The engine has been given the US military designation F125.

The heart of the IDF's avionics system was to be a multi-mode pulse-Doppler radar, offering true beyond visual range (BVR) capability. The Kam Lung (Golden Dragon) 53 GD-53, carried in the nose of the in-service Ching-Kuo (named after a former Taiwanese president), is based on the AN/APG-67(V) developed for the

In two-seat form, the Ching-Kuo loses its forward fuselage fuel tank in favour of an instructor's seat. The second seat is not raised and as a result the instructor's view is comparatively poor.

While from above it bears obvious similarities to the F-16, from below Ching-Kuo has much in common with the F/A-18. The first three FSD aircraft, all single-seaters, wore AIDC's smart house colours.

F-20. It incorporates technology from the F-16A's AN/APG-66 and offers similar and, in some cases, superior capabilities.

Tien Chien

In service, the Ching-Kuo has been seen with AIM-9L/P AAMs, but its primary missile armament consists of the indigenous Tien Chien I (TC-1) IR-guided AAM, which is closely related to the AIM-9, and the TC-2 BVR missile. This latter weapon has been claimed to have capabilities similar to those of AMRAAM, but this seems unlikely. The TC-2 employs active radar homing, and an anti-radar version has been developed. Ching-Kuo also has an internal Vulcan cannon and, for air-to-ground work, is compatible with CBUs, Mk 82 and Mk 84 bombs, and the AGM-65B EO-guided missile. For the anti-shipping role, the aircraft employs the indigenous Hsiung Feng II AShM, of which three rounds can be accommodated.

In service

In 1985, the IDF design was frozen. With the programme at an advanced stage, the first of four FSD aircraft (A-1) flew on 28 May 1989. These four machines were followed by 10 pre-production aircraft for a comprehensive test and evaluation programme.

Unfortunately, the first aircraft was damaged in a very public landing accident before the Taiwanese president and the world's press. A-1 was soon repaired, but the second FSD machine, A-2, was lost in a fatal accident after the port tailplane separated following severe vibration around Mach 1.

Despite these setbacks, the first pre-production aircraft were delivered to the RoCAF around one year early, in early 1992. Production had been planned to encompass some 256 Ching-Kuos, but US promises to supply F-16s saw this requirement dramatically reduced to just 130 aircraft. This down-scaling of the programme immediately made the Ching-Kuo a very expensive product. The Block 20 F-16A/Bs being offered made greater economic sense and the Ching-Kuo was relegated to an 'also-ran', a position which denies this formidable aircraft the recognition it deserves.

F-CK-1B Ching-Kuo

The little-used alphanumeric designation for the Ching-Kuo is F-CK-1A for the single-seat aircraft and F-CK-1B for the two-seaters. This aircraft is shown in 3rd Tactical Fighter Wing colours, based at Kang Air Base. It was one of the four two-seaters in the 10-aircraft pre-production batch.

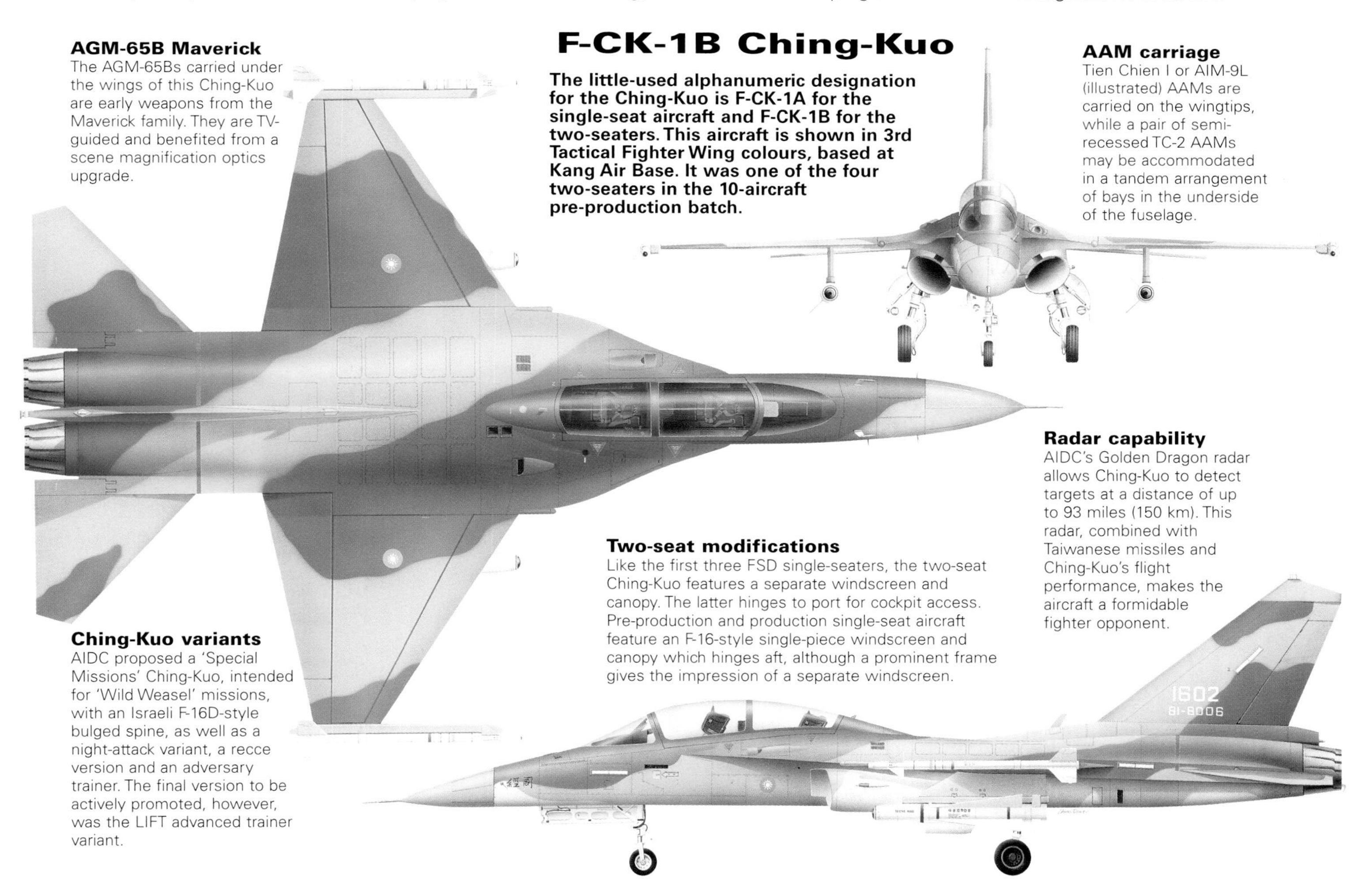

AGM-65B Maverick
The AGM-65Bs carried under the wings of this Ching-Kuo are early weapons from the Maverick family. They are TV-guided and benefited from a scene magnification optics upgrade.

AAM carriage
Tien Chien I or AIM-9L (illustrated) AAMs are carried on the wingtips, while a pair of semi-recessed TC-2 AAMs may be accommodated in a tandem arrangement of bays in the underside of the fuselage.

Radar capability
AIDC's Golden Dragon radar allows Ching-Kuo to detect targets at a distance of up to 93 miles (150 km). This radar, combined with Taiwanese missiles and Ching-Kuo's flight performance, makes the aircraft a formidable fighter opponent.

Two-seat modifications
Like the first three FSD single-seaters, the two-seat Ching-Kuo features a separate windscreen and canopy. The latter hinges to port for cockpit access. Pre-production and production single-seat aircraft feature an F-16-style single-piece windscreen and canopy which hinges aft, although a prominent frame gives the impression of a separate windscreen.

Ching-Kuo variants
AIDC proposed a 'Special Missions' Ching-Kuo, intended for 'Wild Weasel' missions, with an Israeli F-16D-style bulged spine, as well as a night-attack variant, a recce version and an adversary trainer. The final version to be actively promoted, however, was the LIFT advanced trainer variant.

Arado Ar 234

For take-off, the Ar 234A sat on a large trolley that featured a steerable nosewheel and main wheel brakes for taxiing. During the first flights of the V1 prototype, the trolley was jettisoned at altitude, but was subsequently released on the runway.

The first jet bomber

The Luftwaffe's second jet in service and the world's first jet-powered bomber, the Arado Ar 234 showed great potential but was produced too late and in too limited a number to save the Third Reich.

Post-war aviation literature is littered with instances of worthy, even excellent aircraft which have been overshadowed by their more illustrious contemporaries. On the German side, mention the words 'Luftwaffe' and 'jet' and the Messerschmitt Me 262, the world's first jet fighter, immediately springs to mind. Although equally innovative and revolutionary, the Arado Ar 234 – the first operational jet bomber in the world – invariably comes a very poor second.

This undeserved 'also-ran' had begun life late in 1940 as Project E.370. The aircraft was Arado's response to a request for a high-speed reconnaissance aircraft to be powered by two of the new turbojets then being developed by BMW and Junkers. Of clean and simple aerodynamic design, E.370 (soon to be redesignated the Ar 234) mated a narrow fuselage to shoulder-mounted wings, below which would be slung the two jet engines. With the bulk of the fuselage occupied by fuel tanks (dictated by the requirement for a range in excess of 1,243 miles/2000 km), there was no space for an orthodox undercarriage. Arado therefore proposed two alternative, and equally novel, solutions.

The first plan was to combine a centreline retractable bogie comprising nine pairs of small wheels (reminiscent of the company's earlier Ar 232 *Tausendfüssler* (millipede) battlefield transport design) with outrigger skids below the engine nacelles. The second suggestion saw the complex fuselage bogie arrangement replaced with a combination of jettisonable take-off trolley and centrally mounted main landing skid.

Below: The Ar 234B-2 was far more versatile than its predecessor, the Ar 234B-1, being capable of bombing, pathfinding or reconnaissance missions. This model is equipped with **Rauchgeräte** *take-off assistance rockets outboard of the engine nacelles.*

Above: This captured aircraft is an example of the major production model, the Ar 234B-2. The projection above the cockpit is a periscope sight which could serve the two optional 20-mm rear-firing cannon, or give the pilot his only view aft of the aircraft.

Arado 234s line up awaiting another mission during the Ardennes counter-offensive of December 1944 to January 1945. The Ar 234s were used for pinpoint attacks on the advancing Allied positions.

Above: The Ar 234 was involved in **Deichselschlepp,** ***or 'air trailer', trials, aimed at providing the aircraft with an expendable long-range tank. This 616-Imp gal (2800-litre) tank was to be attached to the aircraft by a semi-rigid tube which also acted as a fuel feed pipe.***

Presumably as the lesser of two evils, the latter option was selected to equip the first production model, the Ar 234A.

The first two airframes were completed during the winter of 1941–42, but another year was to pass before Arado took delivery of its first pair of Junkers Jumo 004 turbojets. Even these were pre-production units suitable for static tests only – the Me 262 took first priority in flight-cleared engines. In the event, it was 15 June 1943 before the company's chief test pilot, Flugkapitän Selle, lifted off in the first prototype Ar 234 V1 from Rheine airfield for its maiden flight.

Six further A-series prototypes were constructed. Of these, two were to serve as test-beds for the projected four-engined Ar 234C variant (the V6 had four BMW 003A turbojets in individual nacelles; the V8's powerplants were in paired nacelles under each wing), while the V7 formed part of the follow-on Ar 234B development programme.

By now it was recognised that the Ar 234A's landing skid constituted a serious operational flaw. Once safely back on the ground, the aircraft could not move under its own power but would have to be recovered by a special low-loader. This rendered it dangerously vulnerable to ground-strafing Allied fighters.

Further variants

The first B-series prototype – the V9, first flown on 10 March 1944 – overcame the above problem by featuring a fractionally larger fuselage cross-section, with wheel wells occupying much of the space formerly taken up by the central fuel cell. The main wheels, fitted with large, low-pressure tyres to compensate for the narrowness of track, retracted forwards and inwards. The new nosewheel retracted aft into a well behind the pilot's ejector seat. Other prototypes followed, powered both by the Junkers Jumo 004 and the BMW 003.

On 8 June 1944, the first of 20 pre-production Ar 234B-0s took to the air. These lacked the ejection seat and cabin pressurisation of the V9, but had provision for two cameras. The Ar 234B-1 reconnaissance aircraft was essentially similar, but had the added refinement of an autopilot and provision for drop tanks as standard. The major production model was the Ar 234B-2. This was a far more versatile machine, produced primarily as a bomber capable of carrying a maximum bombload of 3,300 lb (1497 kg). It was also completed to various other equipment standards including reconnaissance (Ar 234B-2/b), pathfinder (Ar 234B-2/l) and long-range (Ar 234B-2/r) versions. The final proposed variant of the B-series, the B-3 bomber, was abandoned in favour of the four-engined Ar 234C model.

The first C-series prototype was the V19, which undertook its maiden flight on 30 September 1944. No fewer than eight separate variants of the 'C' were planned, but only a handful of the earliest versions (up to and including the multi-purpose C-3) had been completed by the war's end. At the cessation of hostilities, the number of prototypes that had been built or were under construction had risen to 40, the last 10 of these being intended for the D-series, which was to be powered by two Heinkel-Hirth HeS 011 turbojets.

The Arado design team was also working on plans for an Ar 234E *Zerstörer* (heavy fighter) version, the Ar 234F (a scaled-up model) and an Ar 234P night-fighter. It was estimated that the performance of the last of these variants, the three-seat P-5, would be only slightly inferior to that of the Me 262B-2a.

A rocket-assisted Ar 234 roars into the air. **Rauchgeräte** ***units were employed to assist in short take-offs, with brake chutes used to reduce landing runs.***

Atlas Cheetah

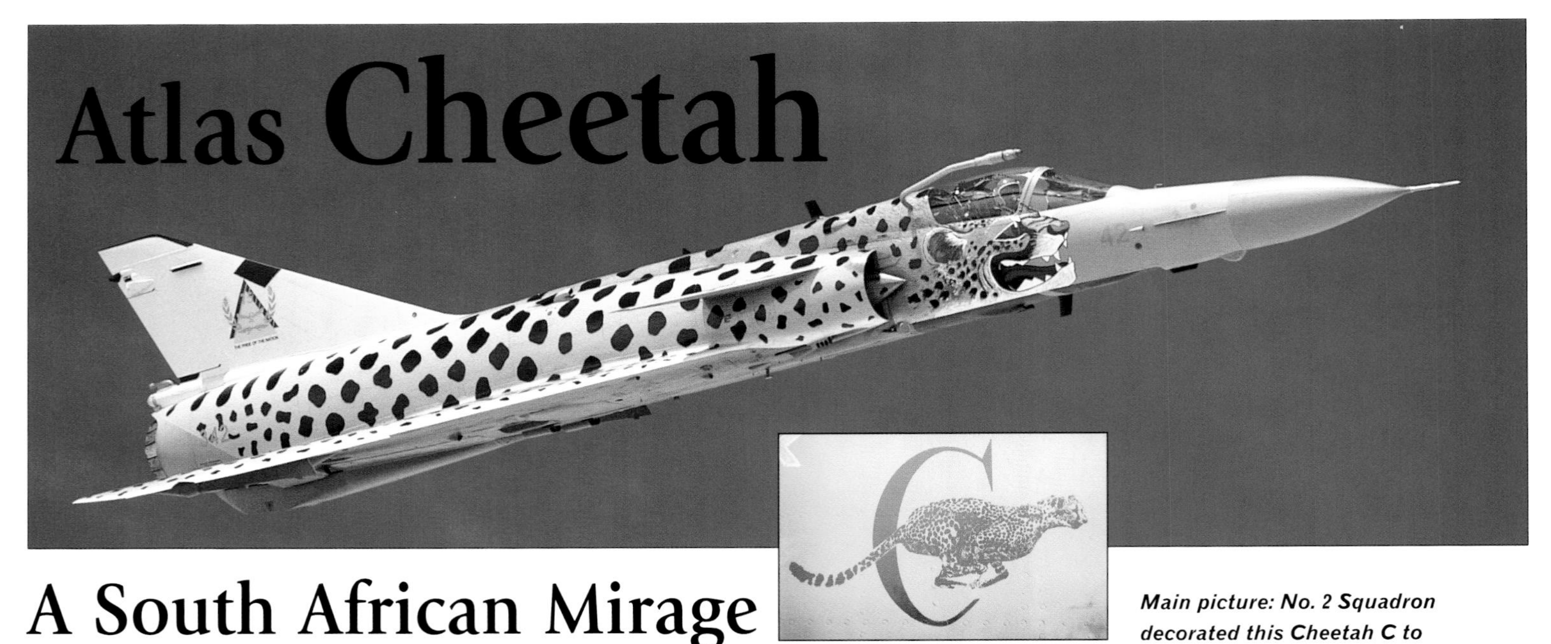

Main picture: No. 2 Squadron decorated this Cheetah C to celebrate the 75th anniversary of the SAAF that was marked in 1995. The aircraft was soon nicknamed 'Spotty' by SAAF personnel.

Inset: All Cheetahs carry the Cheetah emblem, but this personalised form is only carried by the Cheetah C.

A South African Mirage

With the Cheetah, South Africa produced a capable warplane in the face of international sanctions. Pending its forthcoming replacement by the JAS 39 Gripen, the Cheetah C/D remains one of the most potent fighter aircraft on the African continent.

The election of a Labour government in Britain in 1964 led to the imposition of sanctions which cut South Africa off from what had been its main arms supplier, with Britain joining the US and a number of other nations. France initially stepped into the breach, but South Africa was spurred into a drive for self sufficiency and 'import substitution'. Even France imposed sanctions in the late 1970s, and by the mid-1980s the SAAF was facing severe difficulties. Ageing Canberras and Buccaneers were in urgent need of replacement, while the surviving Mirage IIIs were becoming structurally tired and were showing increasingly severe limitations.

South Africa's Mirage F1s remained viable in the air-to-ground role, and it was decided that they would be augmented by upgraded Mirage IIIs. The Mirage III still offered superb outright performance characteristics, and it was felt that an ambitious upgrade and refurbishing programme would extend the type's useful service life and redress its shortcomings. The state-owned Atlas Aircraft Company had amassed considerable experience in supporting and maintaining a wide range of aircraft types, and had even licence-assembled Mirage F1AZ fighter-bombers and built MB-326s (as Impalas).

Mirage upgrade

The South African Mirage upgrade programme was based on Israel's Kfir – itself an indigenous Mirage derivative. The upgraded South African aircraft, known as Cheetahs, were converted from existing Mirage airframes, and retained Atar engines, whereas the Kfirs were newly built and powered by J79 engines. Like the Kfir, however, the Cheetah was designed as a multi-role fighter/fighter-bomber, and was equipped with much the same suite of avionics.

Atlas converted 16 Mirage IIIEZs to Cheetah E configuration (broadly equivalent to the Kfir-C7), and converted 11 Mirage IIIDZs and D2Zs to Cheetah D configuration (broadly equivalent to the Kfir-TC7). Atlas also produced another five more Cheetah Ds from Kfir or Mirage airframes supplied by IAI, to provide 16 two-seaters in total. The Cheetah D and Cheetah E conversions were undertaken side by side, and the variants respectively equipped No. 89 CFS at Pietersburg from July 1986 and No. 5 Squadron at Louis Trichardt from March 1988. The Cheetah D was primarily used for advanced training, long-range attack and laser designation roles. The Cheetah Es were assigned a dual air defence and ground-attack role, with emphasis being placed on the air-to-ground task.

Common to both Cheetah and Kfir are the filled-in sawcuts in the leading edge of the basic Mirage III wing, which are replaced by a dogtooth. This Cheetah D was photographed overflying the Voortrekker Monument.

It is possible that the two-seat Cheetah Ds may have taken over the Buccaneer S.Mk 50's nuclear strike role for a short time in 1990. The type also allowed the retirement of the SAAF's remaining Canberra B(I).Mk 12s and subsequently served in the attack and training roles.

The Cheetah Es were officially withdrawn in October 1992, but they were replaced by a new Cheetah variant, the Cheetah C.

The SAAF was to have received six Cheetah Rs for reconnaissance duties, but in the event only one Mirage IIIR2Z was converted to Cheetah R configuration, and the reconnaissance role was assumed by Cheetah Cs carrying reconnaissance pods.

The Cheetah C was the final Cheetah, 38 being produced using Israeli-supplied airframe components (possibly from redundant Kfirs, possibly newly built). These aircraft used Atar 09 engines taken from retired Mirage F1s and acquired from abroad. The Cheetah Ds of No. 89 CFS moved to Trichardt (since renamed Makhado) in December 1992, forming a training flight within No. 2 Squadron, which converted to the new Cheetah C and moved from Hoedspruit. Cheetah C deliveries were completed in June 1995.

Whereas the Cheetah E had been equipped with only an Elta EL2001 ranging radar, the Cheetah C is broadly equivalent to the Kfir 2000, and as such has a pulse-Doppler, track-while-scan EUM-2032 radar. The new variant also has a new modern 'glass' cockpit, with a wide-angle HUD and full HOTAS controls. The Cheetah C operates primarily in the air defence role, and is armed with a variety of AAMs, including the indigenous Darter and Israeli Python 3 AAMs.

The surviving two-seat Cheetah Ds were upgraded with Atar 09K50 engines, an uprated Cheetah C-type undercarriage and a wraparound windscreen, following the prototype conversion of one aircraft.

The Cheetahs will be replaced by JAS 39 Gripens, handover of which will be completed in 2012.

Cheetah C

Like all of the South African Air Force's active Cheetahs, this Cheetah C is flown by No. 2 Squadron, based at Makhado (the former Louis Trichardt AFB), in the northeast of the country. The Cheetah C emerged into a relative blaze of publicity in 1995 when the wraps were finally taken off what had hitherto been South Africa's most secret aviation programme. Cheetahs will give way to Gripens in the 21st century, following a $1.76 billion deal to purchase 28 of the Saab fighters.

Single-piece windshield
The new single-piece windshield developed for the Cheetah C, and later available for retrofit to the Cheetah D, is a major advance over the unit inherited from the Mirage III. The stretched-acrylic transparency has better optical quality than its glass and acrylic predecessor and none of the steel struts that obscured the pilot's vision. It is also stronger, being capable of resisting a 4-lb (1.8-kg) birdstrike at >250 kt (287 mph; 461 km/h).

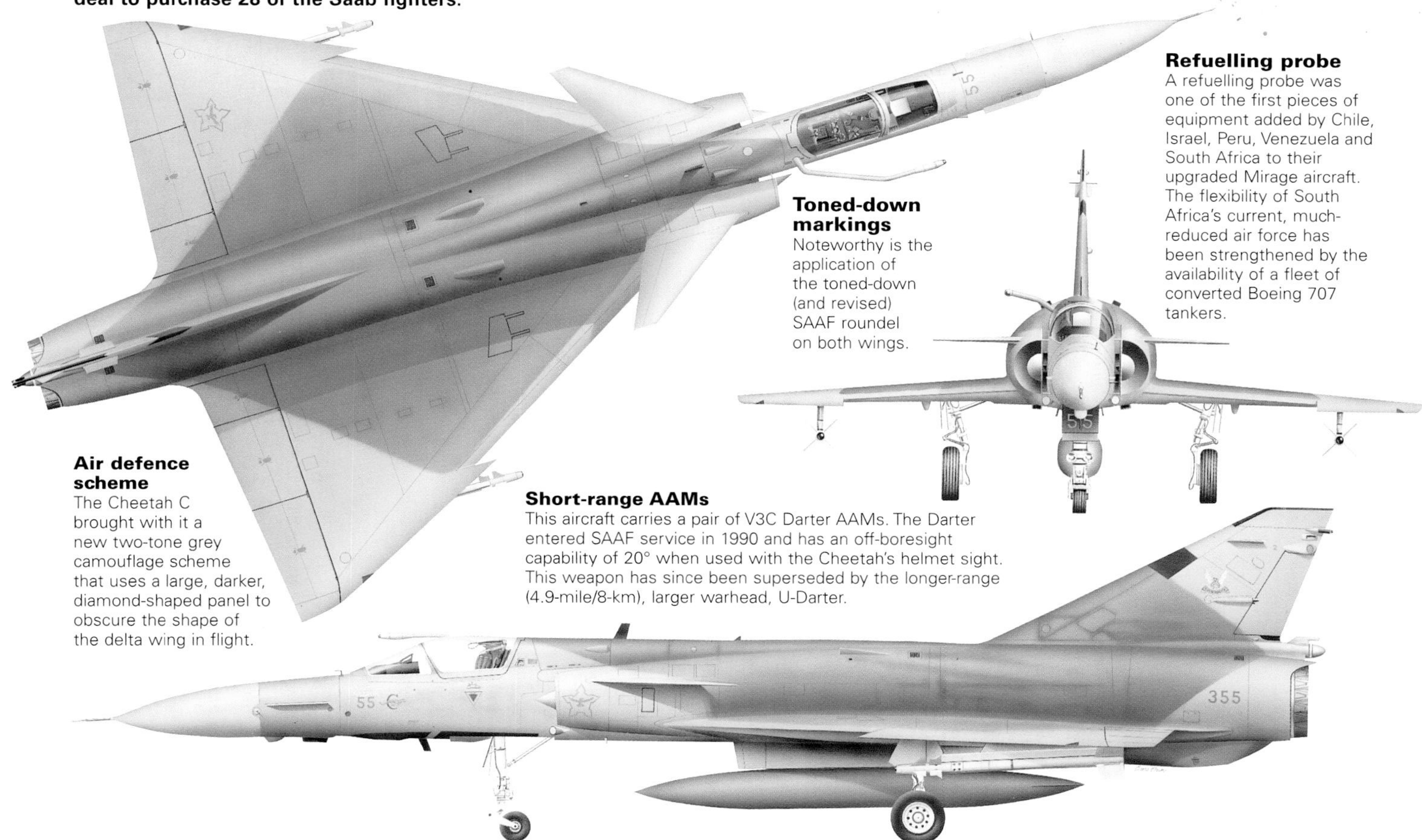

Refuelling probe
A refuelling probe was one of the first pieces of equipment added by Chile, Israel, Peru, Venezuela and South Africa to their upgraded Mirage aircraft. The flexibility of South Africa's current, much-reduced air force has been strengthened by the availability of a fleet of converted Boeing 707 tankers.

Toned-down markings
Noteworthy is the application of the toned-down (and revised) SAAF roundel on both wings.

Air defence scheme
The Cheetah C brought with it a new two-tone grey camouflage scheme that uses a large, darker, diamond-shaped panel to obscure the shape of the delta wing in flight.

Short-range AAMs
This aircraft carries a pair of V3C Darter AAMs. The Darter entered SAAF service in 1990 and has an off-boresight capability of 20° when used with the Cheetah's helmet sight. This weapon has since been superseded by the longer-range (4.9-mile/8-km), larger warhead, U-Darter.

Avro Vulcan
The early years

Above: No. 617 Sqn at ***RAF*** *Scampton was among the first units to receive Vulcan B.Mk 1s, including this aircraft.*

Left: As part of Britain's airborne nuclear deterrent, Vulcan bombers were kept on Quick Reaction Alert (QRA) between 1962 and 1969, initially armed with weapons such as the Yellow Sun free-fall bomb, and later with the Blue Steel stand-off missile.

Below: VX770, the Avro Type 698 prototype, completed its first flight on 30 August 1952. The original wing planform, seen here, was a feature of the first five Vulcan B.Mk 1s. Later aircraft were built with the Phase 2 wing, with its distinctive kinked leading-edge.

Avro's Vulcan was conceived for a deadly mission: nuclear bombing of the Soviet Union. When it finally went into action in the twilight of its career, it was in a very different scenario – attacking a runway in the Falklands, 8,000 miles (12874 km) from its base.

Few aircraft have ever had the impact of the prototype Avro Vulcan. Then simply known as the Avro Type 698, it looked like an almost perfect all-white triangle, but on a gigantic scale. Unknown to the public who watched it at the 1952 Farnborough air show, it had engines of only half the thrust of those for which it had been designed, and much less than one-third as much as those with which it was to mature, yet Avro's chief test pilot, Roly Falk, flung the monster around the sky like a fighter. With a total of one hour in its log book, this said quite a lot about the basic rightness of the design.

Exacting specification

The specification that the Air Staff issued in June 1948 was almost beyond the state of the art. It called for a bomber to carry a nuclear weapon weighing 10,000 lb (4536 kg) and of large linear dimensions to a target 1,725 miles (2780 km) distant at a cruising speed of 576 mph (927 km/h), at heights rising with fuel burn to 50,000 ft (15240 m) over the target. Still-air range was to be 3,858 miles (6209 km). For no evident reason it was stipulated that gross weight should not exceed 100,000 lb (45360 kg), this restriction having the effect of focusing the attention of the design team on means of reducing weight.

After spending the winter of 1946–47 trying to get gross weight below 195,000 lb (88452 kg), Avro's staff began to study the effects of removing the horizontal tail and then of filling in the space behind the swept wing. As the shape approached the delta form, the weights came down until in March 1947 the bold decision was taken to go ahead with this radical shape. Power would come from four Bristol Olympus turbojets mounted in the wingroots. At first the large bomb was to be housed in a bay in the left wing, balanced by fuel on the right, but a better answer was to make the wing thinner, with the engines all in a row, and put the bomb load within the centre fuselage.

To underpin the formula, a series of Avro Type 707 research aircraft was built, and though these designs ran parallel to the Type 698 rather than ahead of it, they contributed valuable data.

VX770, the first Type 698, was ready before its engines, so it was fitted with 6,500-lb (28.91-kN) thrust Rolls-Royce Avon RA.3s and flown at Woodford on 30 August 1952. In 1953 various changes included re-engining with 7,500-lb (33.4-kN) thrust ASSa.6 Sapphires. The second aircraft, VX777, had 9,750-lb (43.4-kN) thrust Olympus Mk 100 engines, as well as a fuselage 16 in (41 cm) longer to increase fuel capacity and accommodate the longer nose leg, a ventral blister for visual bomb-aiming, and a compartment for five crew.

Production Vulcan B.Mk 1s emerged in 1955 with Olympus Mk 100 engines. The latter were soon replaced by Mk 101 engines each rated at 11,000 lb (48.9 kN) thrust, and Bristol then never stopped pulling out more power, to 12,000 lb (53.4 kN) thrust with the Mk 102 and 13,400 lb (59.6 kN) thrust with the Mk 104, the standard for the B.Mk 1.

Kinked wing leading edge

This extra power highlighted a mild buffeting problem in the outer wings that threatened to eat rapidly into airframe fatigue life, and the answer was the Phase 2 wing with a distinctive kinked leading edge. The new wing was introduced on the sixth production Mk 1 aircraft.

By 1958 trials had begun with probes for inflight refuelling, while the RAF built up its Vulcan force. By the time the 45th and last B.Mk 1 was delivered, on 30 April 1959, the Mk 104 engine and inflight-refuelling probe were standard, and the designation had changed to B.Mk 1A with the addition of a large electronic countermeasures (ECM) installation in a redesigned and greatly enlarged rear fuselage.

Bristol's success with the Olympus had, by the second half of the 1950s, forced a complete redesign of the wing. The Mk 200 engine gave 16,000 lb (71.2 kN) thrust; this not only needed larger inlet ducts, but also a Phase 4 wing with span increased by 12 ft (3.66 m), and a considerable further reduction in thickness:chord ratio. Production aircraft so equipped were known as B.Mk 2s, these machines also having provision for launching the Blue Steel stand-off missile.

The first seven B.Mk 2s served as trials aircraft and were fitted with Olympus Mk 200 engines. By 1960 the 17,000-lb (75.6-kN) Olympus Mk 201 was being installed, and the need for rapid getaway led to a pneumatic engine-start system which, when fitted in 1961, changed the engine to Olympus Mk 202. Subsequently, production aircraft were fitted with the Olympus Mk 301 of 20,000-lb (88.9-kN) thrust. This gave a sprightly performance, but at low levels full power could not be used except on take-off. Most Mk 301-powered aircraft served at Waddington, while the Scampton Wing had Mk 201s.

Early operations

On 31 May 1956, 230 Operational Conversion Unit (OCU) formed at Waddington, tasked with the training of Vulcan crew for RAF Bomber Command. After the completion of reliability trials at Boscombe Down in September 1956, 230 OCU finally received its first two Vulcan B.Mk 1s on 18 January 1957. After intensive training, the first five crews of No. 1 Course from 230 OCU became 'A' Flight of No. 83 Squadron on 21 May.

Following Vulcan B.Mk 1 delivery to No. 83 Sqn, the RAF was incorporated into USAF strike plans from July 1958. Later in that year, the squadron received US-made nuclear weapons. With No. 83 Sqn and 230 OCU both based at Waddington, the next B.Mk 1 units to become operational were No. 101 Squadron, established at Finningley on 15 October 1957, and No. 617 Sqn, formed at Scampton on 1 May 1958.

On 1 July 1960 'B' Flight of 230 OCU began to receive the B.Mk 2, although the B.Mk 1s of 'A' Flight were retained until 1965. The first B.Mk 2s joined No. 83 Sqn in December 1960. By 1961, aside from training aircraft and those of the Bomber Command Development Unit, the influx of B.Mk 2s had enabled the B.Mk 1 force to be concentrated at Waddington (home to four units: Nos 44, 50 and 101 Squadrons).

***Above left:** The change to a low-level role brought to the Vulcan Mk 2 fleet terrain-following radar (not fitted here), fatigue meters to measure the severe buffeting experienced at low level, and camouflage.*

***Left:** The last six RAF Vulcans were converted for the less glamorous air-to-air refuelling role. Here Vulcan K.Mk 2 XH560 refuels a No. 9 Sqn Tornado.*

The B.Mk 1 entered service with 230 OCU early in 1957, with the first squadron, No. 83, following in July. The second squadron to operate the type was No. 101 (pictured), receiving its aircraft in October.

Blue Danube to Black Buck

Following their entry into service in 1957, the RAF's Vulcans constituted the sharp end of Britain's nuclear deterrent until 1969, when the responsibility was handed over to the Royal Navy's Polaris ICBM-capable submarines. Thereafter, a range of roles was taken on.

The initial weaponry for the V-force was the Blue Danube free-fall atomic bomb. In June 1954, however, the government initiated development of a more powerful hydrogen bomb, and the Violet Club stop-gap weapon was produced from March 1958. In addition to British weapons, the early Vulcan force could be equipped with American Mk 5 nuclear weapons from 1958.

The Yellow Sun Mk 1, the eventual outcome of the government's 1954 H-bomb requirement, became available in 1960, eventually supplanting the US Mk 5 weapons, as well as the Violet Club. The Yellow Sun Mk 1 was, however, only in service until 1963, before being replaced by the Yellow Sun Mk 2, carrying an improved warhead. Waddington received 24 Yellow Sun Mk 2s to equip its B.Mk 1s, while similar numbers were delivered to the B.Mk 2s based at Honington.

In 1963 – by which time the B.Mk 1 fleet had been upgraded under a modification programme to B.Mk 1A status, with the introduction of B.Mk 2 standard ECM equipment – the V-force was assigned to NATO, and given a part to play in the Alliance's nuclear strike plan.

230 OCU at Waddington was the first Vulcan unit, receiving two B.Mk 1 aircraft in January 1957. This aircraft, the unit's third, was delivered on 3 March, and wears the early silver colour scheme.

Blue Steel

The run-down of the B.Mk 1A force began in earnest in March 1966, when B.Mk 2s began to arrive at Waddington, replacing the earlier Vulcan equipment. On 10 January 1968, the last front-line B.Mk 1A was finally retired from service.

In order to accommodate the new Blue Steel stand-off weapon, the Scampton-based Vulcan B.Mk 2 fleet was modified to B.Mk 2A standard, with provision for the semi-recessed Blue Steel in special bomb-bay doors. No. 617 Sqn received its first B.Mk 2A in September 1961, and the Scampton wing eventually had a fleet of 26 Blue Steel-configured Vulcans. Following the cancellation of the Skybolt air-launched ballistic missile, the proliferation of Soviet surface-to-air missiles (SAMs) rendered existing high-altitude operations ineffective, at least beyond 1965. Meanwhile, Cottesmore's aircraft were optimised for carriage of the WE177B strategic nuclear bomb. The Waddington wing relinquished its B.Mk 1A/Yellow Sun Mk 2 combination in favour of the WE177B-armed B.Mk 2.

With a speed of Mach 2.3 and a range of 115 miles (185 km), Blue Steel was intended to provide the V-bombers with a high-altitude weapon that did not lead them to expose themselves to the air defences of high-priority enemy targets. Blue Steel operational capability was achieved by No. 617 Sqn on 24 September 1962. By the end of 1964, Nos 27 and 83 Squadrons were similarly equipped, sharing weapons with Wittering-based Victor B.Mk 2s of Nos 100 and 139 Squadrons.

However, Blue Steel had been rendered obsolete as a high-altitude weapon by Soviet SAM advances even before service entry, and was adapted for low-level operations from mid-1964. It remained as a peripheral weapon, and free-fall bombs were the only credible high-altitude nuclear weapons option for the Vulcan

Blue Steel operations

Limited Blue Steel capability was attained by the Vulcan fleet in September 1962. Blue Steel (carried by the specially equipped B.Mk 2A) operations were focused around Scampton (home of Nos 27, 83 and 617 Squadrons in 1962) until 1969/70, when the aircraft reverted to free-fall nuclear bombing with the WE177B. Introduced in January 1962, Quick Reaction Alert (QRA) stated that at least one aircraft from each Blue Steel unit was maintained at Cockpit Readiness (above left), with the crew strapped in, allowing the aircraft to be airborne just 57 seconds after the alert had been sounded (above right). Carrying a Red Snow megaton warhead, the Blue Steel stand-off missile (above centre) had a Bristol Stentor rocket motor, fuelled by a volatile mix of kerosene and High-Test Peroxide, necessitating great care in transport and handling.

Below: The B.Mk 1A, seen here taking on fuel from a No. 90 Squadron Valiant B(K).Mk 1, carried the ECM suite developed for the B.Mk 2, providing defence against high-flying interceptors.

fleet. The transition to low-level operations caused serious problems; until the WE177B strategic lay-down bomb could be fielded, the Vulcan had less than ideal weapons. The Yellow Sun and Red Beard weapons required a pop-up to at least 12,000 ft (3660 m) for release, while Blue Steel launched at low level was limited in range. At first, the Yellow Sun force went low-level against primary targets, leaving Blue Steel carriers to attack fringe targets.

QRA stand-down

On 30 June 1969 the Royal Navy's Polaris submarines took over the nuclear deterrent from the V-force, and the Scampton wing gave up its Blue Steel QRA role at midnight. No. 617 Squadron flew the last Blue Steel sortie on 21 December 1970.

A reduction in nuclear responsibilities freed Vulcan B.Mk 2s for other duties. No. 27 Squadron disbanded at Scampton in March 1972, but re-formed at the same base in November 1973 in the maritime radar reconnaissance (MRR) role. Its aircraft partially replaced the Victor SR.Mk 2s of No. 543 Squadron when they retired the following May. Initially, four were converted to B.Mk 2(MRR) standard, with the addition of Loran C navigation equipment and removal of TFR from the nose. Standard Vulcans were operated until four more MRR models were added between 1976 and 1978.

The rest of the Vulcan force soldiered on until it was decided to run-down the entire fleet during 1981/82, replacing them with Tornados. However, the Argentine invasion of the Falkland Islands brought a reprieve and a number of long-distance raids were made during April, May and June 1982 under Operation Black Buck.

The conflict in the South Atlantic spurred development of the last Vulcan variant. Concerns about the Victor tanker fleet led to the hasty modification of six Vulcans to K.Mk 2 standard as inflight-refuelling tankers, with fuel tanks fitted in their bomb bays and a single hose-drogue unit. They were to be the last operational Vulcans, and were finally retired in March 1984.

Right: With the shadow of the Jet Provost photo-platform joining that of the Vulcan, the last aircraft built demonstrates its low-level capabilities. The 'pimple' on the nose housed terrain-following radar.

An obvious change associated with the switch to low-level operations was the use of camouflage, initially applied to Waddington B.Mk 1As in a high-gloss finish. Here, a Cottesmore B.Mk 2 accompanies a white-scheme aircraft from the Finningley OCU.

Blackburn Buccaneer

Anti-ship striker

Developed as a low-level nuclear striker for the Royal Navy, the Buccaneer was also flexible enough to be used in a variety of other roles, if required.

Above: A bombed-up No. 809 Squadron S.Mk 2D is caught at the moment of launch from HMS Ark Royal. *In order to achieve sufficient wing incidence for launch from the short catapult, the Buccaneer was positioned in a nose-up attitude by the use of a hold-back. The 'hands-off' launch prevented the pilot from pulling back on the stick too much at a critical moment.*

The fourth development aircraft, XK849, performs a 'touch and go' on Victorious *during the initial trials of January 1960. Later in 1960, XK849 went aboard* Ark Royal *for another series of trials.*

The Royal Navy's most powerful and advanced British-built aircraft, the Blackburn B.103 Buccaneer was conceived in 1952 in response to the Naval Aircraft requirement NA.39. This called for a high-performance carrierborne strike aircraft, able to attack targets at very low level with an internally stowed weapons load including, if necessary, a nuclear store. The requirement had been drawn up as a counter to the Soviet 'Sverdlov'-class cruisers, after consideration had at first been given to the development of a new surface vessel. A powerful carrierborne attack aircraft was seen to represent a very flexible option which would not be tied to the maritime attack role, should other tasks arise.

Many major British airframe manufacturers produced designs for the NA.39 requirement. Blackburn's design was selected in July 1955 after almost three years of work, and an initial order was placed for a development batch of 20 aircraft. One of the major essentials was a radius of action of 400 nm (460 miles; 740 km), while carrying a full weapons load. This was to be combined with a take-off performance compatible with that of flight-deck operation.

Built to last

To provide sufficient lift while keeping the wing small enough to fold for carrier stowage, the American-pioneered boundary layer blowing system was incorporated. A pair of de-rated de Havilland Gyron Junior engines was selected for the powerplant to keep fuel consumption down and the fuselage was carefully area-ruled for optimum high subsonic performance, this producing the distinctive swelling in line with the wing trailing edge.

It took another three years to build the aircraft, nevertheless the target of first flight in April 1958 was met. The first aircraft was moved by road to RAE Bedford, whence it flew on the last day of the projected month. There followed an intensive programme of trials with the development aircraft, leading up to the first deck-landing on HMS *Victorious* in January 1960.

The first service unit to form was No. 700Z Squadron, the flying trials unit based at

Above: The dummy deck and catapult at RAE Bedford played a significant part in the Buccaneer's naval development. Here, the first S.Mk 2 conversion is seen undertaking trials, armed with 24-round rocket pods (not adopted for service use). Note the photo-calibration marks.

Left: Once airborne, and with careful power control, the Buccaneer S.Mk 1 showed itself to be a manoeuvrable aerobatic mount.

In the conventional attack role, the Buccaneer could carry up to eight 1,000-lb (454-kg) bombs (illustrated). However, for nuclear strikes it was able to deliver the 15-kiloton Red Beard tactical nuclear bomb.

Lossiemouth, and this was followed by the first operational squadron, No. 801. This embarked in HMS *Ark Royal* in February 1963, all the Buccaneers being painted in anti-nuclear flash white, as were the RAF's V-Bombers. No. 809 Squadron formed at Lossiemouth, as a shore-based unit to begin with, and in 1964 the second seagoing squadron, No. 800, embarked in HMS *Eagle*. This completed the service allocation of the Gyron-powered Buccaneer S.Mk 1.

Improved S.Mk 2

Meanwhile, work had been progressing on the next mark, the S.Mk 2, which had a significant increase in the radius of action by the fitting of Rolls-Royce RB.168 Spey engines. When installed in the Buccaneer, this engine increased thrust by about a third over the Gyron, while its lower fuel consumption gave increased endurance. Two development aircraft were re-engined with Speys to serve as S.Mk 2 prototypes and in this form first flew on 17 May 1963. In June 1964 the first production Buccaneer S.Mk 2 flew and aircraft soon began to equip No. 700B Squadron for service trials. All three front-line S.Mk 1 units re-equipped with S.Mk 2s between 1965 and 1967, and in the latter year No. 803 Squadron also formed on the type.

Naval Buccaneers were never required to fly in anger but very useful deterrence flights were made during the Indonesian confrontation, the withdrawal from Aden in 1968, and in Belize. The type also showed its capabilities in 'attacks' on the supertanker *Torrey Canyon*, wrecked off the Scilly Isles in March 1967.

From the mid-1960s the government decided to phase out the Royal Navy's aircraft carriers and, with them, the fixed-wing element of the Fleet Air Arm (FAA). This was complete by the mid-1970s, but a reprieve was given to extend the life of *Ark Royal*, which had been extensively refitted to operate Phantoms. In December 1978, the *Ark Royal* was paid off for the last time and No. 809 Squadron's Buccaneers went the way of its erstwhile companions – to the shore-based squadrons of the RAF.

Seen here turning on the approach over Lossiemouth harbour, No. 700Z Squadron's XK531 was the first Buccaneer to be delivered to an RN unit.

Low-level penetrator

Initially reluctant to adopt the naval Buccaneer into its ranks, the RAF would later reverse its opinion of the aircraft. The Buccaneer, in fact, went on to become one of the most successful and effective strike aircraft ever to have served with the RAF.

*The Buccaneer **XT270** pictured early in its career with **No. 12 Squadron**, firing a pair of **SNEB** rocket pods for a publicity photograph. Always a secondary weapon, the rocket pods were phased out during the 1970s leaving Martel missiles as the main means of attack for the squadron.*

The origin of the RAF's employment of the Buccaneer may be found in the muddled defence thinking of the mid-1960s. Having suffered the cancellation of the TSR.2, the RAF was then promised US-built F-111Ks for the low-level strike role, but these, too, were cancelled, on grounds of economy. Only one option remained, and in July 1968 it was announced that the first batch of 26 Buccaneer S.Mk 2s had been ordered for the RAF, and that some 60 FAA aircraft would be progressively phased into service as the naval force gradually declined.

Newly built aircraft had the complete Martel air-to-surface missile (ASM) fit and were known as S.Mk 2Bs, while around 20 surplus FAA aircraft were converted during 1970/71 as S.Mk 2As with a 'partial' Martel fit. From 1972, most then received full S.Mk 2B plumbing. In addition, a limited number of S.Mk 2Bs were produced directly from S.Mk 2s during 1970. The first aircraft to wear RAF camouflage was XV350, an S.Mk 2A conversion rolled out on 10 January 1969 and first flown on 11 February. The first production S.Mk 2B for the RAF was flown on 8 January 1970.

Honington was selected as the RAF's first Buccaneer base, and No. 12 Squadron formed there on 1 October 1969. Initially equipped with ex-FAA S.Mk 2s, it was later joined by No. 237 OCU for crew training of the squadrons which would follow. Next came No. 15 Squadron on 1 October 1970, this transferring to Laarbruch in January 1971 as the first Buccaneer unit in RAF Germany while, on 14 October 1972, No. 16 Squadron was also established at Laarbruch.

After the initial RAF order, further contracts followed for batches of three, seventeen and then a further three Buccaneers. The last was delivered to Laarbruch for No. 15 Squadron on 6 October 1977, and marked the end of Buccaneer production after nearly 20 years.

Structural fatigue

When a Buccaneer plunged into a ravine during an ultra low-level Red Flag sortie, the investigation revealed the cause as metal fatigue, and the entire RAF Buccaneer fleet of 90 aircraft was grounded for inspection. It soon became apparent that more than half of them were suffering from fatigue cracks. The conclusion was drawn that the extra stresses of

*This picture shows a **No. 12 Squadron** Buccaneer carrying four Sea Eagle missiles during a training flight from **Lossiemouth**. The Sea Eagle is a true 'fire-and-forget' missile, which would have enabled the Buccaneer to continue in the maritime strike role, possibly into the 21st century, had an airframe life extension programme been implemented. However, the cost-effectiveness of operating the Tornado **GR.Mk 1B** in the maritime strike role meant that the Buccaneer was rejected in its favour.*

With No. 12 Squadron's fox emblem on its intake, this Buccaneer S.Mk 2B shows the typical warload for anti-ship operations. The squadron became known as 'Shiny Twelve', dating from when it operated highly polished Fairey Fox biplane fighters. Buccaneer crews continued the tradition by polishing the prominent intake lips of their aircraft.

XW986 was operated by the RAE, later the Defence Evaluation and Research Agency (DERA), now QinetiQ. The huge serial numbers painted on the bomb door (just visible) were reportedly applied by mistake after an MoD officer scribbled the serial across the drawing of the aircraft's proposed paint scheme.

constant overland manoeuvring had proved too much even for the Buccaneer's robust structure. No official announcement was made about the number of Buccaneers incapable of being returned to service, but No. 216 Squadron failed to survive the grounding order and was disbanded, leaving No. 12 Squadron as the sole maritime Buccaneer squadron.

Although plans had already been laid for the eventual replacement of the Buccaneer by the Tornado GR.Mk 1B, the venerable 'Brick' was to see a further decade of service.

Moving from Honington to Lossiemouth, No. 12 Squadron was the sole maritime squadron allocated to Supreme Allied Commander Atlantic (SACLANT) following the decision to deactivate No. 216. This shortcoming was corrected three years later, in the summer of 1983, by the re-roling of No. 208 Squadron. The primary overland commitment of this unit had meant that, until this time, it had remained at Honington as support for the two RAF Germany squadrons. However, with the Tornado coming on stream, it was to be the Germany-based Buccaneer squadrons that were to be the vanguard of conversion. No. 15 Squadron was the first to relinquish its Buccaneers when it became a Tornado squadron on 1 July 1983, followed by No. 16 Squadron in February 1984. This move to the Tornado provided the opportunity to change the role of No. 208 Squadron to fill the gap in SACLANT's defences created by the loss of No. 216 Squadron.

At first, No. 208 Squadron's Buccaneers retained the Paveway system as the primary attack mode, with No. 12 Squadron providing stand-off capability through Martel. At this time, the decision was taken to update 60 Buccaneer airframes over the period 1984 to 1988. This programme was to centre around the new Sea Eagle missile. Also included in the update would be a HUD and improved ECM/ESM equipment. However, by 1986 the programme had been reduced, with the number of aircraft involved shrinking to just 42.

Desert pirates

The Buccaneer was to remain in front-line service with No. 208 Squadron until its retirement on 31 March 1994. The RAF aircraft's call to arms was to be in the twilight of its career, over the deserts of the Middle East. Twelve aircraft were deployed to Muharraq and Dhahran in Saudi Arabia to participate in Operation Desert Storm in 1991. Wearing an overall temporary desert pink camouflage and lurid nose-art, the Buccaneers acted as laser designators for the RAF Tornado GR.Mk 1 fleet as well as dropping bombs themselves.

XV352 refuels from a Victor during a mission over Iraq, clutching a CPU-123 bomb (replacing a Sidewinder) to its port outer pylon. Buccaneers delivered 48 LGBs from 21–28 February 1991, the best known being the two weapons which hit a parked An-12 and a captured C-130 at Shayka Mayhar airfield.

Left: Without the burden of a full fuel load and bombload, the ***B-47*** *was a very sprightly performer, as displayed here. When equipped with* ***RATO*** *equipment, a lightly laden* ***B-47*** *could often outclimb an interceptor, such as the* ***F-101****, during scramble take-offs.*

Inset: The distinctive podded engine layout and the slender lines of the ***Stratojet's*** *fuselage and wing are displayed to advantage in this view of a trio of* ***B-47Bs****. This was the first true production* ***B-47*** *and 399 examples were built.*

Boeing B-47 Stratojet

The first swept-wing jet bomber in service, the B-47 represented a quantum leap in operational capability thanks to the enormous technological advances made by the Boeing team.

Boeing bombers enter the jet age

On 17 December 1947 there took place a flight that revolutionised bomber aviation: the Boeing XB-47 took to the air for the first time. Its swept-back wings, with its six engines underslung in pods beneath, and its sleek, slim fuselage brought the first real jet-age bomber design into being. The high speed of the aircraft brought the world's manufacturers of fighter aircraft to attention, for the XB-47 was capable of outrunning the majority of fighter aircraft that had appeared up to that time.

The newly established USAF had looked upon the design with favour and ordered two prototypes into production. The bomber was originally powered by six General Electric J35 engines, each of which developed 3,750 lb (16.9 kN) of thrust. The 35° swept-back wing was thin and, combined with the extremely high aspect ratio of 11, provided a very fine aerodynamic efficiency. However, this lack of

Making its maiden flight on 17 December 1947, ***Boeing XB-47 Stratojet*** *46-065 was the first of two prototypes of* ***Boeing's*** *revolutionary medium bomber. Swept wings had never previously been used on a large American jet and the positioning of the landing gear and fuel tanks caused much consternation.*

At a cost of $28,500,000, the USAF ordered 10 B-47As – essentially service test versions of the XB-47 – to train crew and ground personnel.

depth made it impossible to house the landing gear or the fuel tanks in the wings. The solution for the landing gear was a tandem gear or 'bicycle' arrangement. One two-wheel main gear was installed just forward of the bomb bay. Small outrigger gears were incorporated into the inboard engine pods to provide stability on the ground. Fuel cells were built into the fuselage above and aft of the bomb bay.

The aircraft normally carried a crew of only three: a pilot and co-pilot housed under a fighter-type canopy, and the navigator-bombardier who flew in the forward nose compartment. The USAF ordered the aircraft into production in September 1948, the first B-47A flying on 25 June 1950. The first 10 B-47As were utilised for development and training purposes. The B-47A underwent a change of powerplant – General Electric J47 engines, each developing 5,200 lb (23.4 kN) of thrust, replaced the J35s, which were utilised only on the first prototype.

The first true combat model of the B-47 was the B-47B variant. This aircraft was fitted with six improved J47-23 engines. The clear nose had been closed, the size of the bomb bay reduced, and the aircraft was fitted with 18 1,000-lb (4.5-kN) thrust solid-fuel rocket (RATO) units. Twin radar-controlled 0.5-in (12.7-mm) machine-guns in the tail comprised the bomber's entire defensive armament.

The B-47 Stratojet rapidly became the backbone of the USAF's Strategic Air Command (SAC), and before the production lines were shut down, 2,289 had been produced. Quantity was such that the Boeing plant in Wichita, Kansas, could not undertake the entire order and aircraft were also built by Lockheed and Douglas.

The first B-47B delivered to SAC went to the 306th Bomb Wing at MacDill AFB, Florida, on 23 October 1951. Before the end of the line, the B-47 equipped 36 SAC wings, one MAC wing and various other small units in the USAF. The units each comprised 45 aircraft. It took until February 1953 before the 306th BW took part in its first simulated combat operation. During that month the bombers pioneered the first SAC deployment to England. These rotational flights became policy in SAC, and one B-47 unit was on duty in England for a 90-day period at all times. This rotational programme continued until 1958.

SAC began to receive the new B-47E in 1953. The B-47E was extensively modified: new and improved engines were installed, which increased individual engine thrust to 6,000 lb (27 kN). A water-injection feature had also been added, which raised thrust to 7,200 lb (32.4 kN) for take-off. The later B-47E models also did away with internal RATO units and incorporated 33 external units on a rack which could be jettisoned following take-off. An improved tail gun position was installed which utilised two 20-mm cannon, replacing the earlier twin machine-guns.

Far East deployment

Modified B-47B and the later B-47E models were all fitted for inflight-refuelling from Boeing KC-97 and later Boeing KC-135 tankers utilising 'flying booms'. The initial exercise featuring inflight refuelling took place in June 1954, when three B-47s of the 22nd Bomb Wing from March AFB, California, flew non-stop to Yokota Air Base, Japan, a distance of 6,700 miles (10780 km), in less than 15 hours.

One exceptional record flight for the B-47 took place on 17 November 1954. Colonel David A. Burchinal, commander of the 43rd Bomb Wing, took off from Sidi Slimane in French Morocco en route to RAF Fairford in England. Upon arrival at Fairford, he was unable to land due to bad weather, so he returned to Sidi Slimane. Upon arrival there, he found again that the weather was too bad for landing. With the assistance of nine aerial refuellings, Burchinal kept flying until he finally landed at Fairford, after a total of 21,163 miles (34058 km) in 47 hours, 35 minutes.

An interesting manoeuvre used with some of the early B-47s was the LABS (Low-Altitude Bombing System) method of atomic weapon delivery. Through extensive modification, the B-47 wing was 'beefed up' for low-level operations, for it was proposed that the bomber would come in at tree-top level, zoom upwards, release its bomb while in a vertical climb, continue up into a half-loop and complete the Immelmann manoeuvre with a half-roll off the top. This would give the B-47 time to make its getaway before the bomb detonated.

Though reconnaissance and weather variants remained in service for some time, the last B-47 bomber was retired from SAC on 11 February 1966.

The ultimate expression of the B-47 bomber was the E model. This was the most important bomber variant, with over 1,500 in service with the USAF at the height of the Cold War.

***Above:* First flying in August 1953, the RB-47E was a modified B-47E with a lengthened nose and a return to the built-in RATO units. The bombardier and his bombing equipment were removed and a photographer/navigator took his place. Eleven cameras were carried, along with 10 photo-flash bombs and supplementary photo-flash cartridges for night photography. An additional 15 RB-47Es were completed as RB-47Ks and differed from the E in having both weather and photo-reconnaissance capability at all altitudes.**

Special missions

While the bomber variants of the Stratojet performed admirably, they never actually came into contact with hostile forces. This dubious privilege went to the reconnaissance and Elint variants of the B-47, which spent years snooping around the borders of the Soviet Union, sometimes with fatal consequences.

In 1953 a new development of the B-47 first flew and this variant would go on serving long after the bomber Stratojet was retired. The RB-47E was not in fact the first reconnaissance Stratojet – that honour going to the RB-47B conversion – but it was the first dedicated reconnaissance variant. The long-nosed RB-47E (and later RB-47K) was built for long-range photo-reconnaissance. Numerous cameras were installed at various points on the fuselage, and in some versions, such as the RB-47H and the ERB-47H, crew members for ECM and reconnaissance tasks were housed in the former bomb bay.

The RB-47s, mainly operated by the 55th Strategic Reconnaissance Wing, regularly flew from bases in England and Turkey, penetrating Soviet airspace in western Europe and the Near East. The super-secretive missions were often completely deniable, especially when flights actually crossed over sensitive Soviet sights. However, the importance of these missions ensured that a hostile reception was often waiting for the Stratojets.

An extended nose was one of the most recognisable features of the RB-47 and was one of a series of modifications made to the airframe to house the mission-critical equipment.

Among the most colourful of the more than 2,000 Stratojets eventually built, this WB-47B operated with the 55th Weather Reconnaissance Squadron and was the only example to be converted.

NACA received a single B-47A (AF 49-1900 and NACA No. 150) on 11 July 1952 and operated it until 1957. The aircraft performed tests at the High-Speed Flight Station at Edwards AFB, California, gathering scientific information for a variety of future high-speed and swept-wing projects.

An RB-47H of the 55th SRW from Forbes AFB, Kansas, was shot down by a Soviet MiG on 1 July 1960. John McKone, the navigator, and Bruce Olmstead, the co-pilot, survived and were captured, while the pilot, Bill Palm, and the three Elint members died. The USSR claimed that the aircraft was on a spy mission over the Bering Sea, while US officials claimed that the Soviets had drawn the aircraft off course and shot it down. The two imprisoned fliers were finally released seven months later.

Several other reconnaissance B-47s were lost or encountered opposition during the Cold War. In May 1954, an RB-47E of the 51st SRW, flying over northern Russia, exchanged gunfire with a MiG-17, but managed to flee. The following year, another RB-47E was lost near Kamchatka, while in 1965 an ERB-47H was damaged by North Korean MiG-17s. It made an emergency landing at Yokota AB, with two engines out.

Additional roles

As well as the conventional reconnaissance role, modified B-47s also engaged in several other roles. QB-47s were modified B-47Es that were converted to radio-controlled drones that could theoretically perform missions that would be too hazardous for a human crew. Their other task was to act as targets for fighter aircraft. However, the aircraft were deemed expensive and were not considered expendable targets, and guided missiles fired against them were programmed to make near misses. Nevertheless, at least one QB-47 was inadvertently downed by a direct hit. Controlling these drones were the DB-47Bs and, later, the DB-47Es, which had their armament deleted and radio equipment installed for control purposes.

Thirty-five obsolescent B-47Es were modified in 1963 as EB-47Ls and these aircraft acted as electronic communications aircraft, serving as relay stations between other aircraft or ground stations.

Several aircraft were also modified for weather reconnaissance as part of Military Air Transport Service. The 9th Weather Reconnaissance Wing's WB-47B/Es were fitted with a range of weather information-gathering equipment, including air-sampling pods and weather radar. Often wearing garish colour schemes, these WB-47s followed their bomber and reconnaissance cousins around the world, with deployments as varied as Hawaii and Scotland.

It was 29 December 1967 before the last RB-47 was retired from the 55th SRW at Forbes AFB, Kansas. Military Airlift Command continued to operate a weather reconnaissance WB-47 until 1969.

Two B-47s were loaned to the US Navy and remained in service long after the last USAF B-47s were retired. The USN used the Stratojet for evaluating the engine of the S-3A Viking and later for ECM testing.

Below: After serving with SAC for a relatively brief period, a number of early production Stratojets were modified to TB-47B configuration, being employed on crew training tasks by the 3520th Flying Training Wing from McConnell AFB, Kansas. The aircraft depicted here was typical of these TB-47Bs.

Boeing B-52 Stratofortress

Boeing's 'Big Stick'

Mainstay of US strategic forces since its service entry in 1955, the B-52 Stratofortress, with its nuclear payload, was the symbol of American might throughout the Cold War. Even with the appearance of new aircraft like the B-1B Lancer and B-2 Spirit, the B-52 is set to soldier on well into the 21st century.

In 1946, Boeing was revelling in its success in building the war-winning B-29 Superfortress, but did not yet know whether or not its post-war B-47 Stratojet would succeed. Approached by the Pentagon to build a new strategic bomber, Boeing began years of design work that ultimately led to the B-52.

By 1950, Boeing's design efforts had yielded the Model 464-49, an eight-jet, swept-wing bomber, built for the USAF in the form of two prototypes, the XB-52 and YB-52. The prototypes were basically the same as the 744 production Stratofortresses that followed. Power was provided by the first jet engine in aviation history to generate 10,000 lb (45 kN) of thrust, the Pratt & Whitney JT3A, known to the military as the J57-P-3.

First flight

XB-52 and YB-52 prototypes were built under conditions of great secrecy and the YB-52 became the first to fly at Seattle, Washington, on 15 April 1952.

Above: The Hound Dog was the first cruise missile deployed on a USAF bomber. It greatly extended the aircraft's combat capabilities, allowing the B-52 to attack three targets simultaneously.

Top: Essentially a production version of the B-52A, the B-52B was outwardly indistinguishable from its predecessor, though it had uprated engines. On 18 January 1957, three B-52Bs completed a non-stop flight around the world in 45 hours, 19 minutes.

The B-52 had been built to the very latest design specifications. It resembled a B-47 Stratojet with its 35° swept wing, podded engines and 'bicycle' undercarriage. From the B-52A model onwards, the canopy was redesigned to provide side-by-side seating. Fuel capacity was greater than in any previous production aircraft at 38,865 US gal (147120 litres) with external tanks, as compared with 21,000 US gal (79493 litres) for the B-36. The eight engines were podded in pairs on four underwing pylons similar to the inboard pylons of the B-47.

Remarkably, the B-52 changed little throughout its 10-year production run. The initial USAF production order was for three

Although rolled out after the XB-52, the YB-52 was the first into the air by five months. During its maiden flight in 1952, it remained aloft for three hours and was well received by the test pilots (who were seated in tandem). The B-52 underwent the most rigorous testing of any aircraft of its time, and some three years elapsed before the aircraft entered regular USAF service.

The XB-52 was first rolled out on the night of 29 November 1951, covered in tarpaulins for security reasons. The two B-52 prototypes differed from their successors by having 'fighter-style' tandem-pilot cockpits and no tail armament.

B-52As with J57-P-9W engines, followed by 23 B-52Bs with J57-P-19W, -29W, and -29WA powerplants. RB-52B reconnaissance models were eventually modified to B-52C standard, in addition to 35 new B-52Cs introduced from March 1956 with extra fuel capacity.

The B-52D, first flown on 14 May 1956, was built in greater numbers (170 in total). These were followed by 100 B-52Es, with minor internal changes, and the manufacture of 89 B-52Fs, beginning in February 1959.

Boeing then produced 193 B-52G aircraft. The B-52G introduced a shorter vertical tail, and a new integral-tank wing with fuel capacity increased to 46,576 US gal (176309 litres) and with underwing tanks reduced in volume to 700 US gal (2650 litres) each. The B-52G was designed for the Skybolt air-launched ballistic missile, which was ultimately cancelled; the aircraft also carried two GAM-77 (AGM-28) Hound Dog cruise missiles. On the B-52G, the gunner was relocated in the main crew compartment, operating the four 0.5-in (12.7-mm) machine-guns via a fire control system.

The USAF ordered 102 B-52H aircraft, taking delivery of the first on 9 May 1961. With the short vertical fin of the B-52G, the H model was powered by eight 17,000-lb (77-kN) thrust Pratt & Whitney TF33 turbofans.

Tail armament of the B-52H was again remotely operated, but now comprised a single 20-mm cannon. The last B-52H was delivered to the USAF on 26 October 1962.

Service entry

On 29 June 1955 the first B-52B models entered service with Strategic Air Command's 93rd Bombardment Wing (Heavy) at Castle AFB near Merced, California. The B-52 was designed to carry the largest US nuclear weapons, to challenge the defences of the Soviet Union, and to get through to targets halfway around the globe via a polar route. When coupled with the KC-135 Stratotanker, the B-52 had global reach.

The reconnaissance mission was a temporary task for the B-52. The RB-52B model introduced a two-man pressurised capsule, equipped with camera or electronic monitoring devices, which could be carried in the bomb bay. B-52C models launched in 1956 retained the reconnaissance capability. By the early 1960s, the reconnaissance function was being ably carried out by other aircraft, whereupon the B-52 reverted to its original role.

The B-52 had many qualities, but at the forefront was its versatility. It had been designed to attack from high altitude, but when Soviet surface-to-air missiles came on the scene the B-52 allowed itself to be re-tasked as a low-level bomber, eventually acquiring terrain-hugging radar and navigation gear. Designed to drop free-fall nuclear bombs, the B-52 was to carry almost every every US air-launched weapon from the Hound Dog missile of the 1960s to the AGM-129 Advanced Cruise Missile of the 1990s.

During its first decade as a Cold War Warrior, the B-52 flew alert missions, staying aloft with nuclear weapons on board, ready to attack the Soviet Union at an instant's notice. The practice of flying aircraft on alert with live nuclear weapons ended in 1967; the practice of keeping B-52s on nuclear alert at the end of a runway was discontinued on 28 September 1991.

The eighth production model of the B-52, the H is set to remain in service until at least 2040. The real strength of the B-52H today lies in its ability to carry a wider range of weaponry than any other US bomber, and including the latest 'J' series of precision munitions.

The reconnaissance/bomber RB-52B had provision for the installation of a removable two-man pressurised capsule in the bomb bays, which allowed the carriage of cameras or ECM equipment. Normal bombloads could alternatively be carried.

B-52s over southeast Asia

A B-52F unloads over a South Vietnamese target during the Arc Light campaign. By September 1967 the last 'Big Belly' B-52Ds had reached Andersen Air Base, Guam, replacing the B-52Fs.

When SAC's B-52s were called upon to bolster the American campaign in southeast Asia, it was not in a strategic bombing role, but in support of ground operations against the Viet Cong – a tactical role that had never been envisaged for the type.

Although use of the B-52 had been seriously considered from the beginning of the 1965–68 Rolling Thunder campaign, doubts were expressed as to whether the aircraft could survive in the skies over North Vietnam against MiGs, surface-to-air missile (SAMs) and 'triple-A'.

Thus, when B-52 bombing operations began on 18 June 1965, Arc Light (as the B-52 campaign was named) was confined to targeting Viet Cong bases in South Vietnam. The aircraft employed were B-52Fs based on Guam, these aircraft typically flying 13½-hour missions from the island, refuelling en route from KC-135A tankers over the South China Sea.

Bombs were dropped from altitudes of 30,000 ft (9144 m) and above, and were delivered with remarkable accuracy, though as the bombing intensified over the next seven years their actual effectiveness was often questioned.

B-52Ds replace Fs

The B-52F was limited to a conventional 'iron' bombload of 27 750-lb (340-kg) bombs, and SAC was soon looking at ways of delivering more ordnance. The solution was to modify the entire B-52D fleet (170 of which were built) to so-called 'Big Belly' standard, this allowing the carriage of no fewer than 84 500-lb (227-kg) or 42 750-lb bombs internally. In addition, these aircraft were able to carry another 24 500-lb or 750-lb bombs aloft on external racks, thus bringing the type's maximum bombload up to a colossal 60,000 lb (27215 kg).

B-52s made their first Arc Light foray into North Vietnam on 11 April 1966, and later that month the first 'Big Belly' B-52Ds began to replace the B-52Fs on Guam. The last B-52Ds were completed in September 1967 and were to bear the brunt of the heavy bombing campaign for the remainder of the war. It was during September, too, that a B-52 encountered a SAM for the first time, though it was to be another five years before a B-52 was finally downed in this way.

Second base

A second base for B-52 missions was opened in April 1967; the use of U-Tapao Air Base in Thailand allowed missions to be flown without inflight refuelling. In the meantime, Arc Light continued into 1968 and, although Rolling Thunder was halted soon afterwards, Arc Light continued.

By 1970 the number and frequency of B-52 raids over the

Ground crewmen at Andersen load 750-lb (340-kg) bombs on to triple ejector racks attached to the underwing pylons of the type designed for use by B-52Gs and Hs, carrying Hound Dog missiles.

Camouflage
For service over southeast Asia, the B-52D fleet wore the camouflage scheme depicted here, standard TO 1-1-4 (comprising two shades of green and tan) covering their top surfaces, while undersides were finished in a gloss black.

Powerplant
The B-52D's eight Pratt & Whitney J57-P-29WA turbojets were required to muster all of their 12,100 lb (54.45 kN) to get the machine airborne with a 54,000-lb (24494-kg) bombload aboard. Water injection was used on take-off, increasing thrust and producing clouds of black exhaust.

Huge span
The B-52's 185-ft (56.4-m), 4,000-sq ft (371.6-m²) wing drooped almost low enough to touch the ground when the bomber was fully loaded; each wingtip sported an outrigger wheel to prevent this from happening.

B-52D Stratofortress

B-52D production totalled 170 machines, 101 from Boeing's Seattle plant and another 69 from the Wichita, Kansas, factory. 56-0676 was one of the latter, allocated to the 307th Strategic Wing at U-Tapao AB, Thailand during Linebacker II. On 18 December 1972 its tail gunner, SSgt Samuel O. Turner, became the first to score an air-to-air kill, downing a MiG-21.

Combat crew
B-52s went into combat with a basic crew of six – a pilot/aircraft commander, co-pilot, radar navigator (bombardier), navigator, electronic warfare officer (EWO) and tail gunner.

Deferred retirement
Early in the Arc Light campaign, US Secretary of Defense Robert McNamara announced that all the older-model B-52s, including the B-52Ds, would be retired by June 1971. This suggested an imminent end to hostilities in southeast Asia, but in the event the B-52D fleet was kept on and in late 1972 over 200 aircraft (including newer B-52Gs) were bombing Hanoi.

Tail turret
The B-52D's only defensive armament was a quartet of 0.5-in (12.7-mm) machine-guns in a radar-equipped turret at the extreme rear of the aircraft. Although the North Vietnamese made claims to the contrary, no B-52 was lost to NVAF fighters, although two B-52 gunners were credited with MiG kills during Linebacker II. The second of these was claimed on 24 December 1972, A1C Albert E. Moore of the 307th SW downing a MiG-21 while aboard B-52D 55-0083.

Massive raid
The largest force of B-52s deployed at once during the Vietnam conflict was 117-strong, sent against Hanoi on 26 December 1972, at the height of Linebacker II.

south had been drastically reduced, although B-52 operations over Cambodia and Laos (Operation Good Luck) kept monthly sortie rates up to around 1,000 in June 1971.

Linebackers I and II

In 1972, however, there was a massive increase in B-52 mission rates and the year also saw the loss of the first aircraft to enemy action. B-52 raids on targets in North Vietnam resumed on 9 April in response to the invasion of South Vietnam by the North Vietnamese on 30 March. On 11 April the first strikes against the interior of the country were launched.

Operation Linebacker, aimed at crippling the North Vietnamese transportation system, began the following month, B-52s playing an important part in its execution. The SAC force in the Far East now comprised both B-52Ds and Gs, a proportion of which were now based on Okinawa, as well as on Guam and at U-Tapao. These aircraft were flying over 3,000 sorties a month by June 1972.

By October the North Vietnamese appeared to have been bombed into submission and a bombing halt over the north was announced. However, the North Vietnamese took this opportunity to regroup and when they finally succeeded, on 22 November, in shooting down a B-52D from U-Tapao and stormed out of peace talks three weeks later, the stage was set for a last-ditch attempt by the US to force Hanoi to the peace table – by bombing Hanoi itself.

Linebacker II began on 18 December, the B-52s spearheading the campaign. In all, 714 sorties were flown by over 200 B-52s. Thousands of SAMs were ranged against the waves of B-52s, 15 of which were lost.

On 28 January 1973, the day on which a ceasefire was finally signed, the last Arc Light raid was flown, bringing the total number of B-52 sorties to 126,615. A staggering 2,633,035 tons (2675274 tonnes) of bombs had been dropped.

Post Vietnam, the Gulf and beyond

Although reduced in numbers since its heyday, the B-52 is still, after more than 50 years of service, one of Air Combat Command's most important bombers. Together with the B-1B Lancer and B-2A Spirit, it shoulders America's power projection role.

A common thread joined the nuclear Stratofortress of the Gen. Curtis E. LeMay era and the conventional Stratofortress which followed: both were meant to fly and fight at high altitude. With SAMs becoming an increasing threat, however, US officers knew that they had no choice but to bring this eight-engined giant down to tree-top level.

As long ago as 1975, the B-52 began to sprout new appendages in the form of bumps, bulges and the prominent jowls of the Electro-optical Viewing System (EVS). The latter was used to enable the bomber to fight at night, using FLIR (forward-looking infra-red) and LLLTV (low-light-level television).

As of 1979, of the 744 B-52s built, 348 were still in the inventory. Many of the D models were for use in the conventional role, and the G and H models in the nuclear, Short-Range Attack Missile (SRAM) and cruise missile-firing roles. The remaining B-52s were the subject of a major modernisation programme and additional mission requirements.

The backbone of SAC

In the late 1970s and, especially, the early 1980s, SAC directives for the B-52 lay in enhanced low-level penetration, cruise missile integration and updating for the conventional role. The majority of the new developments centred around offensive avionics and underwing missile carriage. The result was a pylon that could carry six nuclear AGM-86 ALCM (Air-Launched Cruise Missile) and SRAMs interchangeably. With these improvements, the G and H variants constituted the two definitive post-Cold War SAC models, and the veteran D models were gradually retired.

During the 1980s, the B-52G (193 built) represented the backbone of the command. With the ever-increasing costs of operating these elderly bombers, their numbers slowly dwindled and, by early 1993, only 80 examples remained in service. Serving with the 2nd, 42nd, 93rd, 366th, 379th and 416th Bomb Wings, the B-52Gs were used in the power projection role, using their enormous range and load-carrying ability to haul conventional bombloads to any point on the globe.

An important change to the force occurred in 1991, when SAC eliminated the tail-gunner position (and soon afterwards, the gun as well) from the B-52.

All Desert Storm missions were assigned to the G model,

***Above:** A B-52 crew is a five-strong team. In the forward cabin (illustrated), the flight crew of pilot and co-pilot handle the flying of the aircraft. Behind them, facing backwards, sits an electronic warfare officer. On the lower deck, facing forward, are the radar navigator and navigator.*

***Top:** The B-52H's 12 fuel tanks (including two external tanks) have a total, useable capacity of 48,030 US gal (181812 litres). Even with a maximum fuel transfer of 6,000 lb (2721 kg) per minute, it can take 20 minutes to fully refuel a B-52.*

Above: Seen in 1985, this B-52G wears the mid-1980s colours of two-tone green and grey over white, replaced soon afterwards with an all-over grey scheme.

Right: This B-52H is carrying the AGM-142 Have Nap missile, typical of the new generation of precision-guided weapons introduced to the B-52 from the 1990s. The AGM-142 was combat-proven over Kosovo.

some of which had been converted to carry 12 AGM-86 cruise missiles on the wing pylons, principally for the nuclear role (with the AGM-86B). However, the non-nuclear AGM-86C CALCM (Conventional Air-Launched Cruise Missile) was launched operationally for the first time on the opening night of Desert Storm. Non-cruise-configured B-52Gs were normally assigned a maritime role, including the launch of Harpoon anti-ship missiles, and these aircraft operated as free-fall bombers, attacking Iraq's Republican Guard.

Desert Storm was the final call to action for the B-52G, owing to the reduction in the threat posed by the Soviet Union, and the demise of SAC in 1992 to the more streamlined Air Combat Command. The final examples of the B-52G were retired in 1994, to be replaced by the B-1B Lancer.

The USAF maintains a force of 94 B-52H bombers at two locations – Barksdale AFB in Louisiana and Minot AFB in North Dakota. The B-52H has outlasted the era of ground nuclear alert, which ended in 1991. It is now the longest-serving combat aircraft in history, and is expected to put another quarter-century under its belt. The B-52H 'Cadillac' has a combat radius of 4,802 miles (7730 km) compared with the 4,082 miles (6575 km) of the earlier B-52G.

The image of the H model changed following the continual post-Cold War cutbacks which swept through the USAF. With the reduced nuclear threat, the 68 B-52Hs in regular service (the remainder are kept in reserve) have the ability to respond to both nuclear and conventional conflicts, often deploying over extreme distances from stateside or distant bases. Such missions were performed successfully on 16 December 1998, during Operation Desert Fox. A total of 15 B-52Hs, operating from Diego Garcia, launched CALCMs against Iraqi targets. Over the three-day campaign, some 90 missiles were launched. More significantly, continued unrest in the Balkans as a result of Serbian ethnic cleansing saw Fairford-based B-52Hs launching AGM-69Cs at Serbian positions during a prolonged campaign.

Since then, the B-52H has continued to prove its value in the ongoing war on terrorism. Initially involved in striking strategic targets in Afghanistan during the overthrow of the Taliban regime, B-52s of the 5th Bomb Wing completed some 17,500 combat missions over Afghanistan. The same unit also provided a dozen B-52s to support Operation Iraqi Freedom in 2003 and flew in excess of 120 combat missions in support of the Coalition land campaign.

At the height of the Cold War, this would have been a highly unlikely sight – a B-52 in a non-nuclear role with an Air Force Reserve squadron. This B-52H and A-10 'Warthog' belong to the Reserve's 917th Wing at Barksdale Air Force Base, Louisiana. The B-52H is the only Stratofortress model now in service and has introduced a range of new weapons for the post-Cold War era, including the Joint Direct Attack Munition (JDAM) series, the CBU-105 Wind-Corrected Munition Dispenser and the Joint Stand-Off Weapon (JSOW).

Proudly wearing SAC's 'Milky Way' sash on the nose, the 10th production KC-135A is seen with the type's original short fin. The upper lobe of the 'double-bubble' fuselage was for freight/passenger carriage, while the entire lower lobe and wing interspar area was given over to fuel carriage.

Boeing C-135 Stratotanker

Multi-task transport

Boeing's classic Stratotanker has achieved 50 years of front-line service. Notwithstanding its enormous achievements as a tanker, it has spawned one of the largest and most important families of variants.

On 15 July 1954 Boeing's Model 367-80 jet prototype took to the air for the first time, without any orders backing this brave venture. From this prototype were developed the eminently successful Model 707 airliner and Model 717 (C-135) family of military tankers and transports.

Boeing had for some time been involved in inflight refuelling and had developed the 'flying boom' in service with the KC-97. A need was rapidly arising, however, for a fast tanker able to refuel at speeds more suitable to jets.

Demonstrations of the 367-80 prototype with the 'flying boom' confirmed what the USAF already knew for, shortly after the 367-80's first flight, the first contract for the KC-135A Stratotanker had been placed on SAC's behalf. Between the production aircraft's first flight on 31 August 1956 and 1966, 820 C-135s rolled off the line, the last little changed from the first.

The KC-135A was powered by four Pratt & Whitney J57 turbojets, with water injection to provide extra thrust for take-off. The first 583 examples had short tailfins, and suffered from directional stability problems during take-off. A taller fin and powered rudder were fitted to cure this problem, and were retrofitted to earlier machines.

KC-135s went to work initially in support of SAC's bomber fleet, and remained in SAC's grasp until the command disbanded in 1992. However, from an early date they were also employed to refuel tactical fighters, a role which became prevalent during the US involvement in Vietnam.

Heavy usage of the fleet took its toll, but from 1975 KC-135s had

France's C-135FRs serve with ERV 93 'Bretagne' at Istres. This example demonstrates the use of the short hose/drogue unit fitted to the boom for probe-equipped receivers.

Below: An 18th Wing KC-135R from Kadena AB, Okinawa, refuels an E-3 from the same unit. The KC-135R remains the USAF's standard tanker 50 years after the Stratotanker first entered service.

With one wing and its engine nacelles painted black to avoid glare, the RC-135S Cobra Ball carried cameras to photograph and track Soviet ICBM tests, usually operating from Alaska.

Above: Basically a KC-135 without a refuelling boom, but with a strengthened floor and fuel dumping system, the C-135A was created for MATS to meet a quick-response airlift requirement.

their lower wings re-skinned to greatly extend their useful lives. However, the thirsty and noisy J57's days were numbered, leading to a wholesale re-engining programme. Firstly, from 1981, KC-135s assigned to the Air National Guard and Air Force Reserve were given TF33 turbofans and wide-span tailplanes from surplus 707 airliners to produce the KC-135D/E. More radical was the upgrade of the active-duty fleet with CFM F108 turbofans, revised avionics and onboard APU. The resultant KC-135R/T is the current version of the Stratotanker.

As well as its tanker capabilities, the KC-135R has a capacious hold and cargo door for the carriage of supplies. The type has been heavily involved in all USAF operations since Vietnam and, by the addition of a hose/drogue unit to the boom, can also refuel probe-equipped receivers.

Only one other nation bought the KC-135 from new – France. The Armée de l'Air purchased 12 aircraft similar in configuration to the KC-135A, designated C-135F. These flew with the drogue attachment from the outset. Eleven survivors were upgraded with F108 engines as C-135FRs, similar to the KC-135R. The drawdown of the USAF fleet released some aircraft for export. Three KC-135Rs were acquired by France to bolster the C-135FR fleet. Turkey and Singapore also operate KC-135Rs, re-engined and overhauled before delivery.

Transport and special duties

Early in the KC-135A's career it became obvious that the basic airframe was an excellent basis for a transport. The C-135A was the first transport version, 15 being built from new and three converted from KC-135As. They were followed by 30 C-135Bs, with TF33 turbofans and wide-span tailplane. These high-speed transports were able to take rows of passenger seats or cargo. Most were subsequently converted into special variants. However, five were given VIP interiors (along with two VKC-135As) for staff transport duties.

The C-135 proved an ideal vehicle for many special missions. Five C-135Bs were converted to WC-135B status to perform weather reconnaissance, while seven KC-135As were given Combat Lightning radio relay equipment for service in Vietnam.

Three main special variants families evolved, each of which has played a crucial part in US military operations.

Seventeen aircraft were built as KC-135B tankers from new, but did not serve in the tanker role, being converted with extra communications equipment to serve as EC-135C airborne command posts. These formed the cornerstone of the Post-Attack Command and Control System, under which an airborne alert was maintained to preserve the chain of command in the event of nuclear war. Augmented by radio relay EC-135s, the Looking Glass EC-135C carried a general who could control the US response to an attack. Additional EC-135s were produced to provide command posts for theatre commanders. The EC-135 fleet was retired in the early 1990s.

Strategic reconnaissance was another important mission for the C-135, resulting in many conversions of existing airframes and the purchase of 10 RC-135Bs from new. These aircraft subsequently became RC-135Cs with the addition of cheek fairings for electronic recording gear. Other RC-135 variants were produced, many with an extended nose housing side-looking radar.

In the 21st century the RC-135 fleet is more active than ever. The Combat Sent (RC-135U) and Rivet Joint (RC-135V/W) are an integral part of the USAF's warfighting capability, used to locate and analyse hostile radars and eavesdrop on enemy communications. Other RC-135 variants have been produced to record foreign missile tests.

The last family of major importance are the test and space-tracking aircraft, which have figured prominently in a myriad of experimental programmes. Most of the test aircraft have carried NC-135 and NKC-135 designations. Produced in some numbers, the bulbous-nosed C-135N/EC-135B aircraft were used to track US spacecraft.

The C-135 has been adapted for an almost endless list of experiments ranging from airborne lasers to weightlessness. This is the NC-135A Argus photo-documentation aircraft.

EC-135 variants
Command post aircraft

During the Cold War, EC-135 command posts were the backbone of Strategic Air Command's ability to hit back at the Soviet Union in the event of a nuclear strike.

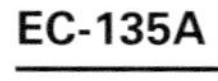

EC-135A

Five KC-135As (61-0262, 61-0278, 61-0287, 61-0289 and 61-0297) were converted to command posts in the early 1960s, serving initially with the 34th ARS at Offutt AFB, Nebraska. The EC-135As initiated the Looking Glass 24-hour alert on 3 February 1961. When the purpose-built EC-135Cs were delivered, the EC-135As went to the 28th Bomb Wing (4th ACCS) at Ellsworth, from where they formed part of the back-up ICBM launch command chain. The aircraft had additional communications and were equipped with the Airborne Launch Control Center equipment.

EC-135C

The only C-135s to be purpose-built for the command post mission were 17 aircraft, powered by TF33 turbofans, serialled 62-3581 to 62-2385 and 63-8046 to 63-8057. Originally designated KC-135B, the aircraft were redesignated as EC-135C once the command post equipment had been installed. Entering service in 1964, the EC-135Cs assumed the primary Looking Glass mission from the EC-135As, and continued the 24-hour airborne alert until stood down on 24 July 1990. After that date daily missions were undertaken. As other EC-135 variants were withdrawn, EC-135Cs made occasional deployments overseas to provide theatre commanders with an airborne command post. Finally, the command post mission was handed over in its entirety to the US Navy's E-6 fleet. By the time the EC-135C was retired, four of the fleet had received the Milstars satellite communications equipment, the antenna being housed in a dorsal fairing. From the outset EC-135Cs were extensively equipped with communications, and added more as the type's career progressed. A 28,500-ft (8687-m) trailing wire and other antennas allowed the EC-135C to communicate across huge distances by very low frequency, usually with other command posts. The task of the EC-135C and its staff was simple: in the event of a nuclear attack on the US, command of Strategic Air Command's nuclear forces could be transferred to the orbiting Looking Glass, which always carried a general to provide the necessary authority to launch ICBMs. The aircraft flew on 8-hour shifts, without a break, for nearly 30 years.

EC-135G

Four EC-135Gs (62-3570, 62-3579, 63-7994 and 63-8001) were produced by conversion from KC-135As. They were primarily intended to take over the launch of Minutemen ICBMs from their fields in the north-central US, and had Airborne Launch Control Center equipment fitted. They served with the 4th ACCS/28th BW at Ellsworth AFB, South Dakota, and with the 305th ARW at Grissom AFB, Indiana.

EC-135J

Three EC-135Cs (62-3584, 63-8055 and 63-8057) were further modified to EC-135J standard to take the national command authority aloft in time of tension. The mission was known as Night Watch and the aircraft served with the 1st ACCS. When E-4As assumed this role in 1975, the EC-135Js were reassigned to the 9th ACCS at Hickam AFB, Hawaii, to provide a command facility for C-in-C Pacific Forces.

EC-135H

The EC-135H was produced to provide theatre commanders with their own command post, and shared many of the communications features of the EC-135C Looking Glass aircraft, including a trailing wire antenna. The first EC-135H (61-0274) was assigned to the 6th ACCS at Langley AFB, Virginia, to support the C-in-C Atlantic in a mission called Scope Light. Four more EC-135Hs (61-0282, 61-0285, 61-0286 and 61-0291) were assigned to SACEUR in a programme codenamed Silk Purse. They were flown by the 10th Airborne Command and Control Squadron, parented by the 513th TAW at RAF Mildenhall, UK. Having been converted from KC-135As, the aircraft initially retained J57 turbojets, as seen on the 6th ACCS aircraft (above left). However, they were subsequently fitted with TF33 turbofans and wide-span tailplanes, as illustrated by the 10th ACCS aircraft (above).

Theatre command posts were withdrawn in the aftermath of the Gulf War and the end of the Cold War. Most were dispatched to Davis-Monthan AFB for storage and eventual scrapping, although a few were modified for other special missions. EC-135Cs were deployed on an infrequent basis to practise the theatre command support mission.

EC-135K

Not command posts in the true sense, the three EC-135Ks (55-3118 – built as the first KC-135A – 59-1518 and 62-3536) were employed by the 9th Tactical Deployment and Control Squadron to act as lead-ships for fighter formations transiting over long distances, especially across water. Two survivors were re-engined with TF33 turbofans after '536 was lost in 1977.

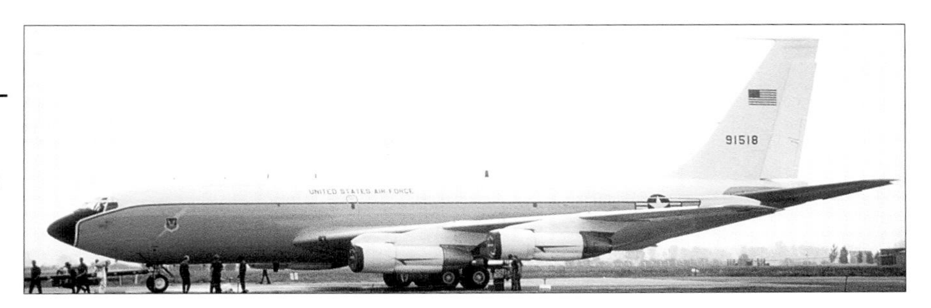

EC-135L

Eight KC-135As (61-0261, 61-0263, 61-0269, 61-0279, 61-0281, 61-0283, 61-0288 and 61-0302) were converted to EC-135L standard, serving with the 70th ARS, 305th ARW, at Grissom AFB, Indiana. Three were subsequently returned to tanker standard, although they retained the inflight-refuelling receptacle added to most EC-135s. The EC-135L's main role was to act as a radio relay platform, extending the reach of SAC's Post-Attack Command and Control System (PACCS) under the mission name Cover All. One flew in Desert Storm.

EC-135Y

This designation covered two aircraft modified as theatre airborne command posts for the Commander of US Central Command. They were converted from an NKC-135A (55-3125) and an EC-135N (61-0327). They were operated on behalf of CentCom by the 19th Air Refueling Wing at Robins AFB, Georgia.

KC-135A Combat Lightning

During the Vietnam War, seven KC-135As (61-0268, 61-0270, 61-0271, 61-0280, 61-0288, 61-0303 and 63-8881) were modified to act as radio relays. The first two in-theatre were initially operated alongside two EC-135Ls, but further Combat Lightning conversions allowed the EC-135Ls to return to their SAC duties.

EC-135P

Originally, five aircraft (58-0001, 58-0007, 58-0018, 58-0019 and 58-0022) were modified to EC-135P configuration, although two ('001 and '018) were later returned to tanker status. The EC-135P fleet was initially assigned to the 6th ACCS at Hickam AFB in Hawaii (above), flying the Blue Eagle mission in support of CinCPAC. When the 6th ACCS acquired EC-135Js, three of the EC-135Ps were reassigned to support CinCLANT and Tactical Air Command operations, flying the Scope Light mission with the 1st ACCS at Langley AFB (above). One of the EC-135Hs, 61-0274, was also assigned to this unit, and later acquired the EC-135P designation. Following the loss of '007 in a ground fire in January 1980, an NKC-135A (55-3129) was converted to EC-135P status to maintain the 1st ACCS fleet at four aircraft. The aircraft were essentially similar to the EC-135C in terms of communications equipment although, like the other theatre-assigned aircraft, lacked the launch control equipment for ICBMs. The 1st ACCS retired its EC-135Ps to the boneyard in 1992.

RC-135 Rivet Joint

RC-135V/W

Despite the collapse of the Soviet threat, the disbandment of Strategic Air Command in 1992 and the introduction of modern spy satellites and J-STARS, the RC-135 remains an important type in the USAF's reconnaissance inventory. During Operation Allied Force in 1999, elements of the RC-135V/W Rivet Joint fleet operated from RAF Mildenhall in the UK as a vital component of the electronic warfare/surveillance effort over the former Yugoslavia. Subsequently, the aircraft have been operational against Afghanistan, during Operation Enduring Freedom, and Iraq, during Operation Iraqi Freedom. It is virtually unthinkable that the US would engage in combat in any theatre without RC-135 Rivet Joint support.

Boeing E-3 Sentry
AWACS in action

Providing airborne early warning, control and communications, the E-3 Sentry is the West's premier air warfare management asset. Defined during the 1960s, it represented a major advance over its predecessors when it entered service with the USAF.

Based on the Boeing 707 airliner, the E-3 Sentry represented a quantum leap over the aircraft it replaced. The large rotodome houses the radar antenna, which turns at speeds of up to 6 rpm.

Large surveillance radars became airborne towards the end of World War II. Unlike previous airborne radars, they were designed to search vast volumes of sky and detect all aircraft present. The most widely used of the early generation of airborne early warning (AEW) aircraft was the EC-121 Warning Star, based on the Super Constellation airliner. In the 1960s, the USAF calculated that a radar in a large jet aircraft at a height of 30,000 ft (9145 m) would 'see' up to a distance of 245 miles (395 km), increasing the time available to give warning to intercept incoming bombers. The weakness of the 1950s radar system was exposed by the move at that time towards low-level attacks. Whereas aircraft flying at high altitude – above the AEW aircraft – had no 'ground clutter' in which to hide, by flying at low level they were able to hide in the reflection of the radar signals from the ground.

In 1965, the USAF began its Overland Radar Technology programme to design a radar that could look down over the land and see jets speeding at 'treetop height'. The answer proved to be pulse-Doppler radar, a radar that uses not only successive pulses of energy, but also the Doppler phase shift of the echoes received back from the target.

There are still certain target angles and ranges where either the target cannot be seen, or the apparent range may be uncertain. Much research was therefore needed to produce an Overland Downlook Radar (ODR) that worked. A very powerful, fast computer was required, which could check each one of the billions of radar pulses and echoes, and display on the operators' screens only the real targets and the true target speeds and distances.

New airframe

The AWACS (Airborne Warning and Control System) tender attracted both Boeing and McDonnell Douglas. Boeing's study included purpose-designed carrier aircraft, but these could not perform much better than the Boeing 707-320 airliner still in production. Boeing won the competition in July 1970, and an order for two EC-137D aircraft was placed to evaluate two competing radar designs. Of these, Westinghouse's AN/APY-1/-2 ODR emerged as the eventual winner.

The radar is located in a saucer-like rotodome carried on two 11-ft (3.35-m) struts above the rear fuselage. On the back of this antenna is mounted a mass of auxiliary equipment inside a large structural beam, so preventing any distortion that might affect accuracy. Attached to this beam is a communications and digital datalink antenna which is used for IFF purposes and for secure communications with perhaps hundreds of other friendly air or ground stations.

When the radar is in operation, a computer processes the incoming radar echoes and feeds the results to nine Situation Display Consoles (SDCs) and two Auxiliary Display Units (ADUs). Immediately behind the consoles is the station for the duty officer. Up front are the flight crew and the station for the computer operator. Further aft is the console for the radar maintenance officer. On a typical mission, an E-3 routinely refuels and stays aloft for up to 18 hours, carrying a crew of 20, including 16 mission specialists.

Following the two prototype EC-137Ds, two further E-3As were ordered for the FSD programme. A total of 30 production aircraft was then funded between 1975 and 1983, and the first flight of an E-3 with full mission avionics was on 25 May 1976. The first delivery to an

After testing two competing radars, the two EC-137Ds were refurbished and upgraded to the E-3 production standard. This is the first Sentry prototype modified as an E-3B, serving with the 552nd ACW at Tinker AFB, Oklahoma.

Ordered in late 1986 and fitted with a refuelling probe, wingtip ESM pods, CFM56-2A-3 engines and finished in an overall grey scheme, the seven aircraft of the RAF's Nos 8 and 23 Squadrons are based at Waddington.

Left: Most NATO countries were unable or unwilling to invest in national fleets of E-3s, so opted for a pooled unit. Based at Geilenkirchen, Germany, the fleet is dispersed to operating bases within Europe.

operational unit was in March 1977, to the 552nd AWAC at Tinker AFB, Oklahoma. E-3s assumed a US continental air defence role in January 1979. Since then, AWACS aircraft have been involved globally in all American combat operations.

The first 24 aircraft were delivered in 'core' standard and the final 10 to the US/NATO 'standard' with the updated AN/APY-2 radar, as fitted to all export aircraft. Core E-3As were upgraded as E-3Bs with the addition of ECM-resistant voice communications, Have Quick communications gear, increased crew capacity and other improvements. The first E-3B was redelivered to the USAF in July 1984. The 10 examples delivered to US/NATO standard were then updated and were redesignated as E-3Cs.

NATO aircraft and exports

Eighteen E-3A 'standards' were delivered to NATO, which also uses three Boeing 707TCAs for training. The 17 NATO Sentries are operated by the NATO Airborne Early Warning Force at Geilenkirchen, Germany.

The E-3 has been exported to three countries. E-3A 'standard' versions were delivered to Saudi Arabia. Ordered in 1982, the aircraft were delivered in 1986 and are supported by eight KE-3A tanker versions. The RAF and Armée de l'Air versions differ markedly from US and NATO E-3s, primarily in the replacement of TF33 turbofans with 106.8-kN (24,000-lb st) CFM56-2A-3 turbofans (also used by the Saudis), and installation of an inflight-refuelling probe in addition to the refuelling receptacle.

Following the cancellation of the Nimrod AEW aircraft for the RAF, the UK placed a contract for six aircraft designated E-3D Sentry AEW.Mk 1 in December 1986, to replace the ancient Shackleton AEW.Mk 2s. An option for a seventh aircraft was converted in October 1987.

At around the same time as the RAF ordered its aircraft, the Armée de l'Air placed an order for three E-3F SDAs (Système de Détection Aéroportée). An order for a fourth aircraft was added later. The E-3Fs serve with EDCA 36 of the Commandement Air des Systèmes de Surveillance et de Communications (CASSIC – Air Signals and Ground Environment Command).

Above: The USAF is by far the largest user of the E-3 Sentry. Initially operated by Tactical Air Command, today Air Combat Command's 552nd ACW at Tinker AFB, Oklahoma, has control over the fleet.

Right: At the heart of the AWACS system is the AN/APY-1/-2 Overland Downlook Radar, which feeds information to the Situation Display Consoles, arranged in rows of three within the cabin.

The second VC-137C, 72-7000, is seen wearing the white and blue upper fuselage scheme of the presidential aircraft.

Boeing C-137 to E-8 J-STARS

The military 707s

For more than 30 years the USAF used the Boeing 707 – as the C-137 – as the transport of America's politicians and VIPs, and the type will always be remembered for its role as 'Air Force One'. With the entry into service of the C-18 in the 1980s, a new chapter in the 707's US military service began.

Having ordered the Boeing Model 717 as the KC-135 Stratotanker, the USAF was quick to realise that the Model 707 would make an ideal VIP transport. Three 707-153s were ordered as VC-137As, with the first taking to the air on 7 April 1959. The new aircraft were fitted with communications stations, airborne headquarter facilities, beds, conference tables and seating areas.

All three VC-137As were modified in 1963, being fitted with Pratt & Whitney JT3D-3 turbofans in place of the original JT3C-6 turbojets, and becoming VC-137Bs. The modification usefully increased the range of the aircraft by about 1,000 nm (1,150 miles; 1850 km).

The USAF ordered a single 707-353B for the Office of President in 1961. The aircraft, the first VC-137C, was delivered in October 1962, and used the call-sign 'Air Force One' when the President was aboard. A second was delivered in 1972.

Change in designation

The VC-137Bs lost the V prefix in the late 1970s, when certain VIP fittings were removed. Since then, the V prefix has only been applied to aircraft and helicopters ordered for presidential use.

When the VC-25As (Model 747s) were delivered, the two VC-137Cs were downgraded as C-137Cs. Two other C-137Cs were later acquired by the USAF. The aircraft have now been replaced by C-32As (757-200s).

Above: The SAAF's fleet of Boeing 707-320Bs equips No. 60 Sqn at Waterkloof. Some of the aircraft have the joint role of tanking and Elint-gathering, carrying Sargent Fletcher pods on the wingtips and sensor packages on the lower forward fuselage.

Below: The first VC-137A, 59-86970, was delivered with short fin and turbojet powerplant. It appeared in Military Air Transport Service colours and the MATS badge was displayed near the tail section.

Wearing the colours of Air Force Systems Command (later Materiel Command), this EC-18B was one of four operated by the USAF. The most prominent feature of the variant was the huge tracking antenna in the 'platypus' nose.

***Left:** Unlike the USAF's E-8s, the US Navy's E-6s were new-build aircraft, with production lasting from 1986 to 1991. The aircraft operate from permanent detachments at Travis AFB, NAS Patuxent River and Offutt AFB.*

***Below left:** Originally designated EC-18C by the USAF, the airborne element of the J-STARS system was later named E-8.*

In June 1981 American Airlines sold eight 707-323Cs to the USAF as C-18As. One aircraft was used for spares before entering service, while the other seven underwent modification for test duties, one being bailed out to Grumman as the sole C-18B.

Four of the aircraft were converted to Advanced Range Instrumented Aircraft (ARIA), as EC-18Bs, to replace EC-135Ns. The aircraft featured the enlarged 'platypus' nose of the EC-135N. The EC-18Bs acted as communications links between satellites and the space centre at Houston, Texas. The final aircraft was retired in August 2001.

Two of the C-18As became EC-18D Cruise Missile Mission Support Aircraft (CMMSA), after being equipped with AN/APG-63 radar for use as flying control stations, tracking and monitoring cruise missile test flights.

The EC-18C designation was given to the original Joint Surveillance Target Attack Radar System (J-STARS) prototypes before they became E-8As. One of the EC-18Bs was converted to become an E-8C, together with both of the EC-18D CMMSAs.

A need to train pilots for the E-3 fleet saw the USAF purchase two ex-TWA 707-331C-H aircraft in 1984 – these became TC-18Es. The US Navy used two TC-18Fs as crew trainers for the E-6 Mercury fleet, two ex-TAP Air Portugal 707-382BA-Hs being acquired in 1987.

The E-6 and E-8 for the USN and USAF are two very different applications of the versatile 707-320 airframe. USN E-6 Mercury aircraft are recent, new-build examples from a second 707 production run in the late 1980s. USAF E-8 J-STARS platforms, by contrast, are rebuilt, former airline 707s, with airframes dating from the 1960s.

TACAMO and J-STARS

The US Navy acquired 16 E-6A Mercurys during the 1980s to carry out a single mission – TACAMO (Take Charge And Move Out). This was the term for LF (low-frequency) radio communication between the White House and Pentagon and at-sea strategic, ballistic-missile submarines. In the TACAMO role, the E-6A Mercury replaced the EC-130G Hercules.

The USN ordered more E-6A TACAMOs than it needed. All have since been upgraded to E-6B standard, with improved electronics installations. The surplus aircraft replaced ageing EC-135s, employed by the USAF for the command and control of strategic nuclear forces.

The Boeing/Grumman E-8 is an airborne command post outfitted for the J-STARS mission, a joint USAF/US Army programme for a battlefield management system that detects, locates, tracks and classifies enemy ground formations at long range.

J-STARS was rushed into use during Operation Desert Storm and was successful in directing fighter-bombers in attacks on Iraqi tanks and other targets detected by the E-8A's radar.

The two prototypes, both previously used 707s converted by Grumman, were equipped with a multi-mode side-looking airborne radar (SLAR) located in a 'canoe' faired into the belly of the aircraft. This radar functions in synthetic-aperture radar (SAR) and Doppler modes out to a range of 160 miles (257 km) to detect and pinpoint stationary objects such as parked missile launchers. The mission crew aboard the E-8 then directs attacks on the targets using the real-time JTIDS (Joint Tactical Information Distribution System).

A total of 17 E-8C J-STARS replaced the E-8A, retaining the same powerplant and configuration but equipped with newer internal systems and better data-processing capability.

707s around the world

Military versions of Boeing's 707 have achieved significant sales success outside the US, with many air forces purchasing ex-airline examples. A notable operator is the South African Air Force, which employs dual-role 707-320Bs for tanking and intelligence missions. In addition to its E-3As, NATO operates three 707s in training and transport roles. Spanish 707s are designated T.17 and operated in transport/tanker, Sigint and VIP configurations.

One of the more recent operators of the 707, Italy acquired four examples in 1992 from Air Portugal, for use in the tanker/transport role. Israel is a major operator, with examples appearing in several different guises, including EW, Elint-gathering, refuelling and transport versions. Pending replacement by the A330, the RAAF operates its aircraft as tankers, with one example used for transport. Most notable of Chile's four 707s is the IAI Phalcon AEW aircraft. Brazil, meanwhile, acquired four KC-137s in 1987 for use in the refuelling and transport roles.

Designated CC-137 Husky, Canada's 707-347Cs were used as transports by No. 437 Squadron. Two examples were later converted for the tanking mission (seen here), but all have since been retired.

BAe Hawk

RAF jet trainer

The BAE Systems Hawk has been in RAF service for more than 30 years. During its years of operations in the UK, the Hawk has been used as the RAF's advanced trainer, taught pilots tactics and weapons skills, became a fighter and thrilled millions as the mount of the Red Arrows aerobatic team.

Today the Hawk is still in production, but as a very different aircraft to that first conceived to meet an RAF requirement of the late 1960s.

The foundations for the Hawk programme resulted from a Royal Air Force need to replace the Folland Gnat and Hawker Hunter for the purposes of advanced training – a role which the two-seat Jaguar B had been due to undertake – and for the same aircraft to take over the upper end of the basic training syllabus conducted on the Jet Provost, although this requirement was later abandoned. This was all encapsulated in a requirement issued at the end of 1970.

However, it was recognised from the outset that the new trainer needed to be exportable, which required it to have a ground-attack potential. The contenders for the requirement were the Alpha Jet, the Hawker Siddeley HS.1182 and the BAC P.59. Design contracts were issued in 1971 to the two British firms and, in October 1971, the HS.1182 was selected as the winner. A contract was placed for 176 aircraft for the RAF in March 1972, the name Hawk being chosen in August 1973. The design was for a tandem-seat, single-turbofan engined (Rolls-Royce/Turboméca Adour) aircraft with provision for five hardpoints.

No prototype

In order to minimise costs, Hawker Siddeley proposed that the Hawk should be built from the outset on production tooling, without building any prototypes. The first pre-production aircraft and the first five off the production line would be used in the flight test phase.

The maiden flight occurred on 21 August 1974. Initial testing resulted in the addition of a pair of ventral stakes under the fuselage (to improve directional stability), as well as wing vortex generators and a small leading-edge fence. The Hawk's first public appearance was at the 1974 Farnborough air show.

Above: Photographed on its roll-out at Dunsfold in August 1974, the first Hawk was a pre-production aircraft, no prototypes being produced. The colour scheme was the original red and white.

Top: The major user of the Hawk in RAF service is No. 4 Flying Training School based at Valley – visible below the aircraft – where advanced pilot training is undertaken.

Four of the schemes worn in RAF service are those of high viz training (red and white), weapons training (camouflaged), point defence (grey) and the display team colours of the Red Arrows.

No. 234 Sqn of No. 1 Tactical Weapons Unit, based at RAF Brawdy, was one of four squadrons that lived on as shadow identities for the TWUs.

The first pair of Hawk T. Mk 1s was delivered to the RAF at RAF Valley on Anglesey, the home of No. 4 Flying Training School (FTS), on 4 November 1976. The first squadron of No. 4 FTS to re-equip was No. 1, the Central Flying School squadron responsible for standardisation and instructor training.

By October 1979, the Hawk had replaced the difficult-to-maintain Gnat and Hunter (which had been used to train pilots who could not physically fit into the diminutive Gnat) in all the No. 4 FTS units. Students arrived at Valley after flying the Jet Provost, or later the Shorts Tucano turboprop basic trainer, to fly just under 75 hours on the Hawk. From Valley, the newly qualified pilots travelled to the pre-Operational Conversion Unit tactical fighter/ground-attack lead-in training courses run at the Tactical Weapons Units (TWUs).

In the mid-1970s a massive fleet of Hunters was occupied in the task of training recently qualified pilots in the art of formation flying, air combat tactics and live weapons firing. The TWU at RAF Brawdy began receiving Hawks for this role from July 1977. The weapons-carrying capability, which had been built in as part of the export potential of the aircraft, and the continuity factor for the pilot – flying the same type for both advanced training and tactical weapons flying – made the Hawk ideally suited to this task.

The aircraft carried the centreline 30-mm ADEN gun pod and had two underwing pylons for rocket pods or practice bomb carriers, no provision being made for underwing fuel tanks. Instead of the original training colours of red and white, the tactical Hawks wore a green/grey camouflage.

The agility of the Hawk gave rise to its secondary (wartime) role of airfield defence. Rewired to be compatible with Sidewinder air-to-air missiles, the aircraft initially received an overall grey scheme and was redesignated as the Hawk T.Mk 1A.

The TWU was a unit of Strike Command and its aircraft formed 'shadow squadrons'. When the TWU split into No. 1 TWU at RAF Brawdy (with shadow squadrons Nos 79 and 234) and No. 2 TWU (Nos 63 and 151 Sqn) at RAF Chivenor (after a brief stay at Lossiemouth), most of the remaining Hunters went to No. 2 TWU, which did not officially convert to the Hawk until April 1981. At this time the TWUs had a principal war role of assisting in the low-level defence of airfields.

Point defence fighter

The successful use of the TWU Hunters as point defence fighters during exercises led to the testing of the Hawk in this role, in which it was found to be more than adequate. In early 1983, a contract was issued to convert 89 Hawks to be compatible with the AIM-9L Sidewinder air-to-air missile, to allow the aircraft to operate in the supplementary air-to-air role in times of emergency. After conversion, aircraft were designated as Hawk T.Mk 1As. The idea was to detect enemy aircraft with the Foxhunter radar of the Tornado F.Mk 3, while the Hawk, which was to be flown by an experienced instructor, fired missiles at the target. It was termed the 'mixed fighter force concept' and a total of 72 aircraft was declared to NATO after the last T.Mk 1A conversion was completed in May 1986.

Red Arrows

After the training school at Valley had retired its Gnats, the only examples of this aircraft left flying, with the exception of a few on test duties with the Ministry of Defence (Procurement Executive), were those with the Central Flying School's aerobatic team, the Red Arrows. Deliveries of Hawks to the 'Reds' began in August 1979 and the team began flying displays on the Hawk during the 1980 air show season.

By 2007, the RAF's Hawk training fleet was centred at RAF Valley, from where the type is operated by two Reserve Squadrons, Nos 19 (R) and 208 (R). The Red Arrows are based at RAF Scampton. A final RAF operator is No. 100 Squadron at Leeming, which uses the aircraft for the advanced training of fast-jet weapons systems officers and for operational support flying.

The RAF's 'legacy' Hawk fleet is due to be replaced from 2008 by the new-generation Hawk Mk 128. Based on the Hawk LIFT, this new development of the Hawk will serve as a lead-in fighter trainer for prospective Eurofighter Typhoon pilots. The Mk 128 is powered by the Adour 951 and can carry a weapons load of 6,614 lb (3000 kg). The original RAF requirement was for 31 such aircraft, although a total of 35 serials have been reserved. A prototype recorded its first flight on 27 July 2005.

The Hawk beat its great rival, the Alpha Jet, to enter service with Abu Dhabi in 1984. Sixteen examples of the Mk 63 were delivered and were followed by another batch of 18. These latter were improved Mk 102s, featuring wingtip Sidewinder air-to-air missile rails, radar warning receivers and revised wing aerodynamics for improved handling. They were later supplemented by four Hawk Mk 63Cs.

Export success

Having already established itself an enviable reputation within the RAF as a fast-jet trainer, the Hawk was actively marketed to a number of European and Middle Eastern countries. Many were to realise the potential of the aircraft, with a succession of orders being placed, and new variants developed.

From the start of the Hawk project, the aircraft was designed for export, especially in the light-attack role. With the Alpha Jet as the main export competitor in its advanced jet trainer category, the export Hawk was initially developed privately. It was marketed at a typical 1976 fly-away cost of around $2.25 million for the standard version, with one centreline and four underwing pylons carrying up to 5,000 lb (2268 kg) of stores over a 280-nm (322-mile; 520-km) combat radius.

Finland became the first Hawk export customer, placing an order for 50 T.Mk 51 versions in December 1977. Only the first four Finnish Hawks were British-built, with Valmet in Finland responsible for final assembly of the remainder. In February 1978, a second Hawk export order was announced, with 12 Hawk Mk 52s for Kenya. A third Hawk order followed in April, with an initial Indonesian contract for eight Mk 53s (subsequently increased to 20 in May 1981).

Although generally resembling the RAF Hawks, with similar Adour engines, the Mk 50 series incorporated several improvements. These included stronger undercarriage, a 30 per cent higher maximum take-off weight, and five stores pylons. Cockpit improvements included a twin-gyro attitude and heading reference system (AHRS), a revised weapons control system incorporating a lead-computing gyro sight, and more comprehensive flight instrumentation.

Engine improvements resulted in a new generation of export versions, known as the 60 series. Zimbabwe was the first customer for the Hawk 60 series, placing an order in January 1981 for eight Mk 61s. The Zimbabwe order was followed in June by a contract for eight Mk 61s from the Dubai Air Wing of the United Arab Emirates. Twelve Mk 64s were bought by Kuwait; 30 Mk 65s were purchased by Saudi Arabia (followed by a further 20 Mk 65A aircraft); 20 Mk 66s were bought by Switzerland; and 20 Mk 67s were purchased by South Korea. The latter aircraft feature the extended nose of the Hawk 100, with a small radome provided for radar.

The Hawk 100 programme was launched in 1982 and incorporated a host of new avionics, including a ring laser-gyro INS. This was linked, via a dual redundant MIL STD 1553B digital databus, to a HUD/Weapons Aiming Computer, radar altimeter, new stores management system and air data sensor for precise low-level navigation and weapons delivery. The Hawk's extensive range of ordnance was also further increased by the ability to carry Sea Eagle anti-ship missiles and the AGM-65 Maverick.

Single-seater

Avionics developed for the Hawk 100 were later applied to the single-seat Hawk 200 derivative. Viewed as 'a more affordable fighter', it was equipped with wingtip-mounted missile rails and an AN/APG-66H radar. Oman was the launch customer for the Hawk 200, placing a contract for 12 Mk 203s in July 1990, and ordering four two-seat Mk 103s at the same time. The second customer for

***Left:** To replace its elderly Vampires, the Air Force of Zimbabwe ordered eight Hawk T.Mk 61s. In doing so, the AFZ became the first customer for the uprated version. However, the first four Hawks delivered in July 1982 were badly damaged by a terrorist attack which resulted in the total destruction of one aircraft.*

***Below:** Australia's Hawk Mk 127s have advanced cockpit instrumentation resembling that of the F/A-18 Hornets for which they provide lead-in training. Thirty-three were ordered for the RAAF, 21 of which were assembled in Australia by BAe Australia.*

US Navy carrier trainer

On 26 January 1988, the US Navy announced the development of the T-45 Goshawk. A heavily converted carrier variant of the Hawk, the Goshawk features a revised wing layout and strengthened undercarriage. Entering operational service on 27 June 1992 with VT-21, the T-45 has replaced the large fleets of TA-4J Skyhawks and T-2C Buckeyes with the US Navy's training wings. A total of 204 aircraft was received.

***Below:** After receiving a batch of 20 Mk 53s beginning in 1980, Indonesia placed orders for eight Mk 109s (one of which is pictured) and 32 Mk 209s. The latter equip Nos 1 and 12 Sqns, TNI-AU.*

the Hawk 200 was Malaysia, with an order for 12 Mk 208s and 10 two-seat Mk 108 trainers placed in December 1990. Indonesia, already a Hawk customer, placed an order for 16 Mk 209s in June 1993, along with eight Mk 109s.

The first of the 'new 100s' was the Mk 115, ordered by Canada in May 1998 to equip the NATO Flight Training in Canada programme. The aircraft was essentially similar to those previously delivered to Abu Dhabi, Indonesia, Malaysia and Oman – but the last of these had been ordered in June 1993.

With a five-year hiatus in orders, the opportunity was taken to refine the Hawk Mk 115's cockpit. Whereas the baseline Hawk 100 had a cockpit with a single central MFD and a pure sensor display to starboard, the Mk 115 had a second MFD in place of the sensor display.

The Mk 115 also forms the basis of the 66 Mk 132s ordered by India. The Mk 132 has a reconfigurable monochrome sensor display to starboard, and some indigenous Indian equipment. India will receive an initial batch of 24 BAE-assembled aircraft, with the final batch of 42 being locally assembled by HAL.

The next customer for the Hawk was Australia, whose Mk 127, ordered in June 1997, was officially designated as the Hawk LIF (Lead In Fighter). The LIF features a new cockpit, with three colour MFDs and new avionics, including a HUD with F/A-18 symbology, a GPS navigation system, and with provision for a detachable, non-retractable refuelling probe.

The Hawk LIF in turn formed the basis of a new variant, the Hawk LIFT (Lead-In Fighter Trainer), with a further improved, fully NVG-compatible cockpit, an enhanced HUD, revised HOTAS moding and compatibility with a wider range of smart weapons. The new version also gained a new powerplant, the 6,500-lb st (28.90-kN) Adour Mk 951, which incorporates FADEC (Full Authority Digital Engine Control) and technologies from the Eurofighter's EJ200 engine. The first LIFT-configured Hawks were the 24 Mk 120s ordered by South Africa in September 1999.

In the late 1980s Oman placed a somewhat ambitious order for eight Tornado ADVs. This was cancelled in 1989 due to cost considerations. Purchased instead were 12 single-seat Mk 203 Hawks. Delivered in 1994, the aircraft serve with 6 Squadron at Masirah in the light-attack role.

BAE Systems Nimrod

The mighty hunter

Derived from the world's first jet-powered airliner, the Nimrod has been constantly updated over the last 30 years to ensure that it remains one of the world's finest maritime patrol and anti-submarine aircraft.

In 1958 the Air Ministry issued a requirement calling for a replacement for the Avro Shackleton as the RAF's principal maritime patrol aircraft. At this time the NATO multinational Atlantic seemed a logical choice. However, the RAF refused to consider the Atlantic, and by 1964 official indecision and rising costs ensured that only a design derived from a current aircraft would be affordable.

Choosing the Comet

The Vickers Vanguard, Vickers VC10, de Havilland Comet and Hawker Siddeley Trident underwent RAF trials. Despite being the eldest of the four designs, the Comet had an efficient wing at all speeds and altitudes in the planned mission, and crews enjoyed the handling and low-level ride. The factor which clinched the decision was that it was possible to shut down two or even three of the Comet's engines while on patrol to extend endurance. Moreover, the latter would be greatly improved by replacing the heavy and thirsty Rolls-Royce Avon 534 engines with the Spey turbofan.

Hawker Siddeley received the go-ahead for the HS.801, later named the Nimrod, in June 1965 and started incorporating the many changes necessary to the Comet 4. The engine inlets and jetpipes were enlarged to accommodate the Spey engine. The fuselage was shortened and an enormous unpressurised extra section was added over almost the whole length, providing room for two tandem weapons bays. Another important addition was the magnetic-anomaly detector (MAD) tailboom.

Development of the Nimrod proved to be painless, and the first Nimrod MR.Mk 1 reached the RAF in October 1969.

Above: Between 1971 and 1977, the RAF had a permanent Nimrod force in the Mediterranean with No. 203 Squadron based at Luqa, Malta. This example is seen in 1973, operating from RAF Gibraltar.

Top: Although never used in anger, the Nimrod can carry two pairs of AIM-9 Sidewinder missiles. During the Falklands War, the type was cleared to engage Argentinian maritime patrol aircraft.

In addition to the purely military anti-submarine role, the Nimrod MR.Mk 1 was used for long-range search and rescue missions and for protecting the UK's territorial waters.

Above: The Nimrod fulfils four roles in RAF service: anti-submarine warfare (ASW); anti-surface unit warfare (ASUW); search and rescue (SAR); and Intelligence, Surveillance, Target Acquisition and Reconnaissance (ISTAR), including communications support.

Above right: The Nimrod MR.Mk 1's weapons bays held 13,500 lb (6120 kg) of stores in six lateral rows. The fuselage aft of the bay was used for storing and ejecting sonobuoys and other stores.

By August 1972, all 38 aircraft in the initial order had been delivered. From its entry into service, the Nimrod proved immensely popular, no other aircraft in its class offering anything like the same combination of performance, spaciousness, mission capability and reliability. The main tactical compartment held the mission crew, comprising a routine navigator, a tactical navigator, a radio operator, a radar operator, two sonics systems operators and an ESM/MAD operator.

In 1974/75, a further eight Nimrod Mk 1s were built, but the British withdrawal from Malta rendered these aircraft surplus to requirements. Seven of the eight aircraft were selected for conversion during the development of the doomed Nimrod AEW.Mk 3 variant.

MR.Mk 2 improvements

Even before the first Nimrod MR.Mk 1 was built, it was recognised that in the course of its service life the original avionics and mission equipment would become outdated. Accordingly, in 1975 a largely new and immeasurably more capable equipment fit was designed. A total of 35 of the MR.Mk 1 aircraft was redelivered as virtually new aircraft, designated Nimrod MR.Mk 2. The first MR.Mk 2 was redelivered in August 1979, and though the flight performance was unchanged, the mission effectiveness was enhanced enormously. The MR.Mk 2 has a completely new avionics and equipment suite, in which all major sensors and equipment items were changed.

The RAF Nimrod fleet has now been reduced to three units – Nos 120, 201 and 42 (R) Squadrons – all based at RAF Kinloss, Scotland, and, since the end of the Cold War, the Intelligence, Surveillance, Target Acquisition and Reconnaissance (ISTAR) mission has come to prominence. The latest Nimrod MRA.Mk 4 configuration, which employs updated flight deck, mission avionics and equipment and BMW Rolls-Royce BR710 turbofans, is being applied to surviving aircraft via a remanufacturing programme that involves an 80 per cent reconstruction of the airframe, a new wing and undercarriage.

Nimrod R.Mk 1 – Electronic eavesdropper

In addition to 46 Nimrod MR.Mk 1s, three further aircraft were ordered as replacements for No. 51 Sqn's intelligence-gathering Comets and Canberras. Security surrounding the aircraft was such that they were delivered to RAF Wyton in 1971 as little more than empty shells, with the RAF fitting virtually all the mission equipment. Shunning publicity, the R.Mk 1 entered service in 1974 as a 'calibration' aircraft, its true Elint role being disguised. The R.Mk 1 (early version pictured below) differs from maritime versions in having no MAD tailboom, instead being fitted with dielectric radomes in the nose of

each external wing tank and on the tail. Constant updating has resulted in increasing numbers of antennas above and below the fuselage as well as wingtip ESM pods. Extra internal equipment has also led to the deletion of several cabin windows and the current aircraft (illustrated below) are fitted with underwing chaff/flare dispensers. The R.Mk 1s almost certainly have a computerised 'threat library', allowing a detailed 'map' of potential enemy radar stations, navaids and defence systems to be built up. With an estimated crew of about 25, No. 51 Sqn R.Mk 1s gained a Battle Honour after the Falklands War and operated from RAF Akrotiri during Desert Storm. In May 1995, one R.Mk 1 ditched into the Moray Firth, resulting in an MR.Mk 2 being converted to Elint standard as a replacement.

Above: Although the Nimrod fleet is shared between the three units, No. 42 Sqn applied special markings to this Nimrod MR.Mk 2 for public displays in the UK and around Europe in the mid-1990s. The latest Nimrod MRA.Mk 4 version is due to enter service in 2011.

British Aerospace Sea Harrier

A naval 'jump-jet'

The RAF's revolutionary Harrier had already proven the viability of VTOL operations at sea, so when the Royal Navy ditched its conventional carrier fleet in 1978, a navalised Harrier was developed to take the place of the Phantoms and Buccaneers which had previously provided the Navy's carrierborne muscle.

XZ451 was the second production Sea Harrier and was preceded by three trials aircraft. When the 30-mm ADEN cannon pods were not fitted, ventral strakes were added to preserve aerodynamic qualities, notably in terms of recirculating air while in the hover.

When, in 1964, the Labour government cancelled the supersonic VTOL P.1154RN and bought the F-4K Phantom instead, it appeared that the Royal Navy was committed to conventional carriers. However, by the end of 1978 the Phantom and the carriers had gone, replaced by three 'Harrier-carrier' vessels ('Invincible'-class through-deck cruisers) plus an interim converted carrier (HMS *Hermes*), none able to support conventional fixed-wing aircraft. The only aircraft available was the Harrier, suitably navalised and optimised for fleet air defence.

The navalised Harrier differed from the RAF model in the vital respect that it had radar and a cockpit floor raised 10 in (25 cm) for greatly improved pilot's vision. Development problems associated with the Sea Harrier were few, for 24 exercises had been conducted on warships by 'land' Harriers over a 10-year period from February 1963. As a concession to the salt air, however, magnesium components were replaced in the airframe and engine, the latter becoming the Pegasus Mk 104, still with the 21,500-lb st (96.75-kN) rating.

Seen during deck trials aboard Hermes, this aircraft served with No. 700A Flight, the intensive flight trials unit formed to clear the Sea Harrier for front-line service. Other trials aircraft were assigned to the manufacturer at Dunsfold and the A&AEE at Boscombe.

Naval roles

The military designation, Sea Harrier FRS.Mk 1, denoted fighter, reconnaissance and strike duties. As a fighter, the aircraft was intended to defend the fleet against Soviet long-range bombers approaching at medium altitude and launching cruise missiles. For this, Ferranti Blue Fox pulse-modulated I-band radar was developed. This gave search and attack modes for both air and surface targets, with weapon-aiming data presented in the HUD, as well as boresight ranging for targets of opportunity. Twin 30-mm ADEN cannon pods could be fitted, the main air-to-air weapon being the AIM-9L Sidewinder, one of which was initially carried on each outer wing pylon. A twin-rail launcher was hastily developed during the Falklands War and entered service in August 1982.

Photographic reconnaissance was minimally catered for by a single F95 oblique camera in the nose. Used only in daylight, the starboard-side F95 had two interchangeable lenses.

Strike implied loft-bombing with the lightweight version of the British WE177 nuclear weapon, but conventional

The Sea Eagle anti-ship missile was an important Sea Harrier weapon and is seen here being carried by one of the pre-production aircraft during land-based ski-jump trials.

weaponry also figured prominently in the Sea Harrier's armoury. Inboard underwing pylons stressed to 2,000 lb (907 kg) could carry free-fall and retarded bombs, or a Sea Eagle anti-ship missile.

Avionics changes from the Harrier included a Ferranti attitude reference and heading system linked to Decca 72 Doppler as a replacement for the FE541 INS, which could not be aligned on a moving deck. Smiths Industries provided a new HUD, linked to a weapon-aiming computer; there was a radar altimeter; and a new autopilot eased workload. The radar warning receiver was an improved version of the ARI.18223. AN/ALE-40 chaff/flare dispensers were fitted in 1982.

Production programme

Hawker Siddeley received a study contract for the 'Navalised Harrier' in 1972, Ferranti receiving a go-ahead for radar development in the following year. Announcement of a contract for 24 aircraft, including three pre-series machines for development work, was made on 15 May 1975, the order complemented by a Harrier T.Mk 4A funded by the Navy, but delivered to the RAF as a payback for pilot training services rendered. Follow-on orders increased the total to 57 single-seat aircraft and four trainers, the final three being navalised T.Mk 4Ns with Sea Harrier avionics and stores management systems, Pegasus 104 engines, but no radar. With its small wing, the Sea Harrier required only a folding nose in order to use the deck-lift aboard 'Invincible'-class vessels, but the T.Mk 4N was incapable of being struck below.

First flight of a Sea Harrier took place at Dunsfold on 20 August 1978, in advance of the three pre-series aircraft that had been delayed by problems not of the manufacturer's making. On 15 December 1978, the FAA's last two fixed-wing squadrons of Buccaneers and Phantoms disbanded, but it was not until June 1979 that a first Sea Harrier was handed over at Yeovilton as the first of a new line of fixed-wing, front-line aircraft. Apart from the short-lived trials squadron, four RN units were formed to operate Sea Harriers: 800 NAS and 801 NAS for shipboard deployment and 899 NAS as the normally shore-based headquarters and training unit. 809 NAS was established during the Falklands campaign, but the squadron disbanded soon after.

***Left: India's front-line Sea Harriers serve with INAS 300 'White Tigers'. After training at Yeovilton, the first aircraft left for India in December 1983 for service aboard INS* Vikrant. *In August 1987 the Sea Harriers switched to INS* Viraat, *previously HMS* Hermes.**

Indian deliveries

The only export order for the Sea Harrier was from India, which bought 23 FRS.Mk 51 single-seaters and four T.Mk 60 two-seaters; the survivors of these are the only Sea Harriers remaining in service, and go to sea aboard the carrier INS *Viraat*. Two additional ex-RAF T.Mk 4s were acquired in 2003, and converted to T.Mk 60 standard. The Indian aircraft are essentially similar to the RN machines, but use Magic 2 missiles instead of AIM-9s. At least 12 single-seat aircraft and two T.Mk 60 trainers have been written off in Indian service, but the remainder continue in service with original operator INAS 300, while pilot training is handled by INAS 552. An upgrade for 14 FRS.Mk 51s was announced in 2005, adding Elta EL/M-2032 multi-mode fire control radar and new AAMs.

Bearing the crossed swords and trident badge of 800 Naval Air Squadron on its tail, this FRS.Mk 1 displays the all-over Extra Dark Sea Grey paint scheme adopted for the Falklands campaign.

Sea Harrier FA.Mk 2

In refining the Sea Harrier as a more capable interceptor, while retaining its reconnaissance and attack capabilities, British Aerospace made some significant changes to the airframe. The result was the FA.Mk 2, one of the world's most able fighters when it entered service with the Fleet Air Arm in 1993.

*The Sea Harrier **FRS.Mk 1/AIM-9L** combination was a potent one in the Falklands War, and the second-generation aircraft retained Sidewinder capability. This aircraft is also fitted with two underfuselage 30-mm **ADEN** cannon pods, which could be replaced by **AIM-120 AMRAAM** launch rails or aerodynamic strakes.*

British Aerospace received a contract in January 1985 for the project definition phase of the Sea Harrier update programme, which included two conversions of the Sea Harrier FRS.Mk 1 to FRS.Mk 2 (later FA.Mk 2) standard. Initially (in 1984) it had been reported that the MoD was planning to award a contract to BAe and Ferranti to cover a mid-life update of the entire Sea Harrier fleet, but these plans were substantially revised (in 1985) to cover an upgrade of some 30 airframes. The upgrade would include Blue Vixen radar, JTIDS, AIM-120 AMRAAM provision and an enhanced RWR fit. The original BAe proposal also covered the installation of wingtip Sidewinder rails. These additions, along with several other aerodynamic refinements, were eventually cut from the project, but a kinked wing leading edge and wing fence were retained. The first test aircraft was flown on 19 September 1988, followed by a second in March 1989. Despite the addition of an extra equipment bay and a recontoured nose to house the Blue Vixen radar, the FRS.Mk 2 was actually nearly 2 ft (0.61 m) shorter overall due to the elimination of the extended pitot head probe of the earlier variant. No increase in wingspan was found to be necessary to carry additional stores, which included a pair of 190-Imp gal (864-litre) drop tanks plus AIM-120 AMRAAMs on each of the outer pylons. Ferry tips were available to increase the wingspan to 29 ft 8 in (9.04 m).

The FA.Mk 2 cockpit introduced new multi-function CRT displays and HOTAS controls to reduce pilot workload. The FA.Mk 2 was powered by a Pegasus Mk 106 turbofan, a navalised version of the Mk 105 as fitted to the AV-8B, but with no magnesium in its construction. On 7 December 1988, a contract was awarded for the conversion of 31 FRS.Mk 1s to Mk 2 standard. On 6 March 1990, an order was placed for 10

Fleet Air Arm air defence, 1990s style: a Sea Harrier FA.Mk 2 from No. 801 Sqn shares deck space on HMS Illustrious with a Sea King AEW.Mk 2 from No. 849 Sqn. The Sea Harrier's Blue Vixen radar provided the pilot with an excellent air picture – in operations over Bosnia FA.Mk 2s were occasionally used to fill in blanks in the overall AEW coverage.

Fitted with Sidewinder acquisition rounds, fuel tanks and gun pods, a Sea Harrier FA.Mk 2 positions itself over the carrier deck prior to landing. The bolt-on refuelling probe was regularly used for ferrying, allowing the aircraft to refuel from RAF tankers.

new-build FA.Mk 2s to augment the conversions, attrition having by that time reduced the RN's Sea Harrier inventory to 39 aircraft. A further contract in January 1994 covered 18 more FA.Mk 2s and an additional five FRS.Mk 1 conversions.

Carrier qualification trials were conducted aboard HMS *Ark Royal* in November 1990 and, among other favourable factors, these proved the FA.Mk 2 capable of operating safely from a 12° ramp. The two aircraft involved in the trials were configured as pre-production aircraft, although there was only one radar between the two. In order to enhance pilot conversion training, a new two-seat trainer conversion, designated T.Mk 8N, was provided, with four aircraft replacing Harrier T.Mk 4Ns in 1996. Essentially a reconfigured T.Mk 4N, this variant duplicated FA.Mk 2 systems, with the exception of the radar.

AMRAAM trials

The primary air-to-air missile for the Sea Harrier FA.Mk 2 was the AIM-120 AMRAAM. Trials for this weapon included 10 live firings against sub-scale drones and full-scale, supersonic QF-106 drones, commencing in March 1993. A serious setback occurred with the loss of one of two radar-equipped trials aircraft in a crash on 5 January 1994.

A trials unit was formed at Boscombe Down in June 1993, receiving the first production FA.Mk 2 on the 21st of that month. The Sea Harrier FA.Mk 2 OEU, which also undertook trials at Boscombe, was an offshoot of No. 899 Squadron. Four aircraft from this OEU then undertook a limited combat cruise aboard HMS *Invincible* from August 1994, prior to full-scale deployment on HMS *Illustrious* by No. 801 Squadron in January 1995. No. 800 Squadron also formed on the type, becoming a stalwart of operations over the former Yugoslavia.

The Sea Harrier was retired prematurely in favour of the upgraded Harrier GR.Mk 9 attack aircraft, the last examples being withdrawn on 28 March 2006.

Sea Harrier FA.Mk 2

Sea Harrier FA.Mk 2 orders for the Royal Navy totalled 38 conversions from existing FRS.Mk 1s plus some 28 new-build aircraft. These served with two front-line squadrons (No. 800 – '12x' codes, and No. 801 – '00x' codes) and a Yeovilton-based training unit (No. 899 Sqn). Under the 1998 UK Strategic Defence Review, the Sea Harrier force joined the RAF's Harrier GR.Mk 7 fleet in a joint-services command, allowing integrated FA.Mk 2/GR.Mk 7 air groups to be carried aboard Royal Navy carriers.

Blue Vixen radar
The heart of the FA.Mk 2 upgrade was the GEC-Marconi Blue Vixen, a lightweight multi-mode radar offering full lookdown/shootdown capability over sea or land. Designed from the outset to be fully compatible with AMRAAM, the radar allowed the ripple-firing of all four missiles carried by the Sea Harrier. Working in I-band with variable pulse repetition frequencies, the radar offered a wide range of air-to-air and air-to-surface modes, the latter supporting sea search missions.

Cockpit
Although it retained the original HUD (head-up display) from the FRS.Mk 1, the FA.Mk 2 cockpit was considerably redesigned to incorporate two MFD head-down displays. All vital inputs were made via a HOTAS (hands on throttle and stick) system or via a UFC (upfront controller). JTIDS datalink integration was initially specified, then shelved, and later reinstated.

Rear fuselage
An extra 1-ft 2-in (0.35-m) plug was inserted aft of the wing trailing edge of the FA.Mk 2 to offer greater internal capacity for avionics equipment.

Defences
The FA.Mk 2 was adequately protected thanks to its Sky Guardian 200 radar warning receiver, which presented a threat array in the cockpit. Mechanical countermeasures were launched from AN/ALE-40 chaff/flare dispensers.

Missile armament
The FA.Mk 2's standard air-to-air loadout consisted of four AIM-120 AMRAAMs carried under the wings and fuselage (the latter displacing the ADEN cannon). On the fuselage stations, the AIM-120 used the LAU-106/A ejector launcher, while those carried underwing were suspended from Frazer-Nash Common Rail Launchers. The wing AMRAAMs could be replaced by up to four AIM-9 Sidewinders on LAU-7 rails. Paveway II LGBs could be carried, but not self-designated.

Air-to-ground weapons
Although tailored more closely to the air defence mission than the FRS.Mk 1, the FA.Mk 2 could carry CRV-7 rocket pods, 1,000-lb (454-kg) bombs, Lepus flares and other air-to-ground ordnance, if required.

Finished in the white over dark blue colour scheme that has adorned the USAF's T-37Bs in recent years, these two aircraft were based at Reese AFB, Texas, in 1992. In 2007, 419 'Tweets' remained within the USAF's Air Education & Training Command, training aircrew from 12 nations.

Cessna T-37/A-37 Dragonfly

Long-serving trainer

Cessna's T-37 'Tweet', or 'Tweety Bird', is the USAF's primary trainer and the first real training aircraft in which a potential new pilot receives instruction. Since the late 1950s, more than 100,000 pilots have earned their wings after starting out in the T-37. The production T-37B will remain in service well into the 21st century.

The T-37B is a conventional, all-metal, twin-jet with a student pilot in the left seat and an instructor on the right beneath a broad clamshell canopy, giving the instructor a 'hands-on' relationship with the student. The aircraft is configured with two small engines in the wingroots with nozzles at the trailing edge. Tricycle landing gear is low and wide-tracked to ease landing and airfield performance. The aircraft's horizontal tail is mounted above the fuselage, one-third of the way up the fin, to ensure that the airstream flowing past it is undisturbed by jet exhaust.

The XT-37 prototype made its first flight on 12 October 1954, followed by the first production T-37A on 27 September 1955. Service use finally began in 1957 after considerable development work, including changes to the cockpit and other modifications. With the T-37 the USAF intended to introduce trainee pilots to jet aircraft from the *ab initio* phase, but the delay in the introduction of the T-37 meant that it was initially only flown by pilots who had begun their flying on the piston-engined Beech T-34A.

In November 1959, the USAF introduced the T-37B (Model 318B) with more powerful engines and improved navigation and communications gear and, in April 1961, the USAF achieved its goal of all-jet pilot training, with students beginning on the 'Tweety Bird' from the outset.

A T-37C version, with wing hardpoints for ordnance and provision for armament, was not adopted by the USAF (though it was exported). The YAT-37D was an armed version evaluated in the early 1960s. Attempts to adopt the T-37 for an air-to-ground role had begun in 1958, when the US Army evaluated three T-37s. However, the statutory bar on the US Army operating fixed-wing combat aircraft proved to be the programme's undoing.

Combat in Vietnam

During the Vietnam War, efforts to find a combat role for the basic T-37 resumed. On 2 May 1967 the USAF began to fly the A-37A Dragonfly, a converted T-37B, for close air support (CAS) and special operations missions. Thirty-nine A-37As were built by converting T-37Bs on the production line. Some were assigned to the South Vietnamese air force.

The A-37B which followed was virtually a new aircraft, weighing

Re-engined with General Electric J85s producing over twice the power of the T-37's J69s, the A-37B featured an inflight-refuelling capability and eight hardpoints able to carry up to 4,100 lb (1860 kg) of underwing stores. Its airframe was stressed for 6g rather than the 5g of the T-37.

Numerous T-37B, T-37C (a variant of the B-model with underwing hardpoints) and A-37B aircraft have been exported. A-37Bs, like this one, are the primary offensive type of the Fuerza Aérea Uruguaya. Sixteen were acquired from ex-USAF stocks in 1992 and 1993.

nearly twice as much as a T-37 trainer, and being powered by two 2,850-lb (12.8-kN) thrust General Electric J85-GE-17A turbojets. 'You have to remember that this was a robust aircraft', says former Cpt. Cort Durocher, who flew A-37Bs with the 604th Air Commando Squadron in Vietnam. 'This was not just a trainer with weapons. All in all, the A-37B was about twice the size of the "Tweet", and when it got into a fight it gave a good account of itself.'

Five hundred and seventy-seven A-37Bs, of which at least 130 later became OA-37B forward air control (FAC) aircraft, served with USAF and Air National Guard units until 1992. The FAC aircraft replaced Cessna O-2As and were issued to three ANG Tactical Air Support Groups, as well as regular units based in South Korea and Panama, where they superseded OV-10 Broncos.

Foreign operators

Numerous foreign air forces have operated the T-37B, T-37C and (O)A-37B. In 2007 T-37s remained in service with Bangladesh, Colombia, Germany (these aircraft being based in the US for the training of Luftwaffe aircrew, and carrying US serials and markings), South Korea (where replacement is underway by the indigenous T-50 Golden Eagle), Pakistan (planned to be replaced by the NAMC/PAC K-8 Karakorum) and Turkey. Chile, Colombia, Ecuador, Guatemala, Honduras, South Korea (where they are also flown by the Black Eagles aerobatic team), Peru, El Salvador and Uruguay fly Dragonflies, and many of these are likely to do so well into the 21st century.

While the US has retired its A-37Bs, the T-37B trainer has been forced to soldier on. The 'Tweet' was to have been replaced by the Fairchild T-46A, but this was cancelled in 1986. A T-37 derivative, the T-48, was proposed by Cessna's then owner, General Dynamics, but this attracted little support. From 1989 Sabreliner Corporation began supplying SLEP (Service Life Extension Program) modification kits to the USAF to allow surviving T-37s to be structurally rebuilt for extended service. The aircraft will eventually be replaced, though only very slowly, by the Raytheon T-6A Texan II (a US-built derivative of the Pilatus PC-9), the first operational example of which was delivered to a training unit in May 2000.

According to USAF instructor Major Bill Gray, the T-37B is one aircraft whose time has come – and gone. Says Gray: 'The T-37 does little to prepare pilots for modern cockpit and navigation systems, is very hard on student pilots by being very hot in the summer, is a gas-guzzler of the highest order, is the air force's champion of both *g*-induced loss of consciousness rates (because a *g*-suit is not worn when flying it) and physiological incident rates (no cabin pressurisation with frequent trips to over 22,000 ft/ 6706 m), and is old enough to be too expensive to improve with modifications.'

Below: From 1979 to 1993, the 169th Tactical Air Support Sqn, Illinois ANG, flew OA-37Bs in the FAC role. 'Southeast Asia' camouflage, seen here, eventually gave way to a 'Europe One' scheme.

Above: The second attempt to develop an 'armed' T-37 derivative resulted in the YAT-37D (later YA-37A), a product of the need for a light CAS and armed reconnaissance aircraft for the war in Vietnam. Redesignated A-37A, 39 T-37Bs were converted for the role and evaluated in-theatre in late 1967.

Convair B-58 Hustler

Space-age bomber

The world's first supersonic bomber, the B-58 represented a massive leap forward in aviation technology. Designed in response to a USAF request for a high-performance bomber, the Hustler, with its huge weapon pod and breathtaking speed, was one of the most dramatic aircraft of its era.

Above: 43rd Bomb Wing B-58s are seen at Carswell AFB. The Hustler lacked flaps, so landings were always 'hot' affairs. The aircraft typically came across the fence at some 200 kt (230 mph; 370 km/h).

Below: YB-58 55-663 was used as a testbed for the drop pods, and was the first aircraft to drop the two-component pod (TCP) (carrying fuel and nuclear weapons) at supersonic speeds.

Today it is almost a cliché to refer to the Convair B-58 Hustler as a milestone, but it truly was one of the most significant aircraft of the early days of high-performance jet aviation. It was the world's first supersonic strategic bomber and was arguably the most successful in terms of accomplishing the goals set for it. However, it was withdrawn after just a decade of service, and failed to be replaced by anything that could match its outstanding performance.

The B-58 had its origins in the late 1940s, when the USAF (USAAF until September 1947) solicited a number of advanced bomber studies under its Generalized Bomber Study (GEBO). Between 1949 and 1951, a second stage of this study narrowed the concept to what was to be a supersonic bomber capable of operating at twice the speed of sound (i.e. Mach 2). By early 1951, the evaluation process had come down to a choice between two design study concepts: Boeing's B-59 and the Convair B-58.

In October 1952, after evaluating the two proposals, the Air Research & Development Command selected Convair over Boeing to proceed with its B-58 design, and the contract was officially signed in February 1953. This contract called for both a B-58 bomber version and an RB-58 reconnaissance version, which were given the respective weapons system contract designations, WS-102A and WS-102L. The aircraft, which would also carry the designation of Convair Model 4, was to be designed with the revolutionary delta wing created by Convair for the F-102 interceptor – this aircraft was approaching its first flight even as the B-58 contract was being inked.

The B-58 was also unusual in that its weapons payload would not be carried in a conventional bomb bay, but rather in a huge streamlined weapons pod carried beneath the fuselage.

Initial orders

The USAF later expanded the initial order for two XB-58 prototypes to include 11 YB-58A flight test aircraft that would be delivered as YB/RB-58s. An additional 17 Block 10 YB-58As ordered in 1958 would be completed as YB/RB-58As. The RB-58A prefix was subsequently abandoned when the USAF decided not to produce a dedicated reconnaissance variant.

However, the USAF response to the B-58 project was mixed. General Curtis LeMay, Commander in Chief of SAC, was concerned about the aircraft's range, which would be about half that of the B-52 Stratofortress that was entering squadron service in the mid-1950s. Although LeMay never fully embraced the B-58 programme, the advent of the KC-135 jet aerial refuelling aircraft helped to render the use of the B-58 slightly more appealing to him.

The first XB-58 prototype (carrying the serial 55-660) made its maiden flight from Fort Worth on 11 November 1956, with Convair test pilot Beryl Erickson at the controls. Initially tested without the big MB-1C weapons pod, aircraft 55-660 went supersonic for the first and second time in two separate flights on 30 December, achieving a maximum speed of Mach 1.31 at 35,000 ft (10668 m). During February 1957, the second

***Left:* The first B-58 Hustler to complete inflight refuelling trials was 55-661. 55-664 is seen here in June 1958 lining itself up with a Boeing KC-135A Stratotanker. During its time in service, the Hustler gained a reputation for being a relatively easy aircraft to handle during inflight refuelling due to its excellent stability.**

***Below left:* Hustler crews practised low-level bombing missions, usually at an altitude of around 1,000 ft (305 m). For the final attack run, the aircraft was handed over to the navigator, although the computer 'flew' the aircraft to the bomb-release point. The end of an audio tone signified bomb release, allowing the pilot to regain control.**

Hustler, designated a YB/RB-58, joined the test programme and made the first supersonic flight with the weapons pod in place. The first flight at the required operational speed of Mach 2 occurred on 29 June 1957, while carrying the MB-1 mission pod.

Meanwhile, two aircraft had been sent to Kirtland AFB, New Mexico, for tests involving the dropping of the weapons pods. A subsonic drop took place on 5 June 1957, followed by the first supersonic drop from an altitude of 40,000 ft (12192 m) on 30 September.

Among other things, flight testing pointed to the need for an operational trainer version of the Hustler, and eight YB-58As were converted to dual control TB-58As, with the first delivery occurring in May 1960. Flight testing of the YB-58A aircraft officially concluded in April 1959, although production flight testing would continue until delivery of the last B-58A in October 1962.

On 15 March 1960, the first B-58A Hustler assigned to an operational unit went into service with the 43rd Bomb Wing at Carswell AFB. On 1 August, SAC officially assumed control of the B-58 programme from the Air Material Command, marking the beginning of a decade of service for what was the world's first supersonic bomber.

Low-level mission

While the B-58 had been designed initially for nuclear strike missions at high altitudes, advances in Soviet radar and surface-to-air missiles led to new tactics. Thus, in addition to training for the original high-altitude scenario, B-58 crews also underwent training for supersonic low-level strike missions. For much of its existence, the B-58's principal operational role was to sit on nuclear alert, although, unlike the B-52 force, the aircraft were not armed.

When the decision was made to withdraw the B-58 from service, it was met with controversy. On the one hand, it had achieved the design goals set for it and it was the fastest strategic bomber to serve with the USAF. On the other, the SAC never fully accepted the Hustler because of its limited range. Furthermore, its service career coincided with a serious debate within the USAF over whether the role of nuclear deterrence was better performed by manned bombers or intercontinental ballistic missiles. Another important and inescapable issue was the cost – especially at the peak of the war in southeast Asia – of maintaining an aircraft so sophisticated and with so many unique parts.

The end of the B-58's career came abruptly. It was announced in October 1969 that both Little Rock AFB and Grissom AFB would be closed and that the entire B-58 fleet would be mothballed within three months. Around 80 aircraft were stored at Davis-Monthan AFB until 1977, when the order came for them to be scrapped. Six B-58s were preserved for posterity.

A B-58 approaches a KC-135 tanker for refuelling. Tanking was vital to the Hustler's strategic mission, owing to the aircraft's comparatively short legs at operational speed.

Above: The F-106B was declared operational in 1960 and more than 60 examples were built. Today, however, only four remain in collections or museums.

Left: The angular-looking F-106 had a reputation as a speedster – it broke the world air speed record in 1959.

Ultimate interceptor

Although the F-106 never fired a shot in anger, its duties saw it intercept many Soviet aircraft. Fondly remembered, it equipped USAF and ANG units for nearly 30 years.

On its first take-off, the F-106 was devoid of the extensive MA-1 system. In general, the flight development programme was very successful; not only was almost the entire envelope of predicted speeds and heights attained, but the manoeuvrability was better than that of the F-102A. This was despite the considerably greater weight, most of which was due to the internal fuel capacity being increased from 1,070 US gal (4050 litres) to 1,440 US gal (5456 litres).

Considerable development went into the cockpit in the course of 1956, with improved radar displays, optical sight, projected-map navigation display, vertical tape instruments and modified twin-grip stick. Six further batches were procured with 1957 funds, followed by 57-2507, the first of a new tandem two-seat version – the F-106B. Launched in June 1957, this was intended as a dual trainer but with full combat capability. Unlike the TF-102A, the two-seat F-106 carried a fully operational fire-control system, and the only disadvantage of the second seat was the loss of one of the forward fuselage fuel cells. Flight performance was generally regarded as identical, though take-off and landing speeds were slightly higher.

First operational unit

The first F-106B flew on 9 April 1958, by which time the first production F-106As were in the air. Deliveries to Air (later Aerospace) Defense Command began in May 1959, and the first combat unit to be declared operational with the Dart was the ADC's 539th Fighter Interceptor Squadron (FIS) in June 1959. Two other FISs were declared combat ready by the end of the year, and the F-106A eventually equipped 13 FISs, or half of the manned interceptor force of ADC, by the time the 277th and last was delivered on 20 July 1961. Each FIS also received a few F-106Bs, which were delivered in parallel. However, the small combined total of 340 of the two models meant that the intention of replacing the F-102A was not to be realised until the Command itself shrank in the late 1960s.

In service the Dart, more often called the 'Six', fulfilled every wish of the USAF and of its pilots, proving delightful to fly and solidly reliable. Partly because of the stand-off interception style of ADC operations, it was not for 11 years that the potential of the F-106 for close air combat was realised (many USAF pilots consider it to have been the best air-combat aircraft of any kind in the US inventory until the arrival of the F-15).

Improvements to the aircraft in service began in 1960 and continued into its last years. Many concerned the radar and its visor display which was initially somewhat outmoded by modern standards. A new ejection seat cleared for supersonic flight arrived in 1964, by which time improved underwing drop tanks were available, with increased capacity and clearance for use at over Mach 1.

Other improvements included an inflight-refuelling receptacle halfway along the dorsal spine, a solid-state digital computer and radar-slaved gunsight. By 1964, all aircraft had a sensitive IR seeker in the nose, extended by the pilot upon demand ahead of the windscreen, where it was normally recessed. This was a valued aid in conditions of heavy radar clutter or ECM. The 'Six'

The F-106 was perhaps the last modern US fighter to wear easily identifiable bright colour schemes and, while the replacement F-15s initially kept these decorations, they are now a thing of the past.

Above: The first F-106 is seen here repainted in high-visibility Dayglo trim. It is now on display at Selfridge AFB, Michigan.

Right: Taking part in the Brave Shield XVI exercises in 1977 was this F-106A from the 498th FIS 'Geiger Tigers'.

also acquired improved EW capability with some aircraft having radar-homing and warning receivers, and provision for an anti-chaff missile mode. Throughout the 1960s, contracts placed by San Antonio Air Materiel Area administered five improvement programmes, which brought in new DC electric power, better radar, improved flight control electronics and other updates.

Combat capability

A major change in 1969 was the testing of an M61A1 20-mm gun. This gun was part of Project Sixshooter (which looked at the F-106's potential as a dogfighter), and it became a regular fit from 1973 along with a superb lead-computing gunsight, digital flight controls and an AWACS datalink.

Surviving F-106s of both models continued until the final disbandment of Aerospace Defence Command on 1 October 1979. NORAD (North American Air Defense) subsequently retained six FISs in TAC and five in the state-organised ANG. By mid-1983 the number of active 'Sixes' had fallen to about 130, in five ANG Air Defense units. By this time, the F-15 had entered service, and in 1988 the last F-106s departed the Atlantic City-based 119th FIS.

F-106A Delta Dart

This particular aircraft, 59-0021, was the 186th F-106 built and was first assigned to the 319th FIS at Bunker Hill in 1960. Three years later, it moved to the 438th FIS at Kincheloe AFB. Later, it was assigned to the commander of the 21st NORAD region and there it remained until it was hit by lightning on 15 May 1973, which caused it to crash, killing Major General James D. Price.

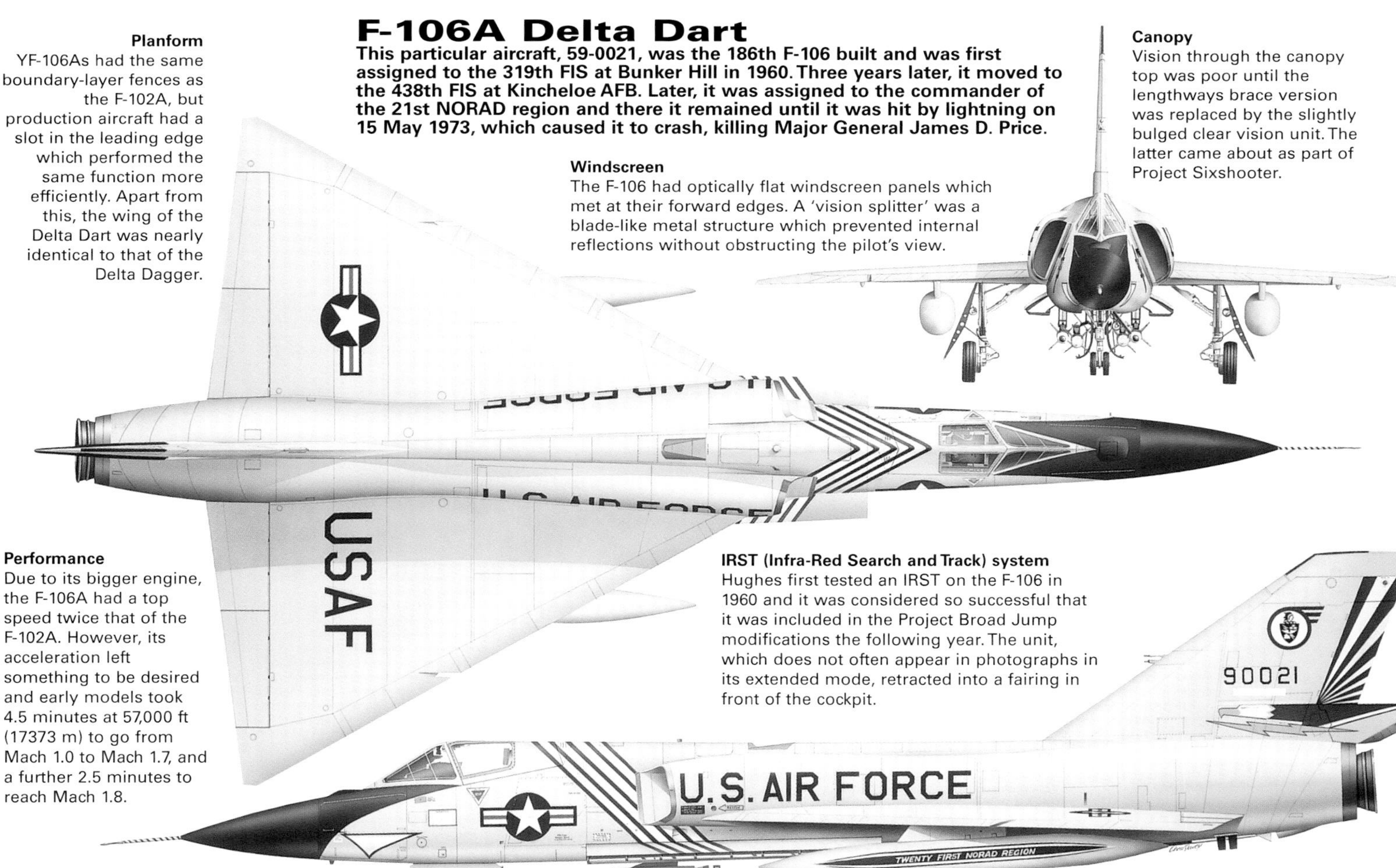

Planform
YF-106As had the same boundary-layer fences as the F-102A, but production aircraft had a slot in the leading edge which performed the same function more efficiently. Apart from this, the wing of the Delta Dart was nearly identical to that of the Delta Dagger.

Windscreen
The F-106 had optically flat windscreen panels which met at their forward edges. A 'vision splitter' was a blade-like metal structure which prevented internal reflections without obstructing the pilot's view.

Canopy
Vision through the canopy top was poor until the lengthways brace version was replaced by the slightly bulged clear vision unit. The latter came about as part of Project Sixshooter.

Performance
Due to its bigger engine, the F-106A had a top speed twice that of the F-102A. However, its acceleration left something to be desired and early models took 4.5 minutes at 57,000 ft (17373 m) to go from Mach 1.0 to Mach 1.7, and a further 2.5 minutes to reach Mach 1.8.

IRST (Infra-Red Search and Track) system
Hughes first tested an IRST on the F-106 in 1960 and it was considered so successful that it was included in the Project Broad Jump modifications the following year. The unit, which does not often appear in photographs in its extended mode, retracted into a fairing in front of the cockpit.

Dassault Etendard/ Super Etendard

France's naval air arm, the Aéronavale, received 69 production Etendard IVM attack fighters from 1962 onwards.

Carrierborne strike fighter

For an aircraft produced in comparatively small numbers and operated by only three air arms, the Etendard series has seen an unusual amount of combat, gaining notoriety in the Falklands conflict.

The original Dassault Etendard (standard, or national flag) was the company's entry in a 1955 NATO light strike fighter competition. As a private venture, Dassault installed the much more powerful SNECMA Atar 08 turbojet and this version, which first flew on 24 July 1956, was designated Etendard IV. After NATO nations rejected the Etendard VI in favour of the Fiat G.91, the Etendard IV underwent modification to meet an Aéronavale requirement for a carrier-based attack and reconnaissance aircraft.

Initial deployment

The first version was designated Etendard IVM and deployed aboard the carriers *Foch* and *Clemenceau*. The prototype flew for the first time on 21 May 1958, and was followed by six pre-production aircraft. The first of 69 production Etendard IVMs for the French navy was delivered in 1962, and production was completed in 1964. The Etendard IVM was withdrawn in July 1991.

The seventh Etendard was the prototype of the Etendard IVP, a reconnaissance/tanker version, of which 21 were ordered. The Etendard IVP was slowly phased out of use, to be replaced by the Standard 4 Super Etendards.

After much political in-fighting, a mid-1970s French naval requirement for 100 new carrier-based strike-fighters eventually resulted in a 1973 contract to Dassault-Breguet for 60 developments of the Etendard IV. The upgraded Super Etendard was planned with an 11,025-lb st (49-kN) SNECMA Atar 8K-50 instead of the original 9,923-lb (44-kN) Atar 8C, and some 90 per cent airframe commonality.

To widen its anti-ship strike and air-to-air capabilities, the Super Etendard featured a new nav/attack system and an Agave I-band monopulse radar, revised avionics and HUD. Three Etendard IVM airframes were converted as Super Etendard prototypes, flying from 29 October 1974. Once the Super Etendard had achieved all of its development criteria, 71 production aircraft began replacing Etendard IVs and Crusader interceptors from June 1978.

By the time the Falklands War started, in April 1982, the

A fighter for NATO?

During early 1954, a NATO committee led by Professor von Kármán was installed in the Palais de Chaillot in Paris, France still being a full member of NATO at the time. Its tasks were to examine the several proposals submitted by European firms to meet the light fighter need, embodied in NATO Basic Military Requirement No. 1. The NBMR-1 aircraft was to weigh between 8,000 and 10,000 lb (3629 and 4536 kg) and be capable of operations from small or even grass runways, with minimal 'turnaround' time on the ground between missions. Dassault's offering was the Etendard VI, intended for frequent, short 'bomb truck' sorties to the front line in support of ground troops. NATO was also sponsoring a new engine to power NBMR-1 – the Bristol Orpheus. However, its inclusion plus additional avionics systems saw the length of the aircraft increase to 42 ft 3⅞ in (12.90 m). Together with the Breguet Taon and Fiat G.91, the Etendard VI (illustrated) was chosen for a fly-off. Only one of the three Etendard VIs was completed and this flew on 15 March 1957. The aircraft was evaluated by British, French, Italian and US pilots, but came second place to the G.91; this infuriated the French, who refused to buy the G.91. Also used in these trials was the Etendard IV, which first flew in July 1956. Equipped with the Atar 101E4 engine, the Etendard was turned down by the Armée de l'Air in favour of the Mirage III, but a navalised variant attracted the attention of the Aéronavale. Accordingly, a semi-navalised prototype, designated Etendard IVM, was ordered, and flew for the first time in May 1958.

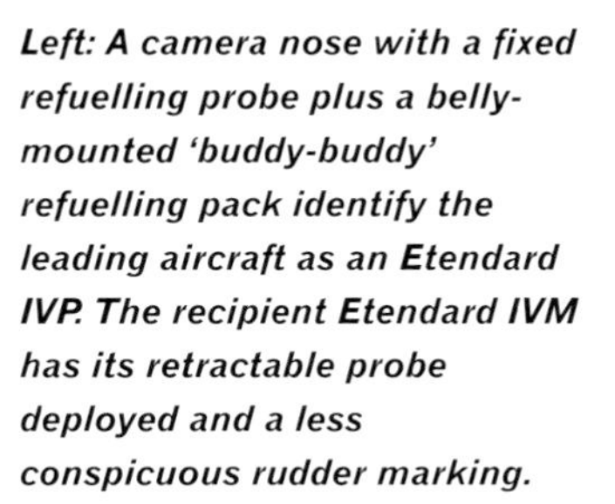

Left: A camera nose with a fixed refuelling probe plus a belly-mounted 'buddy-buddy' refuelling pack identify the leading aircraft as an Etendard IVP. The recipient Etendard IVM has its retractable probe deployed and a less conspicuous rudder marking.

Below left: The 'SuE' has seen recent combat over the former Yugoslavia and Afghanistan, but is being replaced by the swing-role Rafale M Standard F2.

Argentine navy had received the first five of 14 aircraft, together with five AM.39 Exocets. These made their operational debut sinking HMS *Sheffield* on 4 May 1982. The remainder are still operated by 2ª Escuadrilla of 3 Escuadra, from Cdte Espora.

In October 1983 five Aéronavale Super Etendards were leased to Iraq for use against Iranian tankers in the Iran/Iraq war, scoring many successes. The four survivors were returned to France in 1985.

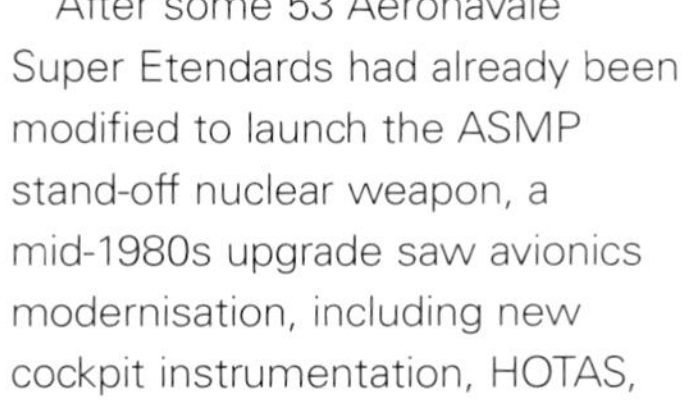

After some 53 Aéronavale Super Etendards had already been modified to launch the ASMP stand-off nuclear weapon, a mid-1980s upgrade saw avionics modernisation, including new cockpit instrumentation, HOTAS, and Anémone radar. Meanwhile, airframe changes were made to extend fatigue life. The prototype upgraded 'SuE' first flew in 1990.

'SuE' today

The five-stage Super Etendard Modernisée (SEM) modernisation programme has given the 'SuE' new capabilities. By the time of Allied Force, the Standard 3 SEM had been delivered, this version employing the ATLIS laser designator to launch the GBU-12 Paveway II LGB and the AS.30L laser-guided missile.

The next phase of the SEM permitted the LGB/ATLIS combination to be carried simultaneously by one aircraft, and gave the option of carrying a new reconnaissance module, allowing retirement of the last Etendard IVPs. Standard 4 also added a new self-defence package. The final Standard 5 delivered from 2006 adds a night precision-attack capability, with FLIR, night-vision goggles and Damoclès laser designator pod.

Above: The first of 14 Super Etendards for Argentina's naval air arm is seen prior to delivery. Five aircraft had been received by the time the Falklands War started, of which one was used as a spares source. The others destroyed two British ships.

Right: While Super Etendards handled* Foch*'s offensive sorties, the Etendard IVPs of 16F were used on recce sorties during Allied Force over Yugoslavia.

Pakistan is the last major operator of the Mirage III/5 family, having acquired second-hand examples from various sources including Australia, France, Lebanon and Libya.

Dassault Mirage III

Dassault's deltas

Dassault's concept of a lightweight, ultra high-performance fighter resulted in a simpler and cheaper aircraft than its more sophisticated contemporaries. Many advances were incorporated and the aircraft spawned a myriad of variants that achieved considerable export success.

Unquestionably the aircraft that restored the global reputation of France as a leader in aeronautical design was the Dassault Mirage III.

'Mirage' became a generic name for subsequent Dassault warplanes, the initial series being the III, 5 and 50. Adopted by a score of air forces, the combat-proven Mirage enjoyed a production history in excess of three decades, and has been refurbished and modified for service well into the 21st century.

Genesis of the Mirage may be traced back to early 1952 when Dassault received a study contract for a variant of its Mystère fighter series, designated M.D.550 Mystère Delta. Some preparatory work had therefore been done when, on 28 January 1953, the Air Staff promulgated a requirement for a light fighter. Parameters included a 4-tonne maximum weight, top speed of Mach 1.3, carriage of a single air-to-air missile and a landing speed less than 112 mph (180 km/h). Power choice was to be made from – if necessary in combination – the new SNECMA Atar afterburning turbojet, light turbojets, liquid-fuel rocket motors and even solid rockets.

Among the responses, it was the Sud-Est Durandal, Sud-Ouest Trident and Dassault Mystère Delta that received orders for two prototypes each. First flown on 25 June 1955, the rocket-boosted Mystère Delta – soon to be re-named Mirage I – was too small to carry radar plus effective armament. Also on the drawing boards were the twin-engined Mirage II; the Mirage III with a single Atar turbojet and 'area ruled' fuselage later incorporating simple variable-geometry air intakes; and the Mirage IV.

The last-mentioned and most futuristic project impressed upon the Air Staff that the light fighter concept was a *cul de sac* in combat aircraft design and strategic defence. Accordingly, in 1956, the original specification was upgraded to 'Stage II', which called for a multi-role, radar-equipped fighter, which only Dassault was in a position to supply before the end of the decade.

Rapid development

Skipping the Mirage II stage, the firm developed the III to the required standard, while the IV was scaled up into a strategic bomber. With incredible speed, Dassault produced a Mirage III fuselage within the year, permitting the aircraft to take to the air on 17 November 1956.

Turning a research machine into a service fighter was the task of 10 pre-production Mirage IIIAs, which gradually incorporated Cyrano Ibis intercept radar and combat avionics during 1958/59. Considerable time was spent perfecting the rocket installation in the lower rear fuselage, although it was little used in squadron service and aroused no interest in foreign customers. The rocket was to improve high-altitude performance, and was certainly not necessary lower down where, on 24 October 1958, IIIA No. 01 achieved twice the speed of sound with only the Atar operating. This was the first unassisted turbojet flight at that speed by a European aircraft.

Deliveries of the definitive Mirage IIIC interceptor to the first operational squadron began in July 1961. Equipped with Cyrano II air intercept radar, the

Powered by an Atar 9 turbojet, Mirage IIIA '05' was the first Mirage completed with a production-standard airframe. Although it had a nose radome, the Cyrano Ibis radar was not fitted.

Initially, the RAAF considered having its locally built Mirage IIIOs powered by Rolls-Royce Avon turbojets and, although a prototype was flown, the Atar was finally chosen in the interests of simplicity. Of 100 examples, all but two were built by the Commonwealth Aircraft Corporation, the type serving on the RAAF front line until 1988.

Armée de l'Air's Mirage IIICs were armed with a large Matra R.511 (later R.530) radar-homing AAM under the fuselage as a complement to twin internal 30-mm cannon. Ground attack ordnance could also be fitted, and during the 1980s a pair of underwing Matra Magics was added to replace the optional AIM-9 Sidewinders.

The Mirage became truly multi-role on 5 April 1961 with the maiden flight of the first 'stretched' IIIE. The IIIEs were assigned a battlefield air superiority role as well as surface attack with conventional ordnance or the AN.52 tactical nuclear weapon. A related variant, the IIIR, provided tactical reconnaissance for the French air force until phased out in 1988.

Export success

Australia adopted the Mirage III as its primary fighter, and Israel made it the top combat machine in the IDF/AF. It was in the Six-Day War that the Mirage III conclusively demonstrated its versatility. On 5 June 1967, wave after wave of Mirages and other IDF aircraft decimated the Egyptian, Jordanian and Syrian air forces on the ground.

Israel was well pleased with the Mirage and ordered a follow-on batch of a simplified variant, lacking radar. A fighter-bomber with fair-weather visual intercept capability, the resultant Mirage 5 opened new markets for Dassault by offering a low purchase price and reduced maintenance requirements.

Abu Dhabi, Egypt, Libya and Pakistan all received aircraft with 'Mirage 5' painted on the side, but which were IIIEs in all essential respects, including Cyrano radar.

Other derivatives

Meanwhile, the Mirage 5 launch customer had been denied its aircraft when France correctly divined that there was more money to be made by selling arms to the neighbouring Arab nations. After its Mirage 5s were embargoed, Israel built its own copy, the IAI Nesher, from 1971. A redesigned derivative with a US engine and Israeli avionics, the IAI Kfir, followed and was first delivered to squadrons from April 1975.

Chile and Venezuela purchased the Mirage 50, a Mirage 5 variant with an uprated Atar 9K50 engine of the type fitted to the Mirage F1.

Several Mirages have undergone mid-life improvement programmes featuring upgraded avionics and other changes. Chile and South Africa utilised Israeli technology to produce their own upgraded aircraft, namely the Pantera and Cheetah, respectively. In all (including licensed production), 1,422 Mirage IIIs, 5s and 50s were built.

The key to the Mirage's ubiquity and longevity was in the careful blending of simplicity with adapted technology. It was a 'minimum risk' programme, relying on constructional materials and manufacturing techniques readily available in Europe during the mid-1950s. One must be clever to make things look simple, and the genius of Dassault was to make an aircraft that was more than the sum of its component parts.

Above left: As with most new single-seat fighters of the period, there was a two-seat trainer variant – the Mirage IIIB. Examples were purchased by the Armée de l'Air and the air forces of Israel (IIIBJ), Switzerland (IIIBS) and South Africa (IIIBZ).

Left: Spain's Mirage IIIEEs were known locally as C.11s. The Ejército del Aire planned to upgrade its Mirages, but budget cuts saw their premature retirement in 1992.

Mirage III in service

Above: The South African Air Force operated a plethora of Mirage III variants, though only the advanced Cheetah C/D remains in service today. This Mirage IIIEZ of No. 2 Squadron is seen firing a salvo of unguided rockets at a ground target.

The Mirage III family was sold to a wide range of customers, many of whom could not afford, or were forbidden, to own the latest American aircraft and so turned to France to meet their needs.

The Armée de l'Air took delivery of 59 Mirage IIIB trainers, 95 Mirage IIICs and 183 Mirage IIIEs, together with 70 Mirage IIIRs and IIIRDs. The trainers and combat aircraft equipped the 2e Escadre de Chasse at Dijon/Longvic from 1961 (consisting of EC 1/2 'Cigognes', ECT 2/2 'Côte d'Or' and EC 3/2 'Alsace'), the 3^{e} Escadre de Chasse at Nancy/Ochey from 1965 (consisting of EC 1/3 'Navarre', EC 2/3 'Champagne' and EC 3/3 'Ardennes'), the 4e Escadre de Chasse at Luxeuil from 1966 (consisting of EC 1/4 'Dauphine' and EC 2/4 'La Fayette'), the 5e Escadre de Chasse at Orange from 1966 (consisting of EC 1/5 'Vendée' and EC 2/5 'Ile de France'), the 10e Escadre de Chasse at Creil (with one squadron in Djibouti) from 1974 (consisting of EC 1/10 'Valois', EC 2/10 'Seine' and the Africa-based EC 3/10 'Vexin'), and the 13e Escadre de Chasse at Colmar from 1966 (consisting of EC 1/ 13 'Artois' and EC 2/13 'Alpes').

The Mirage IIIRs served with the 33^{e} Escadre de Reconnaissance at Strasbourg from 1963 (consisting of ER 1/33 'Belfort', ER 2/33 'Savoie' and ER 3/33 'Moselle'). EC 5 converted to the Mirage F1C in 1975, while EC 10 followed between 1981 and 1988. EC 2 converted to the Mirage 2000C in 1983, EC 4 stood down prior to re-equipping with the Mirage 2000N in 1987, while EC 3 converted to the Mirage 2000N in 1994. EC 1/13 converted to the Mirage F1CT in June 1992, while EC 2/13 had converted to the Mirage 5F in 1977. The reconnaissance unit, ER 33, re-equipped with Mirage F1CRs between 1983 and 1988.

Export aircraft

The Spanish air force received the first of 30 Mirage IIIs (six IIIDE trainers and 24 IIIEE fighters) in June 1970, equipping Ala de Caza 11 at Manises/ Valencia. Initially used in the interceptor role, with AIM-9B Sidewinder and R.530FE AAMs, the aircraft were later relegated to the fighter-bomber role.

Switzerland's reconnaissance Mirage IIIRSs served with detachments of Fliegerstaffel 10 until 1992, when these were redesignated as Fliegerstaffel 3 and Fliegerstaffel 4.

Switzerland procured a fleet of 61 Mirage IIIs, mostly IIIS interceptors, but also including a single IIIC, four IIIBS and two IIIDS trainers and 18 IIIRS reconnaissance aircraft. Some 34 of the IIISs, three BS trainers and the reconnaissance aircraft were locally built. The aircraft entered service during the mid-1960s. The Mirage IIIS fighters flew with Fliegerstaffel 16 and 17. All of the surviving aircraft were upgraded with canards, RWRs and improved equipment during the 1980s. The IIIS interceptors were finally retired in December 1999, followed by the IIIRS recce aircraft in December 2003.

Israel received 72 Mirage IIICJs between July 1961 and July 1964, and five Mirage IIIBJ trainers. These equipped Israel's front-line air defence fighter squadrons until they were themselves replaced by F-4E Phantoms and the indigenous Nesher and Kfir Mirage derivatives from the late 1960s, following relatively heavy attrition during Israel's various wars. The Mirage III operators were Nos 101, 117, 119, 253 and 254 Squadrons. The final 19 Mirage IIICJs and three Mirage IIIBJs were sold to Argentina in 1982.

South America

Argentina ordered 10 Mirage IIIEAs and two IIIDAs in October 1970, and these finally entered service in July 1973. Seven more IIIEAs (compatible with the R.530 AAM) were delivered in 1979.

This Mirage IIIB is seen wearing the markings of SPA 94 of ECT 2/2 'Côte d'Or', the old conversion and training unit for the Armée de l'Air's Mirage IIIs. This unit now operates Mirage 2000-5Fs as EC 2/2 at Dijon.

These equipped Grupo 8 de Caza's I Escuadrón de Caza at Buenos Aires, operating detachments at Comodoro Rivadavia and Rio Gallegos during the Falklands War. The unit gained two more trainers post-war, but the parent Grupo 8 disbanded in February 1988, and I Escuadrón transferred to Grupo 6 at Tandil.

Here it joined the Daggers of Escuadrónes II and III de Caza. A total of 19 ex-IDF/AF Mirage IIICJs and three Mirage IIIBJs was delivered as attrition replacements and equipped Escuadrón 55 which formed within Grupo 4 at El Plumerillo, Mendoza, in 1983. The Mirage IIICJs were grounded in 1996, and Escuadrón 55 was disbanded. As Argentina's final remaining Mirage III operator, II Escuadrón of Grupo 6 maintained a dwindling fleet of Mirage III aircraft at Tandil in 2007.

Brazil received the first of 22 Mirage IIIEBRs and 10 two-seat IIIDBR trainers in 1972. The last six aircraft (four single-seaters) were ex-Armée de l'Air machines delivered from 1988, after refurbishing and modernising with new avionics, canard foreplanes and other improvements. Brazil's 10 surviving original EBRs and two DBRs were subsequently upgraded to the same standard. The Mirages equipped 1° Grupo de Defesa Aerea at Anápolis.

Replaced by 12 ex-Armée de l'Air Mirage 2000B/Cs, the last Brazilian Mirage IIIs were retired in December 2005.

Venezuela's fleet of Mirages consisted mainly of Mirage 5s and 50s, but included seven IIIEV interceptors (equivalent to Armée de l'Air Mirage IIIEs) and three IIIDV trainers. All were upgraded to Mirage 50 standard, with refuelling probes, canard foreplanes and advanced systems, from 1990. The aircraft serve with Grupo Aéreo de Caza 11 at Maracay/Palo Negro.

The Royal Australian Air Force took delivery of 49 fighter-configured Mirage IIIO(F)s and 51 IIIO(A) fighter-bombers, together with 16 Mirage IIID two-seat trainers. Deliveries began in 1963, equipping No. 81 Wing at Williamtown and No. 78 Wing at Butterworth, Malaysia. Between 1968 and 1971, all surviving single-seaters were brought to a common Mirage IIIO(F/A) standard. Conversion to the F/A-18 began in July 1987, but the last Mirages were not retired from experimental and trials duties until early 1989. Fifty aircraft were sold to Pakistan.

South Africa ordered 16 Mirage IIICZ interceptors and three IIIBZ trainers in 1962. They were followed by 17 multi-role Mirage IIIEZs and by three Mirage IIIDZ and 11 Mirage IIID2Z trainers, and four IIIRZ and four IIIR2Z reconnaissance aircraft. Most of the Mirage IIICs were withdrawn from use in 1990. The Mirages were replaced in service by the Atlas Cheetah from July 1986, some of these being produced by conversion of the original French-supplied airframes.

Pakistan ordered 18 Mirage IIIEP interceptors in 1967, augmenting these with three Mirage IIIRPs and three Mirage IIIDP trainers. These equipped No. 5 Squadron from late 1967. Two IIIDPs and 10 IIIRPs arrived in 1970 and 1975, accompanying a number of Mirage 5s. The IIIDPs were used by the newly forming Mirage 5 units, while the reconnaissance aircraft went initially to No. 20 Squadron, before being gathered together with the IIIEPs in No. 5 Squadron. Pakistan subsequently purchased 50 ex-RAAF Mirage IIIOs and IIIDO trainers, and after these arrived in 1990, refurbished enough of them to equip two air defence units. As of 2007, examples of the Mirage III remained in front-line service alongside Mirage 5s, serving with Nos 32 and 34 Wings.

Above: No. 81 Wing at Williamtown was the home-based RAAF Mirage III wing, initially consisting of Nos 75, 76 and 77 Squadrons (an aircraft from the latter unit is pictured) and No. 2 OCU.

Right: The Brazilian F-103E (Mirage IIIEBR) fleet was operated by a single squadron, 1°/1°GDA at Anápolis, until 2005.

Mirage 5/50

While the original Mirage III is fast disappearing from active service, the later Mirage 5 and 50, along with a host of derivatives, serve with several air forces whose resources do not stretch to fourth-generation fighters.

The Mirage 5 stemmed from an Israeli requirement for an attack aircraft having as much as possible in common with the Mirage III, but without radar. Based on the Mirage III, the Mirage 5 dispensed with the SEPR rocket and added sixth and seventh stores hardpoints.

The most noticeable alteration was the removal of the nose radome. Extra space to the rear of the cockpit was used for additional fuel, boosting combat radius from 745 to 800 miles (1200 to 1288 km).

First flown on 19 May 1967, the Mirage 5 suffered a setback when the 50 Israeli 5J aircraft were embargoed by the French government. They went instead to the Armée de l'Air as Mirage 5Fs in the attack role. Eight more were delivered from 1983 to 1985.

Mirage 50

This out-of-sequence designation derives from the fitment of an uprated Atar 09K50 powerplant in place of an 09C to both the basic Mirage III and non-radar 5. The Mirage 50 uses 90 per cent of the structural parts of the III/5 and 95 per cent of the systems, while its extra thrust gives performance advantages.

At first the Mirage 50 was seen as an uprated Mirage 5, with Aïda 2 ranging radar, radio-altimeter, air data computer and gyro weapons sight. Options were the 50A with Agave radar and 50C with Cyrano IV, and all could have RND 72 Doppler coupled with a computer or a conventional INS.

The Atar 09K50 became airborne in the Milan S-01 on 29 May 1970. Next, four IIIR2Zs were exported to South Africa without fanfare, despite being the first 'production' aircraft. On 15 April 1975, the former Milan flew as the official Mirage 50 'first' prototype with Aïda nose.

First Mirage 50s to be exported under that name were eight Mirage 50FCs delivered to Chile during 1980 in the form of re-engined ex-Armée de l'Air Mirage 5Fs, the initial new production concerning a further six for the same customer, designated Mirage 50C and fitted with search radar, radar warning receivers and fin-base fillet. Also delivered were three Mirage 50DC two-seat trainers.

Belgium acquired 106 Mirage 5s, consisting of 63 Mirage 5BA

Above: Colombia's two-seat Mirage 5CODs are equipped with reduced-size (50 per cent less area), Kfir-style canard foreplanes. The Fuerza Aerea Colombiana's Mirage 5COA/CODs operate in the air defence and attack roles with Grupo de Combate 11.

Top: These Mirage 5PA3s equip No. 8 Squadron of the Pakistan Fiza'ya (Pakistan armed forces) based at Masroor.

Most of the Mirage 5s that Chile purchased from Belgium had undergone the MirSIP programme, and in Chilean service were known as Elkan-status Mirages. However, the type still proved inferior to the indigenous Chilean ENAER Pantera C (illustrated).

The first Mirage 5BA flew from Bordeaux on 6 March 1970 and the subsequent 62 examples replaced Belgium's F-84Fs. Despite the beginning of the MirSIP update programme, the last Belgian Mirages were retired in 1993.

fighters, 27 Mirage 5BR reconnaissance aircraft and 16 Mirage 5BD trainers. The first of each variant was built by Dassault, but the remainder were built under licence. Some 20 of the Belgian aircraft began to undergo the MirSIP upgrade, but all were withdrawn by 1993.

Pakistan took delivery of 70 Mirage 5s. These comprised two Mirage 5DPA2 trainers, 28 basic radar-less Mirage 5PAs, 28 Mirage 5PA2s with Cyrano WM radar, and 12 Mirage 5PA3s with Agave radar and Exocet ASMs.

Although designated as Mirage IIIR2Zs, South Africa's last four reconnaissance Mirages were powered by the Atar 09K-50 engine and, as such, were effectively Mirage 50s.

Libya took delivery of 110 Mirage 5s, comprising 53 basic 5Ds, 15 two-seat 5DDs, 32 radar-equipped 5DEs and 10 5DR reconnaissance aircraft.

From 1973 Egypt received 32 Mirage 5SDEs and six Mirage 5SDE trainers (the single-seaters being broadly equivalent to the Mirage IIIE with Cyrano radar and Doppler). It later bought 22 more SDEs, six recce-configured SDRs and 15 Mirage 5E2s.

Gabon ordered four two-seat Mirage 5DGs, five single-seat Mirage 5Gs and two Mirage 5RGs in 1975 and 1982, although the 5RGs were never delivered. Zaire received eight single-seat Mirage 5Ms and three two-seat 5DM trainers from 1975. Abu Dhabi received 12 Mirage 5AD fighter-bombers, 14 radar/Doppler-equipped Mirage 5EADs (Mirage IIIEs in all but name), three Mirage IIIDAD trainers and three Mirage IIIRAD reconnaissance aircraft.

South America

Argentina's Mirage IIIEAs and Daggers were augmented by 10 ex-Peruvian Mirage 5Ps. The aircraft were upgraded to Mara standard (broadly equivalent to Dagger/Finger standard).

Eight ex-Armée de l'Air Mirage 5Fs were modified to Mirage 50FC standard (with 09K50 engines) and were delivered to Chile in 1980. These were augmented by six new-build, radar-equipped Mirage 50CHs and two 50DCH trainers in 1982/83, with an attrition replacement trainer being delivered in 1987. All were upgraded locally to Pantera configuration, with Kfir-type noses and canards, and with a fixed refuelling probe. The Panteras were augmented from 1995 by 15 Belgian Mirage 5BA/BDs which had been converted to MirSIP standard, plus five additional aircraft, all of which were further modified with Chilean-specified systems as Mirage 5MA and 5MD Elkans. Chile also received four unmodified Mirage 5BRs for reconnaissance duties, and one unmodified trainer.

Colombia took delivery of 14 Mirage 5COAs, two Mirage 5COD trainers and two reconnaissance-configured Mirage 5CORs from 1972. The survivors were upgraded to Kfir-C7 avionics standard from 1988, with a Kfir-style nose, inflight refuelling probe and reduced-size canards.

Peru received 40 Mirage 5s, comprising 22 Mirage 5Ps, 10 Mirage 5P3s, two Mirage SP4s and six Mirage 5DP and 5DP3 trainers. Ten Mirage 5Ps were supplied to Argentina in 1982, and the survivors were converted to Mirage 5P4 and Mirage 5DP4 standards.

Venezuela received six Mirage 5Vs alongside its original Mirage IIIs in 1972/73, before receiving nine upgraded, canard-equipped Mirage 50EVs and a Mirage 50DV two-seater in 1990/1991, when surviving Mirage IIIs and Mirage 5s were modified to the same standard.

Above: Venezuela's Mirage IIIDVs have been upgraded to full Mirage 50DV standard with refuelling probe and canard foreplanes. The Mirages are also equipped with nose-mounted vortex generators.

Right: A pair of Mirage 5Fs from EC 3/13 'Auvergne' and EC 2/12 'Alpes' formates with an EC 1/13 'Artois' Mirage III. France took 58 Mirage 5s: 50 from an embargoed Israeli order and eight new-builds. The last examples were retired in 1994.

Mirage IV Strategic bomber

The unusual flattened dome on the undersurface of the Mirage IV formerly covered a DRAA 8A navigation radar, replaced in Mirage IVP aircraft by the Arcana, an all-weather pulse-Doppler unit capable of providing a high-resolution ground map for accurate navigation. This recce-configured IVP carries the CT 52 sensor pod.

Of the 62 Mirage IVA strategic bombers of the Force de Frappe, which allowed France to leave NATO and provide its own nuclear deterrent, 18 were converted in the late 1980s to IVP standard, carrying ASMP.

In 1954, the French government decided to create a Force de Frappe (strike force) as the main element of a national nuclear deterrent capability. A key element of this capability was a manned bomber to deliver the AN.22 weapon, a French-developed free-fall nuclear bomb.

At this time Dassault was involved with the design of the Mirage III interceptor powered by one SNECMA Atar 101G-1 turbojet engine and one SEPR booster rocket, and the Mirage IV heavy fighter with a powerplant of two Atar 9 turbojets. Ultimately, all proposed variants of the Mirage IV fighter were abandoned, but the company's work was not wasted as the Mirage IVC became the basis for the medium strategic bomber required by the French air force. After a year of work trying to turn the Mirage IVC into such a warplane, Dassault rightly opined that greater size and weight were necessary to provide the warload, speed and range demanded by the Armée de l'Air.

This enlarged type would have had a powerplant of two Pratt & Whitney J75-B turbojets, but the air force then decided that inflight refuelling offered greater capabilities, and this led to the purchase of 12 Boeing C-135F tankers to support pairs of bombers, of which one would carry the nuclear weapon and the other additional fuel and a 'buddy' refuelling pack.

The bomber finally developed for this role was the Mirage IVA, which first flew on 17 June 1959

Left: The Mirage IVP navigator was provided with twin inertial platforms and could call upon an enhanced self-defence suite. This included Serval radar warning receiver (RWR) antennas on the outboard wing leading edges and on the rearward extensions to the afterburner cooling air intakes.

Right: EB 1/91 was redeclared operational with ASMP on 1 May 1986 and officially commissioned a week later at Mont-de-Marsan, plus a detachment at Orange. EB 2/91 followed on 1 December 1986, its main base at Cazaux being augmented by a dispersal at Istres. Each squadron had an establishment of seven Mirage IVPs, while a further three were assigned to the strategic force's OCU, Centre d'Instruction des Forces Aériennes Stratégiques 328 'Aquitaine' at Bordeaux.

Left: ***Mirage IVs formed the original cornerstone of France's independent airborne nuclear deterrent. The last offensive examples were the ASMP-armed IVPs which equipped the remaining two of an original nine strike squadrons. After the loss of this role in July 1996, the few remaining aircraft adopted a reconnaissance role, which they performed over the former Yugoslavia and Afghanistan.***

This specially-marked Mirage IVP commemorated EB 2/91's 32 years (1964-96) of operating with the type at the time of its disbanding. At its nine-squadron peak in 1968, the Mirage IV force comprised 36 aircraft each armed with a single AN.22 free-fall nuclear bomb.

as a large warplane with a low/mid-set delta wing, the navigator/systems operator in a small cabin behind the pilot's cockpit, a powerplant of two Atar 9 afterburning turbojets side-by-side in the rear fuselage, and retractable tricycle landing gear. This last was optimised for the Mirage IVA's dispersed-site role, which envisaged rocket-assisted take-off from unprepared strips.

Pre-production batch

The prototype was followed by three slightly larger pre-production aircraft. The first of these flew in October 1961 with a powerplant of two 14,109-lb st (62.76-kN) Atar 9C turbojets, and the third of them flew in January 1963 to a standard fully representative of the Mirage IVA production bomber with Atar 9K50 turbojets, an inflight-refuelling probe on the nose, operational avionics and provision for armament. The first of 62 Mirage IVA bombers went to Escadron de Bombardement 1/91 'Gascogne' at Mont-de-Marsan to enable it to be declared operational on 1 October 1964. By 1 February 1966, nine squadrons had formed within three wings, each squadron having four aircraft at various stages of readiness, the most immediate at 15 minutes. Each bomber was equipped with DRAA 8A surveillance radar, Doppler navigation, Dassault mission computer, and provision for one AN.22 weapon semi-recessed into the lower fuselage.

During the mid and late 1980s, with their free-fall bombing capability now obsolete, 18 Mirage IVA bombers were converted to carry the ASMP stand-off missile with the revised designation Mirage IVP. This type equipped two squadrons and was optimised for low-level penetration with the aid of new Arcana radar, upgraded nav/attack and EW equipment including the Serval RWR, dual Uliss INS, and underwing chaff/flare dispensers.

Some 12 Mirage IVPs were converted for the high/low-level strategic reconnaissance role with special navaids, revised EW system and specific sensor systems. These latter included the CT52 pod, which fitted the underfuselage recess previously used for the AN.22, and carried vertical, oblique and forward cameras (typically three low-level Omera 35 and three high-level Omera 36 units) or a Super Cyclope IR linescanner in place of the Omera 36 cameras. Four to five of these aircraft remained active going into the 21st century, and the final examples were retired in June 2005.

To celebrate 30 years of operational flying, France's Forces Aériennes Stratégiques (FAS) painted up this Mirage IVP. The original three Mirage IVA squadrons had disbanded on 1 July 1976 (replaced by the S-3 IRBM force) and four more gradually disappeared during the 1980s, the last on 1 July 1988, leaving just two operational squadrons of the 91e Escadre de Bombardement. The last eight Mirage IVs relinquished their nuclear role on 31 July 1996, when EB 2/91 was disbanded, leaving EB 1/91 to continue in the reconnaissance role with the last five aircraft as ERS 1/91.

Dassault Mirage F1

Tactical fighter series

Intended as a successor to the successful Mirage III family, Dassault's 'non-delta' F1 constituted the backbone of the French air force for many years and has seen combat in different trouble spots with nearly all of its operators.

Few aircraft can claim the level of operational service of the Dassault Mirage F1: nine out of its 13 operators have used the aircraft in major combat operations. Such countries include Iraq, whose Mirages devastated international shipping with their Exocet missiles and then, years later, fell to the latest Western fighters while, at the other end of the scale, Ecuador's 1995 skirmish with Peru saw F1s claiming two Peruvian 'kills'. The aircraft has undeniably acquired the knack of being in the right conflict at the right time.

This ability to appear in regular conflicts cannot be totally attributed to chance. France pursued an aggressive sales policy, pushing its aircraft to countries which have been blackballed by the United States for political or ethical reasons. At times, no less than 70 per cent of the F1's export customers were hostile to the US or subject to some sort of trade embargo imposed by Washington. As a result, the aircraft was always more likely to enter conflict as soon as sales were concluded. With the Mirage F1, its operators received an aircraft with the qualities of the Mirage III – a rugged, reliable airframe – at a reasonable price.

French demands

During the 1960s, France sought a new dual-role aircraft; it would be an interceptor capable of Mach 2 dash and armed with a cannon and two air-to-air missiles. Alternatively, the aircraft could act in the tactical fighter role, carrying conventional or nuclear weapons. A number of ideas, broadly based on the Mirage III, was put forward and one proposal, the Mirage IIIF, was carried forward through the design stages, eventually being scaled down and ultimately being renamed the Mirage F1.

Easily outperforming its predecessor, the Mirage III, the F1 offers 43 per cent more internal fuel capacity, an extra 2.5 tonnes of gross weight despite a smaller wing area, a 30 per cent shorter take-off run, a 25 per cent slower approach speed and improved manoeuvrability at all speeds. Much of this is to do with the fact

***Above:** South Africa operated both the F1A and F1C variants of the Mirage in combat. During the wars against Angola, SAAF F1s were flown against enemy MiG-21s and repeatedly came out on top.*

***Below:** French F1B/Cs pose for the camera, with Mirage IIIs and Mystères in the background. Only 20 two-seat F1Bs were purchased by France, a relatively small number from a total of 251 F1s delivered.*

***Above:** As the Mirage 2000 began to edge the F1 out of service, the surviving F1 airframes were converted for further service in the ground-attack role as the **F1CT**, replacing the aging Mirage 5s. Aircraft 274 is pictured here during trials wearing **CEAM** (Centre d'Experimentations Aériennes Militaires) codes and fin badge.*

***Right:** Inflight refuelling dramatically increases the flexibility and versatility of the F1, in particular allowing the aircraft to deploy overseas much more easily, a factor that France, with its large number of foreign interests, had to consider.*

that the F1 is fitted with flaps and leading-edge slats, neither of which were fitted to the Mirage III owing to its delta wing.

To meet the interceptor requirements, the F1C was fitted with a Cyrano IV monopulse radar, but there were no ground-mapping or continuous-range options. Single targets could be tracked but performance was degraded in poor weather.

Initially, the F1's armament options were restricted to two 30-mm cannon but, three years into its service, the Matra R.530 missile was issued, with the R.550 Magic heat-seeking missile following a year later. One or two R.530s were carried, options being between a radar-homing or an IR version.

The Armée de l'Air acquired 83 basic F1Cs in 1973 and they equipped two wings. A further 79 machines were subsequently delivered between March 1977 and December 1983. The Armée de l'Air also ordered 20 F1B two-seater trainer variants of the aircraft. The availability of the Mirage 2000 had reduced the number of Armée de l'Air Mirage F1 squadrons to six by 1993. The arrival of the Mirage 2000 also allowed a number of surplus F1C-200s to be converted to multi-role F1CT standard and this variant, along with the F1CR, constitutes the majority of the remaining Armée de l'Air F1s. The French F1's highest profile combat venture was as part of Operation Daguet during the Gulf War of 1991, the aircraft being primarily used in the air defence and reconnaissance roles.

Foreign operators

Exports of the F1C have been made to six countries. South Africa received its 16 F1CZs in 1975 for No. 3 Squadron and these saw action against Angola until the peace of 1992 saw them being placed into storage. Morocco, which received its aircraft in 1978, flew them against rebel guerrilla positions in the Western Sahara. Jordan received its F1CJs in 1981, while Kuwait's F1CKs, which arrived in 1976, fought in the defence of their country against Iraq in August 1990 and during Operation Desert Storm in the following year. Greece and Spain also operate the F1 although, in the case of the former, it was retired in 2003, while the Spanish examples are slowly being pushed out of service by the Eurofighter EF2000.

While most nations were happy to receive the F1C variant, the South African Air Force also wanted a simplified version for day attack missions and so the F1A, which is visually distinguishable by its long nose incorporating the Aïda II ranging radar, was born. The F1E was an upgraded multi-role fighter/attack version for export customers such as Iraq, which used its AM.39 Exocet-armed F1s during the war against Iran and then later in Desert Storm. Twenty-four examples defected to Iran, where they continue to serve.

Mirage F1 variants

Though intended for the air interception role, the Mirage F1 proved itself able to perform attack and reconnaissance missions, leading to a host of variants.

Above: The Armée de l'Air ordered only a limited number of F1B two-seat conversion trainers, and these were not delivered to squadrons until some way into the single-seat operational service. The F1B retains full combat capability.

Top: Performing both air interception and ground-attack missions, Ecuador's F1JAs are similar to the F1E. The aircraft underwent a major upgrade programme which allows them to carry Israeli weaponry, including the highly agile Python AAM.

Despite its suffix, the Mirage F1C was the initial production version. The private venture prototype flew on 23 December 1966 and was officially adopted in May 1967, when three service prototypes were ordered. Power was provided by a 15,873-lb st (70.61-kN) SNECMA Atar 09K50 reheated turbojet.

To meet the prime requirement for an all-weather interceptor, the F1C is equipped with a Cyrano IV monopulse radar operating in the I/J band. A later modification added limited look-down capability, although only single targets can be tracked.

French service

The Armée de l'Air acquired 83 basic F1Cs from 1973, of which the final 13 were fitted with BF radar warning receiver 'bullet' antennas on the fin. Later models were delivered with fixed refuelling probes as the F1C-200.

The Armée de l'Air ordered 20 F1B tandem-seat trainers for pilot conversion. Incorporation of a second cockpit adds only 12 in (30 cm) to the standard F1C's length, as remaining space is made by deleting the fuselage fuel tank and both internal cannon. Otherwise, the F1B is combat capable.

Reconnaissance variant

As soon as it was clear that the Mirage F1 would support a major production run, Dassault studied a dedicated reconnaissance version, the customer being the Armée de l'Air. Designated Mirage F1CR-200, the first example flew on 20 November 1981. For its mission the Mirage F1CR carries a wealth of reconnaissance equipment both internally and externally. A Super Cyclope infra-red linescan unit is installed in place of the cannon, and an undernose fairing houses either a 75-mm panoramic camera or 150-mm vertical camera. Other internal equipment includes a Cyrano IVMR radar with extra ground-mapping, blind let-down, ranging and contour-mapping modes, when compared to the fighter's radar, and provision for a navigation computer and INS.

Additional sensors are carried in various centreline pods, these including Raphaël TH side-looking airborne radar, Harold long-range oblique camera or ASTAC electronic intelligence pods. Various combinations of cameras can also be mounted in a pod. An inflight refuelling probe is fitted on the starboard side of the nose, as on the F1C-200.

Sixty-four F1CRs were ordered, and the first production aircraft flew on 10 November 1982. The the first squadron, Escadron de Reconnaissance 2/33 'Savoie', became operational at Strasbourg in July 1983. ER 1/33 'Belfort' and ER 3/33 'Moselle' followed, conversion from Mirage IIIRs being completed in 1988. F1CRs were dispatched to Saudi Arabia for participation in Desert

Pictured participating in a USAF Red Flag exercise at Nellis AFB in Nevada, this French F1CR displays the bulged undernose fairing housing the aircraft's panoramic camera. The F1CR is also able to carry the Raphaël SLAR 2000 pod on its central fuselage pylon.

Shield/Desert Storm, where they were used for reconnaissance missions before being grounded to prevent confusion with Iraqi Mirage F1EQs. When allowed to resume flying, they displayed their little-known secondary ground-attack role by bombing Iraqi positions, their radar making them more effective than the alternative Jaguars.

While most export customers for the Mirage F1 interceptor series were content to specify aircraft based on the original Armée de l'Air F1C, Dassault recognised the advantages of a simplified version for day attack missions. The Mirage F1A is visually distinguished by having a slender conical nose, resulting from the removal of the large Cyrano IVM radar. In its place is the Aïda II ranging radar. The main advantages of the Mirage F1A are its relatively low cost and extra range. The main avionics racking is moved from behind the cockpit to the nose, making room for an extra fuselage tank. Other additions are a Doppler radar, and a non-retractable inflight refuelling probe. In addition to Aïda radar, South African F1AZs were fitted with a laser-ranger.

Multi-role F1E

On 22 December 1974 Dassault flew a prototype Mirage F1E, powered by the then-new M53 engine. This aircraft failed to win orders, and the M53-powered version was abandoned. Instead, the designation was then applied to an upgraded multi-role version for export customers. Outwardly resembling the F1C, the F1E has a SAGEM inertial system, EMD.182 central digital computer and VE.120C head-up display. Like all F1 versions, the F1E can be fitted with radar-warning receivers, chaff/flare dispensers and ECM jamming pods. The Mirage F1D is essentially similar to the F1B trainer procured by the Armée de l'Air, differing only in being based on the F1E single-seat export variant.

Most export F1D/Es have been fitted with the BF radar warning receiver and VOR aerials located in the fin. In addition, some aircraft received an HF fillet aerial at the forward joint of the fin. Basic multi-role aircraft (F1EQ, F1EQ-2) were followed by the F1EQ-4 with inflight refuelling probe and reconnaissance pod capability, and F1EQ-5 and EQ-6 with Agave radar and Exocet capability. The F1EQ-6 had RWRs from the outset, and these were also retrofitted to F1EQ-5s.

A logical product of the shortfall in French ground-attack capability and a surplus of air defence fighters following Mirage 2000C deliveries, the Mirage F1CT derives its designation from being a tactical air-to-ground version of the F1C interceptor – specifically, the probe-equipped F1C-200. Two prototypes were converted, the first flying on 3 May 1991, and 55 more had been completed by 1995. Deliveries began on 13 February 1992, allowing one squadron at Colmar to achieve IOC in November of that year.

The F1CT programme upgraded interceptors to a similar standard to the tactical recce F1CR. Radar changes from Cyrano IV to IVMR, with additional air-to-ground modes, and is backed by a Uliss 47 inertial platform, M182XR central computer, VE.120 HUD, TMV630A laser rangefinder beneath the nose and improved radar warning receiver.

Structurally, the wing is strengthened and modified for activation of the outboard hardpoints, while the port cannon is removed to make space for the additional equipment. The F1CT carries bombs and rocket pods for its new mission, but retains the ability to launch AAMs as a pure interceptor.

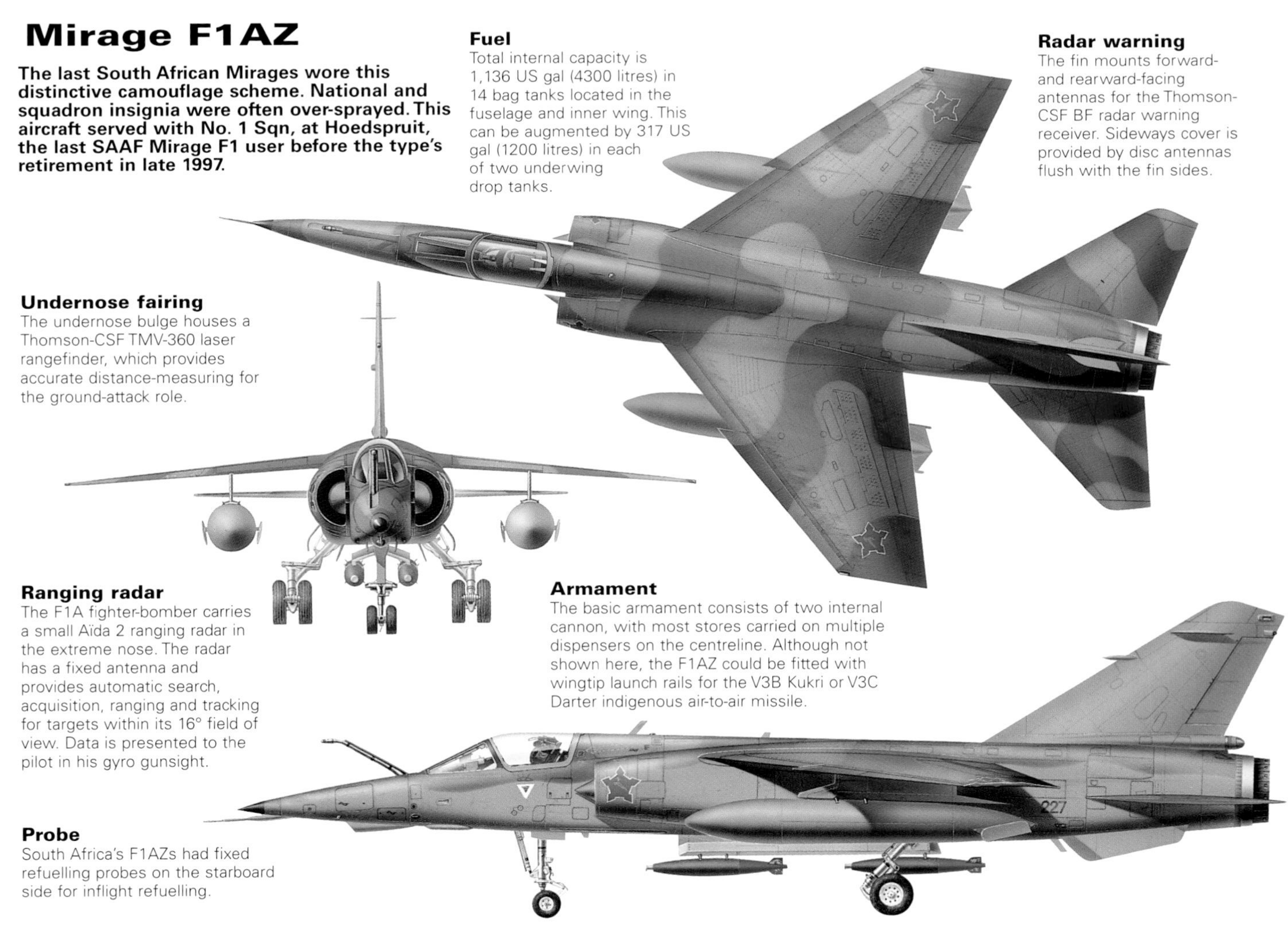

Mirage F1AZ

The last South African Mirages wore this distinctive camouflage scheme. National and squadron insignia were often over-sprayed. This aircraft served with No. 1 Sqn, at Hoedspruit, the last SAAF Mirage F1 user before the type's retirement in late 1997.

Mirage F1 operators

Dassault was assured of a ready-made home market for the Mirage F1, but also wished to continue the export success achieved by the Mirage III/5 series. The F1 did not match its predecessor, but did notch up sales to 10 export customers.

France

F1 deliveries to France consisted of 20 F1B two-seaters, 162 F1C single-seat fighters and 64 F1CR tactical reconnaissance aircraft. Major fighter units were EC 5, EC 10, EC 12 and EC 30, of which EC 30 at Reims-Champagne was the first to become operational, receiving its initial aircraft on 20 December 1973. In addition to France-based units, the F1C also equipped a detachment in Djibouti (EC 4/30, later EC 4/33). All of the F1CRs (an example in desert camouflage is shown top right) were delivered to the ER 33 at Strasbourg. When the Mirage 2000 replaced the F1C in the air defence role, 55 survivors were modified as F1CTs for a multi-role attack tasking, being delivered to EC 13 (right) at Colmar. This unit has subsequently been renumbered as EC 30, and together with ER 33 is the last French F1 operator, each of the two wings having two squadrons on strength. A handful of trials units have also operated the type.

Ecuador

Unable to buy Kfirs, Ecuador turned to France in the late 1970s, resulting in 16 Mirage F1JAs (similar to the F1E) and two F1JE trainers being delivered from 1978 to 1980. The aircraft serve with Escuadrón de Combate 2112, part of Grupo 211 at Base Aérea Taura, Guayaquil. Ecuador's Mirages have a multi-role tasking, and have been updated by Israel. Israeli-made Python AAMs are among the available weaponry.

Greece

Greece's inability to procure F-4 Phantoms in the early 1970s led to an order for 40 Mirage F1CG single-seaters to equip 334 and 342 Mire of 114 Ptérix at Tanagra for the defence of Athens. Such was the urgency of the order that 16 F1Cs were diverted from an Armée de l'Air batch. Virtually identical to French F1Cs, the Greek aircraft initially did not have BF radar warning receivers, although these were subsequently added. The arrival of Mirage 2000s for the defence of Athens saw 334 Mira move to Iraklion as part of the 126a Smirna Makis, while 342 Mira remained at Tanagra until the type was retired.

Iraq and Iran

Iraq ordered a total of 110 Mirage F1EQ single-seat multi-role aircraft and 18 F1BQ two-seaters, although not all were delivered because of arms embargoes. Following 16 F1EQ and 16 F1EQ-2 air defence aircraft were 28 F1EQ-4s with attack and reconnaissance capability. More important were the 20 F1EQ-5s with Agave radar, in place of Cyrano IV equipment, and Exocet missiles. These were used during the Iran–Iraq war in the mid-1980s, during the course of which F1EQs accounted for about 35 claimed 'kills', and an F-14 Tomcat was damaged. A few F1EQ-6s were delivered. Several Mirage F1s were shot down during Desert Storm and others were destroyed on the ground. Twenty-four F1EQ/BQs were among the aircraft which escaped to Iran, where they have been operated from TFB 14 at Mashad since 2003.

Jordan

Having been denied F-16s, Jordan acquired 17 Mirage F1CJs and three F1BJs with Saudi funding. Intended for air defence, this first batch was delivered in light grey to No. 25 Squadron at Azraq. A subsequent batch comprised 17 F1EJs for multi-role duties, these camouflaged aircraft (below) going to No. 1 Squadron.

Kuwait

Kuwait acquired 18 Mirage F1CK interceptors with two F1BK trainers. These were followed by nine F1CK-2s and four F1BK-2s. The aircraft served with Nos 18 and 61 Squadrons at Ali al Salem. Fifteen escaped to Saudi Arabia when Iraq invaded, at least one Iraqi helicopter being shot down in the process. The aircraft were subsequently returned to service before being replaced by the F/A-18 Hornet.

Libya

Libya acquired 38 Mirage F1s, comprising 16 F1AD radarless attack aircraft, six F1BD trainers and 16 F1ED multi-role fighter-bombers (below). They saw some action in the 1980s during operations in Chad. The survivors are believed to serve at Okba bin Nafi, near Tripoli, with an interceptor and a ground-attack squadron.

Morocco

Morocco's 50 Mirage F1s break down as 30 F1CHs and 20 F1EHs, six of the latter being equipped with refuelling probes. First deliveries were made in 1978. The aircraft saw action in the 1977–88 war with Polisario guerrillas, during the course of which at least three were lost to SAMs. The survivors continue to serve with an interceptor and a ground-attack squadron at Sidi Slimane.

Qatar

Having first equipped a training squadron in France, Qatar's Mirage F1s did not arrive in-country until July 1984, where they were assigned to No. 7 Squadron at Doha. The order comprised 12 Mirage F1EDAs and two F1DDA two-seaters. The aircraft had a multi-role tasking, and could carry reconnaissance pods. Having undertaken local air defence missions during Desert Storm, they were sold to Spain. Spain has in turn made efforts to sell the aircraft to other parties.

South Africa and Gabon

South Africa became the first customer for the radarless Mirage F1AZ attack variant, receiving its first of 32 aircraft in November 1975. Sixteen F1CZs were also acquired. The F1AZs served with No. 1 Squadron while the CZs were operated by No. 3 Squadron, both at Waterkloof. Mirage F1s were active in the skirmishes in Angola, including three confirmed 'kills' over MiG-21s. No. 3 Squadron was disbanded in 1992 and its F1CZs retired. Three ex-SAAF F1s were transferred to Gabon in 2006.

Spain

Between 1975 and 1983 Spain received 45 Mirage F1CEs (local designation C.14A), six F1BE trainers (CE.14A) and 22 F1EE multi-role aircraft (C.14B). The CEs were used to equip two squadrons of Ala 14 at Albacete/Los Llanos, while the F1EEs (illustrated below) went to Escuadrón 462 of Ala 46 at Gando, in the Canaries. Subsequently, Ala 11's Escuadrón 111 also transitioned to the type, flying from Manises. Attrition has been made good by the acquisition of surplus F1Cs from France, and by the purchase of the Qatari F1EDAs and F1DDAs, the latter equipping Esc 111. The remaining variants had been due to retire in late 1998. In 2007 the aircraft remained in active service with two squadrons of Ala 14 at Albacete. The aircraft were used for the Baltic Air Policing mission in 2006.

Dassault Mirage 2000

A new Dassault delta

The latest in a long line of distinguished warplanes to bear the Mirage label, the 2000 began life as a fighter designed to re-equip France's interceptor squadrons, but has emerged as a true multi-role performer.

As France's principal fighter manufacturer, Dassault has long had a policy of reusing titles which have proved successful. After the Mirage III had boldly imprinted the name of Générale Aéronautique Marcel Dassault on the map of world military aviation during the 1960s, its differently shaped successor became the Mirage F1. During the 1980s and into the 1990s, Dassault built a third generation of Mirages, once again changed radically – in sophistication, if not in shape – from its predecessors.

However, it must be said that, when the Mirage 2000 began life as a 'back-burner' project, few ever expected it to see the light of day. Dassault's design office commenced work on its Delta 1000 project in 1972, while a far greater proportion of work was being expended on the Avion de Combat Futur (ACF) – the proposed next-generation combat aircraft. But the ACF project was eventually deemed too expensive and fell away, while the Delta project, now given the designation Mirage 2000, began to take shape.

For this new aircraft, Dassault returned to the tailless delta configuration that was so successful in the Mirage III, 5 and 50, and the Mirage 2000 also shares with its predecessors the big high-lift wing and large internal volume.

French operation

Mirage 2000C deliveries to the 2e Escadre de Chasse commenced in 1984. The Mirage 2000 is now standard equipment for the French fighter arm and is operational in a number of variants. A two-seat trainer, the Mirage 2000B flew in production form on 7 August 1983 and is only 7½ in (19.05 cm) longer than the single-seat 2000C, the standard single-seat interceptor. French air force 2000Bs and 2000Cs are sometimes, and confusingly, known as Mirage 2000DAs ('DA' for Défense Aérienne – Air Defence).

For nuclear attack missions, Dassault decided to modify a two-seater Mirage with fuselage enhancements and more accurate positioning systems. The result was the 2000N, which could carry the ASMP missile, and which now provides France's aerial nuclear strike capability. Modifications to the 2000N have resulted in the Mirage 2000D, which is a conventional strike aircraft and, while unable to take the ASMP, it is capable of carrying a wide range of French air-to-surface weaponry.

Above: One of the most versatile operational embodiments of the Mirage 2000 is the D variant, essentially a 2000N which has been optimised for conventional attack missions. This, the first true D model, is carrying Matra laser-guided bombs, an ATLIS designator pod and Magic 2 missiles for self-defence.

Despite reservations from other aircraft manufacturers, Dassault proved the validity of the delta-wing configuration. The Mirage 2000 offers a large number of underwing hardpoints combined with excellent agility, but has yet to match the sales success of previous Mirages.

A further Dassault modification is the Mirage 2000-5 – an upgraded 2000C with enhanced avionics incorporating a weapons management system, improved self-defence options and powerplant. A proportion of French Mirage 2000Cs have been modified to this standard, along with a number of those operated by Greece and the UAE.

The latest variant is the export-optimised Mirage 2000-9. This was specifically developed to

This is one of the UAE's unique Mirage 2000RADs, albeit without a centreline sensor pod. The Gulf nation's commitment to the type resulted in a 1998 order for 32 second-generation Mirage 2000-9 warplanes. At the same time, a total of 30 kits was ordered to upgrade earlier aircraft to Dash 9 standard.

series (2000EM/BM for Egypt, 2000H/TH for India and 2000P/DP for Peru) was based closely on the standard 2000C/B with RDM radar (with CW illuminator) and standard French-specification EW suite. However, there were some small differences. India's first few aircraft had the M53-5 engine and were known as 2000H5s and 2000TH5s. They were subsequently re-engined with M53-P2s. The Egyptian aircraft featured an additional radar warning antenna on the fin.

In terms of armament the first export batch had similar weapons to the French Cs, including Super 530F and Magic 2 missiles. Attack options include a variety of free-fall bombs and laser-guided weapons, designated by the ATLIS II pod.

The second export series comprised 2000EG/BGs for Greece and 2000EAD/DADs for the UAE. This batch has the improved ICMS Mk 1 EW suite, characterised by additional antennas on the fin. Radar in the Greek aircraft is designated RDM3, with improvements over the original unit. Armament options are also expanded, some Greek aircraft being able to launch Exocet anti-ship missiles, while UAE Mirages have been integrated with the Alenia-Marconi PGM series of guided missiles.

Reconnaissance

Included in the UAE's batch were eight reconnaissance aircraft designated 2000RAD. Externally, the 2000RAD differs little from the standard single-seater, but has the ability to carry one of three reconnaissance systems on the centreline. These comprise the Raphäel side-looking imaging radar, Harold long-range oblique photography camera and the COR2 multi-sensor general-purpose reconnaissance pod, which contains cameras and an infra-red linescan.

Mirage 2000C-S4

This aircraft was the last of the S4 variants to be built, fitted with the RDI J2-4 radar. It is seen as it appeared during Operation Daguet (France's contribution to Desert Storm) while based at Al Ahsa AB in Saudi Arabia.

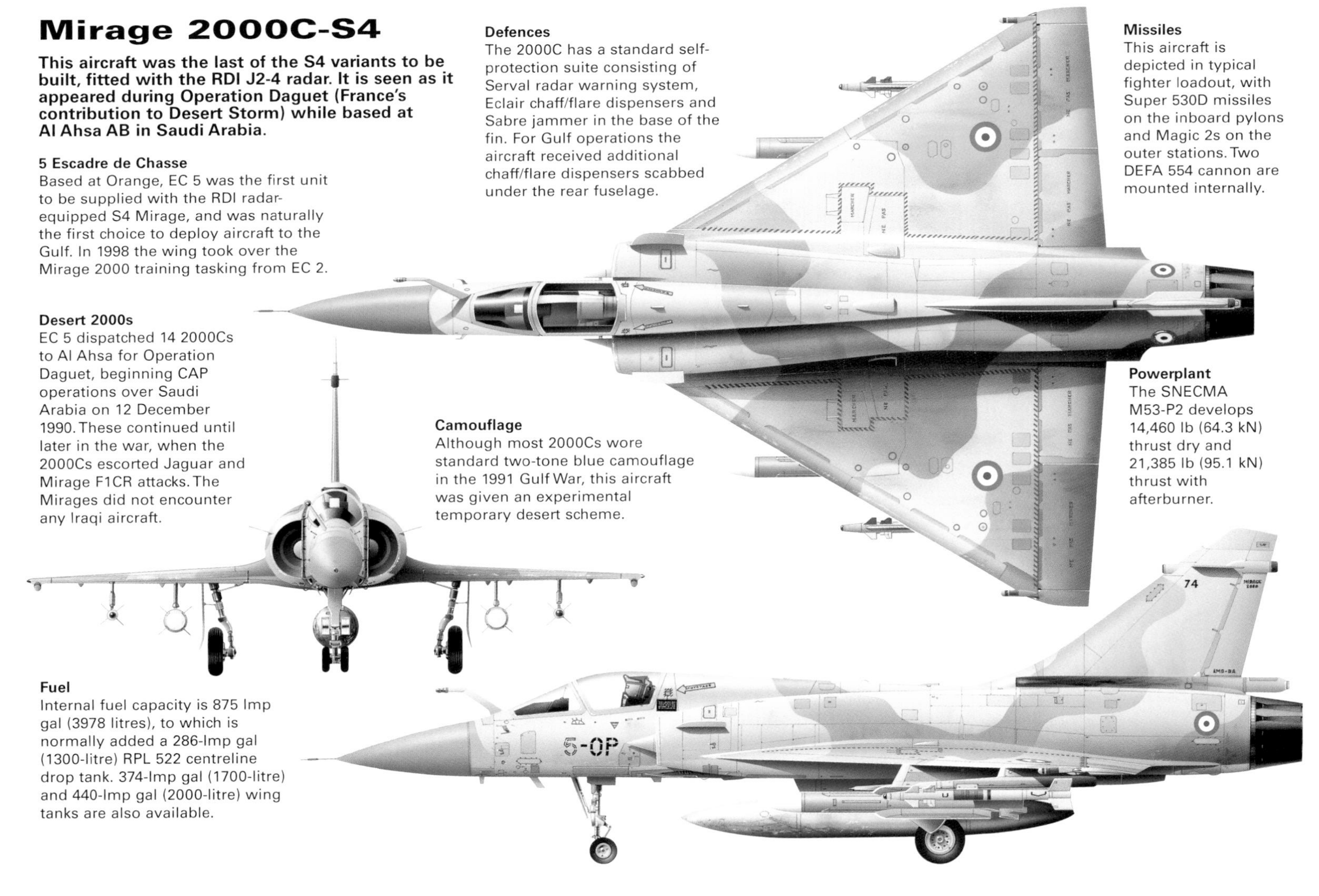

5 Escadre de Chasse
Based at Orange, EC 5 was the first unit to be supplied with the RDI radar-equipped S4 Mirage, and was naturally the first choice to deploy aircraft to the Gulf. In 1998 the wing took over the Mirage 2000 training tasking from EC 2.

Desert 2000s
EC 5 dispatched 14 2000Cs to Al Ahsa for Operation Daguet, beginning CAP operations over Saudi Arabia on 12 December 1990. These continued until later in the war, when the 2000Cs escorted Jaguar and Mirage F1CR attacks. The Mirages did not encounter any Iraqi aircraft.

Fuel
Internal fuel capacity is 875 Imp gal (3978 litres), to which is normally added a 286-Imp gal (1300-litre) RPL 522 centreline drop tank. 374-Imp gal (1700-litre) and 440-Imp gal (2000-litre) wing tanks are also available.

Defences
The 2000C has a standard self-protection suite consisting of Serval radar warning system, Eclair chaff/flare dispensers and Sabre jammer in the base of the fin. For Gulf operations the aircraft received additional chaff/flare dispensers scabbed under the rear fuselage.

Camouflage
Although most 2000Cs wore standard two-tone blue camouflage in the 1991 Gulf War, this aircraft was given an experimental temporary desert scheme.

Missiles
This aircraft is depicted in typical fighter loadout, with Super 530D missiles on the inboard pylons and Magic 2s on the outer stations. Two DEFA 554 cannon are mounted internally.

Powerplant
The SNECMA M53-P2 develops 14,460 lb (64.3 kN) thrust dry and 21,385 lb (95.1 kN) thrust with afterburner.

Mirage 2000

The new generation

With the N, D, Dash 5 and Dash 9 variants of the Mirage 2000, Dassault has dramatically improved the type. The capacity to carry precision-guided weapons and an increased air-to-air capability have ensured that these modern Mirages are selling well, not only in France, but on the export market as well.

Above: Both Dash 5 export customers have acquired two-seaters, in full operational fit. The Qatari aircraft QA86 was the first Qatari Mirage 2000 to fly, late in 1995, and was handed over in France in a ceremony on 8 September 1997.

Below: Two-seat strike/attack variants outnumber the single-seat fighters in French service. Based on the 2000N, the 2000D has a new weapons system, with Antilope 5 radar providing various ground-mapping functions and terrain avoidance.

When the Mirage 2000 was being designed, one of its envisaged roles was that of a nuclear penetrator. The aircraft would be used to deliver the new ASMP (Air-Sol Moyenne Portée – Air-to-Ground Medium-Range) tactical stand-off weapon. Dassault received a contract for two prototypes of an interdictor version of the new Mirage 2000, to be designated 2000P ('P' for 'Pénétration'). However, the designation was soon changed to 2000N ('N' for 'Nucléaire').

The 2000N was based upon the 2000B trainer, but the airframe was strengthened to withstand the stresses of high-subsonic, low-level flight. Antilope V multi-mode terrain-following radar was fitted in the nose. The initial requirement was for 100 Mirage 2000Ns. The first 2000Ns, with ASMP capability, were designated K1 sub-types. From the 32nd 2000N onwards, the designation K2 was used and these aircraft were also capable of carrying conventional ordnance.

In producing a conventional attack version of the Mirage 2000N – the 2000D (Diversifié – diversified) – Dassault took the opportunity to upgrade the aircraft's overall capabilities. Technological advances mean that the crew of the 2000D have more integrated HOTAS controls and are accommodated in what is well on the way to being a 'glass' cockpit.

The key to much of the Mirage 2000D's extra potential in terms of precision weapons is the PDLCT TV/thermal imaging pod carried on a pylon beneath the starboard air intake. This is effective by day or night and is used to direct either an AS.30L missile or BGL 1000 bomb. Also available are the Apache and Scalp EG stand-off weapons.

Variants of the D include the Mirage 2000D-R1N1L (this

The primary role of the Mirage 2000N is to be a launch platform for the ASMP nuclear missile. This aircraft, 301, the first production 2000N, carries the standard configuration of an ASMP, with self-defence Magic 2 AAMs and large wing tanks.

***Left:* Taiwan's 48 Mirage 2000-5EIs serve with the 2nd TFW at Hsinchu. Optimised for air defence duties, they are armed with Magic 2 and Mica missiles.**

***Below:* This 2000D is in typical precision attack fit, carrying two AS.30L laser-guided missiles. The latter is a key weapon of the 2000D, with designation provided by the PDLCT FLIR/laser pod or ATLIS II TV/laser pod.**

designation was given to the first six Mirage 2000Ds). This variant initially had the ability only to launch the AS.30L and BGL 1000, plus Magic AAMs. It gained IOC on 29 July 1993, giving the French air force an urgently needed LGB capability. By June 1995, all had been upgraded to full R1 standard.

The 2000D-R1N1 could carry an increased range of weapons, with 18 aircraft being supplied in this configuration. Another variant, the Mirage 2000D-R1, is able to operate with all the conventional weapons, apart from the Apache and Scalp EG.

In late 1999 production switched to the Mirage 2000D-R2, with the added ability to launch Apache and Scalp EG, as well as full automation of the self-defence suite and provision for ATLIS II laser guidance pods. Conversions to R2 standard were completed in 2003.

Mirage 2000-5

The Mirage 2000-5 brings together the RDY radar, an advanced cockpit, Mica missiles and the ICMS Mk 2 self-defence system in a major update of the original interceptor weapons system. This was first achieved in a two-seat aircraft, which flew initially on 27 April 1991 (it was subsequently converted to the single-place prototype).

Internal aspects of the 2000-5 include the uprating of the engine-driven generators and the installation of an advanced HUD for the pilot. For export, the fully automated ICMS Mk 2 significantly improves upon the self-defence suite of the Mirage 2000D by adding a receiver/processor in the nose and secondary DF antennas on the wingtip pods.

Originally indifferent to the private-venture 2000-5, the French air force was eventually prevailed upon to allocate funding to the conversion of 37 existing airframes to 2000-5F standard. The initial 'production' conversion was handed over on 30 December 1997, but did not transfer to CEAM to begin pilot conversions until April 1998. The initial standard of conversions for the French air force differs slightly from the 2000-5 baseline as promoted for export. The Mirage 2000-5F-SF1 retains the French standard self-protection equipment (Serval, Sabre and Spirale), but with slight modifications. Armament is optimised for the air defence role, the normal configuration being four Micas on pylons beneath the wingroots and a pair of Magic 2s outboard.

Exports of the Mirage 2000-5 were launched in November 1992 and designated 2000-5E, on receipt of a major order from Taiwan for 60. Qatar later announced a contract for 12 and the UAE added 30 more to the order book, as well as funding an upgrade for older aircraft (the UAE batch is described below). Qatar's order of July 1994 included nine single-seat aircraft, designated Mirage 2000-5EDA.

The first squadron of Taiwan's 48 single-seat Mirage 2000-5EIs gained IOC in November 1997. Their configuration is similar to the air defence-optimised Dash 5F, apart from having all five fin antennas. Deliveries to Taiwan began with the arrival of the first five by sea on 5 May 1997.

Export trainers with RDY radar have been supplied to two overseas operators of the Dash 5E. Qatar's three Mirage 2000-5DDAs are partners to nine 5EDAs. Taiwan has 12 Mirage 2000-5DIs, of which aircraft No. 2051 was the first export Mirage 2000-5 to fly, in October 1995. The initial aircraft was handed over in France on 9 May 1996.

Mirage 2000-5 Mk 2

After a protracted competition, a $3.4 billion UAE deal for 32 new Mirage 2000-5 Mk 2s was finalised in November 1998. Some 30 remaining Mirage 2000EADs, RADs and two-seat DADs will be modified to the same standard, which is known as 2000-9 in the case of the UAE aircraft. In 1998 it was announced that the 2000-9 fleet (which includes 12 two-seaters) would be armed with the Black Shaheen, a development of the Scalp EG stand-off missile used by French Mirage 2000Ds.

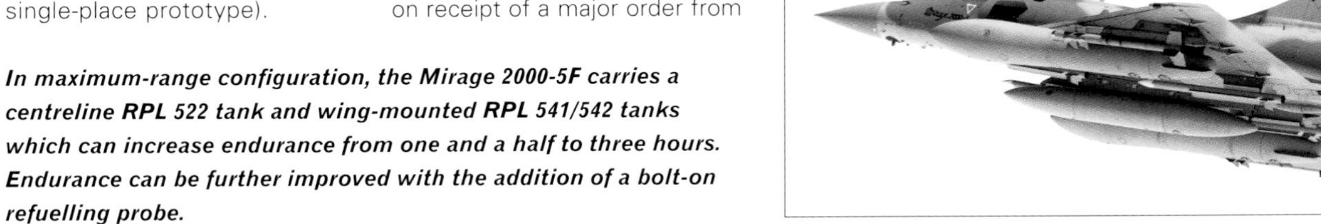

In maximum-range configuration, the Mirage 2000-5F carries a centreline RPL 522 tank and wing-mounted RPL 541/542 tanks which can increase endurance from one and a half to three hours. Endurance can be further improved with the addition of a bolt-on refuelling probe.

Mirage 2000 operators

Mirage 2000s, despite their cost and complexity, achieved notable sales success in the early 1980s. A slump in the late 1980s and early 1990s resulted in the Dash 5, which succeeded in winning back orders.

India

India placed an order for 40 Mirage 2000s, including 36 single-seaters, in October 1982. To expedite deliveries, the first 26 were produced with interim M53-5 engines, and carried a '5' in their designation. KF101 flew on 21 September 1984 and, after pilot training in France, the first batch of seven was delivered by air from 20 to 29 June 1985. Ten final aircraft from the first Indian contract and a follow-up batch of nine, ordered in March 1986 and delivered by October 1988, were supplied with higher-rated M53-P2 engines. The earlier 26 were upgraded to this standard in India. Configuration and colour scheme (black radome) was as for the French 2000C but, by 1993, at least two had received mid-brown and dark-green upper surface camouflage, suggestive of a low-level tasking. A third batch of 10 aircraft were delivered between early 2003 and early 2004, differing from the earlier aircraft in having RDM 7 radar in place of RDM 4, plus upgraded mission computers and navigation suite. IAF Mirage 2000s have always had a dual role, being able to carry Matra Armat anti-radar missiles, Durandal anti-runway bombs, Belouga cluster bombs and ATLIS or Litening II laser designator pods as alternatives to Magic and Super 530 missiles. Operating squadrons are Nos 1 and 7 at Gwalior. India's Mirage 2000 fleet has seen combat against Pakistan, notably in the Kargil conflict.

Peru

The Peruvian air force's intention to order 14 2000Ps (reduced from an original 26, which was to have included four two-seaters) was announced in December 1982 and renegotiated in July 1984 due to financial problems. In all, 10 single-seat Mirage 2000EPs and two Mirage 2000DPs were delivered to Escuadrón de Caza-Bombardeo 412 at La Joya from December 1986 onwards. The initial Peruvian Mirage pilots were trained in France. The aircraft were received together with ATLIS laser designators, 1000-kg (2,205-lb) Matra BGL laser-guided bombs, AS.30L missiles and a selection of free-fall bombs. Peru's Mirage 2000Ps, along with Venezuelan Su-30MK2s and late-model Chilean F-16s, are arguably 'top dog' in South America. Along with Perus's MiG-29s, they represent some of the most capable fighter designs in the region.

Qatar

Qatar's order of July 1994 included nine single-seat 2000-5EDAs and three two-seat -5DDAs. They have the full ICMS Mk 2 defensive aids suite, including five fin antennas, secondary wingtip sensors and provision for Spirale, plus a GPS aerial in the spine. Air-to-air missiles are Mica and Magic 2, but the aircraft also have an air-to-ground role with the Black Pearl stand-off missile (which is an export adaptation of the Scalp EG); AS.30L and BGL 1000, with appropriate designator; and BAP 100, Durandal and Belouga. An 882-lb (400-kg) ASTAC ground radar locator pod can also be carried. The first four Qatari aircraft (including the three -5DDAs) arrived on 18 December 1997, after training in France.

Egypt

Egypt was the first export customer for the Mirage 2000, but the second recipient. The contract placed in December 1981 included 16 single-seat 2000EMs, the first of which flew in December 1985. Four two-seat Mirage 2000BMs were also received. A unique feature of the 2000EM is a single, rear-facing antenna above the Serval unit, high on the fin trailing edge. Based at Bir Ket, the aircraft are in a colour scheme of medium-grey upper surfaces (with a black radome, however) and light-grey undersides. Armament includes Magic, Super 530, Armat ARMs and AS.30L ASMs, with an ATLIS laser designator.

France

The Armée de l'Air marked its 50th anniversary in 1984 by receiving its first squadron of Mirage 2000Cs. Escadron de Chasse 1/2 'Cigognes', the famous 'Storks' squadron, was based at Dijon where, by early 1985, it had achieved full squadron strength, including trainers. Two further wings were soon equipped with the 2000C, replacing Mirage IIIEs and Mirage F1Cs. Incorporated into the Commandement des Forces Aériennes, Mirage 2000Cs are assigned to home defence and overseas intervention, where they have been involved in conflicts such as Desert Storm and Deny Flight over Bosnia. Equipped with the ASMP nuclear stand-off missile, the two-seat 2000N, which was based on the trainer 2000B, was delivered to three squadrons, replacing Mirage IIIEs and Jaguars. EC 1/4 'Dauphiné' was the first unit to receive the 2000N on 12 July 1989. Due to delays in the Rafale programme, further 2000Ns were ordered, including a version without the ASMP interface, and this was eventually designated 2000D. The Ds are used for precision attack, with precision-guided weapons such as the AS.30L, Apache and Scalp EG and equip three squadrons, all based at Nancy. The advanced 2000-5F entered service with EC 1/2 in March 1999. These aircraft are refitted Cs and incorporate new avionics and weapon capabilities. The 2000-5F is operated by just two squadrons within EC 2, both of which are based at Dijon. Other examples are with the CEAM.

Taiwan

Orders for the Dash 5 Mirage 2000 were led by Taiwan, which acquired 60 as part of a major revamping of the RoCAF fighter forces. These comprise 48 2000-5EIs and 12 -5DI two-seat trainers. Magic 2 and Mica air-to-air missiles were included in the deal, and the 2000-5EIs are tasked with air defence missions. Taiwan's Dash 5s serve with three squadrons of the 2nd Tactical Fighter Wing at Hsinchu and, like the aircraft for Qatar, the Taiwanese Mirage Dash 5s have the full ICMS Mk 2 electronic countermeasures suite. Deliveries to Taiwan began with the arrival by sea on 5 May 1997 of the first five aircraft, and were completed in November 1998.

United Arab Emirates

Between May 1983 and 1985, the UAE ordered 22 Mirage 2000EADs. Acceptance was delayed by the customer's dissatisfaction with the standard of equipment installed, and not until November 1989 were the first flown to the Middle East. Self-defence aids include Spirale chaff/flare dispensers in the Karman fairings and Italian ELT/158 radar warning receivers and ELT/558 jammers in place of the standard French equipment, the new fit being known as SAMET. A further unusual feature is the adaptation to carry AIM-9 Sidewinder AAMs as alternatives to Magic (which is also used). Nos I and II Squadrons fly Mirage 2000s at Al Dhafra. The UAE was also the only purchaser of the 2000RAD reconnaissance sub-variant, of which eight were acquired. Six 2000DAD two-seaters were also included in the first batch, finished in a grey scheme. After a protracted competition, the UAE ordered 32 new-build Mirage 2000-9s in December 1997, requiring delivery to take place between late 1998 and late 2001. In the event, final examples were received in September 2004. Some 30 remaining Mirage 2000EADs, RADs and two-seat DADs were also modified to the same standard from 2002. This includes the ability to launch Black Shaheen, an export version of Scalp EG/Storm Shadow.

Greece

Greece's 40 Mirage 2000s were bought primarily for the defence of Athens. A total of 36 Mirage 2000EG and four two-seat Mirage 2000DGs were ordered in March 1985 and were delivered from March 1988 onwards to 331 and 332 Squadrons at Tanagra for air defence duties with Super 530D and Magic 2 AAMs. Greece's two-seaters are fitted with full mission equipment, including ICMS Mk 1. The aircraft have been considerably upgraded, and some have a secondary Exocet anti-ship capability. In addition, Greece placed an order for 18 new-build Dash 5 Mk II aircraft in 2000 and announced its intention to upgrade 10 earlier aircraft to a similar standard. The first production example of the Greek Dash 5 Mk II was flown in May 2003.

Dassault Ouragan/Mystère

Dassault's first jets

Above: Taking to the air with two underwing bomb racks and four rocket rails, this IDF/AF Ouragan wears the tan/dark-green camouflage scheme with pale-grey undersides that was common on the Israeli Ouragan fleet at the time of the Suez Crisis. The aircraft is from 113 Sqn, the first Israeli Ouragan operator, equipped with ex-Armée de l'Air equipment.

The historic Bloch company reappeared post-war, entitled Avions Marcel Dassault. Intent on regaining its position as France's foremost fighter manufacturer, Dassault began an ambitious programme to develop indigenous jet fighters.

Below: Pictured is an EC 3/2 'Alsace' Ouragan, armed with underwing HVARs. The troughs for the port-side pair of 20-mm Hispano-Suiza 404 cannon are clearly evident in the underside of the forward fuselage.

Marcel Dassault's first jet fighter, and the first of such to be ordered in quantity by the Armée de l'Air, the M.D.450 Ouragan (hurricane) established a notable record in speed of design and construction. The design, to an official interceptor specification, was begun in December 1947, the official order for three prototypes was received on 1 July 1948 and the first prototype completed its successful first flight on 28 February 1949.

After successful tests, a pre-production order for 12 M.D.450s was placed, and the first aircraft of this series flew at the end of November 1950. The first production Ouragan flew initially on 5 December 1951. Of the pre-production batch, one example was converted as the M.D.450-30L, while another was fitted with a SNECMA Atar 101 turbojet, the latter making its first flight on 5 December 1951.

The basic production M.D.450 Ouragan was powered by a (Rolls-Royce-designed) Hispano-Suiza Nene Mk 104B turbojet, and 35 per cent of production was sub-contracted to SNCASE (Société Nationale de Constructions Aéronautiques du Sud-Est) and SNCASO (Société Nationale de Constructions Aéronautiques du Sud-Ouest). By no means a revolutionary design, the Ouragan featured a highly polished flush-riveted stressed skin, a pressurised cockpit with Martin-Baker ejection seat, hydraulically retractable landing gear, hydraulically boosted flight controls and four 20-mm cannon.

Ouragan variants

Identified by its twin-wheel 'diablo' main landing gear and brake 'chute fairing, permitting operations from unprepared landing strips, the Barougan (left) was an Ouragan modified by the Armée de l'Air in an attempt to increase its operational usefulness. First flown on 21 January 1952, the M.D.450-30L (right) was the eleventh pre-production Ouragan modified with side air intakes in preparation for the planned M.D.453 (Mystère de Nuit) two-seat, radar-equipped, all-weather interceptor. The SNECMA Atar 101C-powered M.D.451 photo-reconnaissance model remained unbuilt.

Ouragan at war

Both the Indian air force (IAF, Bharatiya Vayu Sena) and the Israeli Defence Force/Air Force (IDF/AF, Tsvah Haganah le Israel/Chel Ha'Avir) took the Ouragan to war. A squadron of ex-Israeli examples was also deployed against rebels in El Salvador in the early 1980s by the Salvadorean air force (FAS), five examples being destroyed by anti-government rebels during an attack upon Ilopango airfield.

IDF/AF
Twenty Israeli Ouragans were operational during 1956 and saw combat that year against Egyptian forces. They wore yellow and black identification stripes. Three Ouragans were lost during the campaign, which saw the type principally employed on ground-attack duties.

Indian air force
This 29 Sqn, IAF, Toofani was briefly operational during the 1965 Indo-Pakistan war over Kashmir. Although the IAF held a numerical advantage over the PAF, the high rates of attrition suffered by IAF Vampires on the first day of conflict saw both these and the Ouragans withdrawn after a single day's combat.

From 1951, a total of 350 Ouragans was produced for Armée de l'Air service. Dassault exported 104 Ouragans to India, where the aircraft was known as the Toofani (hurricane), and 24 to Israel, followed by a further 51 ex-Armée de l'Air machines.

Mystère I and II

Essentially a swept-wing version of the Ouragan, Dassault's first prototype M.D.452 Mystère (mystery) made its maiden flight on 23 February 1951. Two further prototypes were completed to Mystère IIA standard with Hispano-Suiza Tay 250 engines, the first flying on 5 April 1952. An April 1951 order for a pre-production series of 17 aircraft consisted of three Mystère IIAs, followed by three Tay Mk 250-powered Mystère IIBs with two 30-mm cannon in place of the Mystère IIA's four 20-mm weapons. Nine aircraft were finished as Mystère IICs with SNECMA Atar 101D turbojets, revised intake trunking and a modified fuel system. The first Mystère IIC flew on 29 December 1952. The last two of the 17-aircraft order were completed with 8,378-lb st (37.70-kN) afterburning Atar 101F-2 turbojets.

On 28 October 1952 the third pre-production aircraft, a Mystère IIB, fully armed with two 30-mm cannon, became the first French aircraft to exceed Mach 1, in a dive, during trials at Melun.

The production-configured Mystère IIC was the subject of a French government order for 150 examples in April 1953. It was fitted with the 6,173-lb st (27.46-kN) Atar 101D turbojet, without reheat, and carried two 30-mm cannon. The first production Mystère IIC took to the air in June 1954.

Preceding the delivery of export Ouragans, the first Mystère IICs followed the main batch of Armée de l'Air Ouragans, and the total of 150 was delivered from 1954 to 1956.

Despite providing a not inconsiderable advance over the straight-wing Ouragan, the Mystère IIC was destined not to have a long service life, as its successor, the second-generation Mystère IVA, showed tremendous promise. It was built in parallel with the IIC from 1954 onwards, having been the subject of an April 1953 order from the US government for 225 aircraft for the French air force.

Combat record

Although the Ouragan and Mystère IIC saw no combat in French hands, the Ouragan went into battle in Indian and Israeli and, later, in Salvadorean air force colours. The Mystère IIC remained untested in combat, but its immediate successors, the Mystère IVA and the supersonic Super Mystère, would go on to serve in combat with notable success.

***Above:** Mystère IIA number 05 was one of three aircraft out of the 17-machine pre-production batch completed to IIA standard.*

***Left:** Operational Armée de l'Air Mystère IICs of EC 1/10 'Parisis' are seen standing on the rain-soaked apron at Creil. EC 1/10 was formed as a IIC unit on 1 December 1954, and received its aircraft from July 1955. The 10e Escadre de Chasse was complete in 1956, by which time 2/10 'Seine' and 3/10 'Valois' were similarly equipped.*

Mystère IV and Super Mystère

In late 1951, while still in the early stages of the design of the first-generation Mystère, Dassault decided that the aircraft's successor, the M.D.454, or Mystère IV, was to be an entirely new aircraft.

Mystère IVAs of the Escadre de Transformation's ET 1/8 'Saintonge' wore the badges of old squadrons 4C-1 (a lion in yellow and black) and 3C-2 (a black arrow flanked by red wings) on either side of the fin. The Cazaux-based weapons training unit retired its Mystère IVAs in favour of Alpha Jets from 1979 to 1980.

Rolled out from its hangar at Istres in August 1952, the new Mystère IV was superficially similar to the Mystère IIC. However, the IV introduced increased sweepback angles (sweepback at the wing's quarter-chord line was increased from 30° to 38°); a strengthened, longer and deeper oval-section fuselage; a taller and more acutely swept tail and 'all-flying' tailplane; and fully powered flight controls – indeed, not one structural component was common to its predecessor.

The aircraft was powered by a Hispano-Suiza-built Tay derivative, the Verdon, although the first 50 aircraft used the standard Tay 250 unit. The first Mystère IV took to the air on 28 September 1952, and the first production example was delivered to the Armée de l'Air in June 1954. The production IVA differed from the IV in the incorporation of 60 engineering changes, notably a lengthened vertical tail and a dorsal spine, and a lengthened rear fuselage.

An Off-Shore Procurement order funding 225 IVAs was placed by the US, preceding an initial order of 100 examples for the Armée de l'Air; in addition, 110 examples were delivered to India and 60 to Israel. From 1954 to 1958 a total of 421 IVAs was built. Of this total, the Armée de l'Air took 240 (including the US-funded batch). The Mystère IVA saw combat with each of its operators; it was flown by France during the Suez crisis in November 1956.

The Mystère IVA enjoyed a long service life with the Armée de l'Air, with EC 7 retaining examples for general flying practice long after conversion to the Jaguar, while the Fighter School at Tours retained Mystère IVAs as late as 1984. The production IVA was armed with two DEFA 30-mm cannon in the lower forward fuselage, which could be supplemented by an automatic Matra rocket magazine, containing 55 HVARs, aft of the cannon installation. Four underwing pylons could carry bombs, napalm tanks, or Matra rocket containers with 19 HVARs each, or two groups of six air-to-ground rocket projectiles.

Aerodynamic refinement

The Mystère IVB differed from the IVA in the design of the front and rear fuselage, and in its use of a Hispano-Suiza Avon turbojet powerplant. The air inlet duct was directly under the cockpit, rather than dividing to pass on either side of the fuselage. The realignment of this nose air inlet duct necessitated a backwards-retracting nosewheel unit. The nose inlet aperture was similar to that of the F-86 Sabre, with an upper lip containing a radar telemeter. The lengthened rear fuselage incorporated an afterburner.

The Mystère IVB first flew on 16 December 1953, after a batch of six had been ordered in December 1952, and these were built featuring various minor differences. A production version with a SNECMA Atar 101G turbojet was also suggested. During 1956, the IVB completed a series of flight tests equipped with a SEPR liquid-fuelled rocket motor installed under the rear

On the occasion of the departure of the squadron's commanding officer, this Cazaux-based Mystère IVA of ET 2/8 'Nice' was specially painted during July 1981. The scheme was inspired by that worn by an Ouragan display team of the 4e Escadre de Chasse, based at Bremgarten in 1956.

Mystère night-fighter projects

A derivative of the M.D.452 Mystère II, the two-seat, radar-equipped M.D.453 Mystère III 'Mystère de Nuit' prototype (right) utilised the lateral intakes of the M.D.450-30L, and made its first flight on 18 July 1952. The Mystère IVN (below) first flew on 19 July 1954. A two-seat night and all-weather interceptor fighter version of the IVB, the IVN would have carried two 30-mm cannon in addition to 128 HVARs.

fuselage, as part of the early Mirage fighter programme.

Night-fighter development

Developed from the IVB, the IVN, meanwhile, featured a lengthened forward fuselage seating pilot and radar operator in tandem, and was fitted with an F-86D-style nose radome. While the prototype carried the Avon RA.7R, the production variant of this all-weather fighter would have been powered by the afterburning SNECMA Atar 101G, and would have been armed with fuselage rocket packs in addition to underwing-mounted rockets.

Similar in general design to the Mystère IVB, the single-seat Super Mystère B1 featured a thinner, more sharply swept wing with a quarter-chord sweep of 45°, an improved air inlet and better cockpit visibility. The Super Mystère B1 tail was of greater area, with a more pointed top and straight leading edge. The horizontal tail became a one-piece powered 'slab'.

Below: The prototype Super Mystère B1, fitted with an afterburning Avon RA.7, flew for the first time on 2 March 1955, and on its fourth flight the following day achieved Mach 1.2 in level flight.

Super Mystère development continued, with Dassault choosing the afterburning Atar 101G-2 for the production Super Mystère B2 instead of the Avon RA.14R. An original order for 150 Super Mystère B2s for the Armée de l'Air was increased to 370. In French service, the Super Mystère B2 soldiered on until 1977, and was also exported to Israel and, later, to Honduras.

Super Mystère B2

This aircraft carries the markings of Escadron de Chasse 1/12 'Cambrésis', the first B2 operator, normally based at Cambrai. EC 1/12 was also the last B2 operator, giving up its last examples in September 1977. The unit formed with the Ouragan at Mont-de-Marsan in April 1952, switching to the Mystère IVA in autumn 1955.

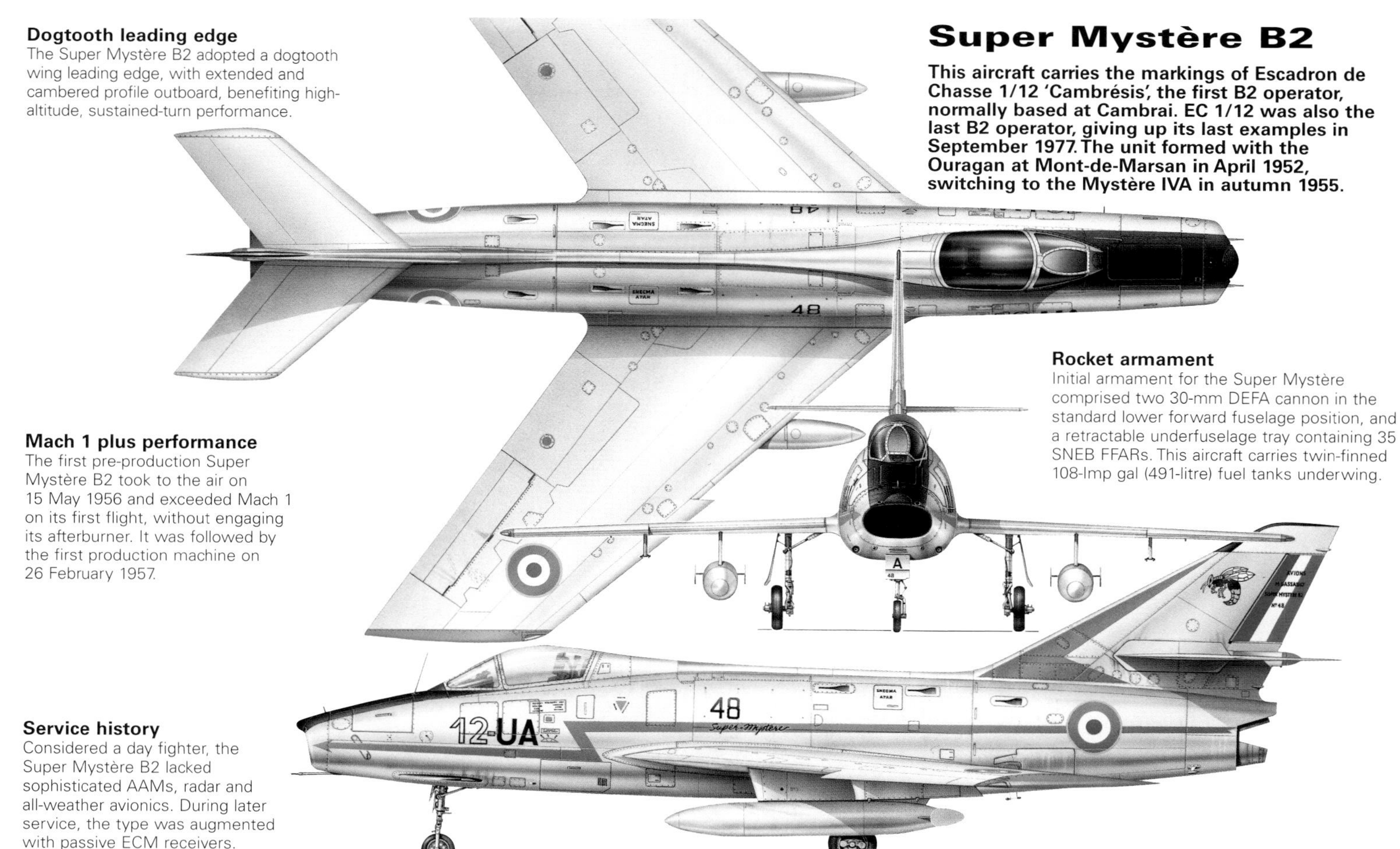

Dogtooth leading edge
The Super Mystère B2 adopted a dogtooth wing leading edge, with extended and cambered profile outboard, benefiting high-altitude, sustained-turn performance.

Mach 1 plus performance
The first pre-production Super Mystère B2 took to the air on 15 May 1956 and exceeded Mach 1 on its first flight, without engaging its afterburner. It was followed by the first production machine on 26 February 1957.

Service history
Considered a day fighter, the Super Mystère B2 lacked sophisticated AAMs, radar and all-weather avionics. During later service, the type was augmented with passive ECM receivers.

Rocket armament
Initial armament for the Super Mystère comprised two 30-mm DEFA cannon in the standard lower forward fuselage position, and a retractable underfuselage tray containing 35 SNEB FFARs. This aircraft carries twin-finned 108-Imp gal (491-litre) fuel tanks underwing.

Dassault Rafale
French superfighter

Rafale is a French combat aircraft with French engines and French avionics – a flagship for its home country's military industries and an affirmation of French determination to be second to none in the Europe of the 21st century.

Public knowledge of what was to become Rafale dates back to June 1982, when Dassault announced that studies were underway to develop a successor to the Mirage 2000, under the acronym ACX (Avion de Combat Experimental). France was then holding discussions with Britain and West Germany with regard to a new multinational fighter, although all three nations continued with their own developments. ACX proceeded with a contract for two (later reduced to one) technology demonstrator in April 1983.

Development of the ACX continued apace, even as the international collaborative effort foundered. In April 1985 ACX was christened Rafale (squall), shortly before Britain, West Germany, Italy and Spain announced that they would proceed without France on what would become the Eurofighter.

There was never any doubt that the Rafale project would not proceed at full pace and, on 4 July 1986, the Rafale A technology demonstrator made its first flight. During the first flight it achieved Mach 1.3, 36,000 ft (10973 m) and pulled 5 *g*. The aircraft showed its Mirage origins by having a near-delta wing, but featured the fourth-generation fighter trademarks of underslung intakes and canard foreplanes. Power

Above: To start its test programme as early as possible, the **Rafale A** *demonstrator initially flew with* **General Electric F404** *engines (as used by the* **F/A-18***). From* **February 1990** *it began flying with the intended* **M88** *engine, initially fitted in the port bay only.* **Rafale A** *eventually contributed* **865** *flights to the flight test programme.*

Top: On its very last flight on **24 January 1994** *the* **Rafale A** *technology demonstrator led all five aircraft then flying for this fine family portrait.* **Rafale A** *was slightly bigger than the four operational prototypes which followed, which comprised a single-seat* **Armée de l'Air** *aircraft* **(C 01)***, two-seater* **(B 01)** *and two single-seaters for the* **Aéronavale (M 01** *and* **M 02)***.*

Still struggling along with ancient **F-8E(FN)** *Crusaders in the fighter role, the* **Aéronavale** *had the most pressing need for re-equipment with* **Rafale***. Consequently, two of the four prototypes were of the carrier-capable* **Rafale M** *variant, which became the first variant in service. The second of these was the main testbed for the operational avionics suite. Here,* **M 02** *launches from* Foch *with a typical air-to-air load of* **Mica** *and* **Magic 2** *missiles.*

initially came from a pair of General Electric F404 turbofans, as SNECMA's new M88 powerplant was far from ready. During early tests the Rafale A easily achieved Mach 2, vindicating the intake/forward fuselage design. On 14 February 1987 the French government formally announced that Rafale would be developed for combat.

During 1987 the aircraft made an important series of approaches to French navy carriers to validate the type's suitability for naval operations. After a lay-up, the Rafale A flew again on 27 February 1990, fitted with an M88 engine in the port bay. The other F404 was later replaced by the intended engine.

Rafale A ended its flight test programme in January 1994, by which time it had been joined by four pre-production combat aircraft. The first of these to fly was C 01, the single-seat prototype for the Armée de l'Air. As well as being smaller than the A, the Rafale C introduced new features, including reshaped wingroot fairings and gold-coated canopy which were part of the 'stealth' features. The airframe was liberally sprinkled with antennas for the Spectra self-defence suite, one of the most advanced in the world and capable of directional jamming. The recontoured nose was yet to house the multi-mode RBE2 radar, first flown in B 01.

Rafale C 01 took to the air on 19 May 1991, demonstrating 'supercruise' (the ability to fly supersonically in dry thrust) on this maiden flight. In 2004, C 01 continued to be engaged in engine trials on behalf of the Rafale text programme.

On 12 December 1991 Rafale M 01 joined the test fleet. The M is the carrier version for the Aéronavale, and features a vastly strengthened undercarriage, arrester hook and unique 'jump strut' nosewheel. Held compressed during the initial phase of the catapult stroke, the nosewheel extends as the aircraft launches, forcing the nose upwards. A series of dummy deck trials in the United States allowed Rafale M 01 to undertake the type's first carrier landing, on *Foch*, on 19 April 1993. Following Mica missile trials and development work associated with the F2 production standard, M 01 was retired in 2003.

Two-seater priority

Next of the prototypes to fly was the two-seater Rafale B 01, which took to the air on 30 April 1993, followed by the second Rafale M on 8 November 1993. The two naval aircraft were extensively involved in a series of deck trials to clear the aircraft for carrier operations with a variety of loads.

In a change of requirement, the Armée de l'Air announced in May 1992 that the majority of its 234 aircraft would be two-seaters, intended to replace attack-roled Jaguars. A two-seat naval variant was launched as the Rafale BM in September 2000. Later redesignated Rafale N, a requirement for 35 aircraft was foreseen, but the naval 'twin-sticker' was abandoned in September 2004 as a result of financial constraints.

Initial Rafale deliveries were to Standard F1 – a lower equipment standard than fully specified in order to get Rafale into service as quickly possible. However, budgetary stretch-outs have slowed down the production programme considerably – the first production example, a Rafale B, took to the air in December 1998, while on 4 December 2000, the first of 60 Aéronavale Rafale Ms was accepted. Service entry with 12F followed on 18 May 2001 and the unit had its full complement of 10 aircraft by September 2002, but it was not until June 2004 that full operational capability was achieved.

Above: The Rafale's cockpit (this is M 01) is one of the most advanced in the world, fully utilising touch-sensitive screen and HOTAS technology. The primary displays are three large multi-function displays and a wide-angle single-glass HUD. The latter can have FLIR imagery overlaid to provide the pilot with a 'window in the night'.

Below: Following Gulf War experience, Armée de l'Air planners altered their requirement to tailor the Rafale B two-seater (previously regarded as a combat-capable trainer) to operational attack missions, the combat workload being perceived to be too high in single-seat attack types for one pilot alone.

Rafale enters service

Rafale M 1, the first navalised production aircraft, maintains 80 per cent structural and systems commonality with the single-seat Rafale C. The initial F1 software standard permits air defence missions against multiple targets, with an armament comprising radar-guided Mica AAMs, IR-guided Magic 2s and onboard cannon.

The Rafale prototype flew before the rival Eurofighter, and for some years the French programme seemed to stay 'ahead' of the multinational Eurofighter effort. This is perhaps unsurprising, since Rafale is in some ways a simpler aircraft, while most of Eurofighter's delays were a function of political difficulties.

In recent years, however, funding problems have delayed the Rafale programme, and the aircraft entered service five years after originally planned.

The Armée de l'Air was originally expected to receive predominantly single-seat Rafale Cs, but in 1991 switched its preference to an operationally equipped two-seat Rafale B, announcing that 60 per cent of its aircraft would be two-seaters. It had once been intended that the aircraft would enter service in three successively more developed standards (*Standard Utilisateur* 0, 1 and 2), though these were replaced by a single Armée de l'Air standard, with an export equivalent, with three successive software standards (F1, F2 and F3).

Production begins

Production of the Rafale was formally launched in December 1992, but was then suspended in November 1995, with work on the first production aircraft halting in April 1996. The programme was effectively relaunched in January 1997, with Dassault and the French MoD agreeing a 48 aircraft production programme (28 firm orders and 20 options) for delivery between 2002 and 2007. The French requirement for Rafales is much greater, of course, with the Armée de l'Air expected to take 234 aircraft, and the Aéronavale taking 60 Rafale Ms.

After the first production Rafale B had been delivered to the CEV (Centre d'Essais en Vol) at Istres for development work, the first production Rafale M took to the

Above: The initial production Rafale B (301) first flew on 24 November 1998 and was assigned to the CEV. The in-service Rafale B is capable of one- or two-crew operations.

Left: B 01, the first Rafale B prototype, and M 01, the first naval prototype, demonstrate different weapon loads. The wingtip pylons accept either Mica (B 01) or Magic 2 (M 01) AAMs. A maximum of three external tanks can be carried.

Rafale M 01 fires a Mica AAM development round during trials. Both IR- and active radar-guided variants of this weapon are available; the Rafale can carry as many as eight in the air defence role.

air on 7 July 1999, while a second Rafale B production aircraft flew later in 1999.

It was once planned that the first 10 Armée de l'Air Rafales would be rushed into service to equip a trials and export promotion half squadron. These plans were quickly abandoned and deliveries finally began to the first trials unit, EC 5/330 'Côte d'Argent', which received Rafale B 304 at Mont-de-Marsan on 22 December 2004. Before the end of the year this unit had received another two Rafale Bs and a single Rafale C.

Operational service

The first operational Armée de l'Air Rafales officially entered service at St Dizier with Escadre de Chasse 7, with an official ceremony on 27 June 2006. The wing was previously equipped with the SEPECAT Jaguar, and had reduced from three Escadrons to a single enlarged Escadron in mid-2001. The first Rafales for EC 1/7 'Provence' substitute the F2 multi-role standard software for the original baseline F1 standard. The F2 software gives the RBE2 radar a number of air-to-ground modes, and allows the aircraft to use the Apache and Scalp EG stand-off missiles as well as GBU-12/-22 laser-guided bombs and the AASM (Armement Air-Sol Modulaire) GPS-guided modular munition. F2 Rafales also have Link 16 MIDS and the OSF IRST system, and are able to use the IR-guided Mica in place of the ageing Magic 2. The first F2 aircraft, Rafale C 102, was accepted on 3 June 2005 by the Armée de l'Air flight evaluation centre at Mont-de-Marsan.

Subsequent Rafales will have F3 software, giving compatibility with the improved ASMP-A nuclear cruise missile, the AM.39 Exocet Block 2 anti-ship missile and the Reco NG recce pod. They will also introduce a buddy-buddy inflight refuelling store and the Topsight helmet-mounted sight for the pilot. All air force and navy Rafales will eventually be brought up to this definitive software standard during routine depot-level maintenance.

Development work on the Rafale continues, and future service aircraft may incorporate additional features. At the 2001 Paris air show at Le Bourget, for example, a Rafale appeared with massive conformal tanks on each side of the fuselage spine, and there have been frequent reports that various 'stealth' features are still being developed for the aircraft.

Aéronavale deliveries

Requiring an urgent replacement for the F-8E(FN) Crusader interceptor, the Aéronavale took delivery of 10 Rafale M aircraft with the original F1 (air defence only) software standard. The first production Rafale M was delivered to Landivisiau on 4 December 2000, while Flottille 12F was reformed on 18 May 2001 in preparation for the arrival of its new charge. Eight F1 Rafale Ms equipped Flottille 12F aboard the *Charles de Gaulle* from 2001, making their first deployment during the Trident D'Or exercise in the Mediterranean in May 2001. In spring 2004 six Flottille 12F Rafale Ms supported by Armée de l'Air C-135FR tankers completed missions in support of Operation Héracles, the French contribution to the anti-terror campaign in Afghanistan.

In 2006 the Rafale M introduced F2 software, and a second unit, Flottille 11F, will be equipped by 2010. The final deliveries will have F3 software (which will then be retrofitted to all earlier Rafale Ms) and the force will eventually be brought up to three squadrons, all shore-based at Landivisiau, and using a core fleet of 40 aircraft, with 20 more kept in reserve. With the French navy having reduced from a two-carrier force to a single carrier fleet (with the carrier *Charles de Gaulle*) significant further Rafale M orders for the Aéronavale seem unlikely.

Operation Serpentaire

Progress with F2 deliveries was such that, in March 2007, a combined Aéronavale/Armée de l'Air force of Rafale F2 standard aircraft could be deployed under Operation Serpentaire, France's mission to support ground troops of the NATO International Security Assistance Force (ISAF) in Afghanistan. The Armée de l'Air aircraft deployed to Dushanbe in Tajikistan, the mission reflecting the fact that air force ground and flight tests and crew training had been completed at Mont-de-Marsan.

The next Armée de l'Air squadron to re-equip with the Rafale B/C will be EC 2/7 'Lorraine', from 2008. This will be a specialist nuclear strike unit with the ASMP-A weapon, and will eventually replace the Mirage 2000N in this role.

Armée de l'Air development airframe B 01 demonstrates a typical air-to-surface weapon load-out, comprising three external fuel tanks in conjunction with four GBU-12 laser-guided bombs and wingtip Magic 2 AAMs. Note also the detachable (fixed) inflight refuelling probe. On a low-level penetration mission with 12 250-kg (551-lb) bombs, four Mica AAMs and 880 Imp gal (4000 litres) of fuel in three external tanks, the Rafale has a combat radius of 655 miles (1055 km).

Dassault/Dornier Alpha Jet More than just a trainer

In celebration of NATO's Tiger Meet held at Beja, Portugal in May 1996, this Portuguese Alpha Jet from Escuadra 301 'Jaguares' was appropriately decorated in 'tiger stripe' markings.

Developed by France as a jet trainer and West Germany as a light-attack aircraft, the Alpha Jet has served its home nations well. The aircraft remains active in France and, for a number of export customers, has proved to be an ideal training and attack platform.

One of the first of a new category of light multi-role military aircraft, the Alpha Jet can perform advanced flying training, weapons instruction and ground-attack missions. Developed jointly by France's Dassault and Germany's Dornier, over 500 Alpha Jets were delivered to 10 air forces, making it one of Europe's most successful post-war aircraft.

The story of the Alpha Jet goes back to the 1960s, when the air staffs of France and West Germany first discussed their future requirements for a jet trainer. The Germans then decided to continue to use US facilities (training on the Cessna T-37 and Northrop T-38). However, Germany would clearly have to replace the Fiat G.91R, of which the Luftwaffe had over 300 in the light ground-attack role. On 22 July 1969 the two governments announced a joint requirement for a new aircraft that could perform either in the training or close support roles, with the intention that each country would buy 200 examples. Ultimately, the two 'launch customers' took an eventual total of 351 aircraft between them.

Basic characteristics

The Alpha Jet is a twin-turbofan aircraft with a high-set swept wing, with increased-thrust Larzac 04 engines mounted in conformal pods on the fuselage sides. The two crew members sit in tandem, with the rear cockpit raised considerably so that, in the flying training role, the instructor can see straight ahead over the student pilot's head. While the French Alpha Jet E (for Ecole, or School) has a rounded nose with strakes for improved spin handling, the German Alpha Jet A (for Appui Tactique, or Attack) close-support aircraft has a pointed nose. Other characteristics of the German aircraft were the installation of a Doppler navigation radar, HUD, and a belly-mounted 27-mm Mauser cannon pod. In its weapons training role, the Alpha Jet E can carry a ventral gun pod with a single DEFA 30-mm cannon. Both variants have four underwing pylons for up to 5,511 lb (2500 kg) of stores, including bombs and rockets.

Above left: The French air force uses the Alpha Jet E for advanced pilot training, weapons instruction and as the mount of its national aerobatic team. Its fleet is divided between bases at Tours and Cazaux, western France.

Below left: With the establishment of two assembly lines, at Toulouse (France) and Oberpfaffenhofen (West Germany), four prototypes were constructed, two for each partner. The first to fly is illustrated lifting off from Istres, France, on 26 October 1973.

Towards the end of the Alpha Jet production run, the ability to carry the AM.39 Exocet anti-ship missile was provided. Along with the Exocet, the Alpha would be able to carry two Magic 2 AAMs and a 138-Imp gal (625-litre) drop tank, thus demonstrating a capability far exceeding that of its original trainer role.

The first of four prototypes made its maiden flight on 26 October 1973, just over two years after the rival Hawk. Alpha Jets entered service with the Armée de l'Air training units in May 1979. The Luftwaffe received its first aircraft a few years later.

The Alpha Jet's success was not restricted to Europe. A number of countries purchased the design, in order to fulfil their training and attack requirements.

The first export customer was Belgium, placing an order for 33 aircraft to fulfil basic and advanced training roles. Further afield, Alpha Jets were ordered by Egypt, Togo, the Ivory Coast, Qatar, Nigeria and Morocco.

Advanced derivatives

All first-hand export customers use aircraft based on the French Alpha Jet A, although Egypt's first batch of trainers was designated Alpha Jet MS (or MS1) and featured an enhanced avionics fit. The Alpha Jet MS2 was a dedicated light-attack aircraft with a new, more pointed nose, accommodating a laser rangefinder. The digital databus-equipped MS2 also featured INS, HUD and a radio altimeter.

The Alpha Jet enjoyed something of a mini-renaissance in the mid-1990s, thanks mainly to Germany's desire to sell off its considerable fleet of stored aircraft that had been retired following the end of the Cold War. The country withdrew the type from front-line use in 1993, and the last few surviving trainers in June 1997. Germany cascaded 50 Alpha Jets to Portugal in 1993, and 12 examples went to the UK's Defence Evaluation and Research Agency (DERA), now QinetiQ. These are employed in the drone-chase, test pilot training and trials support roles. Similar support work is conducted on the Alpha Jet in Canada by the Top Aces company. A further 20 (plus five 'spares ships') were acquired by Thailand. The Alpha Jet has since been flown in civilian hands, most notably with the Flying Bulls display team, which operates three Alphas in Austria.

The Royal Moroccan Air Force's Alpha Jet Hs were delivered from 1979. This pair flanks Alpha Jet Es from GE 314, an Armée de l'Air unit that can trace its origins back to service in Morocco in 1943.

Alpha Jet E

Belgium received 33 Alpha Jets for the training role, delivered between December 1978 and July 1980. Located at Beauvechain, the aircraft are operated by 1 Wing, which also provides schooling on the piston-engined SF.260 basic trainer from the same base.

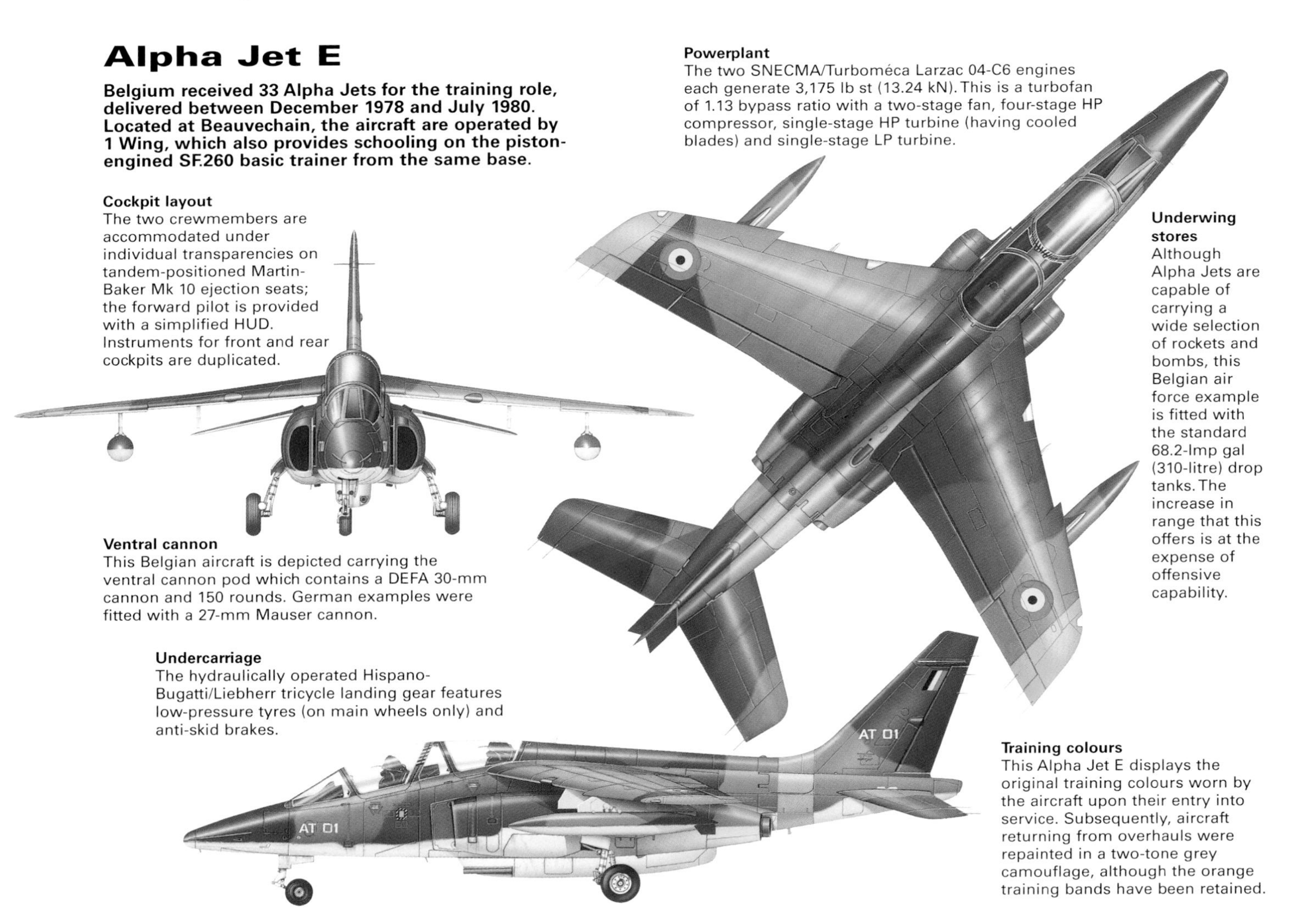

Cockpit layout
The two crewmembers are accommodated under individual transparencies on tandem-positioned Martin-Baker Mk 10 ejection seats; the forward pilot is provided with a simplified HUD. Instruments for front and rear cockpits are duplicated.

Ventral cannon
This Belgian aircraft is depicted carrying the ventral cannon pod which contains a DEFA 30-mm cannon and 150 rounds. German examples were fitted with a 27-mm Mauser cannon.

Undercarriage
The hydraulically operated Hispano-Bugatti/Liebherr tricycle landing gear features low-pressure tyres (on main wheels only) and anti-skid brakes.

Powerplant
The two SNECMA/Turboméca Larzac 04-C6 engines each generate 3,175 lb st (13.24 kN). This is a turbofan of 1.13 bypass ratio with a two-stage fan, four-stage HP compressor, single-stage HP turbine (having cooled blades) and single-stage LP turbine.

Underwing stores
Although Alpha Jets are capable of carrying a wide selection of rockets and bombs, this Belgian air force example is fitted with the standard 68.2-Imp gal (310-litre) drop tanks. The increase in range that this offers is at the expense of offensive capability.

Training colours
This Alpha Jet E displays the original training colours worn by the aircraft upon their entry into service. Subsequently, aircraft returning from overhauls were repainted in a two-tone grey camouflage, although the orange training bands have been retained.

de Havilland Vampire

TG278 was the fifth production Vampire F.Mk I and was built by English Electric at Preston. The first 41 production examples were powered by the Goblin 1 engine, which was replaced in later versions by the Goblin 2.

Twin-boom fighter

Britain's second jet fighter, the de Havilland Vampire retained the good looks (and wooden components) of the company's prestigious forerunners, selling well to the RAF and foreign air forces.

Conceived in 1941 when the early de Havilland Goblin turbojet was showing promise, the de Havilland DH.100 single-engined fighter was designed to Air Ministry Specification F.6/41. Among other demands, this called for a maximum speed of at least 500 mph (805 km/h) and a combat radius of 300 miles (483 km). The aircraft incorporated a twin-boom layout, and the cockpit section was constructed of plywood and balsa sandwich.

Geoffrey de Havilland Jnr first took the prototype DH.100 aloft on 20 September 1943, only 16 months after the initial designs had been drawn. Flight trials with the prototype proved successful and only a small number of changes were incorporated into the two subsequent prototype aircraft. The third prototype also carried the aircraft's standard armament of four 20-mm Hispano cannon.

Britain's fastest fighter

Development trials proceeded rapidly and, on 13 May 1944, a production order for 120 Vampire F.Mk I aircraft was placed. The first production aircraft made its maiden flight on 20 April 1945, less than three weeks before VE-Day. For a short period Vampire F.Mk Is were the fastest British jet fighter, with a top speed of 540 mph (869 km/h).

Three early production examples were experimentally fitted with Rolls-Royce Nene I engines. Designated Vampire Mk II, this variant eventually developed (via the Mk IV) into the Mk 30, built in Australia.

The first RAF unit to receive the Vampire was No. 247 Squadron at Chilbolton in March 1946. Early in 1948 Vampire F.Mk Is began entering service with the 2nd Tactical Air Force in West Germany.

Incorporating a lowered tailplane, rounded fins and rudders and increased fuel capacity (including the ability to carry underwing drop tanks), the

The first Vampire prototype was originally fitted with larger triangular tailfins, but is seen here, post-modification, with the squared-off units applied to the first production examples.

Above: Never initially intended for RAF service, the NF.Mk 10 was adopted as a radar-equipped night-fighter following the cancellation of an Egyptian order and the worsening of relations with the Soviet Union. It served only briefly with the RAF as interim equipment.

Left: No. 247 Squadron was the first operational RAF unit to receive the Vampire Mk I, and made its public debut in the Victory Flypast over London on 8 June 1946.

French manufacturer SNCASE produced 250 SE 535 Mistrals for the Armée de l'Air. Based on the FB.Mk 53, the Mistral was powered by a French-built version of the Rolls-Royce Nene.

Vampire Mk III entered service early in 1948. In July, six examples from No. 54 Squadron became the first jet aircraft to fly across the Atlantic Ocean.

Record-breaker

Another record had been broken on 23 March 1948 when a modified Vampire Mk I, with extended wingtips, established a new world altitude record of 59,446 ft (18119 m). Further development of the airframe eventually led to the Venom.

A new role was introduced with the Vampire FB.Mk 5 fighter-bomber, which featured a strengthened and clipped wing, capable of mounting bombs or rocket projectiles. This variant subsequently became the RAF's standard close-support fighter, serving with 40 squadrons.

To improve both load-carrying and speed performance, de Havilland developed the FB.Mk 6 with the more powerful Goblin 3 engine. The Swiss air force obtained 175 FB.Mk 6s, but the variant was never adopted by the RAF, which instead ordered the FB.Mk 9, of which 324 were eventually acquired. Developed for service in the tropics, the first unit to operate FB.Mk 9s was No. 28 Squadron in Hong Kong.

The Vampire, in both single-seat and twin-seat versions, proved to be a successful export product. The first foreign customer was Sweden, which purchased 74 Vampire Mk Is (operated under the local designation J 28), the first of which was delivered in March 1946. A subsequent order covered 143 Vampire FB.Mk 50s (based on the Mk 5/Mk 6). When retired from Swedish service, a number were sold to Austria and the Dominican Republic.

The survivors of the 175 Vampire Mk 6s delivered to the Swiss air force (100 were licence-built) were among the longest serving Vampires, the last examples retiring in 1990.

Two export customers were found for the Vampire F.Mk 3. The RCAF purchased 83 examples and Norway just four.

Nene-powered variants were bought by Australia which licence-built 80 F.Mk 30s and 29 FB.Mk 31s, along with France which operated 250 SNCASE-built FB.Mk 53s as the Mistral. The Armée de l'Air had earlier acquired over 250 Goblin-powered FB.Mk 5s.

Intended initially for export, the DH.113 Vampire night-fighter was based on the Vampire Mk 5, fitted with an adaptation of the nose and cockpit of the Mosquito NF.Mk 36. It retained the Mosquito's AI.Mk X radar and was powered by a Goblin 3.

The first prototype flew initially on 28 August 1949 and in October of that year Egypt ordered 12 examples. Following the first Arab–Israeli war, arms sales to Egypt were forbidden and the new night-fighters were taken over by the RAF as the Vampire NF.Mk 10. As the RAF's first jet night-fighter the type entered service with No. 25 Squadron at West Malling in June 1951. Production of the Vampire NF.Mk 10 eventually totalled 95 aircraft. The only other operators of two-seat fighter Vampires were India and Italy, both receiving aircraft under the designation Vampire NF.Mk 54.

Private venture

The successful marriage of a side-by-side two-seat nose to the Vampire prompted de Havilland, in 1950, to embark on a trainer version as a private venture. The prototype DH.115 Vampire Trainer first flew on 15 November 1950 and the type was selected as the standard RAF advanced trainer, being ordered in 1951 as the Vampire T.Mk 11.

The T.Mk 11 entered service in 1952 and marked a new era in which RAF aircrew qualified as pilots on a jet aircraft. In addition, 73 examples were ordered by the FAA with the designation Sea Vampire T.Mk 22. Out of the 804 Vampire trainers produced by de Havilland, a large number was destined for the export market as the Vampire T.Mk 55. A number of countries licence-built their own two-seaters, including India and Australia.

Below: Specially modified for the task, Vampire Mk I prototype LZ551 was the first jet-powered aircraft to land on an aircraft-carrier, taking the wire on HMS **Ocean** ***on 3 December 1945.***

Above: The arrival of the Vampire T.Mk 11 (top) ensured that, for the first time, RAF pilots gained their 'wings' on a jet aircraft. Students graduated onto the Vampire from the Provost basic trainer (below).

DH.110 Sea Vixen

All-weather naval fighter

The disastrous crash of the DH.110 prototype on 6 September 1952 put British fighter development back several years and it was not until 1958 that Fleet Air Arm squadrons received their first Sea Vixens.

In 1961 two Sea Vixen FAW.Mk 1s fresh off the Christchurch production line – XN684 and XN685 – were flown to Hatfield and converted to an interim FAW.Mk 2 standard. Once procedures for the conversion programme were established both aircraft were employed in development work concerning the Red Top AAM. XN684 carries four Red Tops in this view and has a special test camera fitted under its nose.

In many ways it is a wonder that the de Havilland DH.110 entered service at all. Proposed to both the Royal Navy and the RAF to fill their respective requirements for a radar-equipped night-/all-weather fighter, the big, twin-engined, two-seat DH.110 was dogged by a fatal crash, subsequent delays, RAF disinterest and, finally, budget cuts that saw the Royal Navy sponsor development of the Sea Venom FAW.Mk 21 instead.

De Havilland submitted one basic design to fill Specifications N.40/46 and F.44/46 (drawn up by the Admiralty and Air Staff, respectively), such was their similarity, allocating the company type number DH.110. The design followed the same basic layout as the DH.100 Vampire, but with twin engines and swept wings.

RAF interest?

In fact it was the RAF that showed the most interest in the aircraft at first, issuing a refined specification in February 1948. This called for a two-seat aircraft with a maximum speed of 525 kt (603 mph; 972 km/h) at 25,000 ft (7620 m), an endurance of at least two hours and the capability of intercepting targets at night and in all weathers. Against this specification nine DH.110 prototypes were ordered, though only as insurance against the failure of the rival Gloster GA.5 (later Javelin), four of which had already been ordered.

At the same time, four aircraft were ordered to meet a similarly revised naval specification – N.14/49. However, in late 1949 both services were hit by budgetary constraints. The N.14/49 prototypes were cancelled in favour of the cheaper Sea Venom and the RAF, faced with delays in GA.5 development, opted for a mixture of interim types. Orders for DH.110s now totalled just two examples.

RAF interest in the de Havilland aircraft formally ceased in 1952, when the GA.5 Javelin was ordered into production, but in the intervening years work on the DH.110 pair continued.

WG236 flew for the first time on 26 September 1951, powered by a pair of 7,500-lb st (33.36-kN) Rolls-Royce Avon RA.7s. WG240 followed in July 1952. Tragically, WG236 disintegrated during a display at the SBAC air display at Farnborough on 6 September, killing its crew and 29 spectators. Structural weaknesses were to blame and it was not until the spring of 1953 that a suitably strengthened and redesigned WG240 resumed test flying.

Even without the crash, the

The DH.110 Mk 20X XF828 was the first 'semi-navalised' prototype and was used for the first carrier trials, aboard* Ark Royal*, in 1956. Powered by production-standard Avon 208s, it sported revised undercarriage, arrester gear and equipment for catapult launching.

***Left:* A concession in the DH.110's design, made to improve the aircraft's suitability for deck operations, was the offset cockpit. This allowed the Sea Vixen's pilot to see forward over the large radome, forward visibility being an important consideration when landing an aircraft on a carrier deck. This FAW.Mk 1, seen being catapulted from the deck of a carrier, has the 'V' tailcode of HMS Victorious.**

***Above:* In 1953 the surviving DH.110 prototype, WG240, was reworked as a fighter demonstrator. Finished in this striking black colour scheme, the aircraft was tested by the navy before being returned to de Havilland for further development testing.**

The last Sea Vixens – the target drones

The last Sea Vixens were a handful converted for use as target drones. An extensive programme for the modification of redundant Sea Vixen FAW.Mk 2s to U.Mk 3 (later D.Mk 3) standard was proposed in the early 1970s. A supply of airframes was made available to Flight Refuelling Ltd, which had considerable experience of this type of conversion. Prior to delivery to FRL, the Sea Vixens were stripped of operational equipment, including radar and armament. FRL then fitted remote control gear that allowed the aircraft to be 'flown' from the ground or from another aircraft, while retaining the ability to carry a 'live' pilot as necessary. Most of the new equipment, including recording devices that enabled the assessment of the 'miss distances' of new weapons, was installed in the observer's compartment. It was 1975 before FRL began actual conversion work and by 1980 only a single aircraft had been completed. By 1983, the Ministry of Defence was unsure whether a requirement for a Sea Vixen drone actually existed. An official specification for the project had never been issued and it had long been underfunded. The MoD was, by now, concerned about the cost of the programme and doubted that it needed such a sophisticated drone. Thus, the entire programme was suspended in 1983 and cancelled altogether in 1984. By then, three Sea Vixen D.Mk 3 prototypes had been delivered to Llanbedr and these went on to see service in conjunction with development of drone control systems. In 1991 the last airworthy example (above) was grounded, bringing the Sea Vixen's service career to an end.

future for the DH.110 had looked bleak. However, the FAA was, by this time, looking for a replacement for its Sea Venoms, and had issued a specification for such an aircraft in 1952. The navy decided that it wanted a twin-engined fighter, with the better performance and greater safety margin that such a machine would offer. De Havilland proposed an updated and navalised DH.110, with uprated Avons and AAMs.

Thus, WG240 was reworked, with new engines and other alterations, as a naval fighter demonstrator. It was followed by a single development airframe designated DH.110 Mk 20X, the 'X' suffix signifying that it was not fully representative of the definitive DH.110 Mk 20 design.

The new aircraft flew on 20 June 1955 and more closely resembled the production Sea Vixen of the future, though it was not fitted with folding wings, radar or armament. Sea trials began in 1956, the first arrested landing and catapult launch taking place in April aboard HMS *Ark Royal.*

Finally, towards the end of 1954, de Havilland was given the go-ahead to begin work on the first production naval DH.110s. In February 1955 an order for 78 DH.110 FAW.Mk 20s was placed. By this time the projected FAW.Mk 20 was a very different aircraft to WG236, for an 80 per cent redesign of the original DH.110 had taken place to create an aircraft for naval use.

The first 21 of these machines were to be pre-production examples. The DH.110 was the first aircraft that the company had developed as an integrated weapons system and therefore radar and weapons, as well as the airframe, would need to be tested. The first aircraft was rolled out in February 1957 and named Sea Vixen in March. Company trials were followed by a spell at Boscombe Down and sea trials.

In 1959 came a designation change, the Sea Vixen FAW.Mk 20 becoming the Sea Vixen FAW.Mk 1, and a further order for 40 aircraft. In early 1961 a final order for 15 Mk 1s was placed, though only the first of these was completed before production switched to the improved FAW. Mk 2.

The Royal Navy took delivery of its first Sea Vixens in late 1958, No. 892 NAS becoming the first front-line unit to take the Sea Vixen to sea. Nos 890 and 893 Squadrons also received the type from 1960; No. 899 Squadron became the shore-based Sea Vixen HQ Squadron in 1961.

Sea Vixen FAW.Mk 2s, with new missiles and a greater internal fuel capacity, entered service in 1964. After 29 new-build aircraft were completed, a further 37 Mk 1s were converted to Mk 2 standard. All four front-line units were eventually re-equipped with the new variant which remained in use until 1971.

Above: The Fleet Air Arm operated three variants of the radar-equipped Sea Venom all-weather fighter. Pictured here is a FAW.Mk 21 with the clear-view clamshell jettisonable canopy and Martin-Baker Mk 4 ejection seat.

de Havilland DH.112 Venom

Vampire reborn

The Venom is often remembered as being little more than a 'warmed over' derivative of the Vampire, outdated and obsolete by the time it entered service, and outclassed by aircraft like the Sabre.

The Venom's reputation for being a barely improved Vampire and obsolete by the time of its service entry is, in fact, far from the truth. The Venom was developed from the Vampire, but featured an entirely new wing and a change of engine, from the very good Goblin to the superb Ghost. These improvements transformed the Venom, giving it better all-round performance and superior handling.

The single-seat Venom was delivered in FB.Mk 1 and Mk 4 forms, with the latter having powered ailerons and re-shaped tailfins. The type entered service in late 1952, equipping nine front-line squadrons in RAF Germany. It subsequently re-equipped six squadrons in the NEAF, including one in Kenya. Three more squadrons received Venoms in the FEAF, together with an RNZAF unit which operated RAF-serialled Venoms 'on loan'. No. 28 Squadron in Hong Kong finally flew the RAF's last Venom sortie on 27 June 1962.

The Venom night-fighter was developed from the single-seat fighter-bomber in just the same way as the Vampire NF.Mk 10 had been developed from the Vampire FB.Mk 5, with a similar two-seat side-by-side cockpit and lengthened radar-equipped nose being grafted on to create the Venom NF.Mk 2, the NF.Mk 2A with a clear-view blown canopy, and the NF.Mk 3 with improved radar. Venom night-fighters equipped eight home-based squadrons, and served from late 1953 until late 1957.

Naval derivatives

The Venom night-fighter in turn formed the basis of the carrierborne Sea Venom. This equipped seven front-line FAA squadrons and two training units from 1955. The last front-line fighters were retired in July 1960, but the type served on until 1966 in the ECM training role. The Sea Venom NF.Mk 52 was designed for France's Aéronavale, which named it the Aquilon, and had it produced under licence by SNCASE. The Aquilon was built in several versions, including the single-seat Mk 203 (with probably the most roomy fighter cockpit of the era), and served between January 1955 and 1965, by which time the last Aquilon 203s were equipped with AAMs!

Below: VV612 was the prototype Venom and first flew from de Havilland's Hatfield plant on 2 September 1949. This view shows the entirely new wing with its swept-back leading edge.

Although the RAF retired its last Venoms in 1962, this was no reflection on the type's capabilities. Contemporary RAF aircraft tended to have short front-line careers and although other types often went on to have long careers in second-line

No. 890 'Night Witches' Squadron, FAA, adorned its Sea Venom FAW.Mk 21s in 1956 with black and yellow chequered wing tanks and black fin bullets in addition to the black witch nose motif.

roles, the Flying Training Schools, target facilities units and similar set-ups were already overflowing with low-houred Vampires, Meteors and even Hunters. Moreover, the RAF's Venoms had been hard-worked in inhospitable climates, and there was little justification for bringing them home.

However, the Venom was still an extremely viable and effective little fighter-bomber, and was destined to enjoy a long career overseas, not least in Switzerland, where the first of 150 Venom FB.Mk 50s and FB.Mk 54s entered service in 1954. These aircraft were licence-built, all but the first 30 having licence-built engines. Twelve aircraft were modified for use in the reconnaissance role.

Right: The de Havilland Ghost Mk 103-powered Venom FB.Mk 1 flew with a total of 16 RAF squadrons serving in the UK, Germany, the Mediterranean and the Middle and Far East.

Swiss survivors

The Swiss Venoms received UHF radios during the early 1970s, and this necessitated the fitting of a new pointed nose-cone. Swiss Venoms soldiered on until 1983, when sufficient Northrop F-5Es had been delivered to allow newer Hunters to be 'cascaded' down to re-equip the fighter-bomber squadrons. Venoms were also exported to Iraq and to Venezuela. Royal Australian Navy Sea Venom FAW.Mk 53s (retired from the front-line fighter role in 1967) served on as target tugs into the 1970s.

Venom FB.Mk 4

Serving with No. 6 Squadron, RAF, this Venom FB.Mk 4 saw action during the November 1956 Suez Crisis, and is shown wearing the appropriate yellow and black theatre bands. Armed for a ground-attack mission, the Venom typically carried eight 60-lb (27-kg) rocket projectiles.

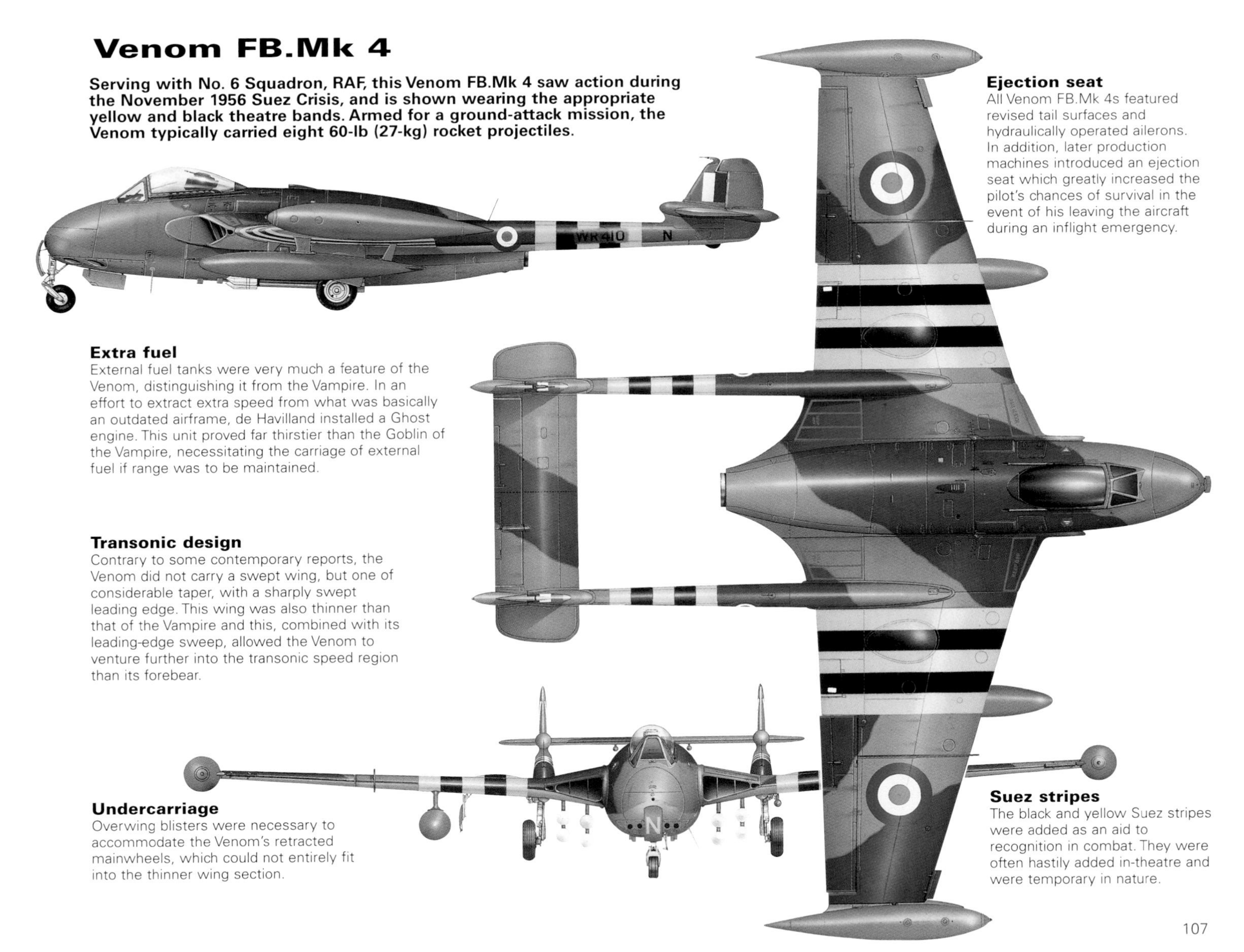

Ejection seat
All Venom FB.Mk 4s featured revised tail surfaces and hydraulically operated ailerons. In addition, later production machines introduced an ejection seat which greatly increased the pilot's chances of survival in the event of his leaving the aircraft during an inflight emergency.

Extra fuel
External fuel tanks were very much a feature of the Venom, distinguishing it from the Vampire. In an effort to extract extra speed from what was basically an outdated airframe, de Havilland installed a Ghost engine. This unit proved far thirstier than the Goblin of the Vampire, necessitating the carriage of external fuel if range was to be maintained.

Transonic design
Contrary to some contemporary reports, the Venom did not carry a swept wing, but one of considerable taper, with a sharply swept leading edge. This wing was also thinner than that of the Vampire and this, combined with its leading-edge sweep, allowed the Venom to venture further into the transonic speed region than its forebear.

Undercarriage
Overwing blisters were necessary to accommodate the Venom's retracted mainwheels, which could not entirely fit into the thinner wing section.

Suez stripes
The black and yellow Suez stripes were added as an aid to recognition in combat. They were often hastily added in-theatre and were temporary in nature.

Douglas A3D/A-3 Skywarrior

Awaiting the launch signal from the catapult officer aboard USS Independence*, a tanker-configured KA-3B from Heavy Attack Squadron 4, 'Fourrunners', prepares for another mission in support of strike aircraft bombing North Vietnam.*

Naval heavyweight

Known by its crews as 'the whale', the Skywarrior was one of the US Navy's most important aircraft of the 1960s and later. It began life as a nuclear strike aircraft, but was to gain fame as an inflight aerial tanker and ELINT platform over Vietnam.

The Douglas company's A-3 Skywarrior (original designation A3D) was the first jet aircraft to be designed from the beginning as a carrier-based strategic bomber. The Skywarrior was developed to replace the interim P2V-3C Neptune and the AJ Savage as a ship-launched, long-range strike aircraft with a nuclear weapon in its internal bomb bay.

Ultimately, the Skywarrior switched jobs. It had only a brief career as a bomber, but for three decades it was a giant success as the fleet's standard air-refuelling tanker and in electronics and secretive reconnaissance duties.

The A-3 was very much the brainchild of Edward H. Heinemann, one of the world's most accomplished aircraft designers and a man whose name was synonymous with decades of achievement by the Douglas Aircraft Company. For Heinemann, the Skywarrior was a step in a new direction since it was created simultaneously with his work on the tiny, bantamweight A4D Skyhawk.

Years later, Heinemann remembered that: 'The principal requirements were to carry a 10,000-lb (4536-kg) device five by five feet by sixteen feet in length, suspected to be an atomic bomb, the distance of a 2,000 miles (3220 km) radius.' Heinemann recalled that he carried out initial design work without knowing any more about the cargo: 'The details of the bomb were so secret that for a long time we didn't even have a drawing. We knew that a certain element had to be inserted in flight through a door from the cockpit which further complicated the challenge.' In retrospect, Heinemann was later to opine that, 'a higher performance machine could have been built had it not been for the great secrecy and the design requirement for the large bomb which never got into production.' The irony was that, by the time the Skywarrior was in service, more than a year behind schedule because of developmental problems with its radar system, nuclear weapons had got considerably smaller.

Flying from the Naval Air Test Center (NATC) Patuxent River, Maryland, this Service Test A3D-1 (BuNo. 135431) was fitted with the more powerful P&W J57 turbojet engines.

Dynamic dimensions

The big, shoulder-winged, twin-engined A3D Skywarrior owed its existence to the development of the atomic bomb. The US Navy – its aircraft carriers overshadowed by the US Air Force's strategic bombers – bred a carrier task force to be part of the US atomic arsenal, poised to unleash a veritable holocaust upon the Soviet Union if the Cold War ever became a hot one.

The second prototype YA3D-1 seen on display at Edwards AFB, finished in an overall Glossy Sea Blue colour scheme and wearing the markings of 'Heavy Two' (VAH-2), the 'Royal Rampants'. A Martin XB-51 prototype can be seen in the background.

The first XA3D-1 Skywarrior completed its maiden flight on 28 October 1952. The Skywarrior introduced a new standard of advanced equipment, including an AN/ASB-1A bombing system which was, however, plagued with problems early on. The prototype Skywarrior was powered by two 7,000-lb (3175-kg) thrust Westinghouse XJ40-WE-3 turbojet engines. The US Navy invested heavily in this engine. Unfortunately, the unreliable J40 did not uphold the high standard set by the same manufacturer's J34, then the Navy's most advanced operational powerplant.

New engines

Fortunately, the Skywarrior's underwing pylon arrangement made it easy to substitute two 10,300-lb (4673-kg) thrust Pratt & Whitney J57-P-10 turbojets.

Douglas built 50 A3D-1 production aircraft (redesignated A-3A in 1962). These were similar to the two prototypes but had improved J57 engines. These bombers were manufactured with twin remotely operated 20-mm cannon in the tail, but these were later removed.

The crew consisted of pilot, bombardier, and navigator/tail gunner, all housed in a pressurised cockpit. Since ejection seats were not yet suitable for this multi-crew configuration, escape chutes were installed. In electronics and training variants, there were no ejection seats either for the personnel in the specialised working space in the bomb bay.

Douglas also turned out 164 A3D-2 bombers, 30 A3D-2P photo ships, 24 A3D-2Q radar reconnaissance aircraft, and 12 A3D-2T trainers. These were redesignated in 1962 as the A-3B, RA-3B, EA-3B and TA-3B respectively.

The A3D-2Q used to detect and monitor hostile radar emissions was actually the first version in service, from 1956. The first A3D-2 bombers reached the fleet in 1957, initially serving with VAH-2.

Right: This A3D-1 is being positioned on the deck edge elevator ready to be taken below to the maintenance hangars, aboard USS* Forrestal *on 5 April, 1956. This Skywarrior was the 13th aircraft off the Douglas production line.

Below: A neat four-ship of A3Ds from VAH-5 'Savage Sons' is seen on exercise over the Mediterranean. Operating from the deck of USS* Forrestal, *VAH-5 won several awards while compiling a brilliant safety record, and made five Mediterranean deployments.

'Whale' of the fleet

Having achieved a highly commendable service record over Vietnam, the Skywarrior went on to perform countless test and support tasks.

Both A3D-1 and A3D-2 variants had folding outer wing panels and a folding vertical tail. Yet despite the Navy's efforts to conserve weight and reduce the Skywarrior's 'footprint' it was the heaviest warplane to operate regularly from carrier decks. The sheer size and weight were illustrated in 1959, when a Skywarrior took off from USS *Independence* at a weight of 82,195 lb (38102 kg). This was significantly more than the routine gross weight of 70,000 lb (31751 kg) – but even at the lower figure, no other shipboard warplane ever came close. In addition it was difficult if not impossible to bail out of an A3D in an emergency, and it handled poorly on final approach to a deck landing – demanding the very best skills of its pilot.

The carrier-based Skywarrior abandoned its nuclear mission to become a champion at electronic warfare (EA-3A, EA-3B), reconnaissance (RA-3B, ERA-3B), radar training (TA-3B), executive transport (VA-3B) and air-refuelling (KA-3B, EKA-3B).

Tanker conversion

Following the success of a few Skywarriors equipped with a detachable air-refuelling kit, no fewer than 85 A-3Bs were converted to tankers in 1968. Engineers removed all bombing equipment and added fuselage fuel tanks and a reel and hose refuelling kit to the underside of the rear fuselage. KA-3B and EKA-3B Skywarriors carried more than 5,000 US gal (18526 litres) of fuel and could loiter over a carrier or, if necessary, venture out into troubled waters to help a fuel-starved battle-damaged warplane tank-up and get home.

***Above:** Ten **RA-3Bs** were converted to **ERA-3Bs** and served as electronic surveillance platforms and communications jammers. Split between **US** Navy electronic warfare squadrons **VAQ-33** and **VAQ-34**, these highly modified examples were finally retired from active military service in 1991.*

***Below:** Introduced into service with **VAK-208**, the 'Jockeys', following the reorganisation of the **Naval Air Reserve** in 1970, the squadron's **KA-3Bs** provided air refuelling and pathfinding for **US Navy** and **Marine** aircraft being ferried to southeast Asia.*

***A Douglas TA-4J of VC-1** formates with **ERA-3B** BuNo. 144827 of VAQ-33 during an exercise in 1978. Note the two ram air turbines (**RATs**) on the **Skywarrior's** fuselage sides and the **AN/ALQ-76** electronics pods beneath the wings. Additional **ECM** equipment was fitted in the bomb bay.*

Above: Following their military service, a mixed fleet of 12 A-3s was acquired by Hughes Aircraft. Test programmes included development work for the Tomahawk and Harpoon missiles and the B-2 bomber.

This A-3B (BuNo. 142630) was modified with the forward component of a previously classified missile. The flat plate area forward of the nose is where the missile was attached.

The 12 A3D-2T/TA-3B trainers launched their naval career with a first flight on 29 August 1959. They were used for navigator and tactical crew training and carried pilot, instructor, and six students. In later years, some were further modified to serve as VIP transports.

The 24 A3D-2Q/EA-3B radar reconnaissance Skywarriors operated with a flight-deck crew of three plus four sensor operators. These aircraft skirted the periphery of Iron Curtain nations at the height of the Cold War, observing and monitoring. Eventually, the EA-3B was replaced in the fleet by the Grumman EA-6A Intruder and EA-6B Prowler.

Also among specialised variants of the Skywarrior were the 30 photo-reconnaissance A3D-2P/RA-3B aircraft. Some later acquired an added electronic mission and received the revised designation ERA-3B.

A warrior in combat

When the US build-up in Vietnam began in 1965, the Skywarrior had been in service for a decade. Skywarriors were used briefly as conventional bombers but were found to be vulnerable to AAA and MiGs. An A-3B from VAH-4 was shot down by a MiG during August 1967. Nevertheless A-3s remained active throughout the Vietnam War, although changed tactics saw to it that they did not venture into SAM or MiG country unless absolutely necessary.

Following Vietnam the Skywarrior was relegated to land-based training units and reserve squadrons, but the A-3 proved to be the ideal platform to fulfil a number of test programmes. Operated by the Pacific Missile Center, the Naval Weapons Center, and a detachment of the Fleet Logistics Support Wing, A-3s sported some of the most radical conversions seen on the Skywarrior. In some cases the entire nose section was replaced by that belonging to an F-14A Tomcat or F-111B; others were fitted with missile warheads in order to test their search and tracking capabilities. These aircraft served in the test role until the early 1980s.

Having been retired from US carrier decks in the early 1980s Skywarriors saw combat one final time during Desert Storm. Deployed to Saudi Arabia and Crete, EA-3Bs belonging to VAQ-2 provided pre- and post-strike reconnaissance to the Red Sea carrier battle groups. A more significant role, however, was coordinating with E-2C Hawkeyes and EA-6B Prowlers for the targeting of HARM missiles against Iraqi radar sites.

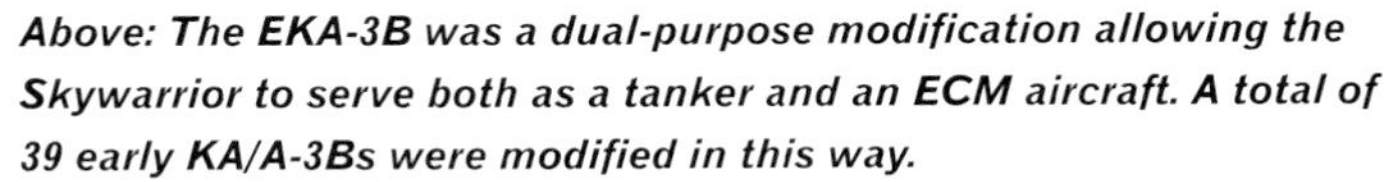

Above: The EKA-3B was a dual-purpose modification allowing the Skywarrior to serve both as a tanker and an ECM aircraft. A total of 39 early KA/A-3Bs were modified in this way.

Left: The last active US Navy Skywarrior, a TA-3B, was retired from military service on 27 September 1991. Many were to end their days awaiting destruction at AMARC, Davis-Monthan AFB, Arizona, having been replaced in the front line by more modern types. However, the durability of the A-3s ensured that a few examples continued to fly, in civilian hands.

Douglas A-4 Skyhawk

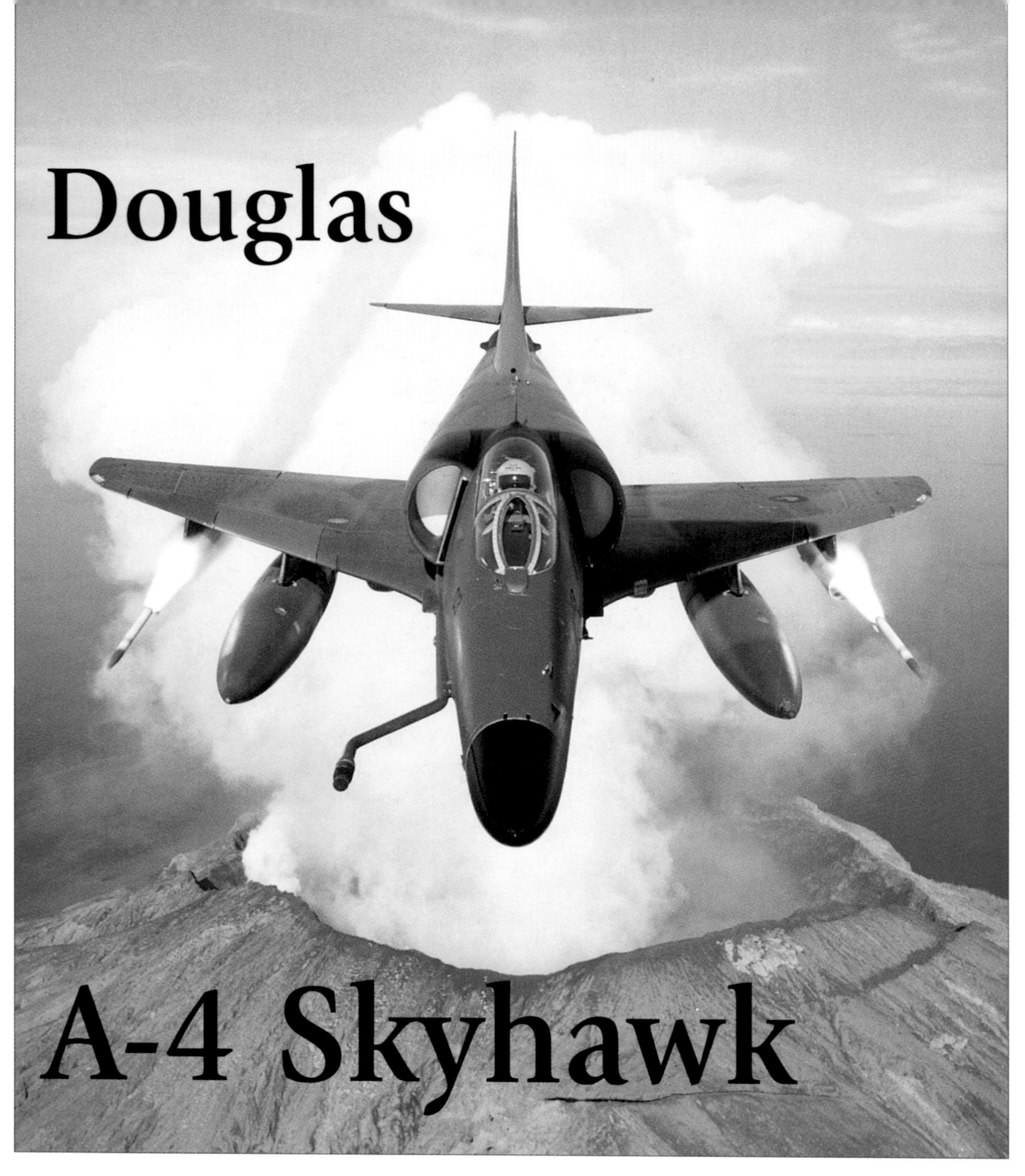

Another A-4 nickname was 'Squawk', applied to the A-4Ks of the Royal New Zealand Air Force. The RNZAF operated the Skyhawk for over 30 years and put its aircraft through a major upgrade in the early 1990s.

'Bantam bomber'

'Tinker Toy', 'Scooter', 'Heinemann's Hot Rod' – few aircraft have acquired so many affectionate nicknames as Douglas's A-4. For more than 50 years it has been proving that the best things come in small packages.

Douglas's A-4 was designed to carry a single nuclear weapon a short way from a carrier deck. In the end, nearly 3,000 were produced to fulfil a myriad of conventional roles.

The A-4 was the first jet combat aircraft to go against the trend of increasing complexity and weight, and therefore cost. Its genesis was during the Korean War, when the US Navy saw the need for a jet replacement for the AD Skyraider that had greater range and carrying capacity than the jets then in combat. Ed Heinemann of Douglas drew up a simple tailed-delta design and claimed that he could produce the aircraft at a weight of 12,000 lb (5443 kg). The USN took up the challenge and approved a single XA4D prototype. During the engineering process, Heinemann rejected many 'off-the-shelf' sub-systems that were heavier than necessary and instructed Douglas engineers to design lighter replacements.

The aircraft's wing, which formed an integral fuel tank, was only 27 ft (8.2 m) in span, obviating the need for wing-folding to fit into the elevators of aircraft-carriers. Elimination of the folding mechanism saved more weight. The aircraft was built around the Armstrong-Siddeley Sapphire, built under licence as the Wright J65.

Although the Skyhawk was conceived with little more than the carriage of a nuclear bomb in mind, the contract issued in June 1952 called for an aircraft capable of dive-bombing, interdiction and close air support, with or without fighter escort. The A-4 proved ably suited to all of these roles and many more.

Skyhawk emerges

The XA4D-1 prototype was flown for the first time on 22 June 1954. The prototype, already named Skyhawk, was 50 per cent lighter than specified, and proved to be 20 per cent faster, with 33 per cent greater range after initial testing. The XA4D-1 was followed by the first batch of 19 A4D-1s, of which nine were used in the test programme. The remainder of the first batch went straight to the fleet. Fleet Introduction Programme (FIP) trials proved that the A4D-1 had the lowest number of maintenance man hours per flight hour of any contemporary USN aircraft, at 26.5.

Deliveries began to the first unit, VA-72 'Blue Hawks', at NAS Quonset Point in October 1956. The following January, Marine squadron VMA-224 'Bengals' took delivery of its first A4D-1s.

The XA4D-1 was built using production tooling which hastened the Skyhawk's introduction to the fleet. There were few changes between the prototype and the following 165 Douglas A4D-1s.

VMA-224 was the first USMC squadron to fly the Skyhawk and soon took it to Japan. One of its A-4s, sent to search for the BOAC 707 airliner that had suffered structural failure in the lee wave of Mt Fuji in high winds in 1960, was subjected to forces of +9 and –3g, but returned without damage.

In total, 165 of the very simple A4D-1s were built, and examples served with no fewer than 18 different USN and USMC squadrons. The type was redesignated A-4A in October 1962. Many were passed to reserve units as newer models became available, and some of these were redesignated TA-4A in order to reduce the apparent size of the attack inventory and so procure more aircraft for use in Vietnam.

Even before the A4D-1 had entered the fleet, an improved version had been ordered. The A4D-2 had increased weapons capability with Bullpup missiles and an improved bomb delivery system. Obvious differences were a refuelling probe fitted along the starboard side of the nose, and the 'tadpole' rudder, with external stiffeners.

Deliveries of the A4D-2 began with VMA-211 'Wake Island Avengers' in September 1957, followed by VA-12 'Flying Ubangis' for the US Navy. The first squadrons to take the A-4 into combat were VA-83 'Rampagers' with A4D-2s, and VA-34 'Blue Blasters' with A4D-1s flying armed reconnaissance missions during the Lebanon crisis in late 1958.

A-4B in Vietnam

The Skyhawk's long association with Vietnam began when the USS *Oriskany* deployed to the South China Sea in August 1963, with the A-4Bs (redesignated from A4D-2 in 1962) of VA-163 'Saints' and VA-164 'Ghost Riders' aboard. The 'Bravo' model only saw one actual combat cruise in the attack role, with VA-95 'Green Lizards' and VA-15 'Valions' on *Intrepid*. The A-4B also had a limited role as a fighter aboard the anti-submarine carriers *Bennington* and *Kearsage*, which were too small for F-8 Crusaders or F-4 Phantoms. These were operated as detachments of attack squadrons, but the final Vietnam deployment for the A-4B was with a new (and short-lived) anti-submarine fighter squadron, VSF-3 aboard *Intrepid* in 1967. Like the earlier detachments on ASW carriers, VSF squadrons provided A-4s for air defence. When the perceived submarine threat failed to materialise, these aircraft were used in the conventional attack role as needed.

A4D-2 (A-4B) production totalled 542 aircraft. As was the case with the A-4A in its later life, some A-4Bs were relegated to TA-4B status, despite no actual changes to the aircraft.

The mid-1950s radar equipment that could have transformed the Skyhawk from simple 'A-bomb basket' into an altogether more versatile light strike platform simply could not be shoehorned into the cramped nose of the A-4A or A-4B to begin with. Within a few years, however, a unit with a limited terrain-following capability was available and Douglas proposed the A4D-3 to take advantage of this, and at the same time give a useful power boost with the Pratt & Whitney J52 engine then under development for the Grumman A2F-1 (A-6A).

Unfortunately, at that time, immediately prior to Vietnam, budget constraints prevented the US Navy from ordering this promising new type.

A series of upgrades means that the Skyhawk remains a viable warplane into the 21st century. This is an Argentine A-4AR Fightinghawk, an ex-USMC A-4M with AN/APG-66 radar and a modernised cockpit.

A-4 Skyhawk

A-4C to Skyhawk II

With a reduction in the US Navy's nuclear air strike role in the late 1950s, the importance of the Skyhawk's original mission declined. The US Navy and US Marines, however, had already found many more uses for the 'Mighty Mite' and developed the A-4 Skyhawk's performance and combat capabilities almost beyond recognition.

As a compromise following the rejection of the A4D-3, Douglas came up with the A4D-2N ('N' standing for 'night') which was essentially the A4D-2 (A-4B) with the new AN/APG-53A radar and navigation system, an autopilot and a blind bombing system all in a lengthened nose. The A4D-2N first flew on 21 August 1958 and entered service with VMA-225 in February 1960. Less than three years later, the last of 638 A4D-2Ns was handed over.

In order to fulfil a US Navy and US Marine Reserve requirement for improved Skyhawk tactical and ECM equipment in the light of the Vietnam conflict, 100 A4D-2Ns (by now known by their A-4C designation) were altered to A-4L configuration. The A-4L featured an uprated Curtiss-Wright J65 engine, wing lift spoilers, and electronics gear relocated to a newly installed upper centre fuselage avionics pod. The initial A-4L first flew on 21 August 1969.

New designations

In October 1962, the designation systems used by the US Army, Navy and Air Force were rationalised. As a result, the A4D-2N became the A-4C, the A4D-2 became the A-4B, and those remaining A4D-1s became designated A-4A. Almost as soon as the A4D-2N/A-4C began production, the USN overcame some of its budgetary problems and contracted for two aircraft to be completed as A4D-5s (the A4D-4 was an unbuilt version with a much larger, folding wing).

Early A-4Es were distinguished from the A-4C model by their nose profile, intake splitter plates and lack of windscreen wiper. Later, A-4Es were retrofitted with avionics humps and bent refuelling probes. This is an early A-4E from VA-55, with Bullpup ASM.

This new version was to include many of the features intended for the A4D-3, such as the J52-P-6A engine which gave an additional 800 lb (3.50 kN) of thrust while offering better specific fuel consumption. New inlet ducts and a redesigned centre fuselage were features of the A4D-5, which was redesignated A-4E within 18 months of its first flight on 12 July 1961. A further increase in nose length housed an AN/ASN-19A navigation computer, Doppler navigation gear and a low-altitude bombing system (LABS). Additional equipment included a new radio altimeter, TACAN and a toss-bombing system. Two additional weapons pylons, combined with airframe strengthening, allowed a maximum catapult take-off weight of 24,500 lb (11113 kg).

Including two aircraft converted on the A-4C production line, a total of 500 A-4Es were produced, the first entering service with VA-23 'Black Knights' in January 1963. During production, a number of improvements was implemented to the A-4E. Most prominent of these was the addition of a large

A4D-1s (A-4As from late 1962) of VA-34 are seen during 1957. The first of 18 USN and USMC units to equip with the A4D-1 were US Navy Attack Squadron 72 (VA-72 'Blue Hawks') and US Marine Attack Squadron 224 (VMA-224 'Bengals'), in 1956.

Above: The A-4 provided the mount for the US Navy's Blue Angels display team from 1974 to 1987. Display aircraft were modified from standard A-4Fs with the addition of a braking parachute, an inverted fuel system, a smoke system and a foldable ladder on the port side.

A TA-4F from US Marine Corps training squadron VMAT-102 looses off a Zuni rocket during combat training. The TA-4F was also used by the USMC in the fast forward air control (Fast FAC) mission.

dorsal avionics 'hump' which contained radio and navigation equipment that could no longer be squeezed into the basic A-4 airframe. ECM in the form of the AN/ALQ-100 system was added, with a transmitter aerial in the tail.

Some USN aircraft were later fitted with the 9,300-lb (41.37-kN) J52-P-8A engine in place of the original P-6A, and those which were stripped of extraneous equipment such as the hump were unofficially known as the 'Super Echo' when used by the 'Topgun' Navy Fighter Weapons School and other units for adversary training.

After the A-4E, the next single-seat production Skyhawk, and the first to be ordered entirely under the post-1962 system, was the A-4F. The 'Foxtrot' was developed to take advantage of lessons learned in Vietnam and to replace the losses of earlier versions in that growing conflict. Chief differences were the modification of the wing flaps to form a spoiler to improve landing performance and the incorporation of nosewheel steering. The engine was the J52-P-8A, as first used on the TA-4E (later redesignated TA-4F). Like the A-4E, the first A-4Fs were delivered without avionics humps, but these were soon added, incorporating additional ECM gear, as was the AN/ALR-45 tail-warning system. First user of the A-4F was again the 'Black Knights' of VA-23 which, along with VA-93 'Blue Blazers', went to Vietnam aboard USS *Ticonderoga* in late 1967.

Blue Angels

In all, 167 A-4Fs were built, a number later being converted to 'Super Foxes' with the 11,200-lb (49.82-kN) J52-P-408 engine. The most famous user of the A-4F was the US Navy's demonstration team, the *Blue Angels*, which replaced the fuel-hungry F-4J Phantom with the diminutive Skyhawk in 1974.

The final single-seat Skyhawk version ordered by the US military was the A-4M Skyhawk II, which was designed exclusively for the US Marine Corps, although some later found their way into USN service. The 'Mike' was powered by the P-408 engine which was smokeless, in addition to providing much greater thrust. A larger canopy and new windscreen were fitted, as was a braking parachute, and the fintip was squared off in profile. Improvements from 1974 to 1977 added AN/ALR-45 ECM equipment and a new Angle Rate Bombing System (ARBS) in the nose. The last A-4 built was the 158th A-4M and the 2,960th of all variants produced in a 27-year production run – the longest of any US combat aircraft to date.

Left: Initially known as the A4D-2N, the A-4C resulted from a need to equip the Skyhawk with greater range through adverse weather and terrain. It became operational in 1960.

Below: The A-4E incorporated more changes from the previous model than any other A-4 variant. Later models were distinguished by their dorsal avionics hump, containing additional radio and navigation equipment.

A-4 Skyhawk
Late models and export

Following a comprehensive upgrade, the RNZAF's A-4Ks (pictured) and TA-4Ks continued to fly with No. 75 Squadron at RNZAF Ohakea and No. 2 Squadron at RANAS Nowra in Australia, until November 2001.

Following the arrival of the ultimate US variant – the A-4M – development of the basic airframe continued for export, notably via a series of increasingly sophisticated upgrades. Meanwhile, two-seat versions continued to provide valuable service in the US and overseas.

The last A-4Ms were retired by USMC Reserve Group MAG-42 at Alameda in 1994, bringing to an end the US career of the attack Skyhawk after 38 years.

As early as 1963, Defense Secretary Robert McNamara had called for a cessation of Skyhawk production, with delivery of the last A-4E. The US Navy had other ideas, however, and issued a revision to the A-4E contract to convert two aircraft to two-seat trainer configuration. The last two A-4Es on the line were converted to TA-4Es with a fuselage plug, dual controls and zero-zero ejection seats. Lift-dumping spoilers and nosewheel steering were incorporated for the first time, as was the improved J52-P-8A engine.

The first two-seat TA-4E made its maiden flight on 30 June 1965. The US Navy saw its first two-seaters when VA-125 'Roughriders' became operational at NAS Lemoore in May 1966. By now, the designation had changed to TA-4F to recognise the many improvements over the A-4E. Production ran to 241 examples and they were mainly used by the replacement air wings as conversion trainers and for check rides as well as 'hacks' by front-line squadrons when land-based.

Fast FAC

The US Marines found another use for the second seat, for a FAC to direct close air support for Marines on the ground in the Fast FAC role. A derivative was the EA-4F, fitted with electronic simulation gear. The EA-4F could also drop chaff and carry jamming pods to simulate an ECM environment.

The TA-4 proved an ideal replacement for the TF-9J Cougar in the advanced training role. After one aircraft was converted to TA-4J standard with the removal of tactical equipment and the lower-rated P-6 engine, an initial batch of 48 was ordered for Training Command. The converted aircraft first flew in December 1968 and, by mid-1969, the first 50 aircraft were in service. In addition to 277 new-build TA-4Js, most TA-4Fs were converted to J standard by deleting radar and weapons equipment, as well as installing the P-6 engine. The gradual introduction of the T-45 Goshawk to Training Command saw the 'Scooter' gradually disappear from VT squadrons, until VT-7 'Eagles' at NAS Meridian, Mississippi, was

Singapore's Black Knights aerobatic team used A-4SUs from No. 145 Squadron. The A-4S was withdrawn from use in Singapore in 2005, but remained in use with No. 150 Sqn at Cazaux, France.

Malaysia's refurbished Skyhawks were delivered in 1986 and served with Nos 6 and 9 Squadrons. Most were replaced by Hawk 200s in 1994, but six were retained as tankers with 'buddy pods' until 1996.

After the Yom Kippur War in 1973, the engine jetpipes of all Israeli A-4s were extended aft to reduce the heat difference between the efflux and the outside air as a defence against infra-red guided missiles.

the last. The last class to graduate on the A-4 did so in late 1999 and included a Brazilian pilot destined to fly his country's first naval jet – the AF-1 Falcoe or A-4KU Skyhawk. On 30 September 1999, the last US Navy Skyhawk 'trap' and launch were made aboard USS *George Washington*, thus drawing to an end 30 years of valuable service.

The final two-seat variant produced for the US was the OA-4M for the Marine Corps. Following its success with the A-4F in the Fast FAC role, the USMC wanted a version equipped with all the air-to-ground radios needed to communicate with the 'mud Marines' on the battlefield and with the ECM equipment necessary to survive above it. The OA-4M was a conversion of the TA-4F, which brought many of its features in line with those of the A-4M, although it retained the J52-P-8 engine. The electronics 'hump' first seen on the A-4E was added and faired into a revised two-seat canopy, and the ECM tail and nose fairings were incorporated. The first of 23 OA-4M conversions flew in July 1978.

On retirement, the OA-4Ms were replaced to a degree by F/A-18D Hornets and were sent to the 'Boneyard'. The bulk of the survivors was obtained by Argentina and refurbished for its air force as the TA-4AR Fightinghawk.

The final US user of the Skyhawk was VC-8 'Redtails', at NS Roosevelt Roads, Puerto Rico. VC-8 retained the TA-4J in the adversary role as well as for drone-launching, FAC training and target-towing, finally retiring the type in April 2003.

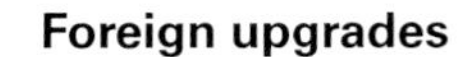

Foreign upgrades

New Zealand's 12 A-4K and TA-4K Skyhawks were basically A-4Fs and TA-4Fs, joined in 1984 by 10 ex-Australian Skyhawks – eight A-4Gs and two TA-4Gs. In 1985 a major refurbishment programme was started on all the aircraft. This involved a structural upgrade and modernising of the avionics and weapons capability, including a version of the F-16's AN/APG-66 radar.

Israel's Skyhawks were in action within two months of the arrival of the first 48 A-4Hs in late 1967. Basically A-4Fs, the A-4Hs also had a braking parachute, a squared-off fintip and extra ECM equipment. In light of combat experience, the IDF/AF soon began to modify these aircraft, as well as the 46 A-4Es transferred from the US Navy, to ensure greater survivability and combat effectiveness. The A-4N, delivered between 1972 and 1976, was in essence an A-4M with Israeli improvements. Israel's TA-4H two-seaters had a combat role as well as their main role of training.

Argentina's air force and naval air arm operated 91 early-model A-4s from 1966. The last Fuerza Aerea Argentina A-4Ps were retired in March 1999. By this time, Argentina had negotiated the purchase of 32 ex-USMC A-4Ms and four OA-4Ms. A version of the F-16's AN/APG-66 radar has been fitted, together with a new cockpit and computerised mission planning system. Argentina has redesignated its aircraft A-4AR and TA-4AR Fightinghawk.

Malaysia obtained 25 A-4Cs and 63 A-4Ls in 1982. The best airframes and components were then used to create 34 A-4PTM and six TA-4PTM aircraft. All the A-4Cs were given an avionics hump to match the A-4Ls.

Brazil became the newest user of the A-4 with the purchase of ex-Kuwaiti A-4KU and TA-4KU aircraft. The 20 A-4KU and three TA-4KU Skyhawks were added to the navy inventory in October 1998. Brazil's Skyhawks (designated AF-1 and AF-1A Falcoe) first went to sea in the *Minas Gerais* in 2001.

Singapore acquired its first Skyhawks in 1972, with the purchase of 50 ex-US Navy A-4Bs. A major upgrade began in 1984 with the local Super Skyhawk programme. A non-afterburning version of the General Electric F404-GE-100D turbofan was fitted and the structure and avionics upgraded. The resultant A-4SU and TA-4SU Super Skyhawk served with Nos 142 and 145 Squadrons, while No. 150 Squadron continues advanced training in France.

Above: Developed for the US Marine Corps, the A-4M Skyhawk II featured more power, a square-cropped tail, relocated braking parachute, head-up display and a considerably enhanced avionics suite. The aircraft forms the basis of Argentina's Fightinghawk.

Right: VC-1 was an archetypal composite squadron which, in later years, was based in the Hawaiian Islands. In the early 1990s the unit continued to operate a mix of A-4Es and TA-4Js (pictured).

Douglas B-66 Destroyer

*The fine lines of the Destroyer were enhanced by the long nacelles of the J71 engines. However, the J57 turbojets fitted to the comparable Navy A3D proved to be a far better powerplant. This is an **RB-66B**, fitted with a turret but no guns.*

Bombers and reconnaissance

Derived from the Navy's A3D (A-3) Skywarrior, the B-66 was hastily conceived in response to an urgent need for a jet-powered light bomber and photo-reconnaissance platform.

During the Korean War the USAF's light bomber was the World War II-vintage A-26 Invader. Recognising the urgent need for a modern replacement, the USAF issued a set of requirements which initially resulted in the purchase of the British Canberra (as the B-57). However, a requirement remained for another fast, agile type that could cover bomber, reconnaissance and electronic warfare roles.

Due to the urgency of the situation, an all-new design was ruled out. Douglas submitted a version of its A3D Skywarrior, which was declared the winner, resulting in a contract for five RB-66A photo-reconnaissance aircraft issued in February 1952.

Although closely based on the Navy aircraft, the RB-66A had notable differences. The wing was completely redesigned with a different planform and roll-control spoilers (later adopted by the A3D). The fuel system was revised to provide greater capacity and allow inflight refuelling via a nose-mounted probe, and hardpoints were provided for underwing tanks. The bomb bay was enlarged to allow carriage of the huge nuclear bombs then in service, and the nose was recontoured to admit the bomb/nav radar (B-66) or search radar (RB-66).

A gun turret was added, armed with two 20-mm cannon and aimed remotely from the flight deck. The cockpit was revised, with the pilot sitting up front with navigator and EWO/gunner facing forwards behind him. All had ejection seats, unlike the A3D.

Most importantly, the B-66 changed to the Allison J71 engine in place of the P&W J57. The Allison engine proved a disappointment in service.

The initial RB-66A first flew on 28 June 1954. Early test flights revealed numerous problems, chiefly concerning buffet and engines. The cockpit glazing had to be redesigned, and a brake chute added. With the bugs ironed out, production got under way with the RB-66B, which was designed as a night reconnaissance version. Instead

*The **RB-66B** was the most numerous **Destroyer** variant, and the first into series production. Although all **Destroyers** were delivered with the tail gun turret, many carried this **ECM** tailcone in operation. In addition to jammers, the fairing contained a chaff dispenser (just visible) on the lower surface.*

***Left:** Only one wing (72 aircraft) of B-66B bombers was built. They were initially assigned to the 17th Bomb Wing at Hurlburt Field, Florida, before being transferred to the 47th Bomb Wing in England. The bomber version had the K-5 bomb/nav radar in place of the RB's AN/APS-27 search radar. The large bomb bay had a perforated baffle ahead of the doors to facilitate weapons separation from the bay.*

***Left:** The small window underneath the wing identified the WB-66D weather recon version. The 36 WB-66Ds were assigned to Shaw (9th TRS) for training, and to Yokota, Japan (11th TRS) and Spangdahlem, Germany (42nd TRS), for operations in the Far East and European theatres.*

of bombs, the RB-66B carried a large photo-reconnaissance pack in the weapons bay, including a battery of cameras and photo-flash bombs for illumination at night. Refuelling probes for use with KB-50 tankers were fitted from the outset, and provision was made for jettisonable RATO equipment for short-field, heavyweight take-offs. RB-66Bs were built with guns, but most later adopted ECM tailcones.

Production of RB-66Bs amounted to 145 aircraft, and they first entered service with the 363rd Tactical Reconnaissance Wing at Shaw AFB, South Carolina, in January 1956. Further deliveries went to the 10th TRW (Spangdahlem, Germany), 66th TRW (Sculthorpe, England and Sembach, Germany) and 67th TRW (Yokota, Japan). The RB-66B proved useful in the photo-reconnaissance role, and was not replaced until 1965 (by the RF-4C). On 10 March 1964, a 19th TRS RB-66B was shot down near Stendal by MiGs some 20 miles (32 km) inside East German territory after launching from Toul in France on a 'routine navigational training flight'. The crew survived, and were briefly held captive.

Bomber Destroyers

Development of the B-66B bomber version ran concurrently with that of the RB-66B. The bomber version was designed to carry the Mk 5 or 6 nuclear bomb or up to 15,000 lb (6800 kg) of conventional weapons. Deliveries began to the 17th Bomb Wing in March 1956, and in June 1958 the B-66Bs moved to Europe and the 47th BW based at Alconbury and Sculthorpe in England.

The B-66B Destroyer was never a great success, mainly due to continuing engine unreliability and problems with the K-5 bomb/nav system. The system did not provide sufficient accuracy for loft bombing, restricting the B-66 to tactically dangerous laydown or dive attacks.

Developments in nuclear technology were such that the size of the bombs themselves had decreased dramatically, in turn requiring much smaller vehicles for their carriage. In June 1962 the USAF's B-66B wing was deactivated, the tactical nuclear role being handed to the Republic F-105. However, the Destroyer did join the rare band of aircraft to drop a live nuclear weapon, releasing at least one B28 thermonuclear bomb during Operation Redwing, the first round of H-bomb tests at Bikini Atoll.

Weather recon

Another important role for the Destroyer was weather reconnaissance. Developed concurrently with the RB-66C electronic warfare version was the WB-66D. Like the RB-66C, the WB had a central crew compartment in place of the weapons bay, which accommodated two systems operators. Assigned alongside RB-66Bs and Cs in units at Shaw, in Europe and in Japan, the WB-66D mapped weather systems over and around the Communist bloc, paying particular attention to likely bomber ingress routes.

Engine testbeds

The podded engine arrangement of the B-66 made it a natural vehicle for engine tests. Above is an NRB-66B fitted with the Pratt & Whitney TF33-P-7 turbofan intended for the C-141A StarLifter, while below the first RB-66A is seen powered by General Electric's CJ805-23 aft-fan engine destined for the Convair CV-990 airliner.

Electronic warfare

Although the B-66/RB-66 was not a huge success in its original roles, it became a true pioneer of modern electronic warfare, with a starring role in the protracted war in southeast Asia.

Having attended to the initial bomber/ reconnaissance requirements of the original specification, Douglas next turned to the electronic reconnaissance role. The RB-66C was therefore produced, with the former weapons bay reworked as a pressurised compartment for four forward-facing systems operators. The antennas for the sophisticated passive receiver suite were housed along the fuselage and, in the case of the direction-finder, in large wingtip pods, which remained the principal distinguishing feature of this variant. Under the belly were canoe fairings, one covering antennas for another direction-finder and another which covered three bell-shaped steerable antennas.

Electronic tailcones

One of the original requirements, namely that of defensive electronics equipment, had been ignored during the early production run of the aircraft. In 1957, however, the USAF ordered 113 ECM tailcones which could be interchanged with the gun turret. Initially these lengthened tailcones housed a chaff dispenser and various receivers/jammers, but were subsequently upgraded throughout the aircraft's life, notably with 'horn' antennas for the AN/ALR-18 receiver.

*Above: An **EB-66C** lifts off from a Thai air base at the start of a combat sortie. The aircraft has the intermediate tailcone with horn antennas for the **AN/ALR-18** receiver.*

*Below: **EB-66C** Destroyers are prepared for a mission at Takhli. By the mid-1960s the antennas had been removed from the characteristic wingtip pods.*

Additional chaff dispensers and jammers could be carried under the wing pylons for further protection. Late in the B-66's career, some aircraft (EB-66Cs and Es) were fitted with a new tailcone that added an infra-red countermeasures system. This was distinguished by a circular plate at the top of the tailcone, cooling intakes and the relocation of the AN/ALR-18 'horns' to the sides.

ECM tailcones were fitted to 13 lucky B-66Bs, which escaped the retirement of the bomber fleet. Under the 1959 programme Brown Cradle, they were equipped with a package of receivers and jammers mounted on a pallet which fitted into the bomb bay. Jamming equipment could only be programmed on the ground to meet expected threats, so the electronic warfare

*This 39th TEWS **EB-66C** wears the **'BV'** tailcode, signifying assignment to the 36th TFW. The wing flew **F-4s** from Bitburg, although the **EB-66s** were based at Spangdahlem.*

The EB-66E was constantly updated to meet ever-changing jamming requirements, but all configurations featured a large farm of blade antennas under the belly. This example has the Mod 2259 tailcone with infra-red countermeasures.

officer had little more than an 'on-off' switch in the cockpit to control the jammers. This was to be the start of a new career for the Destroyer, one which was to be far more important than its original roles. Brown Cradle aircraft initially served in Europe.

As the US Air Force became embroiled in the Vietnam War, strike aircraft encountered SAM and gun-laying radars in growing numbers. In early 1965 the 363rd TRW at Shaw dispatched six RB-66Cs to Takhli AFB, Thailand, to provide EW support, offering both limited jamming coverage and electronic reconnaissance. Two Destroyers would be launched to operate in a semi-escort role protecting F-105 strike packages over North Vietnam. During the course of these early missions, RB-66Cs brought back the first data on the 'Fan Song' radar for the SA-2 missile. Three more RB-66Cs arrived at Takhli in September 1965 to form the 41st Tactical Reconnaissance Squadron, followed by five of the B-66B Brown Cradle jammers.

The latter arrivals were much better equipped for jamming, so the RB-66Cs were moved away to a stand-off role, while the B-66Bs escorted attackers almost to the target. This move depleted the overall jamming assets, so the remaining eight Brown Cradle aircraft were sent to southeast Asia in June 1966, by which time the force had moved to Tan Son Nhut in Vietnam. In September, it shifted back to Thailand, setting up base at Udorn, where the 6460th and 6461st TRSs were established under the 432nd TRW banner. During the year the aircraft were redesignated as EB-66B and EB-66C, while the units became tactical electronic warfare squadrons (TEWSs).

By 1967 the EB-66s were not performing any escort missions, the strikers relying on Wild Weasel support and ECM pods for protection. The Destroyers concentrated on the stand-off jamming of early warning and ground control radars. The wartime need was immense, so the USAF instigated a hasty modification of redundant RB-66Bs into the EB-66E configuration, usually identified by a veritable forest of blade antennas protruding from the belly. Internally, the navigator and EWO stations were transposed (the navigator now sitting to port), while the weapons bay was packed with jammers and receivers, making the EB-66E the most capable of the Destroyer variants in terms of jamming power and frequency coverage.

Squadron and wing designations continued to change, the 6460th TEWS becoming the 42nd TEWS and the Destroyers moving back to Takhli, then finally to Korat (under the 388th TFW). EB-66s were involved in all phases of the air war, and were notable for their contributions during the 1972 Linebacker campaigns. Six were shot down, five falling to SAMs and one to a MiG-21.

Evolving tactics

Throughout the conflict, equipment and tactics were continually updated, including the carriage of double or triple loads of ECM pods from the underwing pylons. Much of the development work was undertaken by the 4416th Test Squadron at Shaw AFB (363rd TRW), which was activated to support the growing EW effort in southeast Asia. Similarly, the 4417th Combat Crew Training Squadron was activated to handle the EW training effort, also at Shaw.

The end of the air war in southeast Asia effectively signalled the end of the B-66's career, the last EB-66Es having already been withdrawn from USAFE's 39th TEWS at Spangdahlem in December 1972. The 42nd TEWS flew its last mission from Korat on 17 April 1973, and stayed in Thailand until January 1974. Back at Shaw, the 39th Tactical Electronic Warfare Training Squadron (formerly 4417th CCTS) was the last Destroyer unit, deactivating on 15 March.

Whatever the questionable qualities of the aircraft, the B-66 had played a massive part in the development of the electronic jamming role. The EB-66s were sorely missed, for it was not until late 1981 that the USAF's next dedicated jamming platform, the EF-111A Raven, entered service.

Radically altered, but still recognisable as Destroyers, the two X-21As were based on WB-66D airframes 55-0408 and 55-0410.

Northrop X-21A – laminar flow testbed

Most radical of the B-66-based testbeds was the Northrop X-21A, a bold attempt to demonstrate the novel concept of laminar flow control. Using two surplus WB-66Ds as a basis, Northrop fitted an entirely new wing which incorporated nearly 17,000 ft (5200 m) of very thin slots. These were connected to two turbines mounted in large fairings under the wings, and which sucked the turbulent boundary layer of air next to the wing skin through the slots, thereby smoothing the airflow over the surface and dramatically improving the efficiency of the lifting surface. Two XJ79 engines were mounted either side of the tail to provide power for flight and bleed air for the turbines. The X-21s were flown by a crew of one pilot and four test engineers, two of whom occupied the former weather observer stations in the central cabin. The first flight was made on 18 April 1963 and the programme showed initial promise. However, the maintenance of the tiny slots proved to be too expensive, both in terms of effort and finances, to be practical.

The first XF4D-1 prototype was photographed here after repainting in a scheme similar to that worn by the second aircraft. The second machine was the only 'Ford' (a nickname derived from its F4D designation) fitted with a sliding cockpit canopy; the first aircraft and all production machines had clamshell canopies.

Douglas F4D Skyray

The fighting 'Ford'

The first carrierborne fighter to break the world's absolute speed record and the first US Navy fighter capable of Mach 1, the F4D Skyray was largely the product of German research into delta-winged craft.

Initial Douglas studies into the delta-wing concept were conducted in response to a US Navy request for a new type of interceptor possessing outstanding climb qualities and featuring the delta wing.

The US Navy Bureau of Aeronautics (BuAer) felt that the Douglas submissions possessed sufficient merit to warrant additional study. In mid-June 1947, the company was awarded a contract for further design work.

The F4D-1's somewhat bulbous nose radome contained the radar for its Aero 13F fire-control system. Armament consisted of four 20-mm cannon, Sidewinder AAMs, bombs and rockets.

Right: This quartet of F4D-1s belonged to VMF-115, the first of seven US Marine Corps units to be equipped with the Skyray.

Continuing study led to further refinement of the XF4D-1 which, by the summer of 1948, was fast being optimised for interceptor duties. Events moved swiftly, BuAer ordering two prototype XF4D-1s and a single static test example on 16 December 1948.

Propulsion hurdles

Propulsion was to be furnished by a single Westinghouse J40 turbojet engine. However, construction of the airframe outstripped development of the powerplant. Douglas endeavoured to sidestep these problems by suggesting that early flights should be made with an Allison J35-A-17 engine.

However, by October the first of many engine-related difficulties had arisen; some redesign was required so that a longer afterburning version of the J40 could be fitted. Ultimately, it was intended to install the more powerful J40-WE-10 variant, and it was this that prompted the change to the airframe design.

By the middle of 1950 assembly of the first XF4D-1 was nearing completion, but the Skyray's maiden flight was delayed until 25 January 1951.

Early aerodynamic problems were fairly easily resolved, unlike the increasing delays being experienced with the proposed J40 powerplant. It was not until February 1952 that the first prototype finally got airborne with the J40 engine. By then, an initial contract had been placed for a batch of 12 aircraft. All of these were earmarked to use the non-afterburning J40-WE-6 and

Production F4D-1s differed significantly from the first two prototypes. When the type finally entered service, Navy Composite Squadron VC-3 at Moffett Field, California, had the distinction of receiving the first examples to join a fleet unit, on 16 April 1956.

this meant that the production machines were significantly different from the first two XF4D-1 prototypes.

Despite the difficulties being encountered in the propulsion field, the type nevertheless showed considerable promise, prompting the US Navy to order a batch of 230 production examples during April 1952.

From J40 to J57

Engine problems began to take on increased magnitude early in the following year. The afterburning variant of the J40 was still not available, and in March 1953 it was decided to switch to the more reliable and more powerful Pratt & Whitney J57 for all production aircraft.

Exploration of the Skyray's full flight envelope eventually got under way during September 1953 following fitment of an afterburning J40-WE-8 in the second XF4D-1. This wasted little time in confirming the Skyray's outstanding performance, setting two world speed records during October.

October also witnessed the first carrier trials, these being undertaken by the original prototype. Further proof of US Navy confidence came with a repeat order for an additional 178 F4D-1s. Almost inevitably, the decision to install the J57 engine in production aircraft led to further delay and it was not until June 1954 that the first F4D-1 made its maiden flight.

Further carrier trials were accomplished during September 1955. Navy Composite Squadron VC-3 at Moffett Field, California, had the distinction of receiving the first production Skyray to join a fleet unit on 16 April 1956, this being followed in a matter of days by Marine Corps Squadron VMF-115 at El Toro, California.

After completing all-weather trials in autumn of 1956, the type was soon well established in US Navy and US Marine Corps service, eventually operating with 26 first- and second-line squadrons. On the way, it took time out to establish no fewer than five time-to-climb world records in May 1958, production terminating in December of that year with the 419th F4D-1.

The Skyray was still in regular service when the unified nomenclature system was introduced in 1962, and was henceforth known as the F-6A. VMF(AW)-115 was the last front-line operator, disposing of its final example in February 1964.

Above: The Skyray was one of the first types able to use the heat-seeking Sidewinder AAM, as seen on this aircraft. The first 100 F4D-1s were completed without this ability, but were later modified.

Left: The first operational fighter squadron to be equipped with Skyrays, VF-74 flew the type from 1956 until 1961. The first Marine Corps unit was VMF-115, which equipped with F4Ds shortly after VF-74.

English Electric Canberra

***Above:* The PR.Mk 9 was intended for high-altitude photographic reconnaissance and was initially designated HA PR.Mk 9 to indicate this fact. At the time of its retirement, the Canberra was the oldest aircraft in RAF squadron service and was operated by No. 39 Squadron, based at Marham.**

No. 213 Sqn operated the Canberra B(I).Mk 6 for 13 years. In this view of two of the unit's aircraft, the underwing pylons and gun pack that distinguished this variant from the B.Mk 6 are evident.

Versatile jet bomber

Britain's first jet bomber was smaller than, and deemed inferior to, the American B-47. However, the Canberra was to go on to be one of the truly great aircraft of the post-war period and was still in RAF service almost 60 years after its first flight.

Design work on the Canberra began in the mid-1940s with the requirement for a turbojet-powered replacement for the de Havilland Mosquito. English Electric chief engineer W. E. W. Petter proposed an aircraft with straight wings of large area, incorporating two of the new Rolls-Royce Avon engines.

When the prototype first flew in 1949, observers were staggered by the aircraft's fighter-like agility, a consequence of the Canberra's low-wing loading, and the aircraft was ordered in B.Mk 2 form for the RAF. Simple to maintain with docile handling and virtually no vices, the Canberra's introduction to service was fairly trouble-free, and early operational exercises showed the aircraft to be almost immune to interception by contemporary RAF fighters. The rate of production built up and, with the introduction of the improved B.Mk 6, there were 25 squadrons operating the type by 1954.

Combat debut

The Canberra was introduced into combat in February 1955 when No. 101 Squadron was detached to Singapore for operations against communist guerrillas in Malaya. Four other UK-based squadrons were also deployed at various times over the following two years before RAF Canberras became permanently based in Singapore.

In late 1956 the Suez crisis resulted in the only major war operation in which RAF Canberras were involved. A total of 13 squadrons participated, with their primary objective being to disable the Egyptian air force by bombing its airfields. During one week of intensive operations the Canberra proved itself in combat, destroying airfield after airfield and, by the time the UN-sanctioned ceasefire was announced in November, only one Canberra had been lost in operations – shot down by an Egyptian MiG-15.

The Canberra also fulfilled another role in the Suez Crisis. The PR.Mk 7 was the second-

Serving with No. 12 Squadron, six B(I).Mk 12s and three T.Mk 4s were delivered to the South African Air Force in 1963/64. The final Mk 12 was the last new-build Canberra to be completed.

***Left:* Based on the B.Mk 6, the PR.Mk 7's most significant advancement over the PR.Mk 3 was its increased range. This was achieved by the addition of extra fuel, located in integral tanks in the wing leading edges. The PR.Mk 7 prototype actually beat the B.Mk 6 into the air, flying on 28 October 1953.**

generation photographic reconnaissance Canberra, having replaced the earlier PR.Mk 3 which had entered service in 1953 at the start of the type's association with the PR role.

A substantial redesign of the Canberra to produce an aircraft dedicated to the aggressive attack role at low level resulted in the B(I).Mk 8. The crew compartment was rearranged to seat the pilot higher and further back, offset on the port side under a fixed but jettisonable fighter-style canopy. The crew was reduced to two and the aircraft could carry an array of weapons including a gun pack containing four 20-mm cannon and rockets or bombs underwing.

The Canberra later served with the RAF/RN in a number of other roles, many of which were undertaken by airframes modified from early bomber variants. These included the U.Mk 10 (later D.Mk 10) unmanned target and research aircraft, T.Mk 11 airborne intercept radar trainer, D.Mk 14 drone used for RN Seacat missile trials, E.Mk 15 with high-altitude calibration platforms, T.Mk 17 ECM trainer, TT.Mk 18 target tug, T.Mk 19 'silent target' aircraft, T.Mk 22 with Blue Parrot forward-looking radar and SC.Mk 9 with radar and installations in the nose for missile tests. In addition, no fewer than 103 Canberras were converted as testbeds for countless trials of engines, missiles, avionics and systems.

Foreign production

The success of Canberra demonstrations at the Farnborough air show in 1949 led to export customers ordering the aircraft in bomber, trainer and photo reconnaissance forms. The Royal Australian Air Force operated the B.Mk 20 (basically a B.Mk 2), 48 of which were licence-built in Australia. These aircraft were among the hardest working bomber examples, serving operationally over Malaya and throughout the Vietnam War.

The US also expressed early interest and eventually licence-built 347 examples as the Martin B-57, the type becoming the first British military aircraft to be built in the US for 40 years.

Additional operators included Venezuela, France, Ecuador, Peru, India, Rhodesia, New Zealand, Sweden, South Africa, West Germany, Ethiopia, Argentina and Chile.

The RAF continued to operate the PR.Mk 9 until the last examples were retired in July 2006. As recently as the 1990s the aircraft had been involved in operations over Bosnia and Kosovo and during the refugee crisis in Rwanda. Latterly they were flown over Afghanistan.

The Canberra won early fame as Britain's first operational jet bomber, and rapidly proved itself to be the most capable and versatile light bomber of its generation, over-shadowing and eventually eclipsing many of the early swept-wing jet bombers. Superb performance and unexpected agility allowed it to outperform most of the fighters of its day, and many of the fighters designed long after it entered service.

The first variant to enter front-line service with the RAF was the B.Mk 2 bomber, when No. 101 Squadron was declared operational in January 1952. The B.Mk 2's bomb bay (seen open here) normally held two triplets of 1,000-lb (454-kg) bombs, but could alternatively carry a 5,000-lb (2268-kg) bomb or nuclear stores.

***Above:* In the late 1960s the Canberra found a new role as the TT.Mk 18 target-towing aircraft. This example, with a Rushton towed target on its underwing pylon, was the first prototype rebuilt by Flight Refuelling and underwent flight trials in 1967.**

***Left:* Fitted with extra fuel tankage in the wings and uprated Rolls-Royce Avon Mk 109 turbojets, the B.Mk 6 entered RAF service in June 1954. This trio can be identified as being from No. 12 Squadron by the unit's fox head badge on the tailfin.**

Canberra variants

As the largest foreign customer, India operated the Canberra into the 21st century. This example wears a striking colour scheme for its role as a target tug for naval AAA. The Indian air force also operated the Canberra in the ECM/EW role.

Designed as a medium bomber to replace aircraft like the Avro Lincoln, the Canberra rapidly became the 'Jet Mosquito' of its day – versatile, adaptable, and popular with operators around the world.

Initial Canberra production of the basic B.Mk 2 reached 412 aircraft before it switched to the improved B.Mk 6, which introduced Avon 109 engines and integral fuel tanks in the wings. Some 106 B.Mk 6s were built, and the B.Mk 2 and B.Mk 6 together equipped 23 front-line home-based Bomber Command Squadrons (reaching this peak in April 1955, when almost 350 were on front-line charge).

Canberra B.Mk 2s based in Germany stood alert with US nuclear weapons, while B.Mk 15s and B.Mk 16s based in Cyprus were equipped with Britain's own Red Beard tactical nuclear bomb.

Bomber Command retired its last bomber-tasked Canberras in 1961, though the overseas-based bombers remained in service into the late 1960s. Nuclear-armed Canberra bombers remained in service in RAF Germany until replaced by Phantoms and Buccaneers between 1970 and 1972.

The most obvious new role for the Canberra was that of photographic reconnaissance, and a small number of B.Mk 2s was hastily adapted for top-secret reconnaissance missions. Even before the B.Mk 2 flew in production form, development of a dedicated reconnaissance version was well underway.

The first of the PR variants was the Mk 3. This had part of its bomb bay replaced with additional fuel tanks and illumination flares. Seven cameras could be mounted in a section inserted in the fuselage.

PR variants

The basic B.Mk 2 formed the basis of a dedicated recce variant, the PR.Mk 3. This married the 'dry' wings and engines of the B.Mk 2 with a modestly redesigned fuselage. The bomb bay was replaced by an auxiliary fuel tank and a flare bay. The forward fuselage was stretched to accommodate a new camera bay, with a variety of oblique cameras. Vertical cameras were carried aft of the flare bay.

The prototype PR.Mk 3 made its maiden flight on 19 March 1950, and in all, 35 PR.Mk 3s were built, entering service with No. 540 Squadron in 1953.

The second-generation Canberra bomber, the B.Mk 6, formed the basis of the PR.Mk 7.

Canberra B(I).Mk 8

The Fuerza Aérea Venezolana was the first overseas customer for the Canberra, taking delivery of bomber, reconnaissance and interdictor variants from 1953. B(I).Mk 8 4B-39 was delivered in 1957 for use by the Escuadrón 39, Grupo de Bombardeo 13, at Barcelona.

Redesigned forward fuselage
The main distinguishing feature of the Mk 8 was its forward fuselage, redesigned to improve visibility for the ground-attack role. The 'fighter-type' cockpit canopy was offset to port. The aircraft's glazed nose required strengthening as the instances of birdstrike increased at low level.

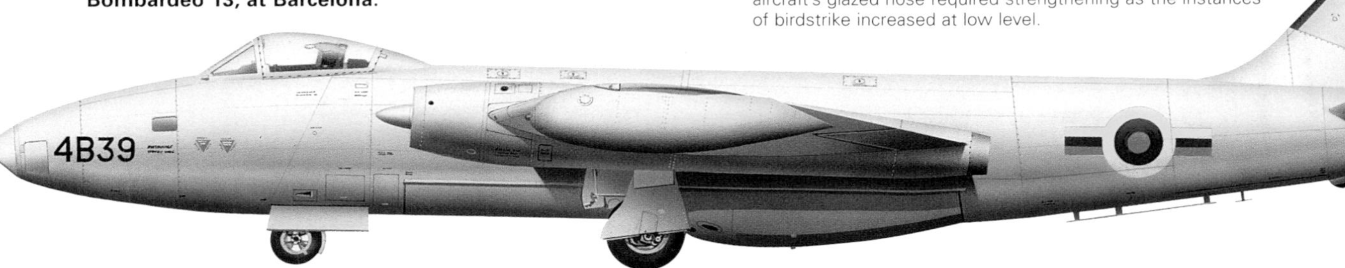

The PR.Mk 7 flew for the first time on 28 October 1953, 74 examples replacing the PR.Mk 3s. At the peak of Canberra reconnaissance operations, Mk 7s equipped reconnaissance squadrons in the Far East, Near East and in RAF Germany. Mk 7s saw active service in support of the Suez operation, and in various other colonial 'hotspots'. The PR.Mk 7 remained in front-line service until December 1981.

The final reconnaissance Canberra was the PR.Mk 9, with Avon Mk 206 engines, and greater wing area provided by increased span and increased chord inboard of the engines. The prototype made its maiden flight on 8 July 1955. Production aircraft had refined noses, with an opening canopy for the pilot, and with the entire nose section hinging to allow the navigator access to his forward-facing ejection seat.

Canberra intruders

It was immediately apparent that the Canberra would provide an excellent basis for an interdictor. The one-off B.Mk 5 (a prototype pathfinder variant) was selected for conversion as the prototype B(I).Mk 8. For its new role, the aircraft was fitted with an entirely new and redesigned nose section, with a fighter-style cockpit canopy offset to port. The navigator sat beside the pilot for take-off, moving forward to a chart table in front of the pilot, or to a prone bomb-aiming couch in the extreme nose. The new variant was provided with an optional cannon pack, which could be installed in the rear of the bomb bay. Three 1,000-lb (454-kg) bombs could still be carried in the forward half and underwing hardpoints were also provided.

Otherwise, the Canberra B(I).Mk 8 was much the same as the B.Mk 6, with Avon engines and integral wing tanks. The definitive B(I).Mk 8 was preceded by 22 interim B(I).Mk 6s, which married the new gun-pack and underwing pylons to a standard B.Mk 6 airframe. A total of 82 B(I).Mk 8s was built for the RAF, though a number were diverted off the RAF contract to go straight to export users. Other new-build interdictors were built specifically for foreign customers. In RAF service, the B(I).Mk 8 served only in RAF Germany, equipping three squadrons; the last examples were withdrawn in June 1972.

The Canberra was a popular choice for conversion to fulfil other roles. Bomber Command used Canberras for ECM jamming, radar calibration, and ECM/EW training. Both these roles initially relied upon modified B.Mk 2s (and a few Mk 6s) and both eventually resulted in dedicated conversions: the E.Mk 15 (for calibration) and T.Mk 17 (for ECM/EW training). From 1953, the Canberra began to enter the world of ELINT, resulting in the B.Mk 6(BS) modification.

Sixteen B.Mk 2s were fitted with new nose sections to become T.Mk 4 trainers, augmenting new-build trainers, while eight more were converted as T.Mk 11s for training night-fighter aircrew. Some 18 B.Mk 2s were converted to U.Mk 10 standard as unmanned target drones and six more became D.Mk 14s for missile tests.

Target facilities units initially employed T.Mk 11s, followed by a handful of B.Mk 2s and T.Mk 4s. As the demand for target facilities grew, specially converted TT.Mk 18s began to be used. The RN also operated the unique Canberra T.Mk 22, a PR.Mk 7 fitted with Blue Parrot radar in a characteristic extended nose.

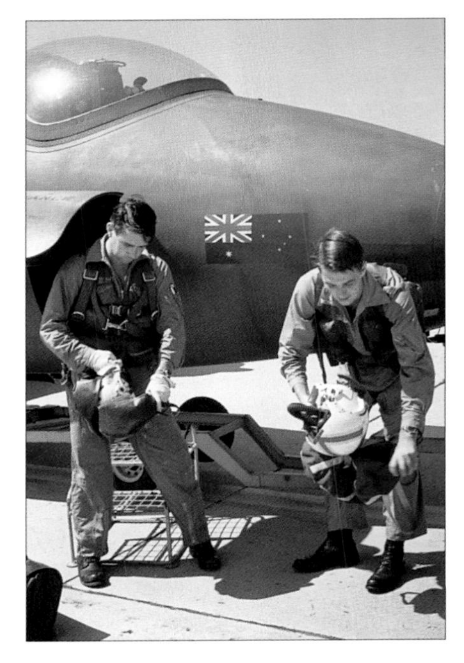

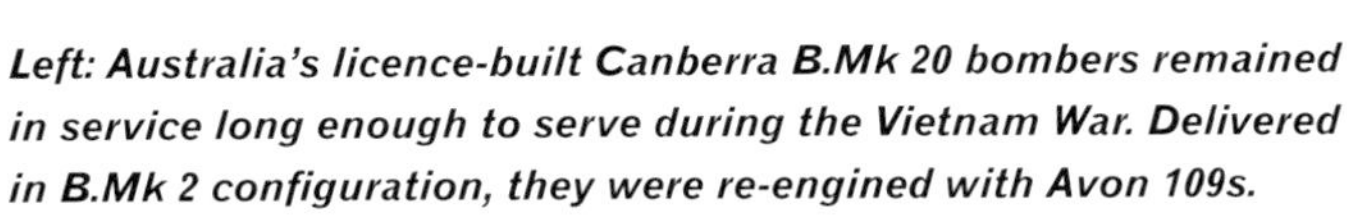

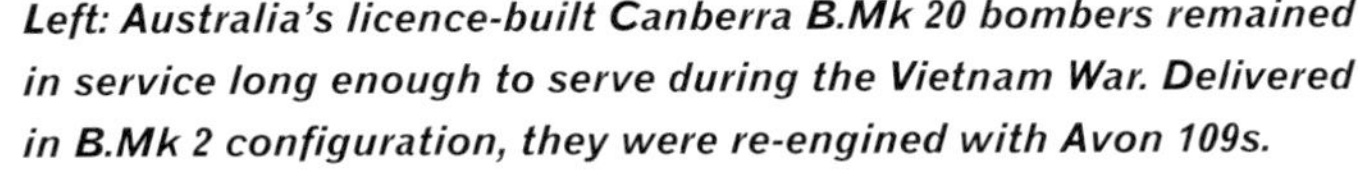

***Left:** Australia's licence-built Canberra B.Mk 20 bombers remained in service long enough to serve during the Vietnam War. Delivered in B.Mk 2 configuration, they were re-engined with Avon 109s.*

***Below:** India received over 100 Canberras. Out of this total, eight PR.Mk 57/67s were received in 1959, forming No. 106 Squadron. Additional attrition replacements were obtained in 1963 and 1975.*

English Electric Lightning

Mach 2 interceptor

Conceived in an era when the future of manned fighters looked uncertain, the Lightning matured into a fine interceptor which assured the defence of the British Isles for over a quarter of a century. The fighter's full potential was never realised, but its astonishing performance ensured it a special place in the hearts of pilots and public alike.

The Lightning's demanding cockpit workload meant that only elite pilots were posted to Lightning units. An early stipulation required potential pilots to have over 1,000 hours on fast jets.

Top: By the mid-1980s, the Lightning's shortcomings as an interceptor were clearly evident, lacking a modern radar and carrying only two missiles. However, it still remained effective for point defence.

Above: For pilots and onlookers alike, the Lightning was best remembered for its phenomenal rate of climb. From brake release, a normally laden F.Mk 2 took less than 150 seconds to reach 40,000 ft (12190 m).

Arguably the best-known of the RAF's post-war fighters, the English Electric Lightning was loved by its pilots and admired by the public for its sheer performance, and perhaps also for its glamorous image. When it entered service, the Lightning marked a dramatic step for the Royal Air Force, and fighter squadrons transitioned straight from their small, drab, subsonic, cannon-armed Hawker Hunters to the shiny silver, Mach 2, missile-armed Lightnings.

More importantly, Lightnings had a sophisticated and automated attack system which allowed pilots to guide their

The Lightning's raison d'être was to intercept and shepherd away potentially hostile intruders such as this Tu-95RTs 'Bear-D' from the British Isles. Good range performance was critical for such missions, and this proved to be the Lightning's greatest shortcoming.

aircraft to the perfect point to fire air-to-air missiles at the enemy, simply by keeping a steering dot centred in the radar display.

In addition to the key role it played in defending Britain's airspace, for much of the height of the Cold War two squadrons of Lightnings in RAF Germany provided an immediate-response interceptor force maintaining the integrity of the north German air defence zone. RAF Lightning squadrons also protected British forces on Cyprus and in Singapore.

The Lightning won valuable export orders, most notably from Saudi Arabia, winning Britain much-needed export earnings and helping to establish its manufacturer (BAC, as it then was) as a major player in the export of military hardware. Ultimately, foreign sales were limited by a lack of British backing for more advanced Lightning derivatives, the two export customers being Saudi Arabia and Kuwait, who purchased close to 50 aircraft between them. Kuwaiti examples (the single-seat F.Mk 53K and two-seat T.Mk 55K aircraft) were retired by 1977, while Saudi Lightnings (single-seat F.Mk 52 and F.Mk 53, and two-seat T.Mk 54 and T.Mk 55 models) were retired in 1986.

Conceived for the strictly limited role of point defence against high-flying supersonic bombers attacking the UK, the Lightning was always handicapped by the fundamental limitations imposed by this task. Even greater limitations were imposed by the timing of the programme. The Lightning emerged in the mid-1950s – an era when many expected manned fighters to be entirely replaced by missiles. The fighter's development was completed only because the aircraft was felt to be 'too far advanced to cancel', and because it was grudgingly accepted that there might be a requirement for an advanced manned interceptor 'in the interim'. Because everyone believed that the Lightning would have only a very short service life, it was never developed as fully as it should have been, and the aircraft's fundamental limitations were never properly addressed.

Elite pilot force

Even by the 1970s, when the Lightning had to face the threat of low-level intruders, the aircraft's exhilarating performance and agility made it a tough opponent, albeit one with a very limited radius of action, endurance and weapon load. The aircraft's high cockpit workload meant that only the best pilots were selected to fly the Lightning, ensuring that the last Lightning squadrons remained an elite force until their final withdrawal in 1988. In addition to single-seaters, two two-seat variants were also built for training duty, these being the Lightning T.Mk 4 and the T.Mk 5, which was developed in parallel with the F.Mk 3 single-seater.

Today, the Lightning is remembered as one of the all-time greats, Britain's only Mach 2 fighter of wholly indigenous design and manufacture, and a worthy successor to aircraft like the Spitfire, Meteor and Hunter.

The Lightning was Britain's only operational supersonic fighter of wholly indigenous design. RAF pilots had to wait until the multinational Typhoon entered service to sample similar high-speed performance in a single-seat environment.

RAF fighters

The first Lightnings offered Britain's air force a major leap forward in terms of capability. The only British-designed supersonic fighter to enter service, the Lightning was the fastest aircraft to have served with the RAF and was much loved by its pilots.

In July 1960, No. 74 Squadron became the first unit to receive the F.Mk 1 and immediately fell under the full glare of the media. Early exercises proved that the Lightning was an excellent short-range interceptor, defeating all known bomber tactics.

By 1956, the government had ordered 50 Lightning F.Mk 1s and, two years later, a larger order was made for F.Mk 2s and two-seat T.Mk 4s. On 3 April 1958, the first of the 20-aircraft Development Batch made its maiden flight. This aircraft, with the original small fin, was powered by a 14,430-lb (64.19-kN) Avon Mk 201 and carried 7,500 lb (3400 kg) of fuel. This was sufficient for a maximum-rate climb to 30,000 ft (9145 m), an acceleration to Mach 1.5, a single-pass intercept, and a return to base.

Into service

Despite its lack of range, the Lightning offered a major leap in capability over the Hawker Hunters and Gloster Javelins that equipped Fighter Command at that time. No. 74 Squadron was selected as the first squadron to receive the Lightning.

Only the first 19 full-production Lightnings were built as F.Mk 1s, XM169 and 27 subsequent aircraft being delivered as F.Mk 1As. The latter had UHF radio from the start and provision for a detachable inflight-refuelling probe below the port wing-root. These aircraft equipped two squadrons at RAF Wattisham: No. 56 (the first to receive the F.Mk 1A on 14 December 1960), followed by No. 111 Squadron from March 1961. However, by the time the F.Mk 1As were flying with these squadrons, it was clear that they would be no more than interim aircraft as further Lightning developments were just around the corner.

When ordered in 1958, the Avon Mk 210-powered Lightning F.Mk 2 marked an improvement over the F.Mk 1, but everyone was convinced that the F.Mk 2 would be both the last Lightning and the last of the manned fighters to be built. The F.Mk 2 made its initial flight on 11 July 1961, and the RAF's first example was delivered to the Air Fighting Development Squadron at Binbrook on 14 November 1962. On 17 December, the variant entered service with No. 19 Squadron at Leconfield, where Nos 19 and 92 Squadrons had been using a quartet of new two-seat T.Mk 4s for training. By then, further progress had been made, so that the F.Mk 2 became no more than another interim Lightning, pending introduction of the 'ultimate' F.Mk 3.

Ultimate Lightning

At the time of its inception, the Lightning F.Mk 3 was regarded as the definitive Lightning but, in truth, it offered only very modest improvements over the basic Lightnings it replaced in service.

The F.Mk 3 received by the RAF was little more than a refined F.Mk 2, stripped of its guns and equipped with the Red Top missile. A total of 70 Lightning F.Mk 3s was built, re-equipping the F.Mk 1 and F.Mk 1A squadrons, and allowing the formation of another unit, No. 23 Squadron. The introduction of the F.Mk 3 at RAF Leuchars, with its standard fit of an inflight-refuelling probe, made QRAs a common event as Lightnings scrambled (with tanker support) to intercept Soviet aircraft far out over the North Sea.

When production switched to the Lightning F.Mk 6, the RAF again received an aircraft which was an improvement over previous variants, but also one which represented only a fraction of what was possible. The new variant introduced an enlarged ventral tank and cambered wing, as well as fuel-filled flaps and overwing fuel tanks.

Development of the long-range F.Mk 3A began in 1963, with an F.Mk 3 and an F.Mk 2 allocated to the programme for development work. The new, enlarged ventral

No. 5 Squadron operated the Lightning F.Mk 6 (Interim) aircraft from 10 December 1965 until late 1966, when these aircraft were upgraded to full Mk 6 standard, with provision for overwing tanks.

tank could contain up to 4,880 lb (2210 kg) of fuel, more than double the capacity of the original ventral tank. The front section could be replaced by a compartment containing two 30-mm ADEN cannon. With guns installed, the capacity of the ventral tank fell to 4,280 lb (1940 kg).

While English Electric built single-role Lightning F.Mk 6s for the RAF, it also developed a very similar – but multi-role – F.Mk 53 version for sale to both Saudi Arabia and Kuwait.

F.Mk 6 in service

The first production F.Mk 6s had begun life on the production line as F.Mk 3s, being modified with the new wing and ventral tank before delivery. These were designated F.Mk 3A or F.Mk 6 (Interim) and were brought up to full F.Mk 6 standard during 1967/68. The F.Mk 6 (Interim) aircraft equipped No. 5 Squadron and a handful subsequently went to No. 23 Squadron. The 16 F.Mk 6 (Interim) aircraft were joined by seven aircraft which first flew as F.Mk 3s, but which were converted to full F.Mk 6 standard in 1967. The RAF also received 39 aircraft which were built and delivered as full-standard F.Mk 6s.

The advantages demonstrated by the F.Mk 6 were sufficient to prompt the RAF to modify 31 surviving F.Mk 2s to F.Mk 2A standard. The F.Mk 2A retained the original Avon engines, which were modified slightly and redesignated Avon Mk 211Rs. Despite an increase in weight, the F.Mk 2A was quite a performer, its well-matched engine and intake making it particularly aerodynamically clean. F.Mk 2A pilots claimed unrefuelled endurance figures of up to two hours at high level – an achievement unheard of in any other Lightning variant.

Below: Viewed as the second-generation Lightning, the F.Mk 3 featured a number of improvements. One noticeable change was an enlarged square-cut tailfin in place of the earlier pointed fin.

Above: No. 11 Sqn was the final RAF Lightning operator. Its F.Mk 6s and two-seat T.Mk 5s (nearest camera) remained in service until 30 April 1988, when they were replaced by Tornado F.Mk 3s.

Lightning F.Mk 1A

No. 56 Squadron became the RAF's second Lightning squadron when it received its first F.Mk 1A at Wattisham on 14 December 1960. During the 1963 display season, the F.Mk 1As of the squadron's Firebirds display team wore very colourful markings, including flame-red fins, spines and leading edges.

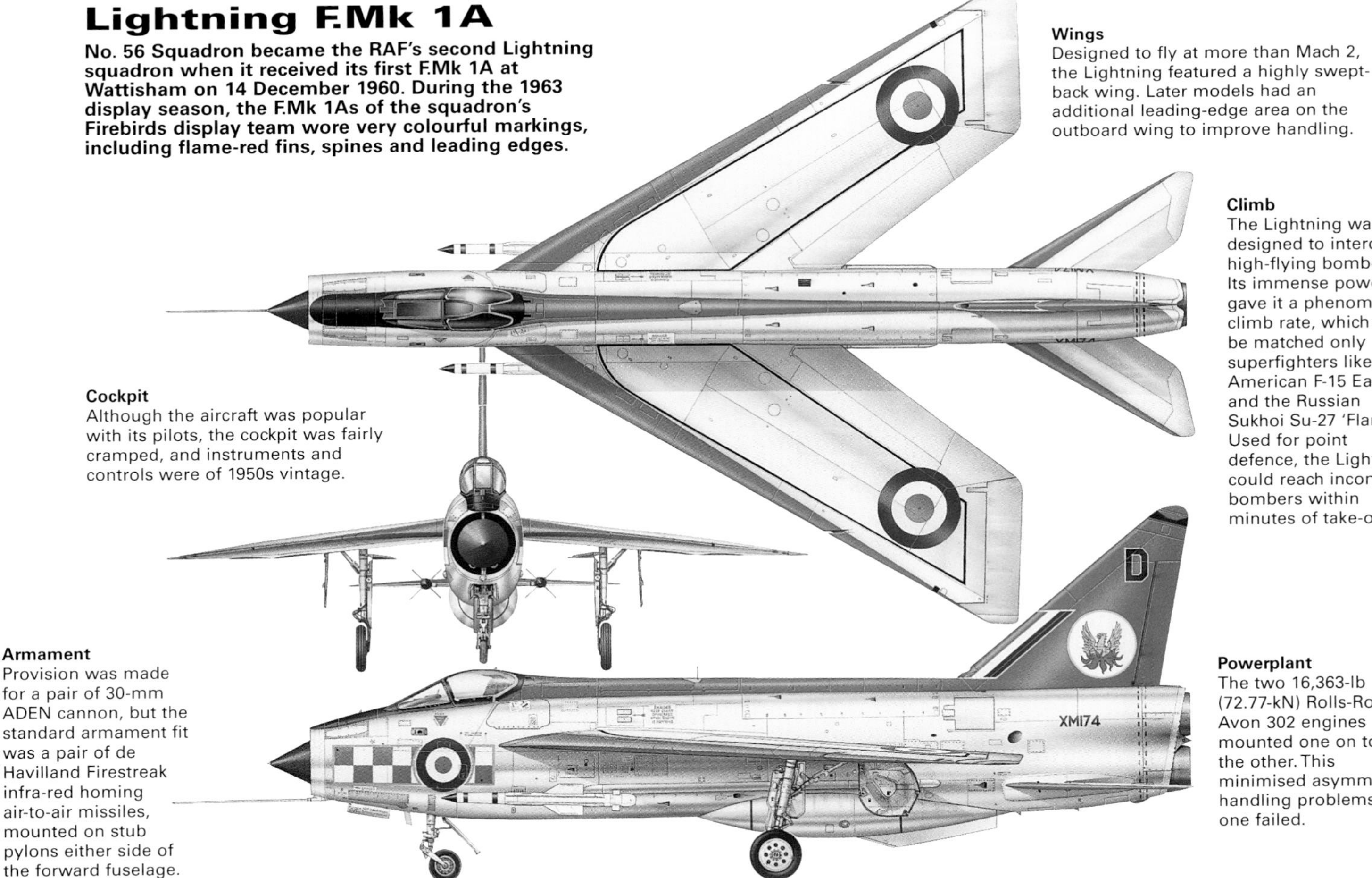

Wings
Designed to fly at more than Mach 2, the Lightning featured a highly swept-back wing. Later models had an additional leading-edge area on the outboard wing to improve handling.

Climb
The Lightning was designed to intercept high-flying bombers. Its immense power gave it a phenomenal climb rate, which can be matched only by superfighters like the American F-15 Eagle and the Russian Sukhoi Su-27 'Flanker'. Used for point defence, the Lightning could reach incoming bombers within minutes of take-off.

Cockpit
Although the aircraft was popular with its pilots, the cockpit was fairly cramped, and instruments and controls were of 1950s vintage.

Armament
Provision was made for a pair of 30-mm ADEN cannon, but the standard armament fit was a pair of de Havilland Firestreak infra-red homing air-to-air missiles, mounted on stub pylons either side of the forward fuselage.

Powerplant
The two 16,363-lb (72.77-kN) Rolls-Royce Avon 302 engines were mounted one on top of the other. This minimised asymmetric handling problems if one failed.

Eurofighter EF2000

Stretching back over 20 years, the Eurofighter programme became a byword for political disagreement and delay. However, the aircraft has been making steady gains recently and is now in front-line service with its first four operator nations.

As a follow-on to the tri-national Tornado programme, the Eurofighter consortium was formed in June 1986 by the same three countries – Britain, West Germany and Italy (soon joined by Spain) – to produce an air superiority fighter by the late 1990s. Other European countries, notably France, had been involved in earlier European Fighter Aircraft (EFA) discussions, but shunned the final consortium to pursue their own independent programmes.

Much experience of the main EFA concepts had been gained from BAe's Experimental Aircraft Programme (EAP). These concepts included an unstable aerodynamic configuration with canard foreplanes, active digital fly-by-wire control system, complex avionics, multi-function cockpit displays, carbon-fibre composites and extensive use of aluminium-lithium alloys, titanium and even direct voice input (DVI). The EAP had been funded by the UK MoD and industry, with some Italian participation. First flying on 8 August 1986, the twin-engined RB.199-powered EAP amassed invaluable data in 259 test sorties totalling over 195 hours before retirement in 1991.

Multinational requirement

Finalised in September 1987, the EFA European Staff Requirement for Development specified a relatively light and sophisticated twin-turbofan single-seat fighter. Optimised for BVR and close air combat, it was also to be capable of secondary air-to-surface roles and operation from short, austere air strips, with a low radar cross-section and high supersonic performance, agility and carefree handling.

Germany and Italy initially sought only air-to-air roles, but accepted the common specification of a 21,495-lb (9750-kg) basic empty weight, 538.2-sq ft (500-m²) gross wing area, and 20,233-lb (90-kN) reheat thrust per engine. These were new EJ200 twin-spool turbofans from the Eurojet consortium, with 30 per cent fewer parts than the Tornado's RB.199, and with a 13,488-lb (60-kN) maximum dry thrust.

A £5.5 billion contract signed on 23 November 1988 covered the building and testing of nine prototypes (including two two-seat versions): three in Britain, two in Germany, two in Italy and one in Spain. The aircraft were funded in proportion to national industrial participation: 33 per cent each by BAe and MBB (now BAE Systems and EADS Deutschland respectively), 21 per cent by Alenia (as it was by now), and 13 per cent by CASA (today also part of EADS).

***Above:* The third phase of Eurofighter flight control system clearance involved air-to-air refuelling. DA2 flew the first such trials, making dry 'prods' into a drogue from an RAF No. 101 Squadron VC10.**

***Top:* Current military experience has demonstrated the need for aircraft that are capable of undertaking offensive counter-air and attack missions on the same sortie. The Eurofighter was designed around this specification from the planning stage.**

Eurofighter systems

Eurofighter initially relies on the AIM-120 AMRAAM as its primary air-to-air weapon. However, in the future, this will be supplemented by the ramjet-powered MBDA Meteor. For shorter-range engagements, RAF Eurofighters use the ASRAAM, while the other three core customers ordered the IRIS-T. An air-to-air configuration could include up to six AMRAAMs and four ASRAAMs. In the air interdiction role, the Eurofighter's 14,300-lb (6486-kg) payload allows it to carry up to two stand-off missiles, two Alarm ARMs, three external fuel tanks plus four AAMs. Other weapons options include the Hellfire-derived Brimstone missile.

The Eurofighter is equipped with the Captor (formerly

The Spanish EF2000 OCU is 113 Escuadrón, with which this CE.16 two-seater is on charge. After Móron receives its complement of 50 aircraft, the next Spanish wing to form on the type will be at Albacete.

Spain will take 87 aircraft (15 of them two-seaters) and these began to equip an operational conversion unit, 113 Escuadrón of Ala 11 at Móron, on 27 May 2004. The first front-line unit is 111 Escuadrón, to be followed by 112 Escuadrón – both also based at Móron – completing Ala 11's transition to the Eurofighter. The next Spanish wing will be Ala 14 at Albacete, with two front-line squadrons: 141 Escuadrón and 142 Escuadrón. These latter are due to receive their Eurofighters from 2011 onwards. Eventually, all Spanish Eurofighter units will be given a multi-role tasking.

The UK will be the largest Eurofighter operator, its 232 Typhoons including 37 two-seaters, known in RAF service as the Typhoon F.Mk 1. The single-seater has been delivered as the F.Mk 2. The first RAF Typhoons began to equip an Operational Evaluation Unit, No. 17 (Reserve) Squadron, on 18 December 2003. This was followed by the type Operational Conversion Unit, No. 29 (R) Squadron, from May 2004. The first 16 RAF pilots and 248 groundcrew were trained at Warton under 'Case White'. This arrangement was designed to reduce risk and ensure a particularly smooth transition to service.

The co-location of the first RAF aircraft alongside BAE's Warton-based Eurofighter development team allowed the service to benefit from on-site support by the manufacturer, and facilitated useful exchange of experience. Deliveries to the RAF will eventually provide for seven front-line squadrons, plus the OEU and OCU, both of which are based at RAF Coningsby. The first front-line RAF unit was No. 3 Squadron, which reformed at Coningsby on 1 April 2006. This was followed on 29 March 2007 by No. 11 Squadron, the RAFs first designated multi-role Typhoon unit.

In common with the other three initial operators, the first RAF Eurofighters were delivered as 'relatively immature, interim' Block 1 aircraft. Block 1 is to the Initial Operational Capability (IOC) standard and as such is fitted with radar, but no DASS. Block 1 also lacks IRST, helmet-mounted displays, and datalink. Despite this, the aircraft are fully compliant with training requirements and can be configured with AIM-120 and AIM-9L Sidewinder or ASRAAM for a limited air-to-air role. Block 2 has full IOC standard avionics and software and additions include IRIS-T capability, datalink, a basic standard DASS and DVI.

The Block 1/2 EF2000 is some way short of the full-spec swing-role fighter envisaged. The aircraft's air-to-ground capabilities are being introduced in stages, starting with the Block 5 deliveries. Block 5 represents the Final Operational Capability (FOC) avionics and software standard, which allows integration with Paveway and Enhanced Paveway series LGBs and the Litening III laser designator pod.

With the Block 5 standard, the Eurofighter has full carefree handling and air-to-ground capability. This means that the aircraft is capable of operating in the 'swing role' mode and pilots can 'swing' from the air-to-surface role to the air-to-air role 'at the push of a button'. Further improvements in capability will come with Block 15, which will add the Meteor AAM as well as expanded air-to-ground weapons options that will include Storm Shadow and Taurus stand-off weapons, a full range of GPS-guided stores, a new designator pod and Brimstone.

Further growth potential will be reflected under the Tranche 3 series of orders, under which sequential Block standards could add new engines, 'stealthy' features and enhanced radar.

Eurofighter for export

The Eurofighter won its first export order from Austria, which will receive 18 single-seat Block 5A aircraft. A formal contract was signed on 1 July 2003. The first Austrian aircraft made its maiden flight on 21 March 2007. The second export customer is Saudi Arabia, which signed up for an initial 24 aircraft under a contract announced in December 2005. The eventual Saudi order is likely to extend to 72 aircraft.

Above: The Luftwaffe's first front-line EF2000 unit is JG 74, based at Neuburg. The wing will initially continue to operate a single F-4F Phantom II* Staffel *alongside the Eurofighter.

Right: Eurofighter is receiving expanded weapons options under a staged programme of Block-by-Block improvements. Here ASRAAM is tested by a No. 3 Squadron Typhoon F.Mk 2.

Fairchild A-10 Thunderbolt II

Scourge of the Iraqi army in 1991, A-10s and OA-10s searched the battlefields for targets. The Thunderbolt's rapid decimation of the opposition forces undoubtedly hastened the Coalition ground forces' advance into Iraq and probably saved the lives of many Allied soldiers.

The 'Warthog'

Flying in the face of popular warplane design, Fairchild produced a slow and ugly CAS aircraft that was to emerge as a premier tank-killer.

Seemingly destined for the scrap heap by 1991, the A-10 earned its survival in front-line service when the 1991 Gulf War showed that it was not too old, too slow or too vulnerable to operate over a modern battlefield. The A-10's critics have always maintained that its armour protection, redundant systems and extreme manoeuvrability at ultra-low level would not guarantee its survival in such an environment. However, the Thunderbolt II, designed to fight a war in western Europe, proved its rugged character and performance in the harsh conditions of the Kuwaiti desert.

The genesis of the A-10 dates from before the Vietnam War, during which some of the Navy's ancient Douglas A-1 Skyraiders were pressed into service by the USAF as CAS and search and rescue (SAR) aircraft.

Learning that speed can sometimes be a liability, and that ruggedness and reliability count for a lot in combat, the USAF's Attack Experimental (AX) programme set out to develop a Skyraider replacement that would have a similarly simple but strong airframe, multiple weapons pylons, great battle damage resistance and excellent low-speed agility. It was determined that, during any war in Europe,

From the very beginning, Fairchild and the USAF were keen to demonstrate the A-10's huge potential for external weapons carriage.

***Above:** Although the A-10 spent much of its career preparing to fight in the grey weather of Europe (or Alaska as illustrated), it actually saw its defining moment of glory over the desert of Kuwait.*

***Right:** While the A-10 force is numerically a shadow of its former self, the aircraft has assumed an important Forward Air Control (FAC) role in addition to its long-standing CAS mission.*

there would generally be 4,000 ft (1219 m) of runway left in operation after an anti-airfield strike. This distance was therefore written into the requirement as the maximum ground roll of a fully armed aircraft. A more lightly loaded aircraft would have to be able to take off in 1,000 ft (305 m). The new aircraft was also to be designed to survive in the 'anticipated groundfire environment of the 1970s and 1980s', which suggested a hitherto-unknown level of armour protection and internal systems redundancy.

Programme launch

The AX programme was launched in June 1966. The USAF issued a request for AX design studies to 21 companies on 6 March 1967, while follow-on study contracts were issued on 2 May 1967. Most studies were of twin turboprops similar in size to the Martin B-57, and with a unit cost (including research and development) of about US$1.5 million. By 1969, however, the USAF was specifying a smaller aircraft with a unit cost of US$1 million, and twin fanjets started to look like a sensible powerplant option, especially since very high-bypass fans were likely to be more economical than turboprops. Turbofan engines could also be located closer to the aircraft centreline, reducing asymmetric handling problems and allowing the airframe to shield the exhaust from heat-seeking SAMs.

Northrop and Fairchild Republic were declared the winners of the AX study on 18 December 1970, each winning the right to build two prototypes.

The first YA-10 flew from Edwards AFB on 10 May 1972. This was shortly followed by the Northrop YA-9 flying on 30 May 1972. The second YA-10 made its first flight on 21 July 1972.

The US Air Force's formal evaluation of the two prototypes lasted from 10 October until 9 December 1972, with the YA-9s logging 307.6 hours, and the YA-10s 328.1 hours. Pilots preferred the handling qualities of the YA-10, but the real advantage was the ease of access to its underwing hardpoints. Other factors included the shorter, easier transition from prototype to production aircraft, the Fairchild aircraft having been built to what amounted to a production standard, at least structurally. The use of an existing engine (the TF34 was also used on the US Navy's S-3 Viking) was also a deciding factor.

Such a new concept in warplane design was always likely to employ a unique weapons system. The specially designed General Electric GAU-8 Avenger cannon lies at the heart of the A-10, offering exceptional anti-armour capabilities in combination with the AGM-65 Maverick missile.

Winning design

Fairchild Republic was announced the winner on 18 January 1973, and set about building 10 (later reduced to six) pre-production YA-10s after signing the production contract on 1 March 1973; simultaneously, General Electric received a contract for TF34 engines for these aircraft.

From April until May 1974, a fly-off was held against an A-7D Corsair II. Despite the initial doubts about the YA-10, the aircraft proved to be far more capable than the Corsair II, being able to spend two hours over the target area, compared to the A-7's 11 minutes.

Pre-production YA-10s joined the test programme from February 1975. The six aircraft were each tasked with specific parts of the test programme.

The first production aircraft flew on 10 October 1975 and was delivered to the USAF on 5 November 1975. The first operational A-10As were delivered to the 355th TFW in March 1976, five months behind the original schedule. The A-10 was christened the 'Thunderbolt II' during the ceremony to mark the delivery of the hundredth aircraft on 3 April 1978. By then the A-10 was already developing into a deadly battlefield warrior within the USAF.

A-10 Thunderbolt II

Service history

The 'Warthog' is best known for its service in Europe, where it equipped the USAF's largest wing. However, it has also served as far afield as Alaska, Korea and locations in the United States.

***Above:* The 354th TFW was the first operational A-10 unit, this pair demonstrating the initial paint scheme to be adopted: MASK-10A. The Wing's aircraft were soon busy on overseas deployments.**

***Top:* Slow when compared to other battlefield types, the A-10 relies on its excellent low-level agility to survive. The traditional anti-armour role has been expanded to include FAC missions.**

Naturally, the first USAF unit to get its hands on the A-10 was the 6510th Test Wing at the Air Force Flight Test Center, Edwards AFB. This unit was responsible for the pre-service tests and trials, using prototype and pre-production aircraft. Another early recipient was the 3246th Test Wing at Eglin AFB, which performed armament trials.

The next step in the introduction to service was the establishment of a training unit, the 355th Tactical Fighter Wing at Davis-Monthan AFB, Arizona, which began trading in Vought A-7s for A-10s in March 1976.

It was the 354th Tactical Fighter Wing at Myrtle Beach, South Carolina, that was the first operational unit to trade in A-7s for A-10s, a process which began in late 1976. In October 1977 operational evaluation work with the 'Warthog' was taken over by the 57th Tactical Training Wing, at Nellis AFB, Nevada. At about that time the critical JAWS (Joint Attack Weapons System) trials took place, which set down the way A-10s would work with artillery and battlefield helicopters.

With training, trials and a US-based organisation in place, it was time to begin equipment of what was arguably the most important wing to receive A-10s: the 81st Tactical Fighter Wing in England. Central Europe was where the A-10 was expected to fight and a large proportion of the front-line force was earmarked for the 81st TFW. From the first aircraft arriving on 26 January 1979, the 81st built up to a six-squadron wing accommodated at the twin bases of RAF Bentwaters and Woodbridge. From here, the A-10s could deploy to six Forward Operating Locations in West Germany.

In the reserves

Following the establishment of the European unit, attentions turned to swelling the ranks of US-based operators who could be called upon to reinforce the 81st in a European war. Five Air National Guard squadrons were

The 355th TFW was the nominated A-10 training unit, although it later added an operational role. The clear skies and extensive ranges of Arizona offered excellent training conditions.

***Right:* Initially envisaged for the war in southeast Asia, the A-10 was eventually tailored to the Central European theatre. Six squadrons were based in England throughout the 1980s, poised to rush into pre-prepared forward bases in Germany to blunt a WarPac armoured thrust.**

***Below:* A pair of A-10s from the 81st FS poses for the camera before dropping away from its tanker while en route for an Allied Force mission in 1999.**

equipped, beginning in May 1979. In 1990/91 two more ANG units began flying the OA/A-10.

Air Force Reserve units also began to receive A-10s in the same time-frame, beginning with the 917th TFW in October 1980. Others were the 442nd TFW, 926th TFW and 930th TFW.

More active-duty units were also formed in the early 1980s, consisting of the 23rd TFW at England AFB, Louisiana, as a second Stateside unit, plus the 51st and 343rd Composite Wings. Both of the latter were based in the Pacific region, the 51st in Korea and the 343rd in Alaska. Both received A-10s in the winter of 1981/82 to complete the initial deployment of the A-10 force.

The A-10 force disposition remained little changed for a decade, although two squadrons of the 81st split off to form the 10th TFW at RAF Alconbury in 1988 – their operational task remained unchanged, however. In October 1987 the 602nd Air Control Wing at Davis-Monthan AFB began its adoption of the 'Warthog' in the forward air control (FAC) role as the OA-10A, introducing a new arrow to the A-10's quiver.

Desert Storm

A-10s went to war in a variety of roles during Desert Storm, aircraft coming from a number of units in the US and Europe to fly with the 23rd and 354th TFW (Provisional), but returned home to face uncertainty. Once slated for complete retirement, the A-10 convinced planners in the 1991 Gulf War that it still had much to offer, especially in the FAC role and for combat search and rescue (CSAR) support duties.

Nevertheless, the end of the Cold War caused dramatic changes in the A-10 community, not least of which was the dismantling of the vast USAFE force, leaving just one squadron based with the 52nd FW at Spangdahlem AB in Germany. This unit has since seen considerable action. Elsewhere, the CONUS force was reduced to just one active-duty unit and several ANG/AFRes units, while a squadron remains in Korea.

Today, each 'Warthog' squadron operates a mix of A-10As and OA-10As, illustrating a mixed attack/FAC tasking, this same division of labour being demonstrated in combat over Bosnia in 1995 and again in Allied Force in the same theatre in 1999. In reality, there is no difference between the two variants and both have also seen extensive combat in recent operations over Afghanistan and Iraq.

Indeed, the A-10 has maintained a presence in the Persian Gulf since the end of Desert Storm, taking part during the 2003 Coalition invasion and its aftermath. Meanwhile, the A-10's future has been ensured by the arrival of the A-10C, an upgrade programme that will keep the 'Warthog' at the front line until around 2020. Based around a new sensor integration, including a targeting pod and datalink, the first A-10C was rolled out on 30 November 2006.

***CONUS*-based A-10As were a key part of the rapid-reaction forces during the later years of the Cold War, being able to fly at very short notice to troublespots. Here, an A-10 taxis in past EAF F-4 Phantoms at an Egyptian base during Exercise Bright Star 1982.**

Fouga Magister

Pioneering jet trainer

Rarely thought of as one of the world's great aircraft, the Magister holds an important place as the first jet trainer ever designed for basic pilot instruction. It was to become one of the major success stories of the French aviation industry in the post-war era.

Totally distinctive in form, the Fouga Magister was the first basic trainer in the world to be jet propelled, and it was also the first lightweight jet trainer of any kind to be ordered by an air force.

In 1948, Fouga submitted to the Ministère de l'Air in Paris a design proposal for a light jet trainer. It was designated CM.130R,and the proposal was attractive, but could be improved. On the power of two Turboméca Palas turbojets, each rated at 331-lb (1.49-kN) thrust, performance appeared rather poor when carrying two pilots, with radio, sufficient systems and, if possible, with a pressurised cockpit. The design was scaled up to larger dimensions and the engines changed to the most powerful of the whole Turboméca range, the Marboré, rated at 882-lb (3.9-kN) thrust. Fouga constructed the aircraft of metal throughout, and the enlarged design emerged as the CM.170R Magister.

Prototype construction

The design was accepted, and in December 1950 Fouga received a ministry contract for three prototypes. Bearing in mind that most trainers at that time in the Armée de l'Air were traditional piston machines, and that no other air force had even considered a light jet basic trainer, it can be seen that the step taken was a radical one, with important consequences.

Above: Israel is the last air arm to operate the Magister in numbers. Survivors were upgraded under the AMIT (Advanced Multi-mission Improved Trainer) programme, and renamed as the Tzukit (thrush).

Valmet of Finland was a licence-builder of the Magister. The company assembled Magisters with an increasing proportion of local parts, and these served with the Ilmavoimat at Kuopio-Rissala, Rovaniemi and the attack school (for guns/rockets) at Pori.

The actual contract was not signed until June 1951, by which time engineering design was virtually complete and the manufacture of parts had commenced. The first prototype took shape in 1952, and made its maiden flight on 23 July of that year. Unpainted except for its name neatly written in black, it looked remarkably similar to the hundreds of Magisters that came after it. The second aircraft was the first fitted with tip tanks, and the third was initially flown with a conventional tail for comparative evaluation of the two designs.

CM.170-2 Magister

Few aircraft can rival the Magister for popularity with national aerobatic teams. At the peak of the Fouga aircraft's service career, no fewer than seven nations equipped their teams with the type. The Magister's success was due to its exceptionally low fuel consumption and outstanding manoeuvrability.

Brazil
Brazil's air force (the FAB) operated the more powerful CM.170-2 Super Magister. The aerobatic team was the *Esquadrilha da Fumaça* (Smoke Squadron) and the Magister was known in Brazil as the T-14.

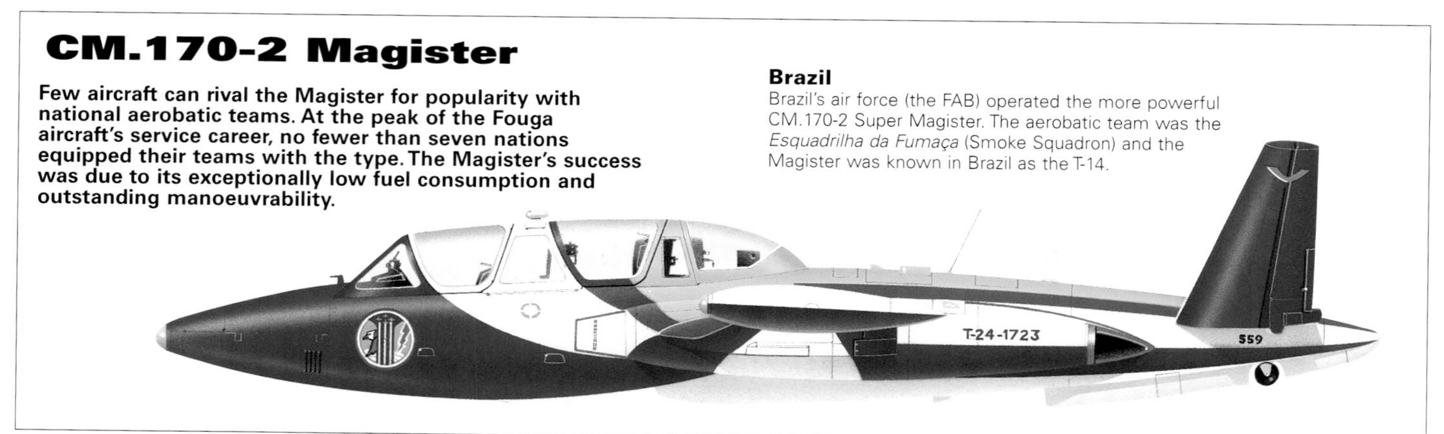

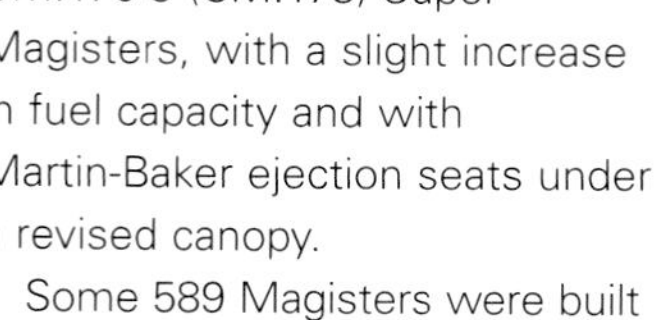

The Belgian air arm has been a loyal operator of the Magister, using the aircraft to equip its national aerobatic team, Les Diables Rouges (The Red Devils), in the 1970s. The final examples serve in the communications role and are also for used for display flying.

Important features of the Magister were the long-span wings and very short landing gear, both coming naturally to a company used to sailplanes rather than to fighters. Structure was stressed-skin throughout, with flush rivetting. The thickness/chord ratio of the wing was high, no less than 19 per cent at the root and 12 per cent at the tip with no dihedral. The engines were mounted recessed into the sides of the fuselage, immediately behind the wing.

The Magister followed the customer's wishes and adhered to traditional tandem seating. Both cockpits had large individual canopies which hinged upwards in clamshell fashion and could, in an emergency, be jettisoned. The instructor's view ahead was augmented by a periscope added early in flight trials. The butterfly tail, rare in production aircraft, had an included angle of 110° and was fitted with static balance weights near the elevator tips.

Following the type's first flight, the French government ordered an initial pre-production batch of 10 Fouga CM.170-1 Magisters (to augment the three prototypes) in June 1953, and in January 1954 ordered the type into full production for the Armée de l'Air. The initial version, with Marboré II engines, was soon superseded by the CM.170-2 with Marboré VI turbojets. Fouga was taken over by Potez in 1958, and was in turn taken over by Sud Aviation in 1967, and by the time production ended, in mid-1969, the company had become part of Aérospatiale.

The last production aircraft were CM.170-3 (CM.173) Super Magisters, with a slight increase in fuel capacity and with Martin-Baker ejection seats under a revised canopy.

Some 589 Magisters were built in France (including prototypes and pre-production aircraft), plus 32 CM.175 Zephyrs, while licence production in Germany (by Flugzeug Union Sud) added 188 more, Finland's Valmet another 62, and IAI a final 36 aircraft, bringing total production to 907 aircraft.

Deliveries to the Ecole de l'Air at Salon de Provence began in 1956, and to the Ecole de Chasse at Meknes (Morocco) in February 1958. The Division des Moniteurs de Pilotage, which was responsible for instructor training, received Magisters from 29 December 1961.

Navy service

A naval version of the Magister (originally known as the CM.175 Esqif) was first flown on 30 May 1959, and two prototypes were followed by 30 production aircraft. Equipped with an arrester hook and other navalised features, the CM.175 (soon renamed Zephyr) entered service with 59 Escadrille de Servitude from October 1959. This unit soon formed an aerobatic team to rival the Armée de l'Air's *Patrouille de France* (similarly equipped with Magisters) – the naval team being known as the *Patrouille de Voltige d'Hyères*.

Even after the last French Magisters were retired from the training role in 1994, the type lingered on in the liaison role, and with instrument training and communications flights at front-line air bases.

Left: The Armée de l'Air eventually received a total of 397 Magisters. In addition to offering basic training, they could be equipped with two 7.5-mm (0.295-in) machine-guns and four underwing rockets for weapons training.

Export aircraft

Although the Armée de l'Air was naturally the largest and most important operator of the type (taking 437 production aircraft), relatively large numbers were exported. Austria took 18, Belgium 48, Brazil seven, Cambodia four, Congo six, Finland 20 (plus its 62 licence-built aircraft), Germany 62 (plus 188 locally built aircraft), Israel 18 (plus 36 built under licence), and Lebanon four.

Second-hand aircraft from Austria, Brazil, France, Germany and Israel were also supplied to Algeria, Bangladesh, Cameroon, Gabon, Ireland, Libya, Morocco, El Salvador, Senegambia and Togo, while Israel also acquired second-hand aircraft to boost the number of aircraft on charge.

Ireland retired its last Magister in September 1999, although Belgium retained the type for staff continuation flying until 2007. Israel's modified IAI Tzukits are the final operational examples remaining in the training role.

Aérospatiale hoped to repeat the success of the Magister with its Fouga 90, which married a Magister wing and tail unit to a new fuselage with a stepped cockpit and a pair of 1,543-lb st (6.94-kN) Turboméca Astafan IIG turbofan engines. The private-venture prototype first flew on 20 August 1978, but no orders were received, and by 1980 the programme has been terminated.

The Aéronavale operated the CM.175 Zéphyr as a basic and carrier trainer. The aircraft was fitted with a deck arrester hook and heavy-frame sliding canopies, allowing carrier operations with open cockpits.

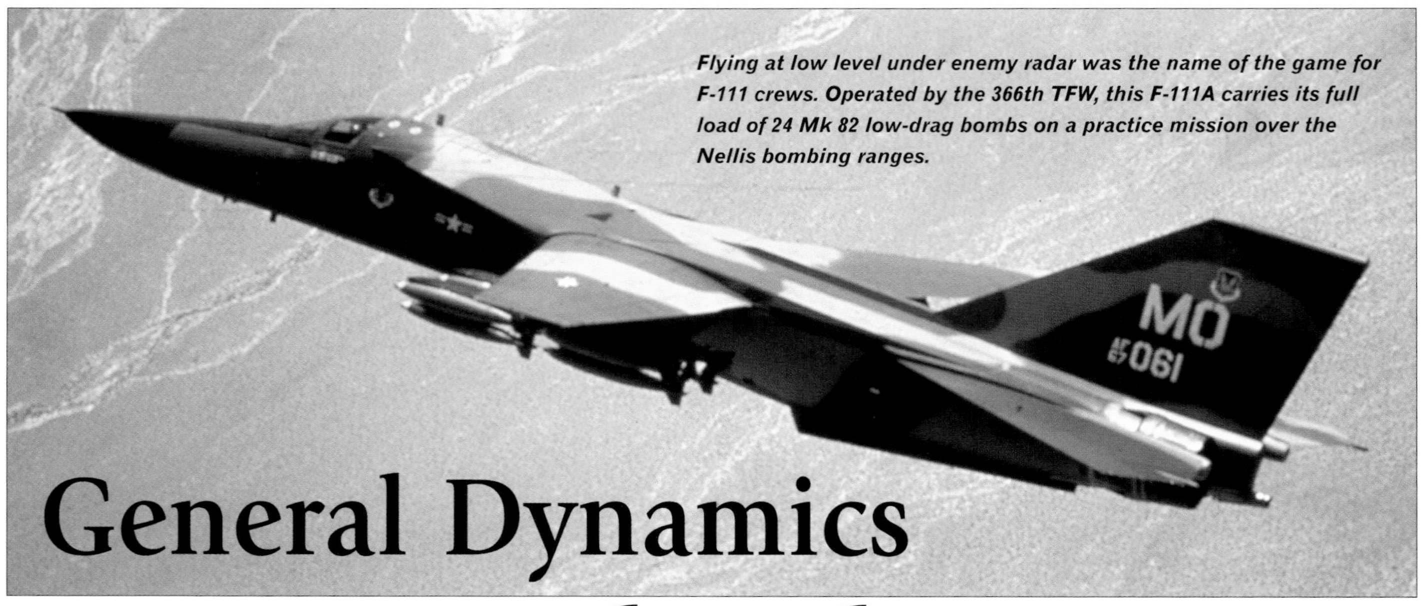

Flying at low level under enemy radar was the name of the game for F-111 crews. Operated by the 366th TFW, this F-111A carries its full load of 24 Mk 82 low-drag bombs on a practice mission over the Nellis bombing ranges.

General Dynamics F-111 Aardvark

Swing-wing striker

With its devastating raid on Libya in 1986, and with high-level deployments to the Gulf region – notably during Desert Storm – the fearsome swing-wing F-111 proved itself as the world's premier pinpoint attack platform. Aardvark crews were confident that their aircraft could undertake their missions in all weathers at great ranges, and be able to deliver their large bombloads with unerring accuracy.

The shorter nose radome of the F-111B is readily apparent in this view, as are the long-span wings. Although carrier operations with the F-111B were successful, by the time these trials took place the programme was virtually dead.

Officially adopting as its name the long-term nickname 'Aardvark', on the eve of its retirement, the General Dynamics F-111 is assured of a place in aviation history by virtue of the fact that it was the first variable-geometry, or 'swing-wing', aircraft to attain quantity production.

Development of the F-111 can be traced back to July 1960, when Specific Operational Requirement No. 183 was issued by the USAF. This called for a new aircraft capable of fulfilling such varied missions as air superiority, conventional and nuclear strike, and reconnaissance. One of the key aspects of SOR 183 concerned the variable-geometry wing, the USAF suggesting that this was the most suitable line of approach. Had the Air Force been allowed to proceed independently the F-111's subsequent history might have been less chequered, but the fact that the US Navy was also engaged in the search for a new fighter to replace the F-4 Phantom II prompted Secretary of Defense Robert McNamara to recommend that the two requirements be combined into a single programme, known as TFX (Tactical Fighter Experimental).

This recommendation was opposed by the two armed forces, but McNamara prevailed, and a new request for proposals was issued in September 1961. Nine responses were received during December of that year, the same month in which the designation F-111 was given to the new fighter. Eventually, after extensive re-design, the General Dynamics submission emerged victorious. Procurement of 23 development aircraft (18 USAF F-111As and five F-111Bs) was authorised. Manufacture of the USAF examples was entrusted to General Dynamics, while the Navy aircraft were the responsibility primarily of Grumman. The two variants made their first flights on 21 December 1964 and 18 May 1965 respectively.

Troubled debut

Like most types then in or about to enter USAF service, the F-111 was introduced to active duty in southeast Asia at the earliest possible date, with the deployment of six F-111As of the 4481st Tactical Fighter Squadron (TFS) to Takhli in Thailand in March 1968. The initial exposure to the hazards of combat proved to be inauspicious, two F-111As being lost during the course of the first 55 missions against targets in North Vietnam. The loss of a further aircraft on 22 April 1968 brought to an end the F-111's combat debut.

Several years were to elapse before the F-111 returned to the rigours of war during the Linebacker II bombing campaign. A total of 48 F-111s was deployed, logging more than 3,000 missions. Despite several losses the deployment was viewed as an immense success.

Although the USAF eventually succeeded in getting the aircraft it had originally wanted, the same claim could not be made

Above: Australia's F-111Cs were actually a hybrid mix of components from several F-111 variants. The fleet underwent a major upgrade programme, fitting them with the Pave Tack FLIR system.

for the Navy, which had never been very enthusiastic about the F-111B. Eventually, unacceptable weight growth, coupled with a serious performance shortfall, resulted in a production hold order being placed on the type during July 1968. By that time, the five development F-111Bs had been joined in the flight test programme by the first two production examples. In August 1968 the programme was officially cancelled, a further blow to General Dynamics which was still recovering from the British decision to abandon plans to acquire 50 examples of a variant designated F-111K.

The second production version of the F-111 first flew in 1969. Designated F-111E, this variant was fitted with an improved version of the TF30 engine and also incorporated an improved terrain-following radar. Entering service with the 27th TFW at Cannon AFB, New Mexico, these aircraft later served with the 20th TFW at Upper Heyford, England.

New capabilities

Next followed the considerably more capable F-111D, with a much revised avionics package for navigation and attack computations. It also incorporated improved engines. In due course a still more-powerful version of the TF30 turbofan was introduced on the later F-111F, but most fundamental to the new F variant was the installation of the Pave Tack system, which enabled targets to be acquired visually by day or night and designated for attack with LGBs.

Perhaps the most formidable of the strike F-111s was the bomber version employed by Strategic Air Command, the FB-111A. These aircraft were viewed as interim machines until the arrival of the Rockwell B-1, but remained in service with Tactical Air Command, though with their strategic modifications removed and re-designated as F-111Gs, until the 1990s.

Most remarkable in terms of their capability were the EF-111A Ravens. Converted from redundant F-111A airframes, the Ravens were equipped with the same systems as the US Navy's EA-6A as well as additional jamming packages. The EF-111As served as radar suppressors. Lacking any offensive weapons their role was to escort strike aircraft all the way to the target and back.

Despite the capabilities of the F-111 just one foreign country, Australia, received the type. Entering service in 1973, the aircraft were designated F-111Cs, being a hybrid mix of earlier models. The Royal Australian Air Force added reconnaissance and anti-ship roles to the long-range attack missions for which the type was originally procured.

The EF-111A Raven programme provided the USAF with a unique jamming platform that could fly the same mission profiles as the strike aircraft it was assigned to protect.

Later combat

In 1986 F-111s struck targets in Libya as part of America's effort to halt Colonel Khadaffi's support for terrorism. Five years later F-111s were back in the Middle East, this time as part of operation Desert Storm. Night attacks were made against strategic targets throughout the war. In the final stages of the conflict the aircraft were also assigned anti-tank missions, delivering LGBs.

Having flown in two wars, and stood alert throughout the Cold War, the end for the strike variants of the F-111 in USAF service came in 1996, when the final F-111Fs of the 27th TFW at Cannon AFB, New Mexico, stood down in October of that year. EF-111A Ravens remained in service until May 1998.

As the aircraft neared the end of their career, USAF F-111 operations were centralised at Cannon AFB, New Mexico. These F-111Gs wear the final overall dark-grey colour scheme.

F-111/EF-111 variants

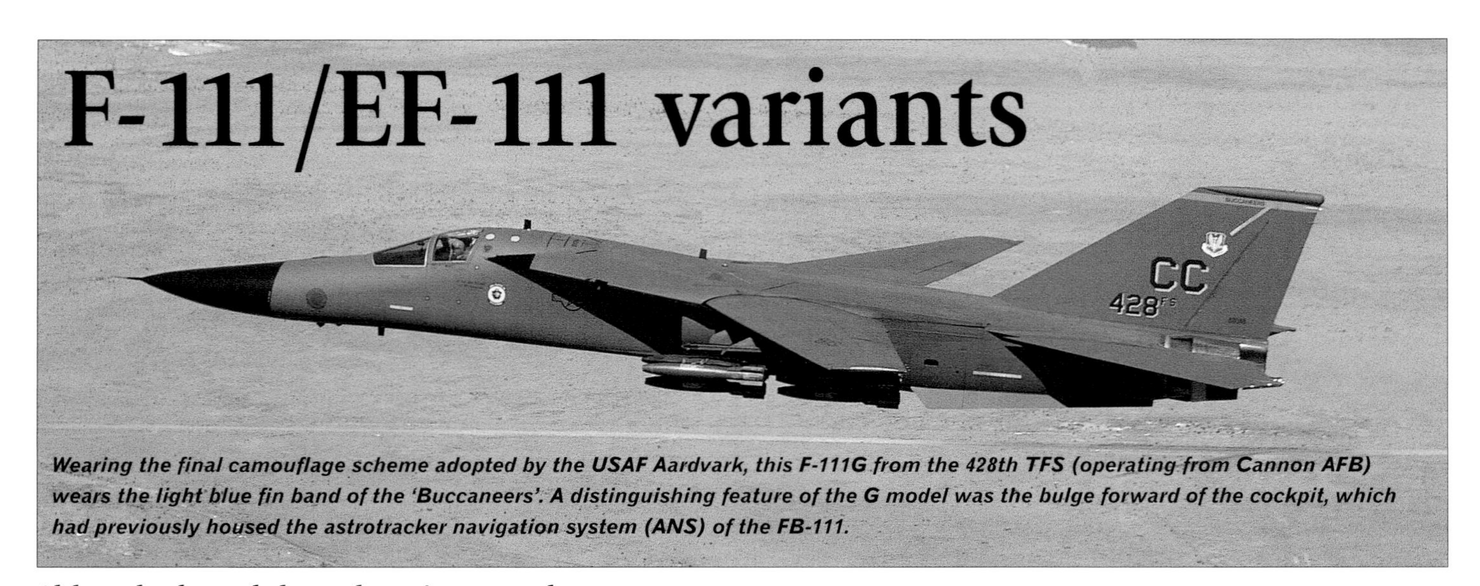

Wearing the final camouflage scheme adopted by the USAF Aardvark, this F-111G from the 428th TFS (operating from Cannon AFB) wears the light blue fin band of the 'Buccaneers'. A distinguishing feature of the G model was the bulge forward of the cockpit, which had previously housed the astrotracker navigation system (ANS) of the FB-111.

Although plagued throughout its career by maintenance problems, the F-111 emerged as a highly capable deep-penetration bomber, giving rise to a succession of sophisticated variants.

F-111A

The F-111A made its first flight on 21 December 1964, 16 days ahead of schedule, with its wings locked at 26° (maximum sweep angle at which flaps and slats can be used). The second flight occurred on 6 January 1965, and saw the wings swept fully aft. The twin TF30-P-1s, the first afterburning turbofan engines to be developed, enabled the F-111 to fly long distances at high speed, with low fuel consumption (later F-111As were powered by P-3s). Later in the programme, the A-model suffered a succession of compressor stalls due to problems with the engine inlets and, despite modification to the inlets and engine blades, the problems persisted. Illustrated is the fifth test aircraft, 63-9770, which had a different tail design to that used on later production F-111s. F-111As were deployed to Vietnam under Operation Combat Lancer in 1968, during which three aircraft were lost. The aircraft were quickly withdrawn, but returned at the end of 1972 to much greater success.

F-111B

Intended as a US Navy replacement for the F-4 Phantom II, the F-111B was built by Grumman, and was planned as a cost-saving measure whereby one common aircraft was developed for both the USAF and US Navy. It was not designed for classic air-to-air combat, but to engage the enemy from up to 115 miles (185 km) away, with its combination of AN/AWG-9 radar in a shortened radome, and AIM-54 Phoenix missiles. The B model was equipped with long-span wings (illustrated below) and an arrester hook mounted between the engines on the underside of the fuselage. Seven aircraft were completed, with carrier trials taking place aboard USS *Coral Sea* in July 1968 (right). The F-111B was well-suited to carrier operations, posing no problems during launch, approach or deck/hangar handling. Of the seven aircraft completed, three crashed, with the loss of four lives. Despite the success of the trials, the F-111B was eventually cancelled due to the aircraft's spiralling increase in weight. Despite frantic weight-reduction efforts by Grumman, the programme was cancelled in favour of Grumman's own proposal, the F-14 Tomcat, which was to utilise the engines and weapons system of the F-111B. The remaining airframes were finally retired in May 1971. The US Navy would have received 231 F-111Bs, which theoretically would have been delivered between 1968 and 1975.

F-111C

The F-111C is an F-111A built for the RAAF. It differs from the US F-111A in its longer wings (as used on the FB-111A) and a removable right control stick. The F-111C also has the larger and stronger landing gear, brakes and tyres of the FB-111A. The first F-111C made its first flight in July 1968, and was quickly followed by 23 further examples. In September the Australian government accepted its first F-111C. After this, all 24 aircraft were put into storage where they were left until problems with the USAF F-111s were corrected. During this period, F-4E Phantoms were leased until the F-111Cs finally arrived on 1 June 1973. Four examples were modified as RF-111Cs for the reconnaissance role, while upgrades to the fleet included the addition of AN/AVQ-26 Pave Tack pods to enhance laser-guided bombing. The retirement of the F-111 from USAF service saw numbers within the RAAF increase. Two variants are currently in service – the RF/F-111C (illustrated) and F-111G.

F-111D

The F-111D followed the F-111E into operational service. It featured an advanced Mk II avionics system, improved environmental control systems, and uprated TF30-P-9 engines. Other changes in the F-111D included the use of larger tyres and parts of the FB-111A's stronger landing gear. This permitted the F-111D to operate at heavier gross weights. The airframe was essentially the same as that of the F-111E, including the Triple Plow II intakes, which featured triple 'blow-in' doors to increase the inlet area. Problems encountered with the Mk II avionics system caused a reduction in the number of D models delivered, the first of which arrived in service on 1 November 1971. The F-111D's unique equipment and its low number of airframe hours made the variant superior to other models. The F-111D, including this 27th Fighter Wing aircraft, ruled the roost at Cannon AFB for 21 years. The wing later transitioned to the F-111F, sending its D models to AMARC at Davis-Monthan.

F-111E/F

The second tactical version of the F-111, the E model became operational in October 1969. It was essentially similar to the F-111A apart from modified air inlets and some minor improvements to the nav/attack system, along with the addition of terrain-following radar (TFR) and a strike camera. All E models were equipped with TF30-P3 engines. Further improvements to the F-111 resulted in the F-111F, which was equipped with the powerful TF30-P-100 engine, but had inferior avionics compared to the D model. It was fitted with Triple Plow II inlets which gave the aircraft a slightly higher speed than earlier models. With the addition of the Pave Tack pod, F-111Fs were able to undertake fully autonomous laser-bombing. During the 1991 Gulf War, the majority of LGBs dropped by the USAF was via the Pave Tack system – illustrated is an F-111F in classic 'laser-bomber' configuration, with its Pave Tack pod fully deployed, an AN/ALQ-131 ECM pod under the rear fuselage and GBU-10 Paveway II LGBs under each wing.

EF-111A Raven

Following the Vietnam War, the US Navy possessed the best electronic jamming aircraft in the world, namely the EA-6B Prowler. An equivalent aircraft was required by the USAF, which would use the same AN/ALQ-99 jamming system mated with an airframe that possessed the required speed and range. The aircraft chosen was the F-111A, those aircraft selected for modification having an average airframe life of 2,000 hours. The first production EF-111A Raven was rolled out on 19 June 1981. The aircraft dispensed with the traditional three-tone southeast Asian camouflage, instead adopting a two-tone grey scheme. The jamming system was an improved version of that used in the EA-6B, and was designated AN/ALQ-99E, the jammers being housed in a canoe fairing in the former weapons bay. UK-based EF-111As, of the 42nd Electronic Combat Squadron at Upper Heyford, served during Desert Storm. The Ravens jammed Iraqi radars, and during one mission, a crew outmanoeuvred an Iraqi Mirage F1 fighter, forcing it to crash into the ground.

FB-111A/F-111G

The FB-111A was based on the F-111A, but incorporated the longer wings of the F-111B, stronger landing gear, extra fuel, and TF30-P-7 powerplants. An improved and expanded avionics suite was also fitted. In addition to carrying nuclear bombs, the FB-111A was unique among Aardvarks in that it was the only variant to be equipped with the astrotracker navigation system (ANS), which was located in front of the canopy, and to have provision for the AGM-69 SRAM (Short-Range Attack Missile) in addition to the incorporation of an Air Force satellite communication capability and a stores management system optimised for its mission as a nuclear bomber. It was also unique in that it had no provision for manually releasing weapons – all releases were via computer. Following the restructuring of the USAF in 1992, which saw the break-up of SAC, FB-111s had their nuclear capability removed, and served instead in the training role. Redesignated F-111G, the aircraft were soon withdrawn from US service, and a number were later sold to the RAAF.

Aardvark operations

For the most part, the USAF's F-111 force was based in the continental United States, with the exception of the USAFE aircraft stationed in the UK. However, combat deployments took the Aardvark further afield, to the Middle East and southeast Asia.

An inauspicious debut – F-111As in Vietnam

In 1967, after years of political and technical struggles and with the war in southeast Asia escalating, there was an overwhelming political need to show what the F-111 could do. The first operational F-111As had joined the 4480th TFW at Nellis AFB in July and were immediately assigned to training tasks. The 4480th became the 474th TFW in January 1968 and six of its aircraft were prepared (under the codename Harvest Reaper) for deployment to Thailand. In March the long flight across the Pacific was completed under Operation Combat Lancer, the F-111As undertaking their first combat missions on the 25th. However, before the end of the month, two aircraft had been lost without trace on low-level missions and, with the loss of a third during April (after just 55 missions in all), Combat Lancer was suspended. Combat Lancer had backfired and it was not until 1972 that the F-111A returned to Thailand. This time, two squadrons were deployed (again from the 474th TFW), pre-positioned crews taking the aircraft into combat within hours of the first six machines touching down at Takhli air base. Operation Constant Guard V, which ended in March 1973, met with much greater success than Combat Lancer, over 4,000 sorties being completed for the loss of just eight aircraft in total. Pictured is a pair of Combat Lancer aircraft – note the ECM pods carried by both machines.

CONUS-based TAC/ACC F-111s

The 474th TFW at Nellis AFB was the first of four TAC wings to operate F-111 bomber variants from bases in the US, fielding three squadrons of F-111As (and a single training unit, which briefly flew a handful of F-111Es from 1969) between 1968 and 1977, when it passed its aircraft to the 366th TFW at Mountain Home AFB. However, it was Cannon AFB, New Mexico, that was to become the unrivalled 'Home of the One-Eleven', receiving its first aircraft in 1969 – 10 F-111As loaned from Nellis. Before the end of the year the 27th TFW at Cannon had relinquished these A-models for F-111Es, which equipped two squadrons. These were passed to the 20th TFW in the UK during 1970/71 and 10 F-111As were again loaned from Nellis pending the arrival of much-delayed F-111Ds, between 1971 and 1973. Until 1980, three operational squadrons and a conversion unit were equipped with the 'D'; one of the operational units then took over the training function, the remaining three squadrons soldiering on until 1990. 1971 saw the re-formation of the 347th TFW at Mountain Home, to take delivery of the first F-111Fs and begin training on the new variant. Three squadrons were established before the wing was redesignated the 366th TFW the following year. In 1973 the 347th was once again re-formed, taking over the aircraft of the 474th TFW at Takhli air base. Moving to Korat in 1974, the 347th's two constituent squadrons remained in southeast Asia until June 1975. Meanwhile, the three squadrons now with the 366th TFW at Mountain Home maintained F-111F operations until these aircraft were passed to the 48th TFW in the UK in 1977. From this point the 366th flew ex-474th TFW F-111As, operating three squadrons of these veteran Aardvarks until 1981, when one unit was replaced with a squadron of EF-111A Ravens. The 366th's F-111A squadrons were disestablished in 1992 and their aircraft retired to AMARC, while its Ravens passed to the 27th FW at Cannon. The early 1990s brought big changes at the New Mexico base, as F-111 operations were concentrated there as the type was slowly withdrawn from service. A fourth squadron joined the 27th FW in 1990, equipped with the handful of F-111Gs (ex-FB-111As) transferred from SAC for training purposes. Ravens formed a fifth squadron in 1992, the same year that ex-48th FW F-111Fs arrived from the UK to replace the 27th's D-models (which were then retired to AMARC). In 1993 the F-111Gs were also retired, their squadron re-equipping with AMP-upgraded F-111Es from the 20th FW in the UK, while the ex-366th EF-111s also arrived at about this time. Cannon was to be the final base of the USAF's F-111s, the final curtain calls coming in July 1996, when the last F-111 bombers (F-111Fs) were retired and, finally, in May 1998, when the final 429th ECS EF-111As were ferried to AMARC. Pictured is a Mountain Home-based F-111A of the 389th TFTS, 366th FW, seen during its last few months of service. Other non-operational units equipped with F-111s included the 46th, 3246th and 6510th Test Wings, the 57th and 4525th Fighter Weapons Wings and the Air Warfare Center, all of which flew a number of different F-111 variants during test and training programmes.

FB-111As in Strategic Air Command

Initially viewed as an interim replacement for the B-58 and some B-52s pending the arrival of the B-1A, the 76 FB-111As were to take on a much greater importance with the cancellation of the new swing-wing bomber in 1977, and remained in service until 1991. The first operational FB-111As were handed over to the 4007th Combat Crew Training Squadron (340th BG) at Carswell AFB in October 1969, this unit undertaking crew training before four operational squadrons were formed. Accordingly, the 509th BW (Medium), comprising the 393rd and 715th Bomb Squadrons, received its first aircraft at Pease AFB in late 1970, while the 380th BW(M) at Plattsburgh AFB – with the 528th and 529th Bomb Squadrons, plus the 530th CCTS (the former 4007th) – was the first to field operational aircraft in July 1971. Both wings were assigned to the 2nd Air Force from the start, though they were reassigned to the 'Mighty 8th' in 1975. After almost 20 years service the 509th was the first to stand down in 1990; the 380th did so the following year. With the arrival of the Rockwell B-1B, 30 aircraft were converted to F-111G standard and transferred to TAC in 1990, equipping the 428th TFTS, 27th FW until retirement in 1993.

Australia's Aardvarks

The F-111 was chosen to replace the ageing RAAF Canberra fleet. An order for 24 aircraft was placed in October 1963, initially for the F-111A, but was later changed to the F-111C. Australia's F-111Cs are a hybrid version, combining the F-111A fuselage, avionics and engines with the longer-span wings, heavier landing gear and wing carry-through box of the FB-111A. Due to problems with the wing carry-through structure of USAF F-111As, the aircraft were placed into storage at Fort Worth in 1968, and it was not until July 1973 that the first four touched down at RAAF Amberley. The aircraft entered service with Nos 1 and 6 Squadrons, as part of No. 82 Wing, and were joined by four ex-USAF F-111As in 1982 as attrition replacements. These latter aircraft were brought up to F-111C standard at Amberley, the only noteworthy difference being the retention of the lower-strength wing carry-through box. The original order included six RF-111As, but this version was not produced and the RAAF had to wait until 1979 before gaining a reconnaissance capability; this was provided by the conversion of four F-111C airframes to RF-111Cs. Fifteen ex-TAC F-111Gs were offered to Australia in 1992, and were duly transferred to RAAF ownership. A number of these are operated by No. 6 Squadron, with the balance being held in rotational storage. In order to allow operation up to the planned retirement date, several shortcomings have had to be addressed, particularly with the 1960s vintage avionics suite. Accordingly, an Avionics Upgrade Programme (AUP) was completed in the 1990s. The digital AUP upgrade confers much greater capability. Coincident with the AUP was the installation of the more powerful TF30-P-109 to the F-111C (pictured) and a hybrid P-107/109 (dubbed P-108) to the F-111G. Thanks to a series of recent upgrades, the F-111s will operate until 2010 at least, after which they will be replaced by 24 F/A-18E/F Super Hornets.

F-111F

The second USAF wing, and the first in USAFE, to receive F-111s was the 20th TFW at RAF Upper Heyford in the UK. F-111Es arriving at the British base in 1970/71 were assigned to three squadrons and remained there (apart from a deployment to Turkey during the 1991 Gulf War) until the wing's disestablishment in 1993. The second USAFE Aardvark wing was the 48th TFW at RAF Lakenheath, which received ex-366th TFW F-111Fs to re-equip its four squadrons in 1977. Representing NATO's most potent strike force of the period, the 48th's F-111s gained fame as the aircraft which formed the USAF component of Operation El Dorado Canyon in 1986 and as, arguably, the most successful Coalition bombers of the 1991 Gulf War. The 48th's aircraft were replaced in 1991/92 by F-15Es. Also involved in operations over Libya and Iraq were UK-based EF-111As. Equipping the 42nd Electronic Combat Squadron (initially within the 20th TFW and, later, with the 66th ECW) from 1984, the Ravens left the UK upon reassignment to the 366th TFW in 1992.

'Statue of Liberty' Wing

Based at RAF Lakenheath in Suffolk, the 48th TFW comprised four squadrons – the 492nd, 493rd, 494th and 495th Tactical Fighter Squadrons. Most of the Wing's aircraft were deployed to Taif AB, Saudi Arabia (as the 48th TFW (Provisional)) from August 1990 until March 1991. This aircraft, flown by the Wing's commander, carries the colours of each squadron on the fin-top bullet fairing.

Pave Tack

Though intended for both the F-111D and F, the Pave Tack targeting pod was destined only to be fitted to the 48th TFW's F-111Fs, under the Pacer Strike upgrade programme. Fitted in the aircraft's little-used weapons bay, the Pave Tack pod had a stabilised turret containing an infra-red sensor and laser designator. This gave the aircraft the ability to make 'smart' weapon attacks by night without the need for third-party designation.

Paveway III LGBs

The F-111Fs of the 48th TFW (Provisional) were employed almost exclusively to drop laser-guided weapons in the Gulf, mostly Paveway IIs and IIIs. The latter weapon is shown here, consisting of a standard bomb (in this case a steel-jacketed BLU-109), to which a laser-guidance system was added. Sixty per cent of all LGBs expended during the Gulf War were dropped by these aircraft, which flew 2,417 sorties over 9,381.2 hours.

Miss Liberty II

F-111F 70-2390 was the 29th of 106 examples delivered to the USAF between 1971 and 1976 and was notable as the first F-111 to drop bombs during both the El Dorado Canyon raid and Desert Storm. On the first night of the latter campaign, 17 January 1991, the 48th TFW(P)'s commander, Colonel Thomas J. Lennon, flew this aircraft with 53 other F-111s to Balad air base, north of Baghdad. *Miss Liberty II*, and a proportion of the other aircraft in the strike packages (comprising between four and eight F-111s), carried a pair of GBU-15 glide bombs, while others dropped CBU-89 Gator area-denial mines.

Radar

The F-111F was fitted with a multi-mode General Electric AN/APQ-144 radar and a Hughes AN/APQ-146 terrain-following radar, which enabled it to carry out low-level operations in all weathers, whatever the visibility.

Gloster Meteor

Britain's first operational jet

Britain's first and only operational jet combat aircraft of World War II was Gloster's extraordinary Meteor, which would go on to serve front-line RAF squadrons in a variety of versions for a further 17 years.

Above: Trials with axial-flow Metro-Vick F.2 engines were carried out by Meteor prototype DG204/G from November 1943 to April 1944. Unlike other Meteors, the engine nacelles were mounted below the aircraft's wing.

Top: In May 1945, as World War II in Europe was drawing to a close, the Meteor Mk IV began to reach RAF units. The aircraft was distinguishable by the long-chord engine nacelles housing the Derwent IV turbojet.

The only Allied turbojet-powered aircraft to see action during World War II, the Gloster Meteor originated in a preliminary study given Air Ministry approval in November 1940. Its twin-engined layout was determined by the low thrust produced by the turbojet engines then available. On 7 February 1941 an order was placed for 12 prototypes, although only eight were actually built. The first of these was fitted with Rover W.2B engines, each of 1,000-lb (4.5-kN) thrust, and taxiing trials commenced in July 1942. Delays in the production of flight-standard engines meant that the fifth airframe, with alternative de Havilland-developed Halford H.1 engines of 1,500-lb (6.75-kN) thrust, was the first to fly, this event taking place on 5 March 1943.

Modified W.2B/23 engines then became available and were installed in the first and fourth

Above: Seen at the forward-operating base of B.158/Lübeck, Germany, in the spring of 1945, this No. 616 Squadron Meteor F.Mk III is finished in standard day-fighter camouflage.

Below: No. 616 Squadron Meteor F.Mk I/IIIs are seen here at RAF Colerne prior to the unit moving to Europe in January 1945. The squadron had been the first to equip with the Meteor in July 1944.

The first Meteor F.Mk I, EE210/G, became the very first Meteor 'export' when, in February 1944, it was loaned to the USAAF for evaluation at Muroc; Britain received a Bell YP-59A Airacomet in return.

prototypes, first flight dates being 12 June and 24 July respectively. On 13 November the third prototype made its maiden flight, powered by two Metrovick F.2 engines in underslung nacelles, and in the same month the second aircraft flew, initially with Power Jets W.2/500 turbojets. The sixth aircraft later became the prototype F.Mk II, with two 2,700-lb (12.15-kN) thrust de Havilland Goblin engines, and was flown on 24 July 1945. It had been preceded by the seventh, used for trials with a modified fin, rudder and dive brakes, and flown on 20 January 1944. The eighth, with Rolls-Royce W.2B/37 Derwent Is, was flown on 18 April 1944.

Early production

Twenty G.41A Meteor Mk Is comprised the first production batch, these being powered by W.2B/23C Wellands and incorporating minor airframe improvements, including a clear-view canopy. After a first flight on 12 January 1944, the first Mk I was delivered to the United States in February, in exchange for a Bell YP-59A Airacomet, the first US jet aircraft. Others were used for airframe and engine development, and the 18th later became the Trent-Meteor, the world's first turboprop-powered aircraft, which was flown on 20 September 1945. The Trent was basically a Derwent engine provided with reduction gearing and a drive shaft that turned a five-bladed Rotol propeller of 7-ft 11-in (2.41-m) diameter. Each engine delivered 750 hp (559 kW), with a residual thrust of 1,000 lb (454 kW).

The RAF's first operational jet fighter squadron was No. 616, based at Culmhead, which was equipped with Spitfire Mk VIIs when its first two Meteor F.Mk Is arrived on 12 July 1944. On 21 July the squadron moved to Manston, receiving more Meteors on 23 July to form a detached flight of seven. The first operational sorties were flown on 27 July, and on 4 August Flying Officer Dean destroyed the first V-1 flying-bomb to be claimed by a jet fighter, using the Meteor's wingtip to tip it over into a spin after the aircraft's four 20-mm cannon had jammed. On the same day, Flying Officer Roger shot down a second V-1.

Conversion to Meteors was completed towards the end of August, and the autumn was spent preparing for operations on the continent. From 10 to 17 October, however, four Meteors were detached to Debden, to take part in an exercise with the USAAF 2nd Bombardment Division and 65th Fighter Wing, to enable defensive tactics against the Messerschmitt Me 163 and Me 262 fighters to be devised. The first Meteor F.Mk IIIs were delivered to Manston on 18 December, and on 17 January the squadron moved to Colerne, where the remaining Mk Is were replaced. On 20 January 1945 one flight of No. 616's Meteors joined No. 84 Group, 2nd Tactical Air Force in Belgium, and in March No. 504 became the second Meteor F.Mk III unit to operate on the other side of the English Channel.

The Meteor F.Mk III, the second and last mark to see operational service during World War II, had increased fuel capacity and a sliding bubble canopy in place of the sideways-opening hood of the Mk I. Fifteen F.Mk IIIs were completed with Welland engines and 265 with Derwents, some in lengthened engine nacelles. Derwents also powered the Meteor F.Mk IV, later examples of which were modified by a 5-ft 10-in (1.78-m) reduction in wingspan. Of 657 built, 465 were supplied to the RAF, enabling Meteor F.Mk IIIs to be passed to auxiliary units.

At the end of the war the Meteor could be regarded as the best fighter in the world. The Derwent 5-powered F.Mk 4 was outstanding, and few could have any doubts that jet power was the way of the future. However, the ever-growing performance gap between advanced trainers and jet fighters was such that provision of a two-seat trainer now became an imperative.

On 20 September 1945 a Meteor F.Mk I, converted with Rolls-Royce Trent engines, became the world's first turboprop-powered aircraft. The machine was converted back to standard Mk I configuration in late 1948.

Post-war service

Despite its obsolete straight wing layout, the Meteor remained in production until 1955. While the T.Mk 7 trainer introduced a whole generation of pilots to jet flying, the F.Mk 8 was built in large numbers to satisfy the urgent demand for fighters until sufficient swept-wing Hunters and Sabres became available.

***Above:** Having started the Korean War operating Mustangs, No. 77 Squadron, Royal Australian Air Force, converted to the Meteor F.Mk 8 in 1951. Quickly being outclassed by the MiG-15 in air combat, the F.Mk 8 compiled an excellent war record in the ground attack role, and was responsible for at least four MiG kills.*

Gloster's answer to fast-evolving jet training needs was the Meteor T.Mk 7, based on the F.Mk 4 but with a lengthened forward fuselage accommodating tandem seats. The fuselage lengthening improved the directional stability of the type considerably, and was adopted for subsequent single-seat variants. First flying on 19 March 1948, the T.Mk 7 soon became the subject of massive orders from home and overseas.

Interim fighter

Drawing on the longer T.Mk 7 fuselage, Gloster created the F.Mk 8. Powered by 3,500-lb (15.57-kN) thrust Derwent 8 engines, the F.Mk 8 used the extra space of the fuselage extension to house additional fuel. This extra weight, plus the forward movement of the four 20-mm cannon, threw the centre of gravity beyond the limits of previous versions, necessitating a redesign of the tail unit to a more angular shape.

On 12 October 1948 the first 'true' F.Mk 8 (in fact, a converted Mk 4) took to the air. F.Mk 8s entered service with the RAF in huge numbers, beginning with No. 43 Squadron in August 1949. Export deliveries were made from 1950, Australia becoming the first recipient. In Europe the F.Mk 8 was chosen to replace existing F.Mk 4s by both Belgium and the Netherlands, and licence production was undertaken in both countries.

In the Middle East, embargoes held up exports, but in the event F.Mk 8s were delivered to Egypt, Israel and Syria. Ultimately, Brazil became the largest export customer, acquiring 60 F.Mk 8s and 10 T.Mk 7s in 1953/54.

Gloster had already been working on Meteor night-fighter studies when a specification calling for a two-seat, twin-engined, all-weather fighter was issued. A night-fighter version of the Meteor was drawn up, to be based on the two-seat Meteor trainer, modified to carry all necessary operational equipment. The Gloster design studies were handed to Armstrong Whitworth, who would produce night-fighter variants of the aircraft.

***Below:** No. 85 Sqn was among the 10 RAF squadrons to operate the Meteor NF.Mk 14. When it entered service in 1954, it was virtually incapable of intercepting the latest jet bombers, thanks to a combination of increased weight and low power.*

Recce jets

Camera installations had been tested in several early Meteors, but it was the F.Mk 8 airframe which provided the basis for the two reconnaissance versions to enter service, which were developed concurrently.

First to fly, on 22 March 1950, was the FR.Mk 9, a minimum-change fighter-reconnaissance version which retained the F.Mk 8's armament but featured a single F.24 camera in the nose, which could be ground-aligned to peer either sideways or forwards. The 126 FR.Mk 9s replaced FR Spitfires, first entering service with No. 208 Squadron in July 1950, and mostly served in Germany, where they were soon replaced by Swift FR.Mk 5s and Hunter FR.Mk 10s.

A more radical modification was applied to the PR.Mk 10, intended to replace high-altitude Spitfires and Mosquitoes. It was based on the lengthened F.Mk 8 fuselage, but reverted to the long-span wings and rounded tail of the Meteor F.Mk III. It was unarmed and could reach 47,000 ft (14326 m) in clean configuration. First flying on 29 March 1950, the PR.Mk 9 entered service in February 1951. Production totalled 59.

***Above:** The high-altitude Meteor PR.Mk 10 served with Nos 2, 13, 81 and 541 Squadrons. Note the rounded wingtips and fin.*

***Right:** The FR.Mk 9's forte was low-level armed recce operations, especially in Germany. This machine is from RAF Germany's No. 79 Squadron.*

The fourth production T.Mk 7 served as the NF.Mk 11 prototype and received a lengthened nose and PR.Mk 10 outer-wing panels, modified to carry four 20-mm cannon. Finally, the decision was taken to fit the larger and more streamlined F.Mk 8-type tail unit.

The NF.Mk 11 prototype first flew in October 1949, without operational equipment. The success of this aircraft led to a production order for 200 Mk 11s, and three prototypes. The three prototypes were equipped to virtually full operational standards, with AI.Mk 10 radar in the nose.

The first front-line delivery went to No. 256 Sqn in October 1950, the Meteor NF.Mk 11 re-equipping four home-based squadrons, and serving with an additional three units for a brief period. The type also went on to equip four squadrons within RAF Germany, and orders were increased to an eventual total of 338 aircraft.

In 1953, the Meteor NF.Mk 12 entered service. The 97 examples completed featured a much improved US AN/APQ-43 radar, installed in a slightly lengthened nose. The Mk 12 was also fitted with new Derwent 9 engines.

A batch of 40 tropicalised Mk 11s were completed as Mk 13s, for issue to two MEAF squadrons.

The definitive Meteor night-fighter and final production variant was the NF.Mk 14. Distinguished by a new bubble canopy and an even longer nose, the Mk 14 was, effectively, an improved Mk 12. In all, 100 were built and, as the Mk 14 utilised the same radar set as the Mk 12, both variants served alongside each other in 10 RAF night-fighter squadrons. Night-fighter Meteors were phased out between 1956 and 1961.

Production of the T.Mk 7 trainer for the UK amounted to 640 aircraft, including 43 for the navy. This trio is from the Central Flying School at Little Rissington.

Meteor F.Mk 8

First delivered to Fighter Command in August 1949, the F.Mk 8 became the UK's principal day fighter until replaced by the Hunter from 1954. Large numbers also served with the Royal Auxiliary Air Force.

No. 500 Squadron
No. 500 'County of Kent' Squadron was formed in 1931 as part of the Special Reserve, but was transferred to the RAuxAF in May 1936. It was re-formed post-war, flying night-fighter Mosquitoes before adopting Spitfire F.Mk 22s in 1948. It then flew Meteor F.Mk 3s, 4s and 8s.

Undercarriage
The various structural and equipment changes introduced by the Mk 8 increased maximum weight to 19,100 lb (8664 kg). The stronger undercarriage of the NF.Mk 11 was fitted to handle the extra load.

Markings
RAuxAF units were renowned for their colourful squadron markings. This aircraft, the personal mount of Squadron Leader Desmond de Villiers, had the unit colours extended to the fin. The blue represented the English Channel, the white was for the Dover cliffs and the green was for the fields of Kent.

Ejection seat
The pilot sat on a Martin-Baker Mk 1 or Mk 1E ejection seat. The latter featured automatic separation of the seat from the pilot. Some aircraft were later fitted with Mk 2E seats, which had a Duplex drogue chute allowing safe ejections down to heights of 125 ft (38 m).

Royal Auxiliary Air Force
Re-formed on 10 May 1946, the RAuxAF was essentially a home defence organisation, equipped largely with Spitfires and Mosquitoes. From 1949 to 1951 eight squadrons received Meteor F.Mk 4s for a brief period. Between June 1951 and August 1952, 10 squadrons (Nos 500, 504, 600, 601, 604, 609, 610, 611, 615 and 616) were equipped with the Meteor F.Mk 8, which was to be their last equipment before the RAuxAF was disbanded in March 1957.

Armament
The Meteor F.Mk 8 retained the four 20-mm cannon armament of its predecessor. This was adequate for the air-to-air mission, and also proved to be ideal for strafing, as discovered by the RAAF during its ground-attack missions in Korea.

Powerplant
Power came from two Derwent 8s rated at 3,500 lb (15.57 kN) thrust. The Derwent was a scaled-down version of the centrifugal-flow Nene.

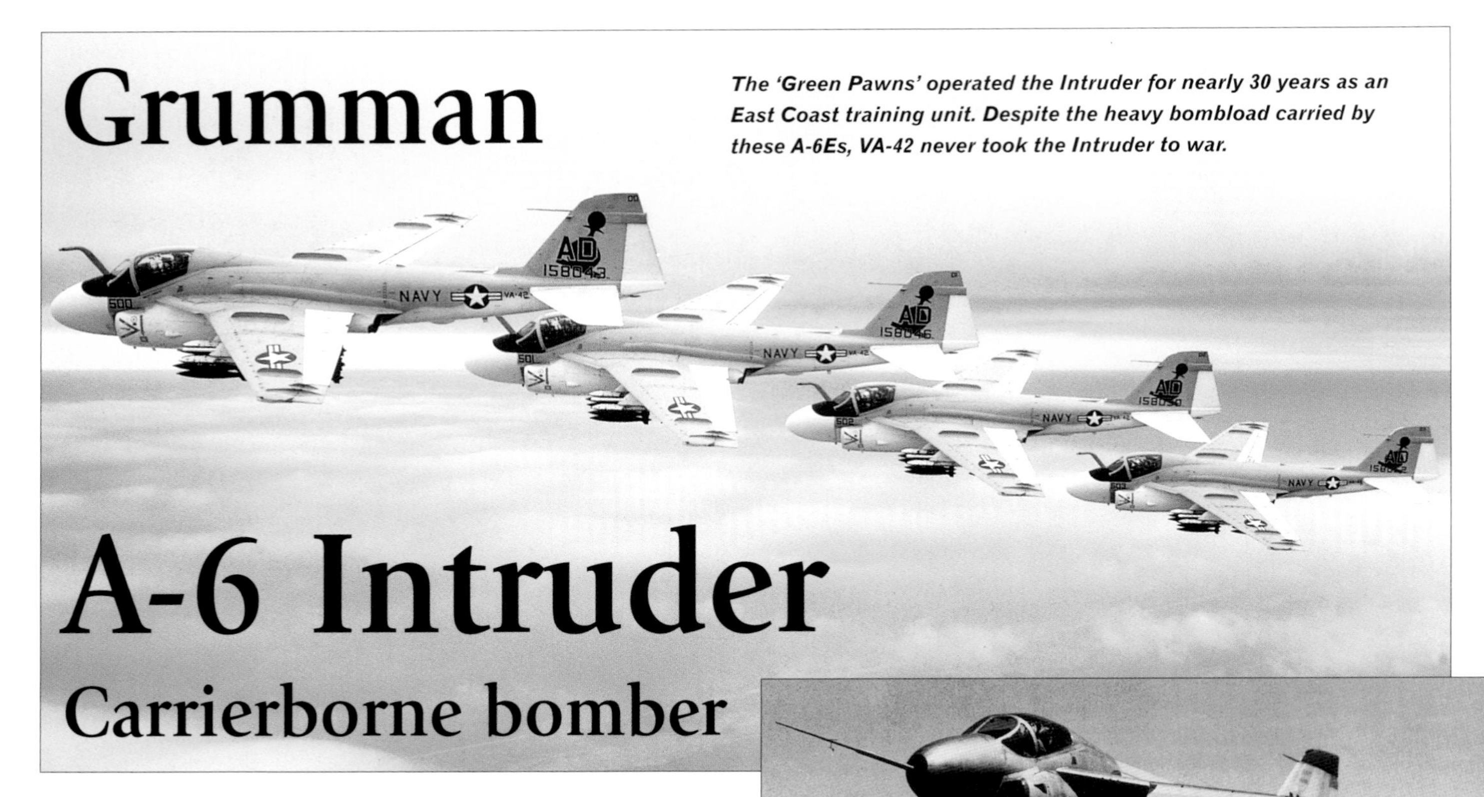

Grumman A-6 Intruder

Carrierborne bomber

The 'Green Pawns' operated the Intruder for nearly 30 years as an East Coast training unit. Despite the heavy bombload carried by these A-6Es, VA-42 never took the Intruder to war.

Entering service with the US Navy in 1963, the Intruder was for many years the sole equipment of the US Navy's medium attack community. Although since replaced by the F/A-18 Hornet, the Intruder's career stretched from Vietnam to Desert Storm.

Based on their Korean War experiences, the US Navy became convinced of the need for a specially designed jet attack aircraft that could operate effectively in the worst weather.

In 1957 eight companies submitted 11 designs in a US Navy competition for a new long-range, low-level tactical strike aircraft. Grumman's G-128 design, selected on the last day of the year, was to fulfil that requirement admirably, becoming a major combat type in the later war in southeast Asia, and leading to a family of later versions.

Eight development A-6As (originally designated A2F-1) were ordered in March 1959, and Grumman started construction of the first aircraft in the same year. The A-6A Intruder was to offer real value for its assigned mission. Included were several 'firsts': the first cockpit display to provide fully integrated data on CRTs (cathode ray tubes), the first contact analogue flight director display and one of the earliest integrated weapons control and status systems.

The first flight of the A2F-1 was made on 19 April 1960. The jet pipes of its two 8,500-lb (37.81-kN) static thrust Pratt & Whitney J52-P-6 engines were designed to swivel downwards to provide an additional component of lift during take-off. This feature was omitted from production aircraft, which instead had jet pipes with a permanent slight downward deflection. The first production A-6As were delivered to US Navy Attack Squadron VA-42 in February 1963, and by the end of the following year 83 aircraft had been delivered to squadrons of the US Navy and to VMA(AW)-242 of the USMC.

The first unit to fly on combat duties in Vietnam was VA-75, whose A-6As began operating from USS *Independence* in March 1965, and from then Intruders of various models became heavily involved in fighting in southeast Asia. Their DIANE (Digital Integrated Attack Navigation Equipment) gave them a first-class operating ability and efficiency in the worst of the weather offered by the local climate. With a maximum ordnance load of over 17,000 lb (7711 kg) they were a potent addition to the US arsenal.

Production of the basic A-6A ran until December 1969 and included 21 EA-6As. The latter were developed primarily to

The prototype A2F-1 Intruder makes its maiden flight at Long Island on 19 April 1960. On the first trip aloft in the new aircraft, test pilot Robert Smyth flew over the manufacturer's facility at Calverton and Bethpage, delighting workers who helped to produce the Intruder.

An early A-6A (formerly A2F-1) displays the tilting tail pipes and perforated fuselage speed brakes which were a feature on early models. The long nose-mounted instrumentation probe was utilised for test purposes only.

provide ECM support for the A-6As in Vietnam and to act as Elint gatherers. They were also a useful step in the evolution of the derived EA-6B Prowler, which remains in service as the only surviving member of Grumman's A-6/EA-6 dynasty.

A number of other variants based on A-6A airframes soon emerged, including the AGM-78 Standard ARM-capable A-6B and the night attack A-6C, which featured FLIR and low-light-level TV equipment in a turret under the fuselage. In addition, a prototype conversion of an A-6A to KA-6D inflight-refuelling tanker standard was flown on 23 May 1966, and 78 A-6As were subsequently modified. The US Navy had also identified a need for an altogether more capable all-weather strike platform, and Grumman therefore produced the upgraded A-6E.

The first A-6E completed its initial flight on 27 February 1970. Procurement of 445 of the new version was undertaken for the USN and USMC, of which some 240 were newly built and about 205 were converted from A-6A/B/Cs. The basis of the A-6E was a new avionics fit, founded on the addition of an AN/APQ-148 multi-mode navigation/attack radar and an AN/ASQ-133 computerised navigation/attack system. Nine A-6E Intruders were further revised, for use in the air-to-air tanker role.

It was the Marine Corps which was the prime mover behind the EA-6A, seeking a replacement for the elderly EF-10B Skyknight. The Corps also took the EA-6A into battle. This example served with VMAQ-2 and wore the famous Playboy bunny on its rudder.

Following the first flight of a test aircraft on 22 March 1974, all Intruders were progressively updated still further under a programme known as TRAM (Target Recognition Attack, Multi-sensor). This added a turreted electro-optical package of FLIR and laser detection equipment integrated with the aircraft's radar and CAINS (carrier airborne inertial navigation system). The A-6E TRAM could now perform automatic carrier landings and deliver automatic-homing and laser-guided air-to-surface weapons.

Grumman developments

Further development of the design resulted in the A-6F, a revised A-6E airframe with new radar, digitised avionics and F404 turbofans. Three prototypes were flown, but the variant was cancelled when the Navy began the pursuit of the 'stealthy' A-12. Grumman for a time continued development of the A-6G, basically the F model but retaining the ageing J52 engines, but this too came to nothing. The subsequent cancellation of the A-12 left the Navy with no choice but to procure the F/A-18E/F as its next-generation attack aircraft.

A series of upgrades kept the A-6E viable until its retirement in February 1997. In 2007, the EA-6B dedicated ECM platform remains in front-line service, however, and has in recent years assumed an ever more important place in US military operations.

With the USAF's EF-111A force having disbanded, HARM-armed USN and USMC Prowlers now provide ECM coverage for both naval and USAF strike packages. Stand-off jamming, escort jamming and lethal SEAD are essential EA-6B roles for the survivors of the 170 Prowlers built, and which will ultimately be replaced by the EA-18G Growler – a derivative of the same Super Hornet airframe that replaced the A-6E strike aircraft on the US Navy's carrier decks.

Above: Seen flying over the Persian Gulf, an EA-6B Prowler (foreground) from VAQ-140 illustrates the similarities to the A-6 (rear). Developed for the electronic warfare role, the Prowler carries a crew of four: a pilot and three EWOs.

Left: The A-6F Intruder II made its first flight in 1987, replacing the J52 turbojets with non-afterburning General Electric F404 engines. However, the USN was then committed to the stealthy A-12, and the Intruder II was cancelled in 1989.

A-6 variants

VA-85 *'Buckeyes' began converting to the* A-6E *in* December 1971, *with* TRAM *aircraft coming a decade later. This unit was involved in strikes against* Lebanese *targets, saw action against* Libyan *targets during* Prairie Fire *and against* Iraqi *targets in* Desert Storm*.*

A2F-1 to A-6E SWIP

The introduction of the A-6 Intruder (designated A2F until 1962) heralded the beginning of a revolution in the US Navy's attack capabilities. The A-6A and later models were built in a host of configurations.

Entering service with the US Navy in 1963, the A-6 Intruder was improved throughout its service life. Several different versions were built, including standard attack aircraft, specialised attack versions (including the A-6C SEA TRIM), tankers and electronic warfare aircraft.

Early experience with the Intruder led the US Navy to begin a series of upgrades to the aircraft, a process which would continue for 30 years. In mid-1966, the USN embarked on a SIP (Systems Improvement Program) for the A-6A, aimed at improving the search and track radars, the AN/APQ-92 and the (new) AN/APQ-112.

SEA TRIM

The Intruder proved to be an extremely useful addition to the US Navy's efforts in Vietnam. Two specialised versions were developed for the conflict, the A-6B and the A-6C. The first fully equipped version of the A-6C SEA TRIM (South-East Asia Trail/Roads Interdiction Multisensor) flew on 11 June 1969. The A-6C SEA TRIM, converted from the A-6A, was equipped with the same TRIM system employed by the Lockheed AP-2H Neptunes of VAH-21 for night and all-weather, low-level operations against the North Vietnamese supply network, referred to as the Ho Chi Minh Trail. It was accepted by the USN on 26 May 1970. The variant carried LLLTV (low-light-level television) and the Black Crow receiver, a sensing device which detected emissions from vehicle exhausts. Twelve A-6C SEA TRIM aircraft were built and the variant was employed by VA-34, VA-35 and VA-165, although only the last-named took it into combat.

The 11 A-6C survivors were later modified as A-6Es, a fate that was to await many of the original A-6As. Others were converted as tankers (KA-6D) or for EW (EA-6A). In all, 488 A-6As were built, and the type was replaced in service by the A-6E.

Half a dozen years after the Intruder commenced flying, the US Navy explored the possibility of using the Intruder airframe as an inflight-refuelling tanker to supplement EKA-3B Skywarriors and combat aircraft employing 'buddy' refuelling packs. In April 1966, the USN demonstrated a possible Intruder tanker when a specially equipped test A-6A refuelled an F-4B Phantom.

The first KA-6D Intruder tanker made its initial flight on 16 April 1970. The KA-6D was in many respects a 'stripped' warplane, with the bomb-aiming and radar

Photographed in November 1966, these VA-35 A-6A Intruders were deployed aboard CVAN-65 (USS* Enterprise*) within a month, heading out to Vietnam for their first operational tour.

Above: *Inclusion of the KA-6D within the air wing allowed carriers to undertake wide-ranging operations without the need to divert other aircraft from primary missions to carry out refuelling duties.*

Below: Three of VA-165's A-6As are seen, while on a cruise on USS **Ranger**, *during one of the squadron's two tours as part of CVW-2; it operated off the Vietnamese coast between late 1967 and mid-1969.*

systems removed and with minimal controls for the second crew member, whose only duties were navigation and refuelling.

As of the early 1970s, an Intruder squadron typically consisted of 10 attack and four tanker aircraft. The initial US Navy contract called for 71 KA-6Ds, which were converted from A-6A airframes. Follow-on orders resulted in 95 being built. When rebuilt from A-6A standard, KA-6Ds received all-new fuel tanks, with two fuselage bulkheads being replaced and the wing rebuilt.

Definitive version

An updated member of the Intruder family, the A-6E Intruder (a converted A-6A), made its maiden flight on 27 February 1970. The first new-build A-6E flew on 26 September 1971. This aircraft was accepted by the US Navy on 1 December 1971.

Powered by two 9,300-lb (41-kN) thrust Pratt & Whitney J52-P-8B turbojets – little different from the -8A engines on all previous Intruders – the A-6E introduced a new central computer, multi-mode radar and weapons release system. The AN/ASQ-133 digital computer and AN/APQ-148 multi-mode radar were incorporated.

To meet fleet requirements within funding limits, the USN adopted a two-tier approach to its A-6E purchases. While new-built A-6Es rolled off the production line at the rate of a dozen aircraft per year from 1972 to 1977, 240 existing A-6As were also rebuilt to A-6E standard in a CILOP (Conversion In Lieu Of Procurement) programme. Not all A-6Es, as it turned out, were exactly the same – there were about a dozen minor differences, ranging from the instrument panel to the dive brakes.

In the 1970s, the basic A-6E gave way to the A-6E CAINS (Carrier Airborne Inertial Navigation System) aircraft, which introduced the AN/ASN-92 inertial navigation system.

A more profound change in the A-6E came with the A-6E TRAM (Target Recognition Attack Multisensor) aircraft. The A-6E TRAM Intruder, introduced in September 1979, had a metallurgical update as well as state-of-the-art laser and infra-red targetting systems. TRAM incorporated a laser designator, laser rangefinder and infra-red sensor mounted in a turret protruding from the bottom of the A-6E radome, just forward of the nosewheel.

The first development flight by an A-6E TRAM Intruder took place on 29 November 1978. The US Navy accepted the first A-6E TRAM on 14 December 1978. TRAM made its first operational deployment with VA-35 aboard USS *Nimitz* during the Iranian crisis in 1979/80.

Initially, 32 aircraft were converted to A-6E TRAM configuration. The number subsequently increased to 228 and the A-6E TRAM became the standard for the fleet.

A-6E SWIP

A closely related improvement to the A-6E Intruder series was that offered by the A-6E SWIP aircraft, which was delivered to US Navy squadrons in 1990/91. Stand-off weapons, including AGM-65E/F Maverick, AGM-84A Harpoon, AGM-84E SLAM and AGM-88 HARM, were available on the type. The SWIP upgrade also encompassed a number of survivability improvements.

The A-6E remained in service for several years before falling foul to USN cutbacks and the growth in capability of the F/A-18 Hornet. The last major conflict for the A-6E/KA-6D was Desert Storm, where nearly 100 aircraft performed admirably, with only minimal casualties. The final A-6E/KA-6Ds were retired in 1997 and the last two units were VA-75 'Sunday Punchers' and VA-196 'Main Battery'.

The large pod under the fuselage of the A-6C contained the low-light-level TV, forward-looking infra-red and passive sensors for interdiction work. This example belongs to VA-165.

EA-6Bs equipped 14 US Navy and four USMC front-line squadrons into 2007. Of these, two USN squadrons are joint USN/USAF squadrons.

EA-6B Prowler

In service since 1972, the EA-6B Prowler is the prime electronic warfare aircraft of the US military services, and is constantly in demand to support both carrier deployments and USAF operations.

Based on the original A-6A Intruder, the Grumman EA-6A was conceived in response to a Marine Corps requirement for an EF-10B Skyknight replacement and entered service with three composite recon/electronic warfare squadrons in the mid-1960s. Production totalled just 27 airframes, of which a dozen were essentially conversions of existing A-6As, and most were retired in the late 1970s. Externally, the most visible difference between the EA-6A and the attack-dedicated A-6A was the bulbous fintip fairing, which housed antennas associated with the electronic warfare equipment. Although mainly employed for electronic warfare, the EA-6A also retained a limited attack capability.

A handful of EA-6As remained in service into the 1990s, operating as electronic aggressors with VAQ-33.

Fundamentally a four-seater variation of the Intruder, the EA-6B entered service during 1971 as a replacement for the EKA-3B Skywarrior. Key equipment includes the TJS (Tactical Jamming System), capable of operating in fully automatic,

The first EA-6A refuels from a pod-equipped A-6A on its first flight. The aircraft's main distinguishing feature was the fintip fairing, housing receivers for the AN/ALQ-86 system.

Above: The USMC took the EA-6A into battle, with aircraft serving with VMCJ-1 and VMCJ-2 in Vietnam. This aircraft wears the markings of VMAQ-2, created in 1975 with the merger of the two EA-6A units.

Below: In 1967, Grumman converted an EA-6B flying demonstrator created from an A-6A Intruder (BuNo. 149481), and this aircraft made its maiden flight on 28 May 1968.

EA-6B 156482 was part of a batch of five new-build pre-production aircraft and was regularly used as a testbed. It can be seen here serving as the test-ship for the ADVCAP variant.

semi-automatic and manual modes and employing 'noise' jamming originating from up to five external transmitter pods.

Progressive updates have resulted in a series of ever more capable versions. Excluding three prototype conversions of A-6As and five development airframes, the first 23 production aircraft were to 'Basic' standard, using AN/ALQ-99 TJS and AN/ALQ-92 with an EW potential that was limited to four specific frequency bands. They were followed in 1973 by the first of 25 Expanded Capability (EXCAP) airframes with improved equipment and the ability to cover threats across eight bands using the TJS.

The next version to appear was Improved Capability (ICAP), which debuted in 1976 and incorporated new displays and reduced reaction times, along with AN/ALQ-126 multiple-band defensive breakers and updated radar deception gear. In addition to 45 new-build machines, 17 surviving Basic and EXCAP airframes were also brought up to full ICAP standard.

Software and display improvements were among the changes made on the ICAP-II version, which flew for the first time in 1980, with all 55 surviving ICAPs being upgraded. ICAP-II is able to handle groups of weapons systems, and embodies such refinements as power management and improved identification of hostile emitters. As with the original ICAP, it has a crew of four and it has also acquired the ability to launch the AGM-88 HARM missile.

New-build and conversions

Procurement of ICAP-II also followed a twin-track approach, with the US Navy and Marine Corps receiving a mixture of remanufactured and new-build aircraft to this standard. These equip 14 deployable Navy squadrons, which are mostly concentrated at NAS Whidbey Island, from where they routinely embark aboard aircraft-carriers of both major fleets. Marine Corps usage of the Prowler is more limited, comprising four front-line squadrons at Marine Corps Air Station (MCAS) Cherry Point.

Production of the US Navy's standard carrierborne electronic warfare aircraft terminated in July 1991 with 170 aircraft built. However, since the Prowler's inception, it has undergone a series of upgrades. After the early ICAP-II variants came the ADVCAP (Advanced Capability) or Block 91. EA-6Bs have been upgraded to two ADVCAP configurations. The basic ADVCAP has new jammer transmission, passive detection capabilities and an expanded chaff dispenser fit.

An Avionics Improvement Program led to a remanufactured ADVCAP/Block 91 EA-6B with new displays, radar improvements, an improved tactical support jamming suite, AN/ALQ-149 communications jamming system and a digital autopilot. Aerodynamic improvements were developed under the Vehicle Enhancement Program (VEP) project. The VEP prototype first flew in 1992 and featured uprated powerplants and two additional HARM pylons. ICAP-II Block 86, 89 and 89A EA-6Bs progressively added new radios, cockpit instrumentation improvements and additional antenna and safety features.

To keep the Prowler serving into the 21st century, the remaining airframes are undergoing ICAP-III development, approved for production in June 2003, and which is replacing the AN/ALQ-99 with improved TJS receivers, introducing a fully integrated communications jamming system and giving the Prowler the ability to react to the latest SAMs. Another new upgrade is the Multifunctional Information Distribution System (MIDS), which adds Link 16 datalink capability.

With the retirement of the F-4G and the EF-111 in the 1990s, the EA-6B has now assumed full responsibility for the electronic warfare mission in US service, with joint USAF/USN squadrons operating the type. The Prowler is expected to remain in service to at least 2010, when the first EA-18Gs are planned to arrive.

EA-6B ICAP-II (Block 89) Prowler

This aircraft was one of those attached to VAQ-134 'Garudas' when that unit sailed aboard the USS *Ranger* before the ship was decommissioned on 10 July 1993. VAQ-134 is now a joint expeditionary Prowler unit.

External stores
The Prowler is designed to carry up to five AN/ALQ-99 jamming pods on its four underwing and single centreline stations. It can also carry a maximum of four AGM-88 HARMs. Beyond this, the only other external stores cleared for EA-6B carriage are standard twin-finned Aero 1D fuel tanks, AN/ALE-41 chaff pods and CNU-188/A baggage pods.

The 'football'
TJS receivers in the bulged fintip 'football' cover frequency bands distinct from those covered by other onboard antennas – such as the twin blister antennas below the 'football' on either side of the fin.

On 19 November 1952 Lt(jg) J. D. Middleton, flying this VF-781 F9F-2 Panther from the USS Oriskany, together with his wingman, Lt E. R. Williams, were credited with two MiG kills. A third MiG was damaged by Lt(jg) D. M. Rowlands. The incident was initially kept secret by the US Navy, in order to avoid international repercussions, as the three MiG-15s in question were Soviet, and based near Vladivostok. USN F9F-2s were credited with eight kills during the Korean War.

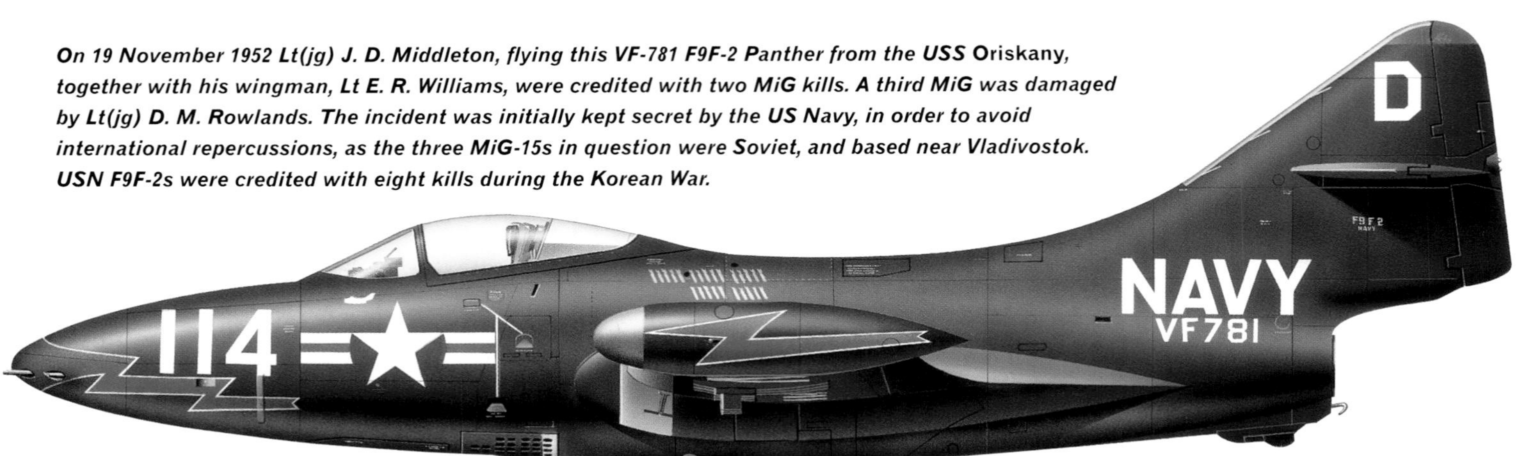

Grumman F9F Panther/Cougar

Naval jet duo

The availability of the Nene engine meant that the F9F was created with speed, meeting the US Navy's shipboard fighter requirements at a time when no operational jet carrier experience existed in the US.

Below: US Marine Corps F9F-2B Panthers of VMF-311 (pictured) first went to Yonpo in December 1950, this being the first jet-equipped USMC unit in the Korean theatre. By March 1951, VMF-311 was at Pohang. The second USMC Panther unit comprised VMF-115, initially based at Pohang from February 1951.

Flying 78,000 Korean combat missions, the F9F was the first naval jet to go to war, and the F9F family was continuously extended by improved versions, until 3,414 had been built.

The family was launched by a May 1945 requirement for a radar-equipped all-weather fighter for the US Navy. On 3 April 1946, Grumman received a contract for its G-75 submission as the two-seat XF9F-1, but the proposal, to be powered by four Westinghouse J30s in the wingroot, remained in a state of flux. Eventually the XF9F-1 was traded for a simpler day fighter, the XF9F-2. Grumman prepared a series of new projects designated G-79, and in August 1946 the US Navy picked the single-engined G-79D. By August 1946 the USN had become interested in the Rolls-Royce Nene engine, providing 5,000 lb (22.5 kN) of thrust.

The Nene spurred US design teams to beat it. Allison responded with its own J33, pushing up its thrust from 4,000 to 4,600 lb (18 to 20.7 kN). Meanwhile, Pratt & Whitney redesigned the Nene as the J42, initially matched to the XF9F-2.

Rival powerplants

To preserve competition, the USN finally settled on J42 power for the first and third XF9F-2s and J33 power for the second aircraft. Grumman received two Nenes in July 1947 and one of these was installed in the first XF9F-2. This machine made a first flight on 24 November 1947.

The second prototype, with one of the first J42 engines, flew in March 1948, and the first of the Allison-engined F9F-3s followed on 16 August 1948. Final carrier trials took place aboard the USS *Franklin D. Roosevelt* in March 1949, and deliveries of the F9F-2 to VF-51 began in May. In July 1950 the USN's F9F went into action, over Korea. Allison supplied J33-8 engines for 54 of a planned 71 F9F-3s, but these engines suffered from bearing failures and from February 1950 the aircraft were re-engined with J42s, becoming F9F-2s. Total production of the F9F-2 amounted to 567, plus 54 converted F9F-3s. In the penultimate block, underwing racks were added for two bombs or six HVARs, as the F9F-2B.

Allison proposed to substitute a new and very powerful engine, the J33-A-16 with major redesign and water injection to give a wet take-off thrust of 6,950 lb (31.3 kN). The first 73 F9F-4s with this US engine were included in the 1949 budget, but though one aircraft (a converted F9F-2) did fly with the J33-A-16 as the XF9F-4, it was the only one with this problem-ridden engine. Allison kept eliminating the snags, and eventually commenced production in the era of the

The F9F-5 was the most numerous Panther variant, with 595 examples built. This aircraft, from the first production batch, featured an experimental refuelling probe installation in the nose, and in 1952 underwent trials with an XAJ-1 Savage tanker.

swept-wing Cougar. Meanwhile, its competition spurred Pratt & Whitney to keep improving the J42. Rolls-Royce had continued to develop the Nene to give much greater thrust as the Tay, and this was eagerly snapped up by Pratt & Whitney, which built it as the J48.

The J48 was further boosted by water/alcohol injection, and provided a welcome boost in all-round performance and agility. The resulting F9F-5 was the most important of the straight-wing versions. The XF9F-5 prototype flew on 21 December 1949, and it introduced a longer fuselage to increase internal fuel to 763 US gal (2888 litres). Development went well, but production had to await termination of F9F-2 contracts in August 1951. By this time, over 300 Panthers were in Korea, on board US Navy carriers and on US Marine airstrips. The Korean War continued to demand massive orders, and 595 of the new F9F-5 model were delivered, as well as 109 aircraft ordered as Allison-engined F9F-4s. In addition, there were 36 unarmed F9F-5P photo-reconnaissance Panthers, making a total of this series of 740.

Panther drones

Panthers continued in front-line USN service until 1956, by which time many earlier examples had been converted as drone targets, or drone control aircraft. Hundreds were refurbished as advanced trainers, and one batch of F9F-2s was reconditioned in 1966 as fighters for the Argentine navy. From 1962 the designation was F-9.

Grumman began swept-wing F9F studies in December 1945, but it was not until March 1950 that the company made a formal proposal for a swept-wing Panther, the G-93.

Grumman received a contract on 2 March 1951 for three XF9F-6 prototypes. The first was flown on 20 September 1951 and was sufficiently different from the straight-wing Panther to merit its new name, Cougar.

The XF9F-6's engine was the J48-8, with water/alcohol injection for a take-off rating of 7,250 lb (32.6 kN). The first production Cougar came off the line in February 1952. By November, the last straight-wing F9F was delivered and VF-32 was working up with the Cougar, which offered considerably enhanced performance.

Altogether 646 F9F-6 Cougars were built, plus 60 unarmed F9F-6Ps with the same camera installation as the F9F-5P. By this time, Allison was at last out of the wood with the J33-16A engine of 6,350-lb (28.6-kN) rating, and this powered 168 examples of the F9F-7, otherwise similar to the F9F-6.

In 1951 Grumman had identified several ways in which the Cougar could be further developed without changing the engine. By late 1952 the G-99 design had been completed and this replaced the F9F-6 and F9F-7 on the production line as the F9F-8, the first example being flown on 18 December 1953, and exceeding Mach 1 in January 1954.

Production amounted to 662, many of which were converted to improved F9F-8B standard, and received launch rails for up to four Sidewinder missiles. The F9F-8P was the corresponding reconnaissance version. The final new-build Cougar version was the F9F-8T dual trainer, a total of 400 of which were delivered, the last in late 1959.

After 1962 the F9F Cougar family received new designations in the F-9 series. The final TF-9J (previously F9F-8T) Cougars were not officially retired until February 1974.

Above: F9F-8B Cougars of VF-81 'Crusaders' from USS** Intrepid **are seen over the Atlantic in August 1958. The F9F-8B introduced a close-support capability with Bullpup radio-command datalink.

Right: The F9F-8T Cougar tandem two-seat operational trainer introduced a lengthened forward fuselage, and remained in service long enough to be redesignated TF-9J in 1962. The prototype YF9F-8T (pictured) first flew on 29 February 1956.

Grumman F-14 Tomcat

Fleet defender

Designed to protect US Navy carriers, the F-14 was the world's finest long-range interceptor for over 20 years, and latterly acquired a potent air-to-ground capability.

As the vanguard of US Navy air defence, Grumman's Tomcat remained one of the world's most potent interceptors until its retirement from US service in 2006. Its AN/AWG-9 fire control system, allied with the formidable AIM-54 Phoenix air-to-air missile, gave it an unmatched ability to intercept and engage targets at ultra-long ranges. The US Navy's Tomcat squadrons were widely regarded as an elite within an elite, and they carried out the vital role of protecting the carrier battle group with supreme confidence and competence for more than 30 years. A new chapter of F-14 operations opened in the 1990s, however, when F-14s began flying ground-attack and precision bombing missions with almost equal facility.

Grumman was determined to produce a fighter that could out-fight aircraft like the Soviet MiG-21 and MiG-23 in close quarter combat, and it succeeded in producing an aircraft whose agility was a

Above: An F-14A of VF-102 'Diamondbacks' launches from USS America. Changes to the composition of each carrier air wing saw the reduction of F-14 squadrons from two to one in the 1990s, but at the same time they began to be tasked with air-to-ground missions.

Top: In the post-Cold War world, the aircraft-carrier assumed a new importance in America's peacekeeping and power projection roles. Until 2006, wherever it went, the US Navy carrier was protected by a supremely capable interceptor, the Grumman F-14 Tomcat.

Left: Iranian Tomcats were delivered in this attractive three-tone desert camouflage with IIAF (Imperial Iranian Air Force) markings. The latter were soon replaced by IRIAF (Islamic Republic of Iran Air Force) titles, and a new 'air superiority' grey camouflage was later adopted.

***Left:* This scene could have been that of USAF F-14s refuelling from a KC-10 if certain planners had had their way. However, USAF concerns that the F-15 might be cancelled, allied with inter-service rivalry, meant that a USAF Tomcat purchase never took place.**

***Below:* Although a fine interceptor, problems with the basic F-14A's TF30 engines led to the F-14D Tomcat with more powerful F110s and upgraded systems. The F-14D introduced a marked leap in performance.**

quantum improvement over that of the F-4 Phantom II which it replaced in USN service.

Although overshadowed in the close-in manoeuvring arena of air combat by more modern, purpose-built air superiority fighters, the Tomcat remained unrivalled in its ability to destroy multiple targets at an unparalleled distance. It could down missile-carrying bombers before they could launch their weapons, or fighters before they could come into range of the carrier battle group.

Like many aircraft, however, the Tomcat had vices as well as virtues; the F-14's development and deployment saw a fascinating mix of triumph and tragedy.

Long-standing problems with the F-14A's TF30 turbofan engines led to the imposition of handling limitations after the loss of around 40 aircraft due to spinning accidents. These problems were only resolved with the F110-powered F-14A+ (F-14B) and F-14D, whose production was eventually radically cut back.

Force contraction

The end of the Cold War brought about a painful contraction of the F-14 force, accompanied by the disestablishment of many historic squadrons. After this consolidation had been completed, the remaining units played a vital and increasingly varied role in US naval air operations, and the Tomcat community enjoyed a latter day renaissance. Being an F-14 pilot or RIO (Radar Intercept Officer) was always a supremely important and enjoyable occupation, and morale remained sky high until the end.

By the time Iran started flying the Tomcat in the late 1970s, the F-14 was also becoming increasingly numerous in the US Navy fleet. CVW-15 (with VF-51 and VF-111) converted in 1979, followed by CVW-3 (VF-11 and VF-31) and CVW-1 (VF-102 and VF-33) in 1982, then by CVW-17 (VF-74 and VF-103) and CVW-14 (VF-21 and VF-154) in 1983. Eventually, each carrier in the US Navy, with the exception of Midway and Coral Sea (whose elevators were too small), had Tomcats aboard.

Birth of the Tomcat

Emerging from an earlier failure by Grumman to produce a shipborne fighter, the F-14 Tomcat's development suffered some early setbacks, yet it soon emerged into an exceptional interceptor.

Above: The first F-14 made its maiden flight one month ahead of schedule, on 21 December 1970. Nine days later, during the aircraft's second flight, disaster struck when a primary hydraulic system failed. The aircraft can be seen speeding back to Grumman's Calverton facility, trailing a plume of hydraulic fluid.

Top: The second F-14 prototype explored the low-speed flight envelope, including spinning and stalling. For spinning trials, the aircraft was fitted with retractable canard strakes on the nose, running forward from the canopy arch to the radome.

During the 1950s, the US Navy began to seek an aircraft that could defend carrier battle groups against long-range bombers carrying stand-off anti-ship missiles. An aircraft able to fulfil these tasks would have to be able to remain aloft for long periods of time and would need to carry missiles with long-range target detection abilities. The only critical parameter was that the aircraft would have to be small enough to be able to operate from an aircraft-carrier; the missile would do the rest of the work.

In 1957 Bendix produced the AAM-N-10 Eagle missile, which had a Mach 4 capability and a 110-nm (126-mile; 203-km) range. In addition, Douglas won a competition between rival aircraft manufacturers to build its XF6D-1 Missileer. This aircraft would be able to loiter for up to 10 hours and carry six Eagle missiles. However, the Missileer was eventually scrapped as it lacked agility and was unarmed apart from the long-range Eagle missiles. Ultimately, one aspect of the Missileer programme did survive and that was the Hughes AN/AWG-9 fire-control system.

More than just a radar, the AN/AWG-9 was an integrated target detection and weapon control system with a long-range IR detection system, lightweight computers, advanced cockpit displays and a two-way datalink to allow aircraft and ship or ground station or even other aircraft to be linked together. The Eagle missile was also reborn as the AAM-N-11 Phoenix (later AIM-54), after the related technology had been transferred from Bendix to Hughes.

This mock-up of the Tomcat was created from the original Design 303E model which only had one dorsal fin and outward-folding ventral fins. Sparrow missiles are also present below the belly, despite the fact the aircraft was designed around the AIM-54 Phoenix.

McNamara's plan

With President Kennedy's inauguration in 1961, Robert S. McNamara was made Secretary of Defense. One of his major ideas on how to save money was a decree that the US Air Force and Navy should adopt a common fighter called the TFX (Tactical Fighter Experimental). However, the Air Force had been looking for a long-range fighter-bomber while the Navy was searching for a fighter capable of long-range and close-in combat. McNamara pressed ahead with the single aircraft idea, despite a campaign by the Navy and Air Force.

A request for proposals was issued on 1 October 1961 and a number of aerospace manufacturers submitted designs; it was ultimately General Dynamics that was successful and it set about producing an F-111 to fulfil the roles of both services. General Dynamics' bid had been made in association with Grumman and it was the latter, with its extensive naval aviation knowledge, which was charged with designing the rear fuselage and landing gear of all F-111s and of the F-111B, the TFX-N naval version. Grumman had

Above: Engineers sift through the wreckage of the Tomcat prototype which crashed on approach to Grumman's Calverton base. The pilot and back-seater had ejected safely beforehand.

Below: Three Tomcat prototypes in flight show different wing sweep angles and some of the varied colour schemes applied to the pre-production aircraft.

also done much work on the variable-sweep wing with its abortive XF10F-1 Jaguar. While the Jaguar was discarded, its 'swing' wing, together with the Phoenix missile, were incorporated into the F-111B.

The nautical F-111 prototype was first flown in May 1965. However, as tests progressed, it soon became apparent that the F-111B was not suited to carrier missions. The Navy was vehemently opposed to the F-111B and made every attempt to highlight any problems with the aircraft, which were further magnified by the loss of a prototype. In a Senate Armed Services Committee, the chiefs of the Navy and the Naval Secretary expressed their severe misgivings about the naval variant and work on it was halted. The TFX programme, the notion of commonality and the F-111B programme were all killed off, though the USAF's F-111 did mature into a potent low-level, long-range bomber.

F-14 genesis

Although the F-111B was totally discredited, the US Navy still pushed ahead with its requirement for a new fighter. F-8 Crusaders and F-4 Phantoms were considered to be reaching obsolescence and the rapid advancement of Soviet aircraft offered a major threat.

The VFX (Carrier-based Fighter Experimental) programme was initialised and a number of companies submitted designs. In October 1967, Grumman proposed the idea of developing a new aircraft which would, however, retain the avionics, missiles, engines and weapon systems of the discredited F-111B. The Navy had no objections to this and Grumman came up with a design that promised to be superior to the F-111B in all aspects. The following year, McDonnell Douglas's Model 225 and Grumman's Design 303 were selected for further testing. Ultimately, Grumman's design was chosen and, in January 1969, it was awarded a contract for the building of six prototypes, and a provision for the production of 463 aircraft.

The aircraft was now known as the F-14 Tomcat; it would utilise the AN/AWG-9 weapon control system and would be fully compatible with the Phoenix missile. The first 67 aircraft, including the prototypes, would be powered by the TF30-P412 turbofan engine, while subsequent aircraft would be built to VFX-2 standard which would have a new, more powerful, advanced engine, and would be designated F-14B. This new engine was cancelled and then later reinstated: VFX-2 eventually resulted in the F402-engined F-14B. The original F-14B was meant to enter service in December 1973, but was ultimately cancelled.

Two full-scale mock-ups of the F-14A were produced, with the original version having a single fin – the second model introduced twin fins. The design was then frozen in March 1969 and the first prototype rolled out of the Grumman plant later that year. A first flight for the new fighter was earmarked for January 1971, but the aircraft had actually made it into the air on 21 December 1970. Nine days later, another flight ended in disaster when a hydraulic system failed. The two crewmen ejected, but the Tomcat itself was destroyed.

Flight testing

A correction to the Tomcat's hydraulic system was relatively easy to fix and, on 24 May 1971, the next fighter flew. This aircraft was assigned to low-speed and critical stall/spin trials. No. 3 aircraft flew envelope-expanding trials with steadily increasing loads and speeds. Nos 4, 5 and 6 went to NAS Point Mugu, the fourth for integration of the weapon system, the fifth for systems, instrumentation and compatibility tests, and the sixth for weapon system and missile separation tests. Of these, No. 5 was lost during a Sparrow separation on 20 June 1973.

Most of the F-14 Tomcat prototypes carried large areas of Dayglo to increase conspicuity and enhance optical tracking by ground-based observers.

Left: A VF-32 'Swordsmen' F-14A keeps a watchful eye over a Soviet navy 'Kresta II'-class guided missile destroyer which is shadowing the Tomcat's carrier battle group. Note the aircraft's full missile armament.

Below: VF-1 and VF-2 had the distinction of being the first fleet units to receive the F-14. The fighter made its first operational deployment aboard the USS Enterprise, *the two squadrons forming the defensive shield for the carrier's air wing, CVW-14.*

Early deployment

With the introduction of the F-14 into Fleet service, a Grumman 'Cat' was once more operating onboard US Navy aircraft-carriers. Despite engine-related groundings, Navy fighter squadrons deployed from the mid-1970s with what was undoubtedly the world's finest interceptor.

The first US Navy squadron to receive the F-14 was VX-4 at Point Mugu, which undertook operational evaluation from September 1972. The first F-14A went to VF-124 at NAS Miramar on 8 October 1972, just 21 months after the type's first flight. VF-124 became the Navy's West Coast fleet replenishment (or readiness) squadron (FRS), tasked with type conversion training prior to fleet service. Later, a second East Coast-based conversion unit for the Tomcat, VF-101 'Grim Reapers', trained crews at NAS Oceana.

After training F-14 instructors, VF-124 was ready by 1973 to begin training crews who would fly the F-14 in the first operational fleet squadrons – VF-1 and VF-2 – which had been commissioned in October 1972. They began their carrier qualifications in early 1974.

On 12 September 1974 the 24 Tomcats of VF-1 and VF-2 left NAS Miramar for loading aboard the USS *Enterprise*. Five days later, the carrier slipped its moorings, marking the first carrier deployment by a Grumman 'Cat' since VF-111's F11F Tigers had returned to the US aboard the USS *Hancock* in March 1961.

The Atlantic Fleet began converting its fleet air defence units to the F-14 in June 1974, with the delivery of the first F-14A to VF-14 at NAS Oceana.

As a new and sophisticated weapons system, the F-14's introduction into service was not

Below: The F-14's combat debut came during its first cruise, when Enterprise *sailed into the South China Sea to support the US withdrawal from Vietnam.*

Tomcats for the US Marine Corps and US Air Force

Early plans for a Marine Corps purchase of the Tomcat were abandoned because of cost, but not before the first 'Grunt' aircrews and ground crews had started training with VF-124. It was thought that the Marines could only afford a much reduced number of F-14s (50) for the same price as its planned purchase of F-4J Phantoms. However, because Marine Tomcat procurement could be added to batches of Navy aircraft, Grumman was able to offer 100 F-14s for the same funding as had been contained in the request for 138 F-4Js ($891.1 million). The first USMC F-14s were to have been delivered at the end of 1975, but in July the decision was made to axe the Marine Tomcats. Instead, it was announced that the USMC would receive four extra F/A-18 Hornet squadrons, and that the Corps' Phantoms would be upgraded for service in the interim. The Marines' loss was the Navy's gain, however, and the number of USN F-14 squadrons was increased by four.

Another potential customer was the US Air Force. It was suggested that Aerospace Defense Command might order a limited number of F-14s to meet the USAF's Improved Manned Interceptor requirement. It was estimated that 170 F-14s would be required, at a cost of $4,300 million. Changes to the F-14 to allow USAF operation would have been relatively minor. However, the purchase of even a few F-14s would have threatened the entire F-15 programme, and was not allowed to happen. Eventually, both programmes were far enough advanced to be safe from cancellation, but direct comparison was still discouraged. The two fighters eventually did meet, during an exercise in 1978, when F-14s from VF-14 and VF-32 flew DACT sorties against F-15s from Bitburg. The two aircraft were closely matched, with the F-14's RIO giving it the edge in complex multi-bogey engagements, but with the F-15 able to sustain higher turn rates above 15,000 ft (4570 m).

F-14A Tomcat

F-14A BuNo. 158579 carries the markings of VF-1 'Wolf Pack', deployed as part of USS *Enterprise*'s CVW-14. The 'Double Nuts' serial number (or modex) indicates that it is also the aircraft allocated to the commander of the carrier's air wing, known as the CAG.

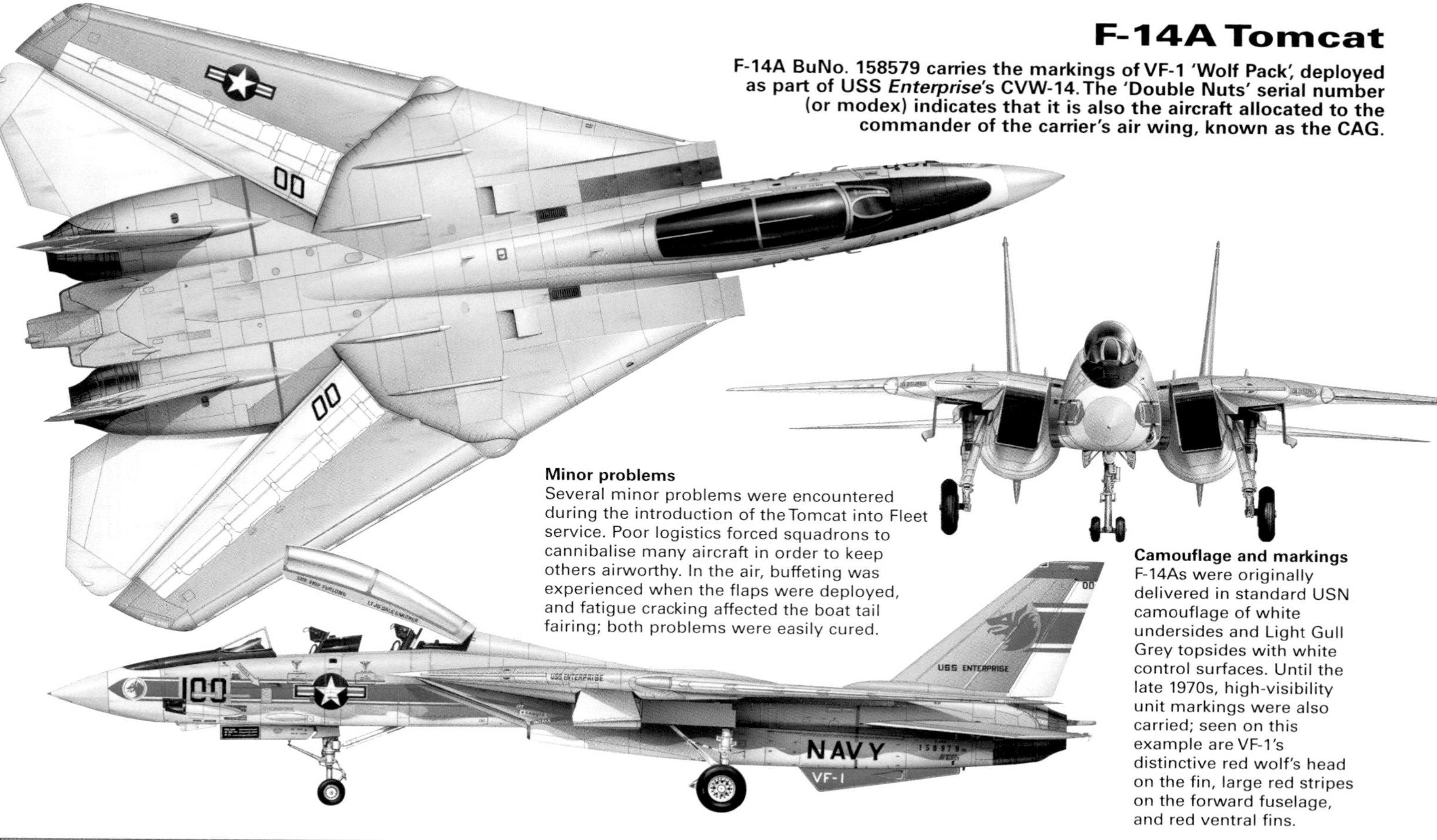

Minor problems
Several minor problems were encountered during the introduction of the Tomcat into Fleet service. Poor logistics forced squadrons to cannibalise many aircraft in order to keep others airworthy. In the air, buffeting was experienced when the flaps were deployed, and fatigue cracking affected the boat tail fairing; both problems were easily cured.

Camouflage and markings
F-14As were originally delivered in standard USN camouflage of white undersides and Light Gull Grey topsides with white control surfaces. Until the late 1970s, high-visibility unit markings were also carried; seen on this example are VF-1's distinctive red wolf's head on the fin, large red stripes on the forward fuselage, and red ventral fins.

***Above:* VF-41 'Black Aces' transitioned to the F-14A from April 1976. Until 1987 the squadron sailed as part of CVW-8 aboard USS Nimitz.**

VF-84 'Jolly Rogers' began conversion to the F-14 in October 1975, and deployed as part of CVW-8 aboard USS Nimitz with VF-41.

entirely trouble-free. Poor logistics and minor aerodynamic problems were solved, but of more serious concern was the TF30 powerplant. Most early F-14 pilots experienced engine flame-outs or even inflight explosions, leading to the loss of several aircraft and subsequent brief grounding orders.

Despite these problems, the commander of the Fighter and AEW Wing Pacific was able to describe the F-14's introduction as 'the most singularly successful fleet introduction programme of a sophisticated aircraft that the Navy has ever had.'

By 30 April 1975 *Enterprise*'s Tomcats were able to claim status as Vietnam veterans by flying top cover for Operation Frequent Wind, the evacuation of Saigon.

The first two Atlantic Fleet squadrons equipped with the new Grumman fighter, VF-14 and VF-32 of CVW-1, undertook carrier qualification between late 1974 and early 1975.

The two units put to sea aboard USS *John F. Kennedy* in June 1975, and were the first F-14 squadrons to work with the E-2C version of the Hawkeye. Their first Sixth Fleet Mediterranean deployment was more successful than the WestPac cruise by VF-1 and VF-2, with only one aircraft being lost, and that through no fault of its own.

Further F-14 conversions

The rate of squadron conversions from F-8s and F-4s to the Tomcat gathered pace. Subsequently, VF-142 and VF-143 of CVW-6 transitioned to the Tomcat at Miramar during 1976, with VF-41 and VF-84 of CVW-8 becoming operational with the Atlantic Fleet during 1976 and 1977 respectively. Between these units, CVW-9's two squadrons (VF-24 and VF-211) and the units from CVW-11 (VF-114 and VF-213) also transitioned at Miramar.

As aircrew learned to master their sophisticated weapons system, the F-14 was gradually integrated into carrier operations. Despite teething troubles, the Tomcat was already turning into the world's finest interceptor.

By the end of March 1985 the US Navy had taken delivery of 509 F-14As from its planned total of 899 aircraft. Two landmark aircraft (the 400th and the 500th) were delivered less than one year apart, both going to the prestigious VF-1.

Iranian orders

The Imperial Iranian Air Force (IIAF) became the first and only foreign purchaser of the Tomcat, ordering 40 aircraft in June 1974 and 40 more in January 1975. Iranian Tomcats were virtually identical to US Navy F-14As and their Phoenix missiles were almost exactly the same, except for deletion of the ECCM suite.

The first Iranian Tomcats were delivered to Mehrabad on 27 January 1976, and eventually equipped four squadrons at Khatami and Shiraz. After 79 of the 80 Tomcats had been delivered, aircraft No. 80 being retained for trials, the Persian state was swept by revolution, culminating in the fall of the Shah. This killed off all prospects for a planned repeat order for 70 more F-14s, and for the supply of 400 additional Phoenix missiles.

Tomcat finale

*A VF-102 **F-14B** takes the wire during exercises. The **F110** engine employed by the **F-14B** and **F-14D** allowed the aircraft to be launched in military power, increased combat radius by 62 per cent and gave the pilot the benefit of carefree engine-handling.*

By 2006, when the last USN Tomcats were retired, the F-14 was almost four decades old. Its replacement is the multi-role F/A-18, especially in its E/F forms. Meanwhile, the Tomcat survives in service with Iran.

During the late 1970s the F-14 Tomcat was widely regarded as the most important aircraft in the US Navy, and was the dream billet for any ambitious trainee naval aviator.

Every US Navy aircraft-carrier (apart from the tiny *Coral Sea* and *Midway*) embarked a pair of F-14 squadrons, and these units were the oldest, most historic and proudest fighter squadrons in the Fleet. Only the Tomcat was felt to be capable of defending the Carrier Battle Group from long-range cruise missile carriers, with its unmatched potential to fire off a salvo of up to six ultra long-range Phoenix AAMs against high- or low-flying targets, and then to deal with any 'leakers' with Sidewinders or the internal 20-mm cannon. And nor was the Tomcat a lumbering bomber-destroyer. Agile and with phenomenal acceleration, the F-14 was a better dogfighter than the F-4 and was superior in a close-in fight to the F-8.

Remarkably, even more than 30 years after it entered service, the F-14 retained a ragged glamour, and, up until its retirement, many regarded it as being the pivotal element within any carrier air wing. However, the credibility of the AIM-54 Phoenix was dented by a poor showing in combat and trials, while the F-14 could not carry the AIM-120 AMRAAM. Plans to integrate the AIM-120 were cancelled, leaving the aircraft reliant on the ageing AIM-7 Sparrow and the AIM-54 in the BVR sector.

Although the weapon recorded numerous successes in Iranian

***Right:** Iran possesses a strong **F-14** force, maintained mostly from local spares sources. The **Hawk SAM** has been integrated onto the aircraft as a medium-range **AAM**, and is known locally as the **AIM-23C Sedjil**.*

*Pictured here is a **USN F-14A** painted for aggressor training. As well as serving in the adversary role with the Naval Strike Air Warfare Center, F-14s performed various test duties.*

The Tomcat left US service in 2006, ousted by Boeing's Super Hornet, especially the two-seat version. The F-14 was active to the last, however, dropping a bomb over Iraq during its final sortie on 8 February 2006.

hands, the only time six USN AIM-54s were ever fired together (against a close-packed formation of radar-signature augmented drones), just three missiles actually hit their targets. Impressive as an air-to-air dogfighter when it entered service, the F-14's agility was never on a par with that of the slightly newer teen-series fighters (F-15, F-16 and F/A-18), nor of aircraft like the Su-27. Against such aircraft, the Tomcat relies on its BVR capability, on superior tactics, and on the greater situational awareness that a well coordinated two-person crew can enjoy.

The original F-14A model was always severely constrained by the unreliability and limitations of its TF30 engines, which accounted for heavy losses of aircraft and aircrew. For many years, the Tomcat had little multi-role versatility, although it proved a remarkably useful tactical reconnaissance platform when equipped with the TARPS pod, and every Carrier Air Wing included two or three TARPS-capable F-14s. This recce capability was enhanced in later years by the addition of a digital TARPS reconnaissance pod and real-time datalink.

A shortage of F-14 airframes, coupled with the realisation that the F/A-18 Hornet was a more versatile aircraft, especially in the post-Cold War world, led to a dramatic reduction in the F-14 fleet. The composition of the Carrier Air Wing was revised, with only a single F-14 unit and three squadrons of F/A-18s (which could include a USMC Hornet unit) deployed aboard most carriers. Only two Air Wings (CVW-7 aboard the USS *Dwight D. Eisenhower* and CVW-8 aboard the USS *Theodore Roosevelt*) retained paired Tomcat squadrons – a result of a shortfall in F/A-18 numbers rather than a deliberate 'pro-Tomcat' choice.

By the mid-1990s, the Tomcat force was thus reduced from 28 squadrons (with separate Atlantic and Pacific Fleet training units) to just 12, with a single training unit. All of these (except VF-154) were based at NAS Oceana. The exception was based at Atsugi in Japan, where it supported CVW-5 aboard the USS *Kitty Hawk*.

This drawdown left three squadrons with the F-14D (VF-2, VF-11 and VF-31), four with the F-14B (VF-102, VF-103, VF-143 and VF-211) and five with the F-14A (VF-14, VF-32, VF-41, VF-154 and VF-213). A shortage of F-14Ds led to the conversion of VF-11 to the F-14B in 1997, though VF-213 subsequently re-equipped with the F-14D version, VF-211 transitioned back to the F-14A, while VF-32 gained F-14Bs.

Persian 'cats

In Iran, the Tomcat also found a single export customer. A peek beneath the veil of security surrounding the aircraft reveals that as many as 44 Iranian F-14s remain operational early in 2007. These have been subject to local upgrade and are now armed with a range of indigenous weaponry, including Fatter IR-guided AAMs (similar in appearance to the AIM-9P Sidewinder) and a reverse-engineered version of the AIM-54 Phoenix. Iran has also tested the F-14 in the air-to-ground role and integrated the Russian R-73 AAM.

The US F-14 force began assuming a limited clear-weather attack capability in 1992, and some began referring to the aircraft as the 'Bombcat'. Limited all-weather air-to-ground PGM capability was then provided through the integration of the LANTIRN (Low-Altitude Navigation and Targeting Infra-Red for Night) laser designator, and the aircraft could deliver a range of LGBs, dumb 'iron' bombs, Cluster Bomb Units and unguided rockets.

Work then moved on to integrating GPS-guided munitions, including JDAM (Joint Direct Attack Munition) though, even with all these capabilities, the only real advantage of the 'Bombcat' over the F/A-18C/D (let alone the far more capable F/A-18E/F) lay in its superior range and radius of action. Its disadvantages included very poor serviceability and huge operating costs.

The US Navy's F-14s remained in active service until 2006, seeing combat during Operation Iraqi Freedom. After 36 years of service, the Tomcat was officially retired by the USN during a ceremony held at NAS Oceana on 22 September 2006.

Open-air maintenance was standard practice at NAS Oceana. The base previously housed A-6s alongside its F-14s, but the A-6 apron was later turned over to the F/A-18.

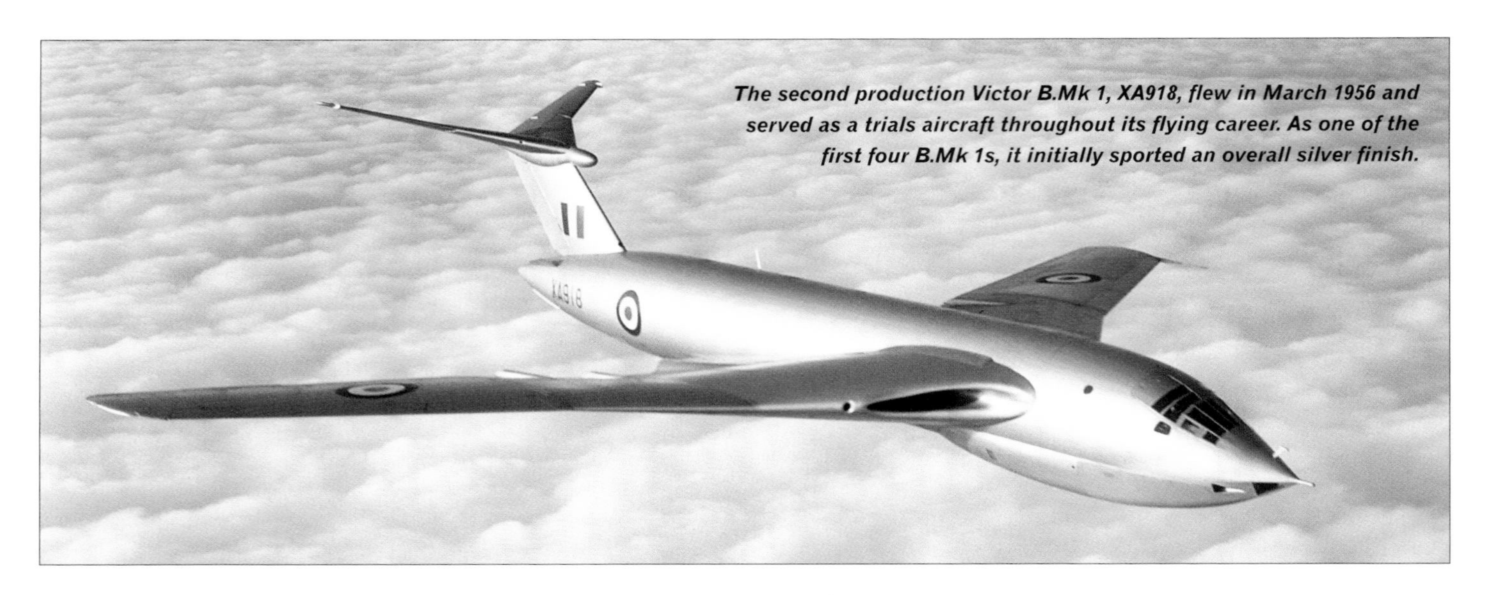

The second production Victor B.Mk 1, XA918, flew in March 1956 and served as a trials aircraft throughout its flying career. As one of the first four B.Mk 1s, it initially sported an overall silver finish.

Handley Page Victor

The third V-bomber

Designed in response to an urgent requirement for a new generation of jet bombers for the RAF, Handley Page's Victor made up one third of the famous triumvirate of V-bombers, along with the Avro Vulcan and Vickers Valiant.

The H.P.88 was a 0.4-scale flying test model for the Victor. A Supermarine Swift fuselage was used as the basis of the airframe which incorporated Krüger nose flaps, elevons and an all-moving tailplane. The sole example was destroyed after breaking up during a calibration run at Stansted, Essex, on 26 August 1951.

One month after Germany's surrender in World War II and, significantly, two months before atomic bombs destroyed Hiroshima and Nagasaki, Sir Frederick Handley Page instructed his staff to examine the practicability of a jet bomber weighing 100,000 lb (45360 kg) all-up and with wings swept at an angle of 40°. Some changes were made in the proposal when German work on high-speed flight was studied during the weeks which followed, and in February 1946 the designation H.P.80 was bestowed on an aircraft powered by four scaled-down Rolls-Royce Avons. With a span of 122 ft (37.19 m), the H.P.80 would carry four crew and a 10,000-lb (4536-kg) load over 5,000 miles (8047 km) at 600 mph (966 km/h).

The Air Staff had also been addressing the problem of bringing Bomber Command simultaneously into the jet and nuclear ages, the result being the issue of Operational Requirements 229 and 230. Both aircraft envisaged in these studies were to carry a bombload of up to 30,000 lb (13608 kg), but the principal store was an atomic device weighing an estimated 10,000 lb (4536 kg). OR 229 covered a medium-range aircraft having an operational radius of 1,725 miles (2776 km), while OR 230 was the long-range counterpart which would weigh up to 200,000 lb (90718 kg) and have a radius of 2,300 miles (3701 km). Soon it became clear that to proceed with OR 230 would cause a considerable drain on limited financial resources. As the medium-range aircraft would satisfy most requirements, OR 229 was translated into an official specification, B.35/46.

Advanced submissions from Avro and Handley Page were selected for further development, but the Air Staff was never able to make a decision between the two designs and so the competitors became partners in RAF service: Avro's Vulcan and Handley Page's Victor.

The Victor shapes up

Several configurations were examined before the H.P.80 adopted its production form. The key to meeting the exacting specification was in the wing design, to which the Handley Page team gave further consideration. Achievement of high speeds at operating altitudes between 35,000 and 50,000 ft (10670 and 15240 m) was

The first H.P.80 Victor prototype is seen here in the company's colours. The aircraft incorporated the original short nose and taller fin, two features that had a major influence on the test programme.

dependent upon ensuring a constant critical Mach number along the whole length of wing, despite its taper. An answer was found in the 'crescent' leading edge in which the sweepback began at 48.5° and then declined to 37.5° for the centre panels and 26.75° outboard. The H.P.88 research aircraft was to have tested this planform at 0.4 scale, but before any useful work could be done, it crashed.

By August 1952 the first of two H.P.80 prototypes (ordered in April 1948) had been named Victor and was taken by road to Boscombe Down for its maiden flight. The Victor took to the air on Christmas Eve 1952.

Structural failure

Testing came to a temporary and tragic end on 14 July 1954 when the prototype crashed after its tailplane broke away during a high-speed run. Investigations revealed that a series of fatigue cracks had developed around the fin, the remedy being to reduce stress in the area – outwardly manifested by a reduction of fin height by 15 in (38.10 cm).

It was therefore the second prototype which began A&AEE handling trials in March 1955, following its first flight on the previous 11 September. The way was then clear for the company to continue with manufacture of the first 25 Victor B.Mk 1 bombers, which had been ordered in June 1952.

Five crew members were required for the Victor, of which two were pilots and the remainder performed functions under the titles Air Electronics Officer, Nav-Radar and Nav-Plotter. Unlike the Valiant and Vulcan, all five were seated at the same level, though only the pilots had ejection seats.

Immediately below the pressure cabin was the H_2S radar scanner, allied to a navigation and bombing computer plus a radar bombsight. With a normal all-up weight of 160,000 lb (72575 kg), the Victor B.Mk 1 had a still-air range of 5,020 miles (8079 km) while carrying a 10,000-lb (4536-kg) bombload, and could cross the target at 50,800 ft (15485 m) in that condition. The Victor's ceiling technically exceeded that of the Vulcan, though the Avro aircraft had more powerful engines. The Victor's four Sapphire ASSa.7 Mk 202s each delivered a maximum of 11,050 lb (49.73 kN) thrust. For overload take-offs, eventually cleared up to 205,000 lb (92986 kg), a de Havilland Spectre rocket of 8,000 lb (36 kN) thrust could be attached below the wing between each pair of engines.

In bomb bay capacity, too, the Victor exceeded its V-bomber compatriots. It could carry (at the expense of range) one 22,000-lb (9979-kg) Grand Slam, two 12,000-lb (5443-kg) Tallboys, three 10,000-lb (4536-kg) conventional bombs, 35 1,000-lb (454-kg) bombs or 17 2,000-lb (907-kg) sea mines. The total of 35 1,000-lb (454-kg) bombs was an RAF operational limit, though no fewer than 48 could actually be stowed internally. For reconnaissance, bomb bay crates held 15 cameras and 150 photoflashes, backed by another 110 of the latter in external carriers.

Supersonic

The first production Victor flew on 1 February 1956. During company trials it smoothly, though accidentally, exceeded Mach 1 in a shallow dive on 1 June 1957, becoming the largest aircraft to have done so at that time.

Service use of the Victor began on 28 November 1957 with the type's issue to 'A' Squadron of No. 232 Operational Conversion Unit at Gaydon, and in April 1958 the OCU's first graduates formed two units. Lesser known of these was the Wyton-based Radar Reconnaissance Flight, whose three aircraft were equipped with Yellow Aster sensors. The first Victor bomber squadron was No. 10 at Cottesmore, to which an initial three Victors were delivered on 9 April.

In the course of 1958, a two-squadron (Nos 10 and 15) wing was established at Cottesmore, equipped with B.Mk 1s. Exercises regularly tested the V-force's ability to scramble and to disperse its aircraft to airfields around the UK. QRA was introduced on 1 January 1962, requiring each squadron to maintain one (later two) aircraft at fully armed 15-minute readiness. During exercises, aircraft demonstrated the capability to get airborne within four minutes of the alert being received.

Beginning at the start of 1959, a second Victor wing was established at Honington, comprising Nos 55 and 57 Squadrons with Victor B.Mk 1As. The B.Mk 1A featured several important modifications, including provision for an inflight refuelling probe, tail-warning radar, the fitting of drooped leading edges, new ECM equipment and the strengthening of the pressure cabin.

Above: The key to the Victor's performance was the crescent-shaped wing, which allowed a high cruising speed without making the take-off or landing speeds prohibitively high.

Below: In the late 1950s the Victor was a graceful, futuristic shape. However, its splendid anti-flash white scheme belied its true purpose: to deliver Britain's strategic deterrent to the heart of the Warsaw Pact. This B.Mk 1 wears the badge of No. 15 Sqn.

Service history

As the last of the V-bombers to enter service, the Victor was overshadowed by the majestic Vulcan. However, for 10 years it played a smaller, yet no less vital, part in the V-force which provided the United Kingdom with its strategic nuclear deterrent.

The first Victor B.Mk 2s arrived in service with Nos 100 and 139 Squadrons at Wittering in 1962, No. 232 OCU having received its first B.Mk 2 on 1 November 1961. A third B.Mk 2 squadron had been planned, to operate alongside the other two in the Blue Steel missile role, but the aircraft were switched, as SR.Mk 2s, to strategic recce, replacing the Valiant B(PR).Mk 1s with No. 543 Squadron.

The major design change on the Mk 2 was the installation of a new powerplant, the 17,250-lb st (77.60-kN) Rolls-Royce Conway RCo.11. Handley Page received a contract for 21 Victor B.Mk 2s in June 1956 and, following ground-testing of the new engines, the wingroot area was redesigned, with the engine bays and intakes deepened and widened.

The Victor B.Mk 1/1A force was withdrawn from the bomber role in 1964/65, beginning with the disbandment of No. 10 Squadron. No. 15 followed, while Nos 55 and 57 transferred to the tanker role, a transition hastened by the retirement of the Valiant.

During Blue Steel trials, a single Victor B.Mk 2 was modified to incorporate additional electronic equipment and certain design changes, including streamlined fairing pods known as 'Küchemann carrots' on the wing trailing edge. This aircraft, with all its modifications, was the first of the new B.Mk 2R version – the 'R' standing for 'Retrofit'.

Victor weapons

When they entered V-force service, Victors were armed with the Blue Danube weapon. This was the UK's first nuclear weapon, and despite its huge size had a kiloton-class yield.

Following the relaxation of nuclear controls by the United States, the RAF began to receive US-owned weapons in late 1958 for use by V-force bombers. To cover for delays in the development of the British H-bomb, Mk 5 hydrogen bombs were stored at V-force airfields and made available for three wings. Vulcans and Valiants were the first recipients, but when the Honington Victor B.Mk 1A wing was established in 1959/60, it was assigned the US weapons. The Honington Victors were the first to give up US weapons, the switch to Yellow Sun Mk 1s occurring on 1 July 1961.

In 1960 two new British weapons were introduced, the megaton Yellow Sun Mk 1 and kiloton Red Beard. Red Beard was in essence a 15-kT tactical weapon, two of which could be carried by the Victor, although this was largely considered a 'reserve' weapon.

In 1961 Yellow Sun Mk 2 was introduced. This had a new Red Snow warhead, as was also fitted to the Blue Steel missile.

When the Wittering Wing began Victor B.Mk 2 operations in 1962, it did so with Yellow Sun Mk 2 as its primary weapon, with Red Beards as back-up. Due to delays with the B.Mk 2R/Blue Steel programme, it was not until 24 October 1963 that No. 139 Squadron flew the wing's first mission with its intended weapon – the Blue Steel missile.

Low-level role

By the time Blue Steel became operational on the Victor, the force had made the switch to

Above: A Victor B.Mk 1A from No. 57 Squadron patrols along the Malayan coast during a mission from Tengah. Although they never dropped bombs, the four-aircraft Victor detachments provided a powerful show-of-force during the Indonesian Confrontation.

Top: From 1963 the Victor force operated at low-level, requiring new tactics and, from 1964, a new paint job. This is a B.Mk 2R from Wittering's No. 139 (Jamaica) Squadron.

After the Falklands War, the Victor fleet acquired the hemp colour scheme, which they wore until retirement in 1993. This No. 55 Sqn aircraft is refuelling a pair of No. 208 Sqn Buccaneer S.Mk 2s.

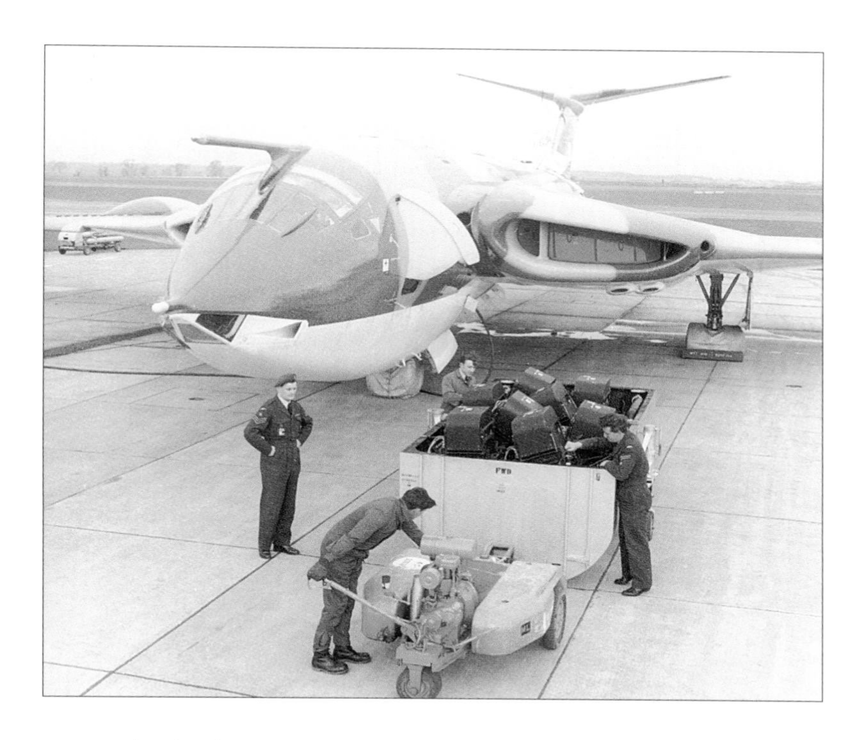

The last nine Victor B.Mk 2R conversions were modified as SR.Mk 2 reconnaissance variants. The SR.Mk 2's day reconnaissance camera crate was housed in the bomb bay, along with two large fuel tanks.

low-level operations, brought on by advances in Soviet SAM technology. Training for the new mission began in March 1963.

B.Mk 2Rs continued in the Blue Steel role until the end of 1968, after which the Royal Navy's Polaris submarines assumed the UK's strategic deterrent duties.

No. 543 Squadron disbanded in May 1974, its role having been taken over by the Vulcans of No. 27 Squadron. However, the reconnaissance role was briefly revived in 1982 when Victors from Nos 55 and 57 Squadrons conducted MRR during the Falklands conflict.

It had been planned that the Victor would replace the Valiant in the tanker role, and conversion work began in December 1964. By May 1965, No. 55 Squadron, which had relinquished its bombing role in March 1965, was fully operational in the tanker role. The intended fitment was a hose pod on each wing and a hose drum unit (HDU) in the rear of the bomb-bay, though such was the urgency that the first six had only the wing units.

More Victors were freed by the disbandment of Nos 10 and 15 Squadrons in 1964, allowing the production of 10 examples of the full-conversion Victor B(K).Mk 1 and 14 full-conversion Victor B(K).Mk 1As. These were redesignated Victor K.Mk 1 and Victor K.Mk 1A in 1968, while the six two-point aircraft became B.Mk 1A(K2P)s.

B.Mk 2 tankers

Tanker conversions of the Victor B.Mk 2 were planned to replace earlier aircraft, and the first Victor K.Mk 2 flew in March 1972. Deliveries began to No. 232 OCU at Marham in May 1974. No. 55 Squadron was declared operational with the new variant in July 1975, followed by No. 57. A total of 24 K.Mk 2s was converted. It was as tankers that Victors took part in the 1982 Falklands War, while the Iraqi invasion of Kuwait in August 1990 provided the Victor tankers with more battle honours before retirement. On 15 October 1993, No. 55 Squadron stood down as a Victor unit and the era of the V-bombers came to an end.

Victor B.Mk 2R

Powered by RCo.17 engines, and fitted with 'Küchemann carrots' and a full ECM fit, the B.Mk 2R was the ultimate Victor bomber version, although it was armed primarily with a single Avro Blue Steel missile. Until the Douglas Skybolt missile was cancelled in December 1962, it had been envisaged that some B.Mk 2s would carry these US-built aero-ballistic weapons.

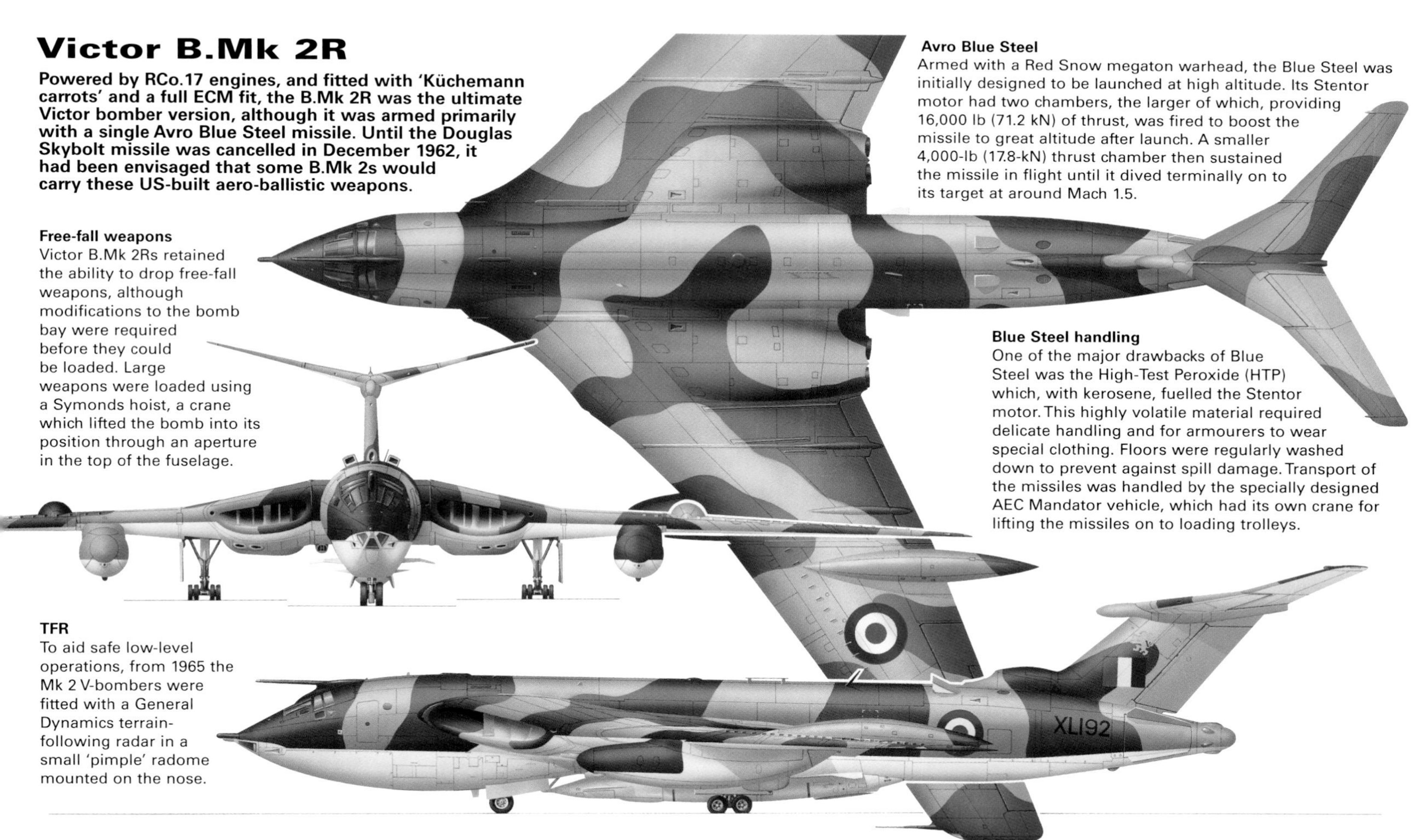

Free-fall weapons
Victor B.Mk 2Rs retained the ability to drop free-fall weapons, although modifications to the bomb bay were required before they could be loaded. Large weapons were loaded using a Symonds hoist, a crane which lifted the bomb into its position through an aperture in the top of the fuselage.

TFR
To aid safe low-level operations, from 1965 the Mk 2 V-bombers were fitted with a General Dynamics terrain-following radar in a small 'pimple' radome mounted on the nose.

Avro Blue Steel
Armed with a Red Snow megaton warhead, the Blue Steel was initially designed to be launched at high altitude. Its Stentor motor had two chambers, the larger of which, providing 16,000 lb (71.2 kN) of thrust, was fired to boost the missile to great altitude after launch. A smaller 4,000-lb (17.8-kN) thrust chamber then sustained the missile in flight until it dived terminally on to its target at around Mach 1.5.

Blue Steel handling
One of the major drawbacks of Blue Steel was the High-Test Peroxide (HTP) which, with kerosene, fuelled the Stentor motor. This highly volatile material required delicate handling and for armourers to wear special clothing. Floors were regularly washed down to prevent against spill damage. Transport of the missiles was handled by the specially designed AEC Mandator vehicle, which had its own crane for lifting the missiles on to loading trolleys.

Hawker Hunter

Camm's masterwork

The Hawker Hunter is undoubtedly one of the world's all-time great fighters. Superb handling won it the love of those lucky enough to fly it, while its graceful lines won it a wider circle of admirers.

Designed by Sidney Camm and his talented team at Hawker – many of whom had previously worked on aircraft such as the Fury, Hurricane, Typhoon, Tempest and Sea Hawk – the Hunter was one of the UK's first swept-wing interceptors. Although the Hunter briefly held the world speed record, it was never at the cutting edge of fighter design, and was actually less advanced, in certain minor respects, than some of the swept-wing fighters from the US which preceded it, including the F-86 Sabre.

Teething problems

On entering service, the first variant of the Hunter was in many ways a disappointment. Limited internal fuel capacity gave the aircraft a tiny radius of action – it was possible to run the tanks dry in 11 minutes at full throttle and very low level. Moreover, the early Rolls-Royce Avon engines powering the Mk 1 suffered from surging problems, especially when the guns were fired at high altitudes.

However, these difficulties proved to be little more than teething problems, and with the advent of the F.Mk 4 (and especially the 'big-bore' F.Mk 6) the Hunter became a highly effective tactical fighter, especially in the air-to-ground role. Development of the Hunter reached its apogee with the RAF's FGA.Mk 9 (and a number of similar export derivatives).

Above: More than 40 years after entering RAF service, Britain was still operating the Hunter in the form of the T.Mk 7 used by the Empire Test Pilot's School at Boscombe Down. This particular aircraft was lost in an accident in 1998.

Above: The Hunter F.Mk 6 single-seat fighter became a favourite formation aerobatic mount for a number of Royal Air Force squadrons (such as No. 111 Squadron's Black Arrows) during the 1950s and 1960s. Here the No. 92 Squadron Blue Diamonds display team of 1963 practises its routine.

Left: A total of 47 Hunters was acquired by the Singapore air force in both single-and two-seat variants. These three single-seat F.Mk 74Bs were operated by No. 140 Squadron in the mid-1980s. Both the F.Mk 74s and the two-seat T.Mk 75s continued in service until the early 1990s.

***Above:* Seen during trial flights in July 1955, this Hunter F.Mk 50 was the first production example for the Swedish air force. Based on the F.Mk 4, this variant lacked the dogtooth wing leading edge.**

***Right:* Among many Middle East customers for the Hunter was Kuwait, which received six single-seat FGA.Mk 57s and five T.Mk 67 two-seat trainers.**

These aircraft combined excellent performance with a heavy warload, yet retained the Hunter's traditionally superb handling characteristics.

The Hunter proved extremely popular with export customers, and its modular construction made refurbishing even the oldest aircraft a viable proposition. Aircraft relegated to ground instructional duties were sold back to Hawker Siddeley which rebuilt them for extended service with new operators. Sales of refurbished, 'second-hand' Hunters made the aircraft one of the most successful products of Britain's aircraft industry in the post-war period.

But while the Hunter won fame as a superb ground-attack weapon, the aircraft was also a useful air combat trainer, with the powerful Avon engine giving good acceleration and the big wing allowing a surprisingly good rate of turn, especially in conjunction with combat flap. The Hunter also packed an impressive punch with its highly concentrated battery of four 30-mm cannon.

Indian Hunters racked up an impressive combat record (contrary to the claims of the Pakistanis and their apologists), proving superior to the Sabre and F-104 in close-in engagements. In Arab hands Hunters proved to be among the toughest opposition encountered by Israeli pilots. In two Middle Eastern wars Jordanian and Iraqi Hunters scored combat victories against Israeli fighters, including the IDF/AF's much vaunted and Mach 2-capable Mirage III.

Missile capable

Air combat capability was dramatically enhanced by the addition of AIM-9 Sidewinders in Swiss, Singapore, Omani and Chilean service, but missile-armed Hunters never saw combat.

Hunters were finally withdrawn from front-line RAF service in the early 1970s, but then went on to serve with great distinction in the advanced and tactical fighter weapons training roles. Elsewhere, Hunters remained in front-line service into the 1990s, and a handful remained active in Zimbabwe as late as 1997.

A handful of air arms still operated the Hunter in second-line duties into the 21st century. The type long remained a fixture with the Empire Test Pilot's School, being prized for its ability to undertake deliberate inverted spinning, the only swept-wing aircraft cleared to do so.

A growing number of Hunters are being restored to flying condition as civilian-owned 'warbirds', and the distinctive note of the Hunter's Avon engine will remain a common sound for many years to come.

From the second batch of refurbished Hunter F.Mk 58As delivered to Switzerland in 1974-75, this ex-RAF F.Mk 4 (WW590) is seen carrying two AIM-9 Sidewinder missiles for the air-to-air role.

British service

No. 208 Squadron took over No. 34 Squadron's Hunter Mk 5s at RAF Tangmere in January 1958, converting to Mk 6s the following month and moving to Nicosia, Cyprus, in March and then to the Middle East. These were the first Hunters to see service in the region.

The first production Hunters finally entered RAF service in 1954, and the type was not retired from front-line service until 1976. Though never a front-line type in the FAA, the Hunter saw over 20 years of valuable service in important support roles.

Meteor F.Mk 8-equipped fighter unit No. 43 Squadron introduced the Hunter F.Mk 1 into RAF service in July 1954 and was followed in its re-equipment by No. 222 Squadron later in the year and No. 54 Squadron in February 1955, both units also relinquishing Meteor Mk 8s. No. 229 OCU also received 25 Hunter Mk 1s for conversion purposes. Although No. 43 Squadron operated its Mk 1s for two years, the early Hunter's career with the other units was shorter – just seven months in the case of No. 54 Squadron. All three units received Hunter Mk 4s during 1956/57.

The Sapphire-engined F.Mk 2s comprised 45 aircraft, No. 257 Squadron taking delivery of the first examples in September 1954. No. 257 was based at RAF Wattisham alongside the only other unit to fly the Mk 2, No. 263 Squadron, which received its aircraft in February 1955. Thus, by this time, the RAF had five Hunter squadrons on an operational footing, but subject to a range of restrictions and hindered by poor endurance.

It was not until the advent of the much improved Mk 4 that RAF Fighter Command had a practical Hunter interceptor. In March 1955 No. 54 Squadron received the first operational examples, No. 98 Squadron, 2nd TAF (RAF Germany from 1 January 1959) following suit in April. No. 118 Squadron at Jever converted to the Hunter in May 1955, and was followed by Nos 4, 14, 26 and 20 Squadrons over the next six months, replacing Sabres and Venoms.

The Hunter F.Mk 5 was, to the Mk 2, what the Mk 4 was to the Mk 1 and incorporated the same improvements to fuel capacity. With no facilities for the maintenance of Sapphire-engined aircraft in Germany, the variant was largely confined to home-based units. Like the Mk 4, the Mk 5 entered RAF service in 1955, serving Nos 56, 41, 1 and 34 Squadrons. The last named pair (forming the Tangmere Wing) were posted to Cyprus in 1956 to provide top cover during the Suez Crisis.

'Big bore' Mk 6

Even in its F.Mk 4 form, the Hunter was a severely restricted aircraft, which failed to fully exploit the design's considerable potential. The aircraft remained deficient in range, and its performance fell far short of the original requirement. Hawker proposed a number of supersonic Hunter designs, but the aircraft that entered RAF service with No. 19 Squadron in October 1956 as the F.Mk 6, was a Mk 4 derivative with more internal fuel and minor changes.

Powered by the improved 10,000-lb (44.48-kN) thrust 'big bore' Rolls-Royce Avon 203, the Hunter F.Mk 6 went on to equip another 18 squadrons at home and abroad.

Both single- and two-seat Hunters were important training types in the RAF. This is a T.Mk 7 of No. 4 TFS, charged with training overseas pilots and RAF trainees too big for the diminutive Gnat.

No. 257 Squadron flew Hunter F.Mk 2s for two and a half years before converting to the improved F.Mk 5. This Mk 2 carries the unit's green and yellow check markings.

Thirty-three Hunter Mk 6s were later converted to FR.Mk 10 standard during 1960/61. All served with units in RAF Germany and in the Middle East, replacing photo-reconnaissance Meteors.

Unique in terms of its procurement in that not a single new aircraft was built, the Hunter FGA.Mk 9 entered RAF service in January 1960, with No. 8 Squadron at Khormaksar (Aden). In the UK No. 1 Sqn also re-equipped in January, followed by the five remaining front-line Hunter units at home and in the Middle East Air Force (MEAF) and Far East Air Force (FEAF).

Middle East Air Force

Beginning in 1960, the Hunter began to take over the ground-attack role from the MEAF's Venoms. The command's 'resident' attack squadron – No. 8 Squadron – received FGA.Mk 9s in January and was followed shortly afterwards by No. 208 Squadron. (Among the first Hunters in the region had been the Mk 6s of No. 208 Squadron, based on Cyprus during 1958/59. Disbanded in March 1959, it had reformed immediately at Eastleigh, Kenya – by the renumbering of No. 142 Squadron – with Venoms.) No. 43 Squadron also received Mk 9s in 1960, moving to Cyprus (from Leuchars) the following year and joining the Khormaksar Hunter Wing in 1963.

The FEAF had two Hunter-equipped squadrons, No. 20 Squadron reforming at Tengah, Singapore, in September 1961 with FGA.Mk 9s. It was joined in May 1962 by No. 28 Sqn at Kai Tak (Hong Kong).

The Hunter had originally been retired by the front-line RAF in 1969, but made a return in 1974 when No. 45 Squadron was formed as a post-Tactical Weapons Unit 'first tour' posting for prospective Jaguar pilots. The squadron later split to form a second unit, No. 58 Squadron; both were disbanded in 1976.

The Hunter was always an important second-line type in the RAF, the service's last examples being those engaged in Buccaneer aircrew training. The Buccaneer OCU disbanded in 1991, its last Hunter T.Mk 7Ds going to No. 208 Squadron for the remaining three years of the Buccaneer's service, which finally ended in 1994.

Royal Navy aircraft

It was in support roles that the Fleet Air Arm's Hunters served. Converted from surplus RAF Hunter Mk 4s, the first of the FAA's 40 GA.Mk 11 tactical weapons trainers entered service with No. 738 NAS in 1962, these machines serving for 23 years, latterly alongside T.Mk 8Cs and a pair of ex-RAF T.Mk 7s.

The Navy also took delivery of 41 'navalised' Hunter T.Mk 8s, in a number of sub-variants, which were issued principally to Nos 736 and 764 NASs for operational conversion and instructor training.

Hunter T.Mk 8

An aircraft of No. 738 Naval Air Squadron based at RNAS Brawdy during 1965, XL598 was one of the first batch of 10 new-build Hunter T.Mk 8s (actually ordered as Mk 7s for the RAF) and made its first flight on 15 October 1958. The aircraft is marked with Brawdy's 'BY' codes and the Pegasus from its squadron emblem.

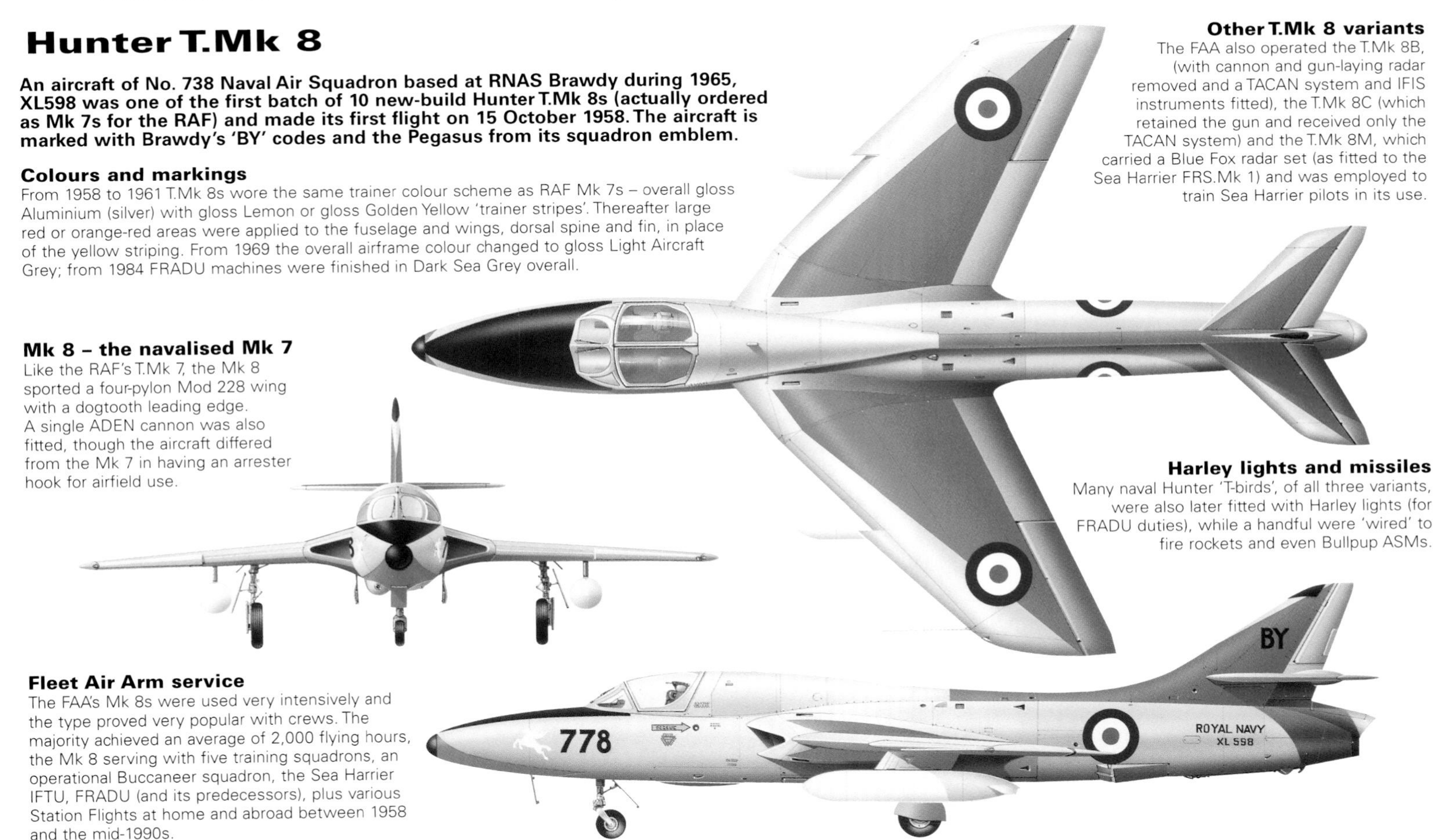

Colours and markings
From 1958 to 1961 T.Mk 8s wore the same trainer colour scheme as RAF Mk 7s – overall gloss Aluminium (silver) with gloss Lemon or gloss Golden Yellow 'trainer stripes'. Thereafter large red or orange-red areas were applied to the fuselage and wings, dorsal spine and fin, in place of the yellow striping. From 1969 the overall airframe colour changed to gloss Light Aircraft Grey; from 1984 FRADU machines were finished in Dark Sea Grey overall.

Other T.Mk 8 variants
The FAA also operated the T.Mk 8B, (with cannon and gun-laying radar removed and a TACAN system and IFIS instruments fitted), the T.Mk 8C (which retained the gun and received only the TACAN system) and the T.Mk 8M, which carried a Blue Fox radar set (as fitted to the Sea Harrier FRS.Mk 1) and was employed to train Sea Harrier pilots in its use.

Mk 8 – the navalised Mk 7
Like the RAF's T.Mk 7, the Mk 8 sported a four-pylon Mod 228 wing with a dogtooth leading edge. A single ADEN cannon was also fitted, though the aircraft differed from the Mk 7 in having an arrester hook for airfield use.

Harley lights and missiles
Many naval Hunter 'T-birds', of all three variants, were also later fitted with Harley lights (for FRADU duties), while a handful were 'wired' to fire rockets and even Bullpup ASMs.

Fleet Air Arm service
The FAA's Mk 8s were used very intensively and the type proved very popular with crews. The majority achieved an average of 2,000 flying hours, the Mk 8 serving with five training squadrons, an operational Buccaneer squadron, the Sea Harrier IFTU, FRADU (and its predecessors), plus various Station Flights at home and abroad between 1958 and the mid-1990s.

Hawker Sea Hawk

Kingston's first jet

The Sea Hawk enjoyed some export success – beginning in 1958, West Germany took delivery of 68 Mk 100s and radar-equipped Mk 101s. VA+229 was an example of the anti-ship Mk 100.

Conceived as a land-based interceptor, the P.1040 nearly failed to leave the drawing-board, the Meteor and Vampire meeting the Air Ministry's post-war requirements. However, modified to fit a Royal Navy specification, the Sea Hawk, as the P.1040 became, went on to see 30 years' service with four nations.

By the end of World War II, Hawker had acquired an enviable reputation as a producer of successful piston-engined aircraft. As the jet age dawned, its staff turned their attention towards this new form of propulsion, in the hope that it could maintain Air Ministry interest in its designs.

Thus, the P.1040 was a private venture – a single-engined jet fighter design aimed at either the RAF and/or the Royal Navy. In early 1946 the Ministry of Aircraft Production, sufficiently impressed with the aircraft, ordered three prototypes for evaluation, though by then any potential RAF interest had waned, orders having been placed for the Meteor F.Mk 4.

The first P.1040, a fairly conventional aircraft with unswept wings and powered by a 4,500-lb (20.25-kN) thrust Rolls-Royce Nene turbojet buried in its fuselage, was first flown on 2 September 1947. It was followed by the remaining prototypes, though these were completed to meet naval specification N.7/46, with folding wings, catapult and arrester gear and four 20-mm cannon in a belly pack. N.7/46 called for a carrierborne jet fighter and successful trials in 1949 aboard HMS *Illustrious* led to an order being placed later that year for 151 Sea Hawk F.Mk 1s, powered by a 5,000-lb (22.5-kN) thrust Nene Mk 101. Other features of the first production variant included an ejection seat, pressurised cockpit and a mainplane of increased span to improve take-off and landing performance.

Armstrong Whitworth

In fact, only the first 35 of these aircraft were actually built and were the only Sea Hawks built by Hawker. With large-scale Hunter production for the RAF about to begin, insufficient capacity at Hawker's Kingston factory led to the transfer of the entire project to Armstrong Whitworth.

Sea Hawk deployment by the FAA peaked around the time of the Suez Crisis. Seen during 1957-58, the deck of HMS* Ark Royal *hosts FGA.Mk 6s of No. 804 NAS (in the foreground) and FB.Mk 5s of No. 802 NAS. To the right are Sea Venom FAW.Mk 21s of No. 893 NAS.

Sea Hawk FGA.Mk 6s of No. 300 'White Tiger' Squadron, Indian Navy, share the deck of the carrier INS Vikrant *with an Alouette III helicopter and a number of Alizé turboprop ASW aircraft.*

No. 806 Squadron, Fleet Air Arm, the first unit to re-equip with the type, received nine Sea Hawks in March 1953, operating from HMS *Eagle* from early 1954. Nos 804 and 898 Squadrons followed suit shortly afterwards, their aircraft including some of the 60 Mk 1s built by Armstrong Whitworth (the balance of the original 151-aircraft Hawker order having been cancelled).

These were followed by 40 Sea Hawk F.Mk 2s (with powered ailerons to correct lateral control problems), most of which went to No. 806 Squadron from February 1954.

The third Sea Hawk production batch, of 116 aircraft, was made up of the most widely-used of the early Sea Hawk variants, the FB.Mk 3 fighter-bomber. This served with five front-line FAA squadrons, from both carrier and shore bases.

The next Sea Hawks off the production line were 97 FGA.Mk 4s, equipped with an extra pair of underwing pylons.

Official concerns about the type's flagging performance resulted in the re-engining of about 50 FB.Mk 3s with Nene Mk 103 engines, rated at 5,200-lb (23.4-kN) thrust. These aircraft, redesignated FB.Mk 5s, re-equipped three FAA units.

Mk 6s in Suez action

A few Sea Hawk Mk 4s were also re-engined with the uprated Nene, as Mk 6s, and were followed by a production order for 86 FGA.Mk 6 aircraft, the last new Sea Hawks for the FAA. The final airframe was completed in 1956, the Mk 6 equipping six FAA units. Five of these squadrons, flying from three RN carriers, were among those aircraft called upon to support the Anglo-French Suez campaign in November 1956.

The Sea Hawk was slowly withdrawn from front-line FAA service, No. 806 Squadron finally disbanding in 1960.

Attempts to sell the Sea Hawk abroad met with moderate success, the production line being restarted twice to fulfil export orders placed by three air arms. From 1957, the Dutch naval air service received 32 Mk 50s (based on the Mk 6) for operation from the carrier HrMs *Karel Doorman*. Later equipped to carry Sidewinder AAMs, the last of these aircraft was withdrawn in 1964.

For land-based operation, West Germany ordered 68 Sea Hawks, including 34 Mk 100s. The balance were Mk 101 night-fighter/reconnaissance aircraft, with radar in an underwing pod.

Finally, India's navy joined the Sea Hawk 'club' in 1959. Its first nine aircraft were ex-FAA Mk 3s, refurbished to Mk 6 standard. These were followed by 14 new≠build Mk 6s and another 23 refurbished examples. When Germany withdrew its Sea Hawks in 1966, India purchased 10 Mk 100s and 18 Mk 101s. Based aboard INS *Vikrant* and at shore bases, India's Sea Hawks saw action against Pakistani targets in the 1971 war, a small number remaining in service until the early 1980s.

Withdrawn from front-line service in 1960, Sea Hawk FGA.Mk 6 WV908 (seen here) was restored to fly in the mid-1970s, taking to the air again in 1978 in the colours of No. 806 Squadron, FAA, having joined the RN Historic Flight.

During the 1968 Farnborough air show, the USMC was evaluating an early Harrier (right), seen here with one of the original T.Mk 2s. This test set in motion an order which would see 110 aircraft join the Corps, all of which were built by BAe at Kingston. The relationship with McDonnell Douglas was to prove crucial to the future of the Harrier programme.

Hawker Siddeley Harrier

V/STOL pioneer

Developed from the concept that numerous hidden dispersals were preferable to a vulnerable fixed base, the ground-breaking Harrier revolutionised aerial warfare and, with its VTOL capability, became one of the world's most instantly recognisable aircraft.

In the mid-1950s, when ideas were being formulated which, by painstaking developments, resulted in the Harrier, forward-thinking tacticians were looking with dismay at the fixed military installations upon which the security of NATO depended. On the principle that a moving target is more difficult to hit, there was an obvious need for a high-performance aircraft capable of operating away from vulnerable airfields. The answer to this problem was the combination of a French concept, American funding and assistance, and British industry. On 21 October 1960 the first Hawker P.1127 raised itself a few inches from the ground, supported on the four columns of air from a Bristol-Siddeley Pegasus vectored-thrust turbofan engine.

Much more work was required before what came to be known as the Harrier entered service with the RAF. At first, the P.1127 was seen merely as a concept-proving demonstrator for the P.1154, which would have also joined the Fleet Air Arm. Nine developed P.1127s, known as Kestrels, were flown, but even as an evaluation unit was being formed, the P.1154 was dropped on grounds of economy and an extensively redesigned aircraft, known as the Harrier GR.Mk 1, was chosen by the RAF.

***Spain's sole Harrier squadron was Escuadrilla 8ª. Working-up commenced in 1976 in the US before this unit was installed at Rota in December of that year for operations from the* Dedalo.**

Introduction to service began on 1 January 1969 with the formation at Wittering of the Harrier Conversion Unit and, on 1 October of that year, No. 1 Squadron was established as the world's first operational fixed-wing VTOL (vertical take-off and landing) unit. Pending arrival of the F-35, to date, only the Soviet Yakovlev Yak-38, with its outdated fixed lifting-engine concept, has joined the unique club founded by the Harrier.

The comparatively modest total of four RAF squadrons flew

A trio of No. 3 Squadron's Harrier GR.Mk 3s is pictured in flight. No. 3 was the last RAF Germany Harrier squadron to form. The unit's badge is a cockatrice perched on a Stonehenge lintel.

Both the surviving YAV-8B prototype, subsequently serialled 704, and this standard AV-8A, 718, were operated by NASA, wearing the blue and white NASA 'house colours'.

Below: The Harrier's baptism of fire came in the South Atlantic when Harriers of No. 1 Squadron (seen here on Ascension Island) were used to great effect in the ground-attack role during the re-taking of the Falkland Islands in 1982.

the early Harriers; these were assisted by an operational conversion unit (OCU) and two flights formed to meet demands in Belize and the Falkland Islands. No. 1 Squadron was assigned to rapid intervention roles and as such was involved in the 1982 Falklands War.

Permanently in the potential front line were the Harriers of RAF Germany. Three units (Nos 3, 4 and 20 Squadrons) were installed at Wildenrath in 1970/71. When No. 20 disbanded, the remaining two units absorbed its aircraft and moved forward to Gütersloh. Off-airfield roles were taken seriously, with the result that, about three times every year, the Gütersloh wing took to the German countryside to practise flying from dispersed sites. Squadrons usually divided into three flights for this purpose, hiding in the woods when not in the air.

For the sake of simplicity, the aircraft has previously been described as having VTOL capability. This is true, but even in its subsequent GR.Mk 3 configuration, with a 21,500-lb (96.75-kN) thrust Pegasus Mk 103 giving 2,500 lb (11.25 kN) more power than the engine first installed in the GR.Mk 1, the Harrier could not lift a worthwhile warload without a short take-off run. Thus, training operations were typically flown from a 200-yard (183-m) strip of aluminium planking, from which the aircraft leapt into the air after gathering forward speed. In wartime, a stretch of road would have sufficed equally well. Landing could be accomplished vertically when weapons had been expended.

US Marines service

Ironically, it was the US Marine Corps – the only American armed service not to take part in the original Kestrel trials – which went on to be the largest operator of all, taking into account the second-generation Harrier II aircraft.

Well before the advent of the Sea Harrier, or the operation of 10 No. 1 Squadron aircraft from HMS *Hermes* during the Falklands War, the US Marine Corps was regularly operating its 102 AV-8As and eight TAV-8A trainers from assault carriers. Delivered between 1971 and 1976, these aircraft were exactly what the USMC sought for close support of amphibious landings.

Spain's naval air force, the Arma Aérea de la Armada, bought an initial six AV-8As and two TAV-8As through the US Navy in 1973, these having the local designation VA.1 and VAE.1 Matador respectively. Five more single-seat aircraft, loosely known by the designation AV-8s, followed directly from the UK during 1980. Spain later turned to the more advanced Harrier II to replace the AV-8As, which were sold to Thailand. In 2007 these remained the only first-generation Harriers in front-line use, although their actual 'deck time' is very limited.

Below: Up to 5,000 lb (2268 kg) of weaponry could be attached to the Harrier's seven strongpoints, three of them beneath the fuselage. Weapons included the Hunting BL755 CBU or a pod containing 19 68-mm (2.68-in) Matra SNEB air-to-surface rockets.

Above: Spain's seven surviving VA.1s and two VAE.1s were sold for operations with the Royal Thai Navy's Air Division. Delivered in September 1997, these are embarked on the carrier **Chakri Naruebet.**

P.1127 to T.Mk 4

Several of No. 4 (AC) Squadron's Harrier GR.Mk 3s gained a colourful fin during their last couple of years of service.

First-generation British Harrier development

Development of the P.1127 family might have ended had not Europe's attempts to produce a supersonic VTOL combat aircraft finished in disaster. Announcement of the P.1154's cancellation was accompanied by a statement affirming the urgent need for a fully militarised P.1127 for the RAF's ground-attack squadrons, a contract for six pre-series machines being issued a mere 17 days after the P.1154's demise.

The Harrier has its origins in a 1957 agreement between Hawker and Bristol Aero-Engines to design a tactical aircraft around Bristol's BE.53 turbofan. This new engine was designed to produce direct jet-lift for vertical take-off and employed four nozzles, in fore-and-aft pairs, which were pivoted to vector the exhaust thrust. Hawker designed a small all-metal, shoulder-wing monoplane around the newly christened Pegasus engine.

Features of the airframe included pronounced anhedral on the wings and tailplane, large semi-circular intakes on each side of the fuselage and accommodation for a single pilot. The undercarriage consisted of single-wheel nose gear and a short main unit with twin wheels. These undercarriage members were mounted in tandem along the fuselage centreline. In addition, small wheels were mounted on a retractable outrigger leg located at each wing tip.

Designated Hawker P.1127, the first of six prototypes hovered for the first time on 21 October 1960. By 12 September 1961, complete transitions were being made between vertical and horizontal flight. Additional stability was provided by reaction control jets mounted in the nose, tail and each wing tip.

Initial contract

With the basic concept proven, Hawker Siddeley was awarded a contract for nine pre-production aircraft. These machines were intended for evaluation as operational fighter/ground-attack aircraft. Designated Kestrel F(GA).Mk 1, the first completed its maiden flight on 7 March 1964. Evaluation was tasked to a three-nation squadron, which included pilots from the RAF, Luftwaffe and three US armed services. Between April 1965 and April 1966 the unit tested the Kestrel under various simulated conditions.

However, the British government had already placed a February 1965 order for another six development aircraft. These machines were the first to be given the name Harrier, and the first of the aircraft made its initial flight on 31 August 1966. By that time the Mach 2 Hawker Siddeley P.1154 multi-role STOVL aircraft for the RAF and Royal Navy had been replaced in official thinking by the Harrier produced only for the RAF.

With 'Hawker Siddeley Harrier' emblazened along the side of its nose, this early production Harrier is appropriately armed with Matra rockets and ADEN cannon for its close support role.

Appointed Chief Designer of the renamed P.1127RAF, John Fozzard was given the brief of adding P.1154 avionics and a more powerful engine to the Kestrel and delivering it to the RAF in record time. The resultant aircraft, though similar in external appearance, shared only seven per cent of the Kestrel's engineering drawings.

With the Harrier, the P.1127 received a new wing. This featured a leading-edge dogtooth and increased span, the tips now extending beyond the outriggers. The wing was, perhaps, a little on the small side, thereby reducing manoeuvrability, but, as weight-saving was considered paramount, it was the best compromise available.

The single-seat Harrier GR.Mk 1 was developed for the ground-attack and reconnaissance roles, and the tandem two-seat Harrier T.Mk 2 for conversion and combat readiness training. Total orders for the RAF subsequently rose to 118 single-seat and 23 two-seat

Left: During August 1973, Harrier GR.Mk 1As of No. 20 Squadron took part in Exercise Grimm Crusade in the North Rhine/Westphalia region. After seven years No. 20 Squadron disbanded in 1977 as attrition forced RAF Germany to reduce to two Harrier squadrons.

No. 1 (Fighter) Squadron Harrier GR.Mk 3s display their temporary disruptive snow camouflage during an exercise in Norway. As can be seen, the 30-mm ADEN cannon and underwing fuel tanks also received the paint scheme.

aircraft, the Fleet Air Arm later acquiring four two-seaters, the first production examples of each model making their maiden flights on 28 December 1967 and 24 April 1969 respectively.

The first of 61 Harrier GR.Mk 1 aircraft officially entered RAF service on 1 April 1969, initially being used to equip No. 233 OCU at RAF Wittering. In the following year, the first of 23 Harrier T.Mk 2s entered service, and each of these initial models was powered by the Pegasus 6 turbofan (which carried the military designation Mk 101), rated at 19,000 lb st (84.52 kN).

Changes from the Pegasus 5 included an all-titanium fan, two-vane nozzles and a water injection system. The four jet nozzles could be rotated through 98° 30' from the fully aft position, allowing the aircraft to employ a slight element of backward thrust for 'reversing' in the air at up to 20 mph (32 km/h). The nozzles were actually an aircraft component, in that they were anchored to the airframe for strength. Rotated by dual motors, their movement mechanism was so arranged that if one nozzle jammed, drives to the other three were sheared, and all four consequently remained in the same position. Extra air for low-speed flight was provided by eight doors on each intake, while a bleed-door in the cockpit side removed the boundary layer.

Engine upgrades

Surviving aircraft (complemented by 17 new-build single-seaters) were later upgraded to the Harrier GR.Mk 1A and Harrier T.Mk 2A standards, by retrofit of the Pegasus Mk 102 rated at 20,500 lb st (91.19 kN). The surviving aircraft (complemented this time by 40 new-build single-seaters) were further upgraded to Harrier GR.Mk 3 and Harrier T.Mk 4 standards by retrofit of the 21,500-lb st (96.75-kN) Pegasus Mk 103. These aircraft equipped four operational squadrons (one in the UK and three in West Germany). The RAF generally operated the Harrier as a STOVL aircraft as a short take-off run allowed the type to carry a greater load of weapons. Equipment included an inertial navigation system, optional inflight-refuelling probe, head-up display, laser rangefinder/marked-target seeker (LRMTS) and radar-warning receiver, the last two being added in new-build aircraft from 1976 and also retrofitted to existing aircraft. Both the one- and two- seat variants had the same weapons-carrying capability, though the two-seater had a greater empty weight.

The Harrier T.Mk 4 (Harrier T.Mk 4N in FAA service) was re-designated Harrier T.Mk 4A when fitted with the LRMTS nose of the GR.Mk 3. The RAF began the process of converting to the Harrier GR.Mk 5 during 1988, and the last examples of the first-generation Harrier had been retired from RAF service by late 1995. The FAA continued to operate seven two-seaters as Harrier T.Mk 8 aircraft, converted from T.Mk 4N and T.Mk 4A standard to provide compatibility with the Sea Harrier FA.Mk 2. These final aircraft had been withdrawn, in common with the Sea Harrier FA.Mk 2 fleet, by March 2006.

Above: A pair of No. 3 Squadron Harrier GR.Mk 3s overflies a German forest. The rear aircraft is wearing an experimental overall-green scheme, later adopted as standard for the GR.Mk 5.

Below: G-VTOL was a BAe company demonstrator built to Harrier T.Mk 2 standard. In this view the elongated fin originally fitted to the RAF's two-seaters is evident.

AV-8 in service

The AV-8A pioneered V/STOL operations with the US Marine Corps, vindicating the Corps' original decision to procure the type in large numbers.

Prompted by a publicity film, a senior USMC officer dispatched two pilots to the 1968 Farnborough air show with instructions to conduct a preliminary evaluation of the Harrier. Main attraction to the Marines was the Harrier's ability to provide close support for the Corps' raison d'être: the opposed amphibious landing. For a battle in which a hastily summoned air strike from a carrier offshore might come too late to save the day, the Harrier was ideal. Pilots were particularly impressed with the Harrier's acceleration and performance at altitude, both parameters being superior to those of the A-4 Skyhawk.

The type offered improved flexibility compared to fast jets that were either tied to large air bases or carriers. The A-4 was the only other close-support aircraft that could come ashore – but only after the engineers had built a runway and fitted it with arrester gear. Able to operate from rough or semi-prepared surfaces, the Harrier could be deployed from a greater number of sites, closer to the front line. This not only improved the response time for close air support, but also gave higher mission frequencies.

Large procurement

Orders were placed between Fiscal Year (FY) 1970 and FY75 in six batches comprising 12, 18, 30, 30 and 12 AV-8As respectively and a batch of eight TAV-8As. All AV-8As were built at Kingston, test-flown at Dunsfold, and delivered as air freight between January 1971 and November 1976.

Known to its makers as the Harrier Mk 50 and to the Marines as the AV-8A, the aircraft initially resembled the RAF's Harrier GR.Mk 1A in having a Pegasus 10 powerplant, although the Mk 11 engine was introduced from the 11th aircraft and retrofitted, the export designation being Pegasus Mk 803 and the DoD calling it F402-RR-402.

VMA-231 'Aces' was the third and final operational USMC AV-8A squadron. It came closest to seeing combat when deployed aboard USS Tarawa *in 1983 for peacekeeping operations over Lebanon.*

The first 59 AV-8As had the FE.541 nav/attack system, which was deleted and replaced on subsequent AV-8As by a simpler I/WAC (interface/weapons aiming computer) attitude and heading reference system that was all that was necessary for the short-range CAS missions envisaged by the Marines. No LRMTS was fitted, and the ejection seat was (eventually) a Stencel SIIIS-3. In other respects, apart from radios and IFF, the aircraft were the same as their RAF brethren.

Four squadrons with a nominal strength of 20 (later 15 due to attrition) aircraft were formed.

In April 1971 VMA-513 became the first unit to form, at MCAS Beaufort. The 'Flying Nightmares' were followed at Beaufort by VMA-542 'Flying Tigers' which was commissioned as MAG-32's second AV-8A unit in November 1972. Both units later transferred to Cherry Point as a component of MAG-20.

Early tasks revolved around learning how to use the Harrier in the USMC's unique combat conditions. It was during 1971/72, as pilots began to explore the Harrier's air-to-air envelope, that the type's most publicised technique was discovered. Known as VIFFing for Vectoring In Forward Flight, and practised during air combat manouevring, this involved the pilot rotating the nozzles from the aft to the forward position, This produced a rapid deceleration and nose-up attitude guaranteed to make any pursuing interceptor overshoot into the Harrier's gunsight or Sidewinder envelope.

The third and final operational USMC Harrier unit was formed at MCAS Cherry Point. VMA-231

Spain's VA.1s carried Sidewinders for the point interception role. The initial AIM-9N variant was replaced by the 'Papa' model as seen on aircraft '885'. Combat persistence was greatly improved with the introduction of twin missile rails.

The AV-8A operated primarily from the Marine Corps' LHA and LPH amphibious assault ships, but also deployed aboard larger aircraft-carriers. These AV-8s are seen aboard USS* Saipan *(LHA-21). The ship's standard complement was eight Harriers.

AV-8A/C weapons

A broad variety of ordnance was cleared for AV-8A fitment, comprising free-fall and retarded 250-lb (113-kg) Mk 81 and 500-lb (227-kg) Mk 82 bombs; free-fall 1,000-lb (454-kg) Mk 83s; LAU-10A (four 5-in/12.7-cm) and LAU-68A (seven 68-mm/2.68-in) rocket launchers; Mk 77 fire-bombs; and APAM and Rockeye 11 cluster bombs. Also specified from the outset was provision for outboard underwing AIM-9E Sidewinder air-to-air missiles. These later gave way to the -9J and -9L variants. The Marine Corps originally planned to change the 30-mm ADEN cannons for an American weapon, but retained the reliable British guns.

An AV-8A of VMA-542 'Flying Tigers' lets loose a 5-in (127-mm) Zuni rocket over a training range.

'Aces' was reactivated on 15 May 1973 as MAG-20. In January 1976 MAG-32 transferred to Cherry Point. Absorbing the resident squadrons, the group now contained the entire operational USMC Harrier force.

In January 1975, VMA-231 made its first operational assignment aboard the USS *Inchon* for carrier qualification. On 4 October 1976 14 Harriers of VMA-231 sailed for the Mediterranean aboard USS *Franklin D. Roosevelt*. This was designed to prove how Harriers could be integrated into a carrier air wing's operations.

In June 1978, Harriers were taken aboard an LHA class vessel (USS *Saipan*) for the first time. Later, in October, six AV-8As made a transatlantic deployment to take part in the Harrier's first participation in European exercises. The three USMC squadrons also shared a rota of six-month detachments to Okinawa.

By the time the Harrier force entered its second decade of service, plans were already well underway for the second-generation version. The AV-8B's new wing had been first flown on 9 November 1978, attached to the 11th AV-8A.

Pending availability of the AV-8B, the USMC upgraded the AV-8A as an interim measure. The service originally intended to cycle some 60 AV-8s to AV-8C standard. In the end only 47 aircraft were modified between 1979 and 1984. In addition to structural modification to increase airframe life to 4,000 flying hours, they received an AN/ALR-45F radar-warning receiver, an AN/ALE-39 chaff/flare dispenser, new secure radios and lift-improvement devices (developed for the AV-8B) that were attached to the gun pods. One deletion concerned the nose oblique F.95 camera. These updated aircraft flew alongside unconverted AV-8As and kept the four squadrons operative until the mid-1980s.

The arrival of the AV-8B in the mid-1980s signalled the end of AV-8A/Cs. From September 1985 AV-8As began to arrive for storage at AMARC as VMA-231 began to transition to the AV-8B. The following year AV-8Cs were also sent to Davis Monthan when VMA-542 too began conversion. VMA-513 conducted the AV-8C's last operational deployment in 1986 and stood down as an AV-8C squadron in August. Pilots started AV-8B conversion at Cherry Point with VMAT-203 in January 1987. The training unit disposed of its five surviving TAV-8As in late 1987.

TAV-8A – two-seat trainer

Like the RAF, the Marines suffered a high loss rate during the first few years of Harrier operations. The type's demanding cockpit workload favoured air crew converting from 'fast movers' such as F-4s and A-4s, as opposed to OV-10s, A-6s, C-130s and helicopters. Formed at Cherry Point in 1975, VMAT-203 was formed to conduct combat-capable V/STOL jet attack training for pilots; the emphasis was placed upon weapons delivery in destruction of ground targets. The unit took all of the eight TAV-8As ordered in FY74, as well as 10 AV-8As. Harrier losses dropped significantly once the training unit had worked up. Carrier qualification of the two-seat Harrier was achieved aboard USS *Franklin D. Roosevelt* in 1976 (although never used operationally), as well as from smaller helicopter-carriers. Although the unit got its first Harrier II in late 1983 it did not relinquish its training role for first-generation AV-8Cs until March 1985. VMAT-203 also became responsible for training those destined to serve with AV-8B squadrons. It relinquished its remaining TAV-8As in late 1987.

Spanish navy service

The only AV-8 export customer was the Spanish navy air arm – the Arma Aérea de la Armada – for use on the carrier *Dedalo*. Spain ordered its first batch of six AV-8A single-seaters and two TAV-8A trainers through the US Navy, which placed a contract with Hawker Siddeley in July 1973. Spanish type numbers VA.1 and VAE.1 (two-seat) were assigned and Octava Escuadrilla (8ª Esc/Eighth Flight) was selected as the operating unit. In August 1977 the Spanish Navy ordered a further five single-seaters. These were delivered between 27 June and 19 December 1980, this time directly to Spain. Final operations with *Dedalo* took place in 1988, although operations with the AV-8S continued until 8ª Esc disbanded in October 1996.

Heinkel He 162 'Salamander'

Volksjäger

Conceived in the dying throes of the Third Reich, the He 162 'Salamander' was intended as one massive last-ditch effort to fend off the Allies. However, for the Nazis, this diminutive jet was too little, too late.

Autumn 1944 saw Hitler's Germany being reduced to rubble under continuous Allied bombing raids. Desperate measures were needed, and under the overall control of Albert Speer's armament ministry, Party Leader Karl-Otto Saur devised a *Volksjäger* (people's fighter). This was to be small (not over 4,410 lb/2000 kg when loaded), simple, jet-propelled and able to outpace and outmanoeuvre Allied fighters. It was to be armed with one or two 30-mm guns, be easy to maintain and make absolutely minimum demands on skilled labour and scarce materials.

The requirement was issued on 8 September 1944 and was immediately studied by the leading aircraft manufacturers. By 15 September, the proposals had been whittled down to two. On every count, the Blohm und Voss P.211 was the better aircraft, but Heinkel forced through its P.1073 so that, on 24 September, it received an official go-ahead.

The final go-ahead was granted on 30 September, with a planned initial output of 1,000 aircraft per month. The programme was given the name Salamander, while the designation was given as He 162. The appellation 'Salamander' for the aircraft was never popularly used by the Germans – rather, it was bestowed by the Allies when they learned of the project name.

Simple design

The He 162's streamlined fuselage was a light-alloy, semi-monocoque structure of circular section, with a moulded plywood nose. The cockpit had an upward-hinged canopy and cartridge-actuated ejection seat while fuel was housed in a tank amidships. Wheels and brakes were taken from the Bf 109G and the chosen engine was a BMW 003 turbojet, attached directly above the high-mounted wing.

Considerable numbers of He 162s were captured by the Allies in varying degrees of repair. This aircraft was flown on 26 flights by the British RAE at Farnborough.

Above: This He 162A-2 was allocated to 3. Staffel/JG 1 at its Leck base in May 1945. By this time, the 50 aircraft had been reorganised into one single* Gruppe*, Einsatz-Gruppe I./JG 1; many pilots from other fragmented units at Leck were absorbed by this new unit.

Production aircraft did not differ greatly from this, the first V1 prototype, except for turned-down wingtips, enlarged ailerons and compound taper on the trailing edge near the wingroot. The V1 had only been flying for four days when it broke up in mid-air.

The programme, centred on Heinkel's Vienna-Schwechat factory, initially produced 10 prototypes, He 162 V1 to V10, which were also considered the pre-production batch. The planned He 162A-1 production fighter was to be mass-produced by a growing number of factories and sub-contractors. The biggest factories were to build up to 1,000 aircraft each per month, with total monthly production from all manufacturers reaching 6,000.

One of the four 'Salamanders' transported to Britain was 120072, which made four evaluation flights from Farnborough after the war. On the last of these, the aircraft broke up in a roll, killing the pilot.

The first prototype made its first take-off on 6 December 1944 and reached its maximum speed of 522 mph (840 km/h). Upon landing, the V1 was discovered to have suffered some structural damage as a result of the use of acids in the construction of the aircraft; moreover, a shortage of time had meant that substitute adhesives had been rushed in. On 10 December, with a large audience of Luftwaffe, RLM (air ministry) and Nazi party officials, the V1 flew from Schwechat airfield. While making a low-level pass over the airfield, the entire port leading-edge broke away and the aircraft crashed.

To show confidence, the first flight of the V2 prototype was made by the Schwechat technical director. Exploring the limits of the flight envelope revealed unacceptable lateral and directional instabilities, especially in tight turns. As a result, the tail was slightly enlarged and the wingtips were tilted downwards.

Armament selection

Since the design team found it impossible to house more than 50 rounds per gun with the requested 30-mm MK 108 cannon, the 20-mm MG 151 was substituted, each gun having 120 rounds. The V1 had 20-mm guns, but the RLM insisted on the V2 having two MK 108s and, in early 1945, trials were conducted with these weapons. Although MK 108s were fitted to the V6, the production He 162A-2 was standardised with the MG 151.

By February 1945 approximately 100 aircraft had been completed, including over 20 prototype and development machines, and the production programme was getting into its stride. However, there was no parallel programme to train pilots. Heinz Bär was posted to activate Erprobungs-kommando (special test unit) 162 at Rechlin in late January 1945.

In spite of the great urgency, the Luftwaffe insisted on checking that the He 162A-2 could serve as a fighter. A few days later, on 6 February, I./JG 1 began converting to the He 162 at Parchim. Subsequently, II./JG 1 also converted, but in the dying weeks of the Third Reich, chaos and fuel shortages were just two factors preventing effective operations. Plans had gone ahead for an entire year's intake of Hitler Youth to carry out brief training on gliders, and then proceed directly to the He 162. At the same time, Heinkel was scheming further variants of the He 162. And, while all this was happening, the Allied forces were overrunning Germany and any further plans for the He 162 were consigned to history.

He 162A-2 'Salamander'

The Heinkel He 162 was the product of a rushed attempt to mass-produce a fighter that would stem the Allied advance. However, the speed of the development process resulted in many structural and aerodynamic shortcomings. This He 162A-2 was assigned to 3. Staffel, Einsatzgruppen I./JG 1, and was the personal aircraft of Staffelkapitän Oberleutnant Erich Demuth. It carried his 16 victory marks on the tail, although these had been gained on other aircraft.

Configuration
Experts predicted that the He 162's unusual top-mounted engine would suffer airflow problems (which to a great extent did not occur), but did not foresee the pitch instability which made the aircraft so tricky to fly and fight in.

Powerplant
The He 162A-2 was powered by a single BMW 003E-1 or E-2 axial-flow turbojet, rated at 1,764 lb st (7.8 kN) with a 2,028-lb st (9.02-kN) emergency rating available for periods of up to 30 seconds. The pre-production aircraft had been powered by the BMW 003A-1, while some prototypes flew with the BMW 003R, combined with the 1,764-lb st (7.8-kN) BMW 718 liquid-fuel rocket. Shortages of BMW 003s led to the investigation of the Jumo 004D as a possible alternative, and this engine was installed in two prototypes.

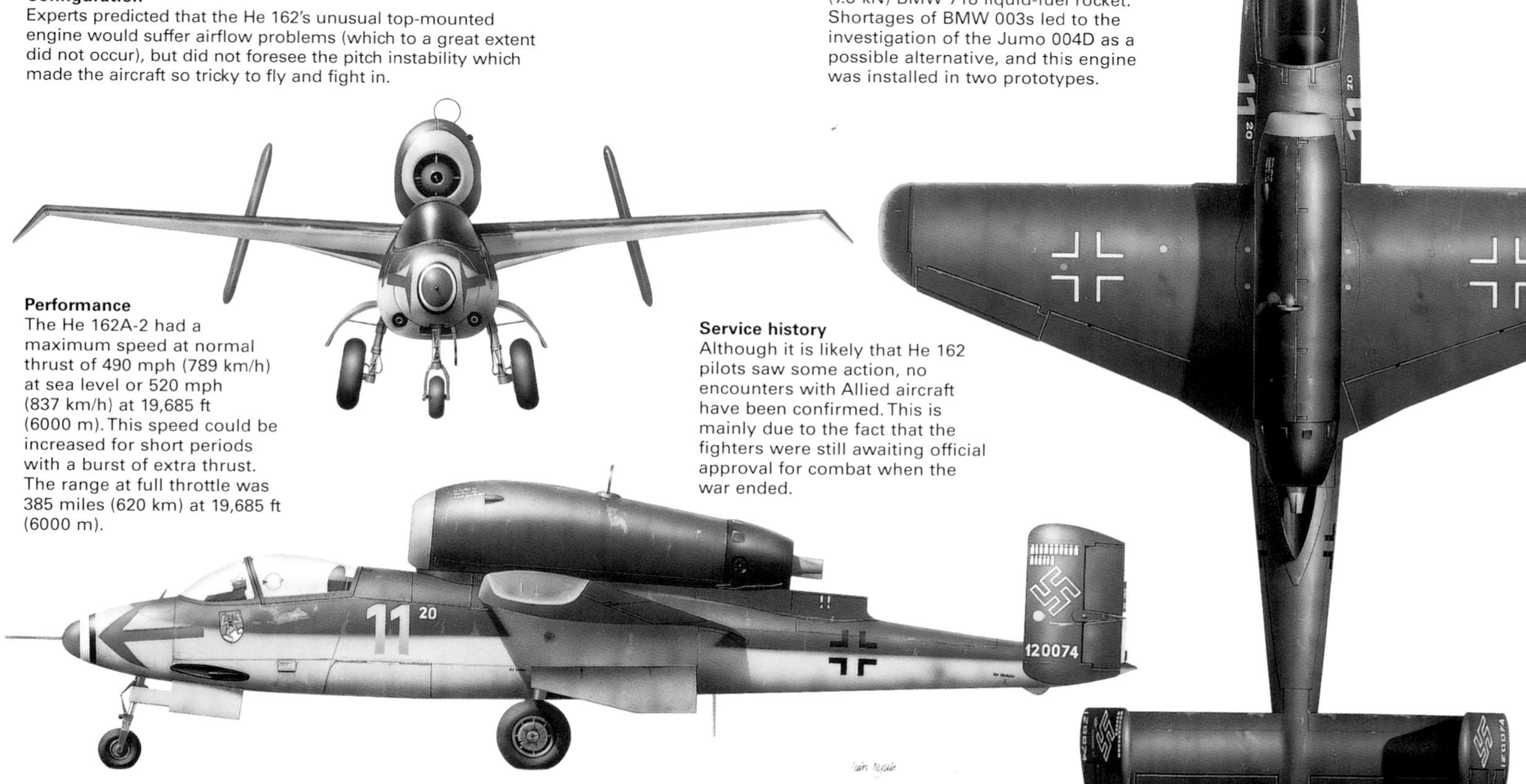

Performance
The He 162A-2 had a maximum speed at normal thrust of 490 mph (789 km/h) at sea level or 520 mph (837 km/h) at 19,685 ft (6000 m). This speed could be increased for short periods with a burst of extra thrust. The range at full throttle was 385 miles (620 km) at 19,685 ft (6000 m).

Service history
Although it is likely that He 162 pilots saw some action, no encounters with Allied aircraft have been confirmed. This is mainly due to the fact that the fighters were still awaiting official approval for combat when the war ended.

By adding canards and a US engine to the Mirage III airframe, IAI improved the airfield performance and manoeuvrability of the French aircraft while also overcoming an embargo on its engine.

IAI Kfir
Desert lion

Forged in the face of embargoes and hostile conditions, IAI's Kfir fought successfully in the wars of the Middle East and has also been exported to several air arms around the world.

Israel was the first export customer for the Mirage III, and used the type to great effect during the 1967 and 1973 wars with its Arab neighbours. Despite its success, Israel was aware of the shortcomings of the Mirage, and the obvious need for improvement, coupled with arms embargoes, forced Israel first to upgrade its Mirages and then to build its own improved Mirage derivatives.

This process resulted eventually in the IAI Kfir (lion cub). Development of the Kfir was made possible by Israel's purchase of the Phantom and its General Electric J79 engine. The first J79-engined Mirage was a French-built two-seater, and this took to the air on 19 October 1970, joined by a re-engined Nesher in September 1971.

The basic Kfir was produced in small numbers (27) and most were later upgraded to Kfir C1 configuration, with small narrow-span fixed canards on the intakes and rectangular strakes on the sides of the nose. Twenty-five survivors were later lent to the US Navy and US Marines for adversary training (between 1985 and 1989) as F-21As.

Avionics upgrades

The Kfir C2 was the first full-standard variant, equipped with nose strakes and large fixed canard foreplanes from the outset. The new variant also had a dogtooth wing leading edge. Canards and strakes were first flown on the J79-powered Mirage IIIB which had served as the Kfir prototype, in July 1974. These aerodynamic alterations improved turn and take-off performance along with controllability.

The Kfir C2 also introduced new avionics, including an Elta ranging radar. Other equipment included an MBT twin-computer flight control system, Elbit multi-mode navigation and weapons delivery system, Taman central air data computer and a new HUD. One hundred and eighty-five C2s and TC2 trainers were built, and remained in IDF/AF service until the mid-1990s.

After long delays in gaining US approval to re-export the J79 powerplant, 10 Kfir C2s and two TC2s were sold to Ecuador in 1982, and another 12 improved C7 models and a single TC7 went to Colombia in 1988-89. Ecuador took a further three C2s and one TC2 in 1996, before signing up in 1999 for two 'new-generation' C10s together with the conversion of a number of the original C2s to C10 standard, with

The US Navy and Marine Corps used the Kfir for dissimilar air combat training in the late 1980s. The aircraft flew in a number of colour schemes, some in two-tone grey, some in Israeli camouflage.

The greater mass flow and higher operating temperature of the Kfir's J79 engine necessitated the provision of enlarged air intakes and extensive heat shielding of the rear fuselage.

helmet-mounted sights and provision for the carriage of Python 4 AAMs. Meanwhile, Colombia's surviving Kfirs received Python 3s and Griffin LGBs, and have been widely used in COIN operations against guerrillas. The latest customer for the Kfir is Sri Lanka which purchased an initial batch of C2s and a single TC2 aircraft in 1996 and used them in offensive actions against the Tamil Tiger rebels. In 2001, Sri Lanka received four more C7s and a second TC2. A number of aircraft have been lost in service. Virtually all surviving Israeli Kfir C2s and TC2s were upgraded to Kfir C7 and TC7 standards.

The C7 designation is applied to upgraded aircraft delivered from 1983 onwards. These incorporate a number of avionics improvements, and have what is effectively a HOTAS cockpit. Equipment improvements involve a new weapons delivery and navigation system, an Elbit stores management system, armament control display panel, video sub-systems and the ability to release 'smart' weapons. Aerial refuelling provision with either probe or receptacle is optional. Jamming pods can be fitted on the port inboard wing pylon.

The only external difference is the provision of an extra pair of hardpoints under the engine intakes, bringing the total to nine and increasing warload to a maximum of 13,415 lb (6085 kg). An engine overspeed provision, referred to as 'combat plus', can be used to boost thrust to 18,750 lb st (83.41 kN).

Kfir C10 upgrade

During 1993, Israel began seeking export customers for its surplus Kfir C2/C7s and, to this end, IAI proposed a further upgrade as the Kfir C10. Features of this version include a new cockpit fit, a new Elta multi-mode radar in an enlarged radome, enlarged radome, more external fuel, a BVR capability with Derby AAMs, and provision for an inflight refuelling probe.

Kfir C2

Ecuador operates one squadron of Kfirs. Escuadrón de Combate 2113 received both C2s and TC2 two-seat trainers, with a number of the C2s later being upgraded to C10 standard, known locally as the Kfir CE. The Kfirs were involved in Ecuador's 1995 conflict with Peru over disputed territory and made at least one confirmed aerial kill over a FAP AT-37B.

Camouflage
Ecuador's Kfirs received a two-tone disruptive camouflage scheme, with light grey undersides. National insignia is applied above the port and below the starboard wing.

Canards
Ecuadorian Kfirs are fitted with the full-size fixed foreplanes associated with the Kfir C2 and C7. These reduce the take-off run by some 1,500 ft (457 m) and have a similarly dramatic effect on turn performances, reducing longitudinal stability by generating lift ahead of the centre of gravity.

Armament
Ecuador's Kfirs are primarily used in the air defence and interception role, though as part of a multi-role wing, they also undergo training in fighter-bomber operations. The aircraft are normally armed with a pair of Rafael Python 3 IR-homing air-to-air missiles. Like all Kfirs, they have a pair of Rafael Defa 553 30-mm cannon ahead of the wingroots, each with 125 rounds of ammunition. In the ground-attack role, the C2 aircraft can carry a variety of US, Israeli or French free-fall bombs, but do not have the extra under-intake hardpoints associated with the Kfir C7.

Wing
The Kfir's wings lack the sawcut leading-edge of the Mirage III and instead have extended outboard leading-edges, giving a pronounced saw-tooth leading edge discontinuity.

Powerplant
The most powerful production variant of the General Electric J79 engine, the J79-J1E powers the Kfir. Because it has greater mass flow than the original Mirage Atar engine, installation of the J79 necessitated larger intakes, and its increased operating temperatures required provision of a dorsal airscoop.

From its introduction into service the Il-28 was a successful and popular aircraft, particularly with crews. This photograph depicts three service-test aircraft, the nearest example having non-standard projections beneath the rear fuselage.

Ilyushin Il-28 'Beagle'

Turbojet bomber

Ilyushin's Il-28, while not an outstandingly innovative design, proved to be a highly effective, jet-powered nuclear strike aircraft, with enough flexibility to be adapted to conventional roles. It eventually became the world's most widely produced jet bomber.

Like the contemporary MiG-15 and MiG-17 fighters, the Il-28 was made possible by the British Labour government's extraordinary decision to supply the latest British jet engines to their erstwhile Soviet allies, despite the fact that the Cold War was already clearly beginning.

Ilyushin mated the RD-45 engine (a copy of the Rolls-Royce Nene) to a fuselage whose design relied heavily on the aid of expatriate German engineers and captured German aircraft. The resulting Il-28 had a long forward fuselage and massive engine nacelles, needed to house the RD-45 with its large frontal area. In plan view, the wing and tail were a strange contrast: the wing was unswept at the leading edge and the trailing edge was raked forward, while the tail surfaces were sharply swept back. This represented a solution to the problems of packing the various components into an airframe small enough to offer good performance, and simple enough to be built in large quantities.

In October 1948, the Il-28 was evaluated against the larger, but similarly powered, Tupolev Tu-78 in the light bomber role; the Il-28 proved faster and more agile, and was selected as the replacement for the obsolescent Tu-2. Preparations for large-scale production proceeded with great urgency and the type entered service in September 1950 and

Above: The only operator to retain the Il-28 in significant numbers into the 21st century was the People's Liberation Army Air Force and Naval Air Force (PLAAF and PLANAF). These aircraft were locally produced as the Harbin H-5 between 1967 and the early 1980s.

Two Il-28s make a low-level pass over a Soviet landing craft during the Odra-Nysa naval exercises of the 1960s. This involved the Soviet Union and its Warsaw Pact allies practising large-scale naval assaults in the Baltic.

became the Soviet equivalent of the British Canberra.

The only major change during development was the switch from the RD-45, used only in the prototype and pre-production aircraft, to the similarly sized but more powerful VK-1. The basic Il-28 remained virtually unchanged throughout its production life. The only visible alteration was the introduction of a small tail-warning radar.

Large-scale production

Like contemporary MiG fighters, the Il-28 was built in vast quantities, including a number produced in Czechoslovakia as the B-228. The only major derivative of the type was the Il-28U 'Mascot' conversion trainer; the student occupied a completely separate cockpit, replacing the navigator/bomb aimer's station.

Other variants included: the Il-28R reconnaissance version which featured cameras in the rear fuselage and auxiliary fuel in the bomb bay and in tip tanks; the Il-28T anti-shipping version with different radar and a modified bomb bay to carry two torpedoes; the Il-28D long-range nuclear attack version with the front guns and turret removed; and the Il-28RT, the only new-build variant, used for Elint with passive receivers and cameras. Various other designations were used for different reconnaissance and EW versions, and the type was also used as an unmanned target drone. Another version was the unarmed and de-militarised Il-20, used by Aeroflot for high-speed package deliveries and, most importantly, to familiarise Aeroflot aircrew with jet operations in the civilian environment.

Nuclear capability

For the 1950s, the Il-28 was an effective light bomber. It had a substantially greater payload and range than any modified fighter of the day. With its internal weapons bay, it could carry large conventional stores such as a 3000-kg (6,614-lb) bomb, or a tactical nuclear weapon.

In September 1962, the arrival of a regiment of Il-28s, along with medium-range Soviet missiles in Cuba, was enough to alarm the US government, which successfully insisted on their removal. However, with the introduction of the Yak-28 in 1963/64, the Il-28 quickly became obsolescent in Soviet service and was rapidly replaced.

The Il-28 was a standard type with Warsaw Pact forces and was widely exported, a marked contrast with the Yak-28, which was exclusively used by Soviet units. The type saw some action in the Middle East and in the Nigerian civil war in the late 1960s, albeit with little distinction. In Nigeria the Egyptian-manned Il-28s proved notoriously inaccurate and in the Middle East the fighting was too intense for the ageing bombers. The greater part of the Il-28s in that theatre were destroyed on the ground by the first Israeli sorties of the June 1967 war.

The biggest operator of the Il-28 outside the Soviet Union was China, which is believed to have received around 500 examples in the late 1950s. After the Sino-Soviet rift of 1959, engineers at China's Harbin plant analysed and copied the Il-28 airframe and systems, and began to produce the aircraft from April 1967 as the Hong-5 (H-5). Production of the H-5 continued in China until the early 1980s, and examples remained on strength with the People's Liberation Army Air Force and Naval Air Force into the 21st century. A handful of exported H-5s also served into the new century with Romania (also an Il-28 operator), although by 2007 the only remaining operator of the H-5 was North Korea.

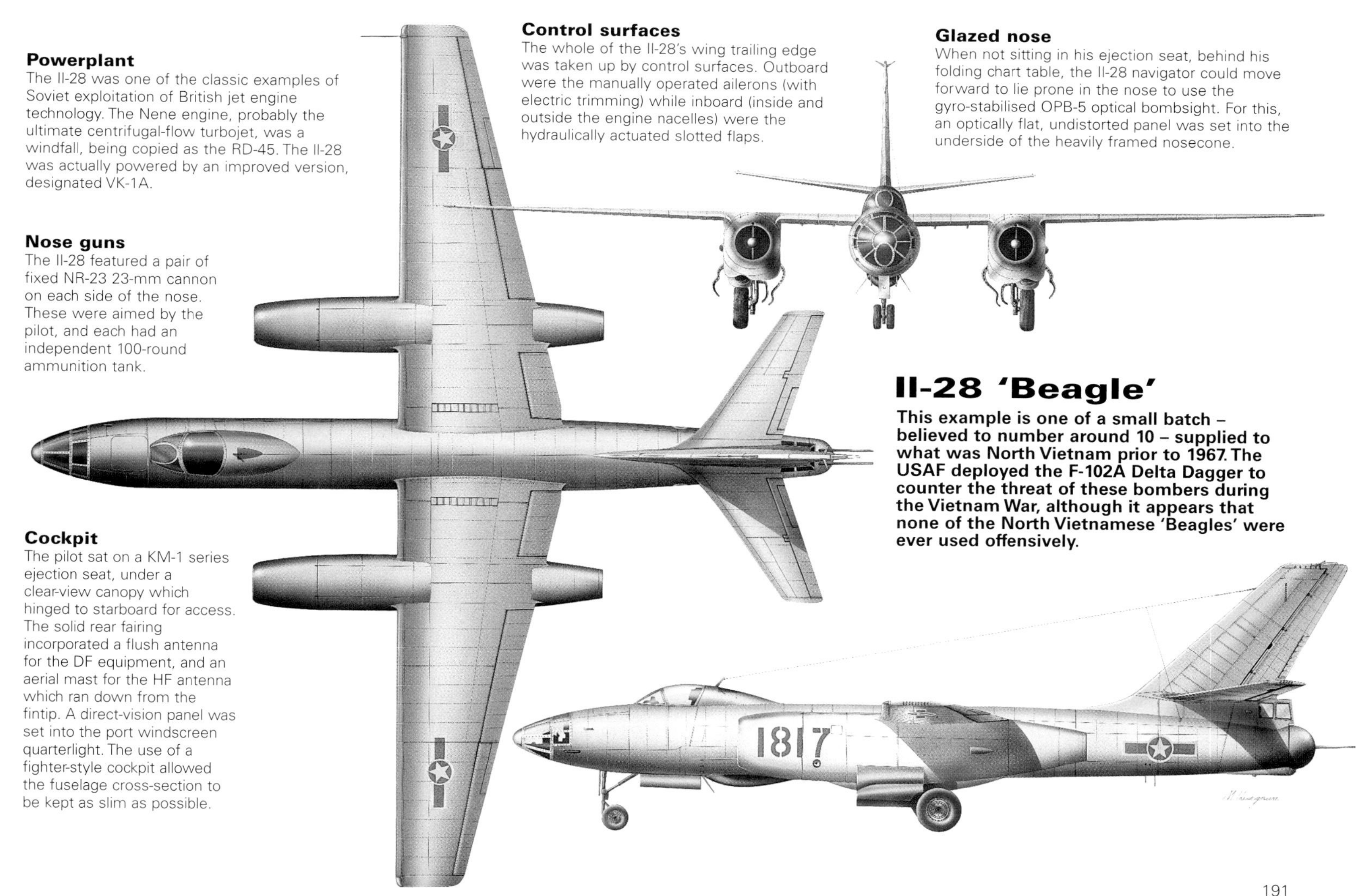

Powerplant
The Il-28 was one of the classic examples of Soviet exploitation of British jet engine technology. The Nene engine, probably the ultimate centrifugal-flow turbojet, was a windfall, being copied as the RD-45. The Il-28 was actually powered by an improved version, designated VK-1A.

Nose guns
The Il-28 featured a pair of fixed NR-23 23-mm cannon on each side of the nose. These were aimed by the pilot, and each had an independent 100-round ammunition tank.

Cockpit
The pilot sat on a KM-1 series ejection seat, under a clear-view canopy which hinged to starboard for access. The solid rear fairing incorporated a flush antenna for the DF equipment, and an aerial mast for the HF antenna which ran down from the fintip. A direct-vision panel was set into the port windscreen quarterlight. The use of a fighter-style cockpit allowed the fuselage cross-section to be kept as slim as possible.

Control surfaces
The whole of the Il-28's wing trailing edge was taken up by control surfaces. Outboard were the manually operated ailerons (with electric trimming) while inboard (inside and outside the engine nacelles) were the hydraulically actuated slotted flaps.

Glazed nose
When not sitting in his ejection seat, behind his folding chart table, the Il-28 navigator could move forward to lie prone in the nose to use the gyro-stabilised OPB-5 optical bombsight. For this, an optically flat, undistorted panel was set into the underside of the heavily framed nosecone.

Il-28 'Beagle'

This example is one of a small batch – believed to number around 10 – supplied to what was North Vietnam prior to 1967. The USAF deployed the F-102A Delta Dagger to counter the threat of these bombers during the Vietnam War, although it appears that none of the North Vietnamese 'Beagles' were ever used offensively.

Ilyushin Il-76/Il-78 & A-50

'Candid', 'Midas' and 'Mainstay'

The unarmed Il-76T 'civilian' version was, together with other Aeroflot assets, operated on behalf of Military Transport Aviation (Voyenno Transportnaya Aviatsiya, VTA) during the Soviet period. This example was used to transport freight to Soviet airbases within East Germany.

Developed as a successor to the An-12 turboprop transport, with short-field and adverse weather capability, the Ilyushin Il-76 was intended for service with transport elements of both the Soviet air force and Aeroflot.

In the same way that the USAF had purchased the jet-driven C-141 to augment propeller-driven C-130s, so the Soviet air force turned to a jet aircraft to augment (and eventually supersede) its An-12s. However, in certain roles, the Soviets found the turboprop An-12 superior, and the Il-76 never entirely replaced the Antonov design in Soviet service. Larger, heavier and more powerful than the C-141, the Il-76 uses extensive high-lift devices, thrust reversers and a high-flotation undercarriage to achieve superior short- and rough-field performance, at the expense of slightly inferior payload and range.

Design philosophy

The Il-76 displays many of the traits of a typical post-war Soviet transport. Most military variants carry a gun turret (with a twin-barrelled GSh-23L 23-mm cannon) in the tail, and all transport versions have an extensively glazed navigator/drop master position in the nose. The cargo hold is fully pressurised and has a titanium floor, with fold-down roller conveyors, and can be rapidly reconfigured by using interchangeable passenger or freight modules. Three such modules can be fitted (each 20 ft/6.10 m long and 8 ft/2.44 m wide), the passenger modules containing 30 passengers in four-abreast seating.

Loading is accomplished with the aid of a pair of internal overhead winches, each of which can mount two 6,614-lb (3000-kg) or four 5,511-lb (2500-kg) hoists. The ramp itself can be used as a lift, with a capacity of up to 66,150 lb (30000 kg).

The first prototype Il-76 made its maiden flight in March 1971, and by 1974, a development

Above: In Indian Air Force service, the Il-76MD is known as the Gajaraj (king elephant), and replaced the An-12BK. The IAF initially received 24 examples, to be shared by Nos 25 and 44 Squadrons.

Below: The definitive military 'Candid' variant is the Il-76MD, as exemplified by this Russian air force machine in Aeroflot colours. Note the rear turret and clamshell thrust reversers.

Il-78 'Midas' – Russia's tanker

The 'Candid' tanker was first trialled using a converted Il-76MD (no. 78782) in 1977, and the design was refined over a period of 10 years, prior to service entry of the Il-78 'Midas-A' at Uzin in 1987, replacing the 3MS2 and 3MN2 'Bison'. The Il-78 carries 90 tonnes of fuel in the wing, and 28 tonnes in the fuselage, including cylindrical tanks in the hold totalling 14,080 Imp gal (64000 litres). The initial Il-78 service aircraft carries a single UPAZ-1A hose-drum unit (HDU) scabbed on the port side of the rear fuselage (below right). A crew of seven is carried. The nose navigator station and radars are similar to those of the Il-76MD, but an observer station replaces the standard military tail turret. Formation lights and ranging radar are carried in the underside of the ramp door. From 1989, UPAZ-1A pods were added under each wing, creating the definitive, non-convertible, Il-78M 'Midas-B' (below left, with a pair of Su-24s). Limits for contact are 6,560 to 29,530 ft (2000–9000 m) at speeds of 249 to 373 mph (400–600 km/h). The Il-78 is operated by Russia (203. Guards Aircraft Refuelling Aviation Regiment at Ryazan) and Ukraine (albeit converted back to transports), while China has ordered eight examples, and India six Il-78MKIs.

squadron was in VTA service, flying tail gun-equipped Il-76s. Series production of the Il-76 began at Tashkent, Uzbekistan, in 1975. The initial production version of the Il-76 received the NATO reporting name 'Candid-A'. The unarmed Il-76T retained the 'Candid-A' codename, but was essentially a civil conversion, with additional fuel tankage in the wing centre section. The final 'Candid-A' variant is the unarmed Il-76TD, with upgraded avionics, strengthened wings and centre fuselage, and uprated Aviadvigatel D-30KP-2 engines, which maintain full power at higher outside air temperatures, and offer improved 'hot-and-high' take-off performance.

Maximum take-off weight and payload are increased compared to earlier models, and range is increased by 745 miles (1200 km) with the carriage of an additional 22,046 lb (10000 kg) of fuel. A single sound-proofed and specially equipped Il-76TD was operated in support of Soviet Antarctic expeditions from 1986.

Similar to the Il-76T is the dedicated military Il-76M 'Candid-B', with provision for the carriage of up to 140 troops or 125 paratroops as an alternative to freight. This version carries a rear gun turret as standard, although this is not always fitted to exported examples. For self defence, the Il-76M carries small ECM fairings on each side of the front fuselage, and on each side of the rear fuselage. Packs of 96 flares are fitted to the landing gear fairings, and further packs can be scabbed onto the rear fuselage sides. Generally similar is the Il-76MD 'Candid-B', which introduced the improvements of the Il-76TD to the dedicated military Il-76M.

Based on the Il-76MD are the Il-76LL testbeds, which have carried a number of engines, including the NK-86, PS-90A and D-18T turbofans, and the D-236 propfan. The Il-76MDP is a fire-bomber conversion carrying up to 44 tonnes of retardant in two cylindrical tanks in the hold.

The Il-76PP is a version of the Il-76MD equipped for ECM, with a Landysh avionics suite in lengthened undercarriage panniers. The type was not adopted for front-line service.

The Il-76VPK (Il-82) airborne command post is based on the Il-76MD, with a prominent 'doghouse' fairing over its satellite communications/IR antenna, a ventral canoe radome and strakes, 14 blade antennas, VLF trailing wire, new APU, and HF probes under the wings.

In addition to around 500 Il-76s built for the Soviet military (including the AV-MF naval arm), and around 120 for Aeroflot service, 'Candids' were exported to the military air arms of Algeria, Cuba, India, Iran, Iraq, Libya, North Korea, Syria and Yemen. Former Soviet states with 'Candids' in their military inventory include Azerbaijan, Belarus and Ukraine. Iraq's fleet included drogue-equipped tanker conversions, the abortive Baghdad-1 with radar inverted under the tail, and the Adnan-1 AEW&C conversion.

AEW conversions

Developed from the Il-76MD from the 1970s as a replacement for the Tu-126 'Moss', A-50 'Mainstay' conversions were begun by Beriev from the early 1980s. The baseline A-50 carries a conventionally located 'saucer' radome and a Liana AEW&C radar, derived from that carried by the Tu-126. The more capable A-50U is equipped with improved Vega Shmel-M radar system in place of the Liana. The 'Mainstay' is equipped for inflight refuelling and has accommodation for 10 mission operators with colour CRT displays. Around 25 'Mainstays' are operational with the Russian air force at Pechora, principally tasked with the control of counter-air fighters for home defence. China has also developed an AEW variant based on converted Il-76 transports.

Related aircraft include the A-60 airborne laser testbed and the Be-976 (or Il-76SKIP) surveillance platform and range control aircraft for the observation of missile and aircraft flight tests, the latter aircraft being externally similar to the A-50, except for the retention of the transport variant's glazed navigator's station in the nose.

The Beriev A-50 'Mainstay', in its improved A-50U guise with three-dimensional pulse-Doppler radar and digital MTI subsystem, is capable of the passive detection of hostile ECM sources, and the detection of a MiG-21-size target within a search radius of 143 miles (230 km). The A-50U can track 50 targets, and guide the interception of up to 10 of them simultaneously. Endurance on internal fuel, at maximum take-off weight, is 4 hours at 621 miles (1000 km) from base.

Lockheed C-5 Galaxy
US heavyweight

Seen in formation with a Lockheed T-33 chase aircraft, the first prototype C-5 undergoes flight trials. An instrument probe was fitted to the nose of the aircraft for the tests.

The world's largest operational aircraft at its time of introduction, the C-5 Galaxy has been the workhorse of US strategic airlifting for nearly 40 years.

Although the introduction of the C-141 Starlifter had markedly increased Military Air Transport Service's airlifting capability, it was not capable of airlifting larger weapons such as main battle tanks and troop-carrying helicopters. To address this shortfall, the USAF began design studies in 1963 for an aircraft weighing in the order of 600,000 lb (272160 kg).

By mid-1964 the programme had been defined, in a more ambitious form, as the CX-HLS (Cargo Experimental-Heavy Logistics System) which specified that the aircraft should be capable of hauling a payload of 125,000 lb (56700 kg) over 8,000 miles (12875 km) and have the ability to operate from semi-prepared airstrips. Contracts for design studies were issued to three manufacturers and two engine companies.

Lockheed won the airframe competition, with power to be provided by the General Electric TF39 turbofan.

Structural shortfall

The demands of the CX-HLS requirement proved to be unrealistic and were never remotely approached by the Lockheed design, by then named Galaxy. In an attempt to save weight, which could be translated into payload, Lockheed compromised on design strength, a decision which would come back to haunt the company soon after the type entered service.

Rolled out on 2 March 1968, the C-5A bore a distinct family resemblance to the smaller C-141, with four podded engines suspended beneath a shoulder-mounted wing, a T-tail and an upswept aft fuselage section incorporating loading doors and a ramp. There the similarity ended, for the Galaxy introduced a much revised forward fuselage with the flight deck situated above the forward part of the hold allowing the fitment of an upward-hinging 'visor' for loading and unloading at the front of the aircraft.

Directly behind the flight deck a cabin area could accommodate 15 passengers, while a second larger

***Above:** On its introduction into service, the C-5 was the world's largest and heaviest aircraft. Almost four decades later, the Galaxy is still the largest aircraft in the US inventory.*

***Below:** General Electric fought off Pratt & Whitney to win the engine contract for the C-5A. Generating 41,100 lb (183 kN) of thrust, its TF39-GE-1 engine was then the most powerful high-bypass turbofan engine to be fitted to a military aircraft.*

cabin (located in the upper fuselage aft of the wing) could take up to 75 troops. The main cargo hold was designed with a capacity of 34,795 cu ft (985.29 m³) for cargo operations and could be re-configured to carry up to 270 troops.

***Left:* In the 1980s, the C-5 fleet adopted the 'European One' camouflage scheme. Although the scheme was successful internal heat problems occurred when operating in hot climates.**

***Below:* The key to successful resupply operations is the ability to carry vital large, heavy and bulky equipment, frequently over long distances. Air-to-air refuelling capability makes the C-5 one of the best aircraft in the world at accomplishing these missions.**

Flight restrictions

The C-5A first flew on 30 June 1968 and the initial tests were relatively trouble-free. However, in the summer of 1969, the appearance of wing cracks in a fatigue test airframe revealed a major shortcoming which was to plague the Galaxy for nearly a decade. In the quest to reduce weight, the strength of the wing box had been compromised. As a result, the Galaxy was only likely to achieve 25 per cent of its intended design life. In November 1969 the procurement was reduced to just 81 aircraft. To help extend operational life a peacetime payload restriction of 50,000 lb (22680 kg) was implemented – less than 20 per cent of the maximum payload. The retrofitting of active ailerons and reinforcement of the wing box helped alleviate some of the flight restrictions imposed but were at best only a partial palliative.

On 6 June 1970 the 3rd Military Airlift Squadron, 437th MAW became the first operational unit based at Charleston AFB. The first to attain initial operational capability (IOC) was the 75th MAS at Travis AFB.

In 1977 the USAF eventually elected to institute a re-winging programme to ensure that the aircraft would achieve their design life of 30,000 hours. A total of 77 C-5As was put through a re-winging programme between 1981 and 1987. At the same time, the production line was reopened to meet an urgent USAF demand for additional heavy airlift capacity.

Fifty C-5Bs with the new wing were built, essentially similar to the C-5A but incorporating some modifications including an improved automated flight control system. Deliveries to the 443rd Military Airlift Wing began in January 1986 and the USAF accepted the final C-5B in April 1989. As the C-5Bs supplemented C-5As in active-duty units, a number of C-5As could in turn be released to AFRes and ANG units.

Air Mobility Command currently operates C-5s from Altus, Dover and Travis AFBs. With Air Force Reserve squadrons at Kelly, Stewart, Westover and Wright-Patterson, and with ANG squadrons at Memphis and Martinsburg, the C-5 remains a vital part of the USAF's resources.

In order to further enhance the C-5's capabilities, the USAF began the C-5M programme in 1998. Core features of this upgrade are new 50,000-lb st (222.4-kN) General Electric CF6-80C2 turbofans and updated avionics, including a 'glass' cockpit.

The C-5 was designed to carry main battle tanks like this M1 Abrams, or large helicopters. The hinged nose greatly decreases loading/unloading time, providing a roll-on/roll-off capability.

Lockheed C-141 StarLifter

Above: The StarLifter could carry a variety of palletised loads and most vehicle types, with the exception of main battle tanks. The C-141's load-carrying ability was called upon many times by the USAF, in actions spanning from the Vietnam War to Operation Iraqi Freedom, beginning in 2003.

Strategic transport

Constant, effective support is essential for any military force, particularly when that force is spread around the world, with a vast range of operational needs. For four decades, the C-141 answered the call for quick and effective logistic support.

At the beginning of the 1960s most of the USAF's Military Air Transport Service (MATS) strategic transport aircraft were prop-driven types. With increasing demand for rapid deployment capability, it was clear that modern jet-powered equipment was urgently needed.

The veteran C-124 continued to serve in considerable numbers as the backbone of MATS' heavy-lift capability, supported by a modest number of C-133s. It was mainly to replace the C-124 that the USAF issued SOR-182, inviting designs for a new turbofan-powered cargo/troop-carrier aircraft.

The USAF judged Lockheed's candidate as best suited to fulfilling the requirement, ordering an initial batch of five aircraft in August 1961.

Flown for the first time on 17 December 1963, the C-141A began to enter operational service with the 1501st Air Transport Wing (subsequently the 60th Military Airlift Wing) at Travis AFB on 23 April 1965. This occurred eight months before MATS underwent a considerable upheaval, being retitled as Military Airlift Command on 1 January 1966. From 1966 to 1977 the StarLifter went on to enter service with five more front-line transport wings. A modest number was also allocated to MAC's principal training unit, at Tinker AFB. After one StarLifter wing became a C-5A unit, five front-line units and a training element continued to operate the C-141 from 1973 onwards, a line-up which remained essentially unchanged until the 1990s.

The C-141A emerged as a four-engined, high-wing aircraft incorporating rear-loading doors facilitating the carriage of extremely lengthy and heavy items, including ICBMs.

The first operational airlift base to receive the StarLifter, Travis served as a key link in the supply chain to Vietnam and, as a consequence, at the height of the war witnessed a near-constant stream of airlift aircraft departing for southeast Asia.

In addition to being employed in support of forces engaged in combat in Vietnam, the StarLifter also began to undertake its fair share of 'special airlift missions'. This involved a diverse range of activities including mobility training exercises, ICBM and outsize cargo shipment, humanitarian tasks and specialised support operations.

***Above:** With events in southeast Asia taking centre stage during the mid-1960s as the **C-141A** began to join **MATS/MAC** in considerable numbers, the type was soon committed to supporting the war effort.*

***Below:** Modification from **C-141A** to **C-141B** (foreground) standard entailed adding a 13-ft 4-in (4.06-m) long plug directly ahead of the wing and a 10-ft (3.05-m) long plug immediately aft.*

By 1967, when a substantial proportion of the 284 examples that were eventually procured had been delivered to MAC, the StarLifter was likely to appear at any air base where American influence was strong or where the US had a vested interest.

Operational experience acquired during the late 1960s and early 1970s revealed that, although in many ways suited to MAC airlift tasks, in its initial form the C-141A suffered from some shortcomings.

If it were to possess true global range, the C-141 would require modification in order that it might be refuelled in flight. At the same time, consideration was given to the C-141's payload capability. Although nothing could be done to increase the cross-section of the StarLifter's hold, it was feasible to 'stretch' the aircraft so that it could operate at weights rather closer to the permissible maximum. In 1976, Lockheed received a contract covering the conversion of a single C-141A into the YC-141B prototype.

Stretching the StarLifter

Modification to YC-141B standard allowed an increase in the number of standard pallets which could be accommodated from 10 to 13. Improved wingroot fairings were fitted, reducing drag and resulting in a slightly higher maximum speed and lower fuel consumption.

Inflight refuelling capability was installed on the YC-141B, which first flew on 24 March 1977. Prototype-testing in mid-1977 led to a decision to modify all of MAC's 270 or so remaining C-141As, this project getting under way in 1978. Acceptance of the first 'production' C-141B took place in December 1979 and the modification programme terminated in June 1982 when the last example was re-delivered to MAC. The fleet-wide modification initiative provided MAC with the equivalent of an additional 90 C-141As at modest cost and without the need to find additional aircrews.

The 'new' StarLifter emphatically demonstrated its value on numerous occasions after entering the MAC inventory, having 'grown' in both the literal and metaphorical senses since entering service. The process of attaining maturity resulted in an aircraft which provided MAC with the ability to move cargo and/or personnel virtually anywhere in the world at short notice.

However, the arrival in service of the far more capable C-17 Globemaster III signalled the end of the road for the StarLifter. The last active-duty C-141B was retired by the USAF in September 2004, leaving just 20 examples of the C-141C with the Reserve. This was a version upgraded with improved avionics (including a 'glass' cockpit) and navigation systems, but it, too, gave way to the C-17, the last examples being withdrawn from service in May 2006.

***Right:** Operationally, the advent of the **C-141B** made a considerable difference to **MAC's** airlift potential, with the ability to refuel in flight meaning that the **C-141's** range became limited only by crew fatigue considerations.*

***Left:** With side-facing canvas seats in place, the **C-141B** could carry 168 fully equipped paratroops. The clamshell rear cargo doors opened outwards for maximum clearance.*

*Lockheed's long-serving **T-33A** prototype, 48-356, itself a converted production **P-80C**, was further reworked as the YF-94/F-94A prototype, first flying in its new guise on 16 April 1949. Note the underwing tip tanks, of the type fitted to the **T-33**, the nose radome and guns.*

Lockheed F-94 Starfire

ADC's first jet interceptor

The F-94 was the first jet-powered interceptor in Air Defense Command (ADC), and the only one for more than three years. The powerful F-94C was the first two-seat aircraft to fly faster than sound. It was also the first production fighter to be equipped with all-rocket armament and the first to use a drag 'chute on landing.

Like most early jets, the F-94 was beset with teething troubles. The F-94C Starfire was initially so handicapped by its engine that the USAF considered cancelling it, and the Hughes fire control system on the F-94C required an enormous effort to make it functional. In the end, the F-94 could never overcome the basic deficiency inherent in its design: it lacked range. As the ultimate development of the Lockheed P-80, the F-94 never had the internal volume to permit greater fuel capacity.

The F-94 was the result of an urgent programme to equip USAF interceptor squadrons with jets to meet the perceived Soviet bomber threat. All-weather fighter jets had been ordered as far back as 1945, but the Curtiss XP-87 had been cancelled and Northrop's XP-89 plagued by development problems.

The USAF took delivery of its first F-94A in December 1949. Initially, F-94As were assigned to the 317th Fighter Interceptor Squadron at McChord AFB and the 319th FIS at Moses Lake AFB in May 1950, replacing the F-82G Twin Mustang. At the time, the defence of the United States was in the hands of CONAC (Continental Air Command). The mission reverted soon afterward to ADC (Air Defense Command). More than three years were to elapse before other all-weather interceptors, the F-86D Sabre and the F-89 Scorpion, joined the Lockheed fighter in service.

The improved F-94B version began to reach the 61st FIS at Selfridge AFB in April 1951. Apart from early maintenance snags with the radar, the F-94A/B was generally reliable, but was too lightly armed and was deemed unlikely to be effective against modern bombers. The USAF wanted an interceptor with greater rate of climb, more range and heavier firepower.

The rocket-armed F-94C model – the only variant in the series ever officially named Starfire – encountered early developmental problems, many of which centred around the unreliability of its E-5 fire control system. Initially, the F-94C had a tendency to flame out when its nose rockets were fired, a problem which was resolved with minor changes to the nose contours. The F-94C was two years behind expectations when it began operational flying with the 437th FIS at Otis AFB in March 1953.

By 1954, the USAF was beginning to phase out the F-94A/B, which had always been seen as performing an interim role. They joined the Air National Guard as replacements for the F-51 Mustang. The F-94's ANG career was brief, but the type equipped 21 ANG squadrons at one stage. The 179th FIS of the Minnesota ANG was the final user of the type, and gave up its F-94s in summer 1959.

Some 854 F-94s came off Lockheed's production line in Burbank, California. In retrospect, the F-94 was an 'interim' solution to air defence. Built in smaller numbers than the F-80 or T-33, it was well known for a brief time, then receded into history.

*Its afterburner producing a long finger of flame, a 319th **FIS F-94B** undergoes engine runs in the dispersal at Suwon (K-13) in Korea, prior to a nocturnal 'Bedcheck Charlie' mission in July 1953. As one of the first and therefore most experienced operators of the **F-94A**, the 319th was one of the first **F-94** units committed to the Korean police action. By the time the unit had arrived in-theatre, it had re-equipped with **F-94Bs**.*

The 15th production F-94C Starfire, 50-970, poses for one of a series of publicity photographs. This aircraft was delivered to the Air Proving Ground Command at Eglin AFB on 3 October 1952 where it was used as a test aircraft in the programme to develop wing rocket pods for the F-94C.

F-94s in Korea

The 68th FIS 'Lightning Lancers' at Itazuke Air Base, Japan, began to receive F-94As on 10 October 1951. The arrival of this new combat aircraft with a profile almost identical to the T-33 trainer was celebrated in the popular 'Terry and the Pirates' comic strip by George Wunder, which had a Communist agent trying to figure out why the nose, with its radar, was different from that of the trainer.

With or without help from the cartoonist or the 'Terry' cartoon's radar operator named Hot Shot Charlie, FEAF (Far East Air Forces) clamped an extraordinary restriction on F-94 operations. Commander of the 68th Major Donald E. McNeil took a pair of F-94As to K-13 Suwon Air Base to stand alert beginning 28 December 1951, only to be given firm orders that he was prohibited from flying the F-94 north of the bomb line. During the day, MiG-15s were wreaking havoc with the Allied air forces; they had wiped out no fewer than six B-29 Superfortresses in one day in October, counting aircraft which brought their crews home but never flew again. This caused FEAF to shift most B-29 sorties to the nocturnal hours, when night intruders dubbed 'Bedcheck Charlie' were causing chaos at American air bases. Some MiGs and possibly Yak-15s were also operating at night. Yet, FEAF was more worried about the F-94's precious new radar falling into enemy hands than about Americans being killed and wounded because the F-94 force was shackled.

The F-94A appeared only briefly in Korea, and the 68th soon converted to the B. The 319th FIS re-equipped with the newer F-94B as well and began operating from Suwon on 22 March 1952, still under orders not to fly over enemy territory, to prevent compromising their secret electronic equipment. The FEAF order merely repeated a policy established by the Air Staff in the Pentagon, who had decided that the radar and fire control system was too valuable to risk. Neither the top brass nor Soviet agents, if there were any around, seemed to grasp the essential reality about the radar: it was unreliable and cantankerous and was, in the words of one technician assigned to keep it running, 'so finicky that it will break down if you look at it the wrong way'. Many early problems were solved with practice and repetition, and with a tremendous support effort by Hughes, but an F-94 crew always taxied out from the revetment not knowing whether the radar would continue to work for an entire flight.

The restriction on use of the F-94 was lifted in January 1953, following a visit to Korea by USAF chief of staff General Hoyt S. Vandenberg. The 319th FIS began flying protective patrols 30 miles (50 km) ahead of B-29 formations. On the night of 30 January 1952, an F-94B flown by pilot Captain Benjamin L. Fithian and radar operator Lieutenant R. S. 'Sam' Lyons was launched against an intruding Lavochkin La-9 piston-engined fighter, which was never seen by the friendlies but was apparently identified via a communications intercept. After another F-94 radioed 'no joy', meaning that his RO (radar observer) could not establish contact using the interceptor's onboard radar, Fithian and Lyons made radar contact, extended air brakes to stay behind the slower Lavochkin, and attacked, firing using the radar scope. Fithian did not see his opponent until his machine-gun rounds set the La-9 afire and sent it spinning into the sea with the canopy closed. It was apparently the first aerial victory in history against an opponent who was never seen during the engagement.

On 10 May 1953, an F-94 in the hands of pilot Captain John R. Phillips and radar operator Lieutenant Billy J. Atto shot down the first MiG-15 to fall to the Lockheed interceptor. Before the war ended in July, Korea-based F-94Bs shot down two more nocturnal intruders. On 3 May 1953, an F-94B crewed by First Lieutenants Stanton G. Wilcox and Irwin L. Goldberg throttled down to 110 mph (177 km/h) to attempt a low-level kill of a Polikarpov Po-2 biplane, and crashed into terrain. Both men lost their lives. On 12 June, Lieutenant Colonel Robert V. McHale, commander of the 319th FIS and his back-seater Captain Samuel Hoster were killed when they apparently collided with a Po-2 they were attempting to intercept.

An F-94C Starfire of the 26th Air Division, winners of the 1955 Rocketry Meet, opens fire. The first three projectiles from the right-hand pod appear to have collided. If the rocket's fins failed to deploy, trajectories were unpredictable. The FFAR relied on the 'shot-gun' effect to score a kill.

In Korea F-94Bs, like this 68th Fighter Interceptor Squadron example, flew night interdiction sorties, dropping 1,100 tons of bombs, as well as intercept and escort missions.

Lockheed F-104 Starfighter

The 'manned missile'

Designed in the 1950s, in the aftermath of the Korean War, as the ultimate clear-air dogfighter – lightweight, simple and with breathtaking performance – Lockheed's F-104 was eventually developed into a sophisticated all-weather interdictor. The F-104 remained in limited front-line use with the Italian air force until 2004.

Few aircraft have attracted such passionate feelings of love and hate, or excitement and fear, as the F-104 Starfighter. Setting out to create a brilliant world-beating air-combat fighter, its designers failed utterly. But the result turned out to be quite good at low-level attack and reconnaissance, and Lockheed sold an improved version to such good effect that it was, for more than 20 years, the leading tactical aircraft of Europe's NATO air arms and Japan, despite the fact that the US Air Force's only interest was to assist sales to others!

Lessons from Korea

It all began with a visit to Korea in 1952 by Clarence L. ('Kelly') Johnson, Lockheed's chief engineer. He found even the F-86 squadrons depressed, because they were unable to outclimb or outmanoeuvre the MiG-15 'Fagots'. They wanted a fighter with the highest possible performance, even at the cost of reduced endurance and armament. Johnson returned determined to achieve superior performance at almost any price.

Lockheed made an unsolicited proposal of the Model 83 to the USAF in November 1952. On 11 March 1953, the USAF issued a letter contract for two XF-104s. The first, powered by a J65 rated

High over San Francisco harbour, a pair of F-104As from the 337th Fighter Interceptor Squadron pass the Bay Bridge. The type proved less than ideal in the defence of the continental United States and enjoyed only a brief career with the USAF.

at 8,000 lb (35.6 kN), flew on 28 February 1954. The second, with an afterburning J65 rated at 11,500 lb (51.16 kN), followed on 5 October 1954. The J65 was envisaged only as an interim engine, pending availability of the more powerful General Electric J79 but, despite this, a speed of Mach 1.7 and height of 60,000 ft (18288 m) were soon reached. The bad news was that, predictably, the XF-104 was a real handful, requiring constant accurate flying.

In July 1954, a cautious USAF ordered 17 YF-104As; these were intended to be very close to production F-104As with a J79-GE-3 engine. The aircraft entered limited service in a test/development capacity with the 83rd FIS at Hamilton AFB. A total of 610 F-104As had been requested, but only 153 were actually built. They were phased out of USAF service in 1960, but were recalled by the Berlin and Cuban crises of 1961/62. Likewise, instead of the planned 112 F-104B tandem-trainers, the USAF received only 26.

Despite the operation of the Tornado and the introduction of the AMX, Italy still retained front-line F-104s into the 21st century. For combat air patrol missions, the aircraft latterly operated in conjunction with Tornado F.Mk 3s, which provided the Starfighters with extra radar information for interception work.

Starfighter reborn

At this point, Lockheed's Starfighter seemed to have been a failure, but Lockheed recognised that the USAF would only be a peripheral customer. It therefore started to organise a sales team to try to persuade foreign customers that, even if the USAF did not want the F-104, the improved Starfighter (now available) would be the greatest aircraft in the sky. The so-called Super Starfighter (F-104G) was equipped with an uprated powerplant, NASARR radar, strengthened fuselage and new mission equipment.

NATO allies were quick to adopt the F-104 Starfighter into service, with no fewer than nine NATO air forces operating the type. The aircraft was built under licence by consortia of Belgium, Dutch, Italian and German companies, and by Canadair.

Outside Europe, the major operator was Japan, which produced 200 F-104J single-seat and DJ two-seat Starfighters under licence. Ex-USAF Starfighters were supplied to Pakistan, Taiwan and Jordan, while Spain received 21 F-104Gs and TF-104G trainers in 1965, in return for the American use of Spanish air bases.

The Starfighter did not see extensive combat during its service life, although Taiwanese examples participated in numerous combats with Communist Chinese fighters, scoring few victories. During the Indo-Pakistan War of 1965, the Pakistan air force's single Starfighter squadron scored several victories for the loss of at least one fighter in combat.

The F-104 remained in front-line service into the 21st century, although in a much modified form, with the Italian air force. Known as the F-104S, this featured extra fuselage missile pylons and an improved radar with a 'look-down' capability. The F-104S underwent a further upgrade programme during 1997 to emerge as the F-104S-ASA-M, finally retired in October 2004.

With its high speed, climb performance and high-altitude capability, the Starfighter was a natural choice for NASA's test fleet. Operating from Dryden's Flight Research facility at Edwards AFB, the Starfighter served until 1983, when it was replaced by the F/A-18 Hornet. This was an ironic move since the F-104 served as a chase aircraft during the Hornet's development.

USAF service

*Left: In the wake of the **Cuban Missile Crisis, F-104As** were taken out of **ANG** control and assigned to the active-duty 32nd Air Division (ADC) at Homestead AFB, Florida. From here the three squadrons provided a rapid-reaction capability to deter any aggression from the south.*

*Below: The 83rd **FIS** had flown the sluggish Northrop **F-89** for most of the 1950s, so the arrival of the swift **F-104** provided an interesting lesson in state-of-the-art technology. It was also a painful one: **ADC** began losing **F-104As** at an alarming rate.*

The USAF took delivery of the first of just 258 production Starfighters in 1958, the type remaining in front-line service for 10 years. The F-104 was finally retired by the Air National Guard in 1975.

The first XF-104 was trucked to the Air Force Flight Test Center (AFFTC), Edwards AFB, California on 25 February 1954 and flew on 5 March. The YF-104A was tested at Edwards beginning 17 February 1956. The first operational F-104A in USAF service reached the 83rd FIS at Hamilton AFB, California on 29 January 1958. Initially slated for Tactical Air Command (TAC) where it had been viewed as an F-100 Super Sabre replacement, the F-104A went to Air Defense Command (ADC) instead, due to ADC's urgent need for an interceptor to fill in between the F-102 and F-106. The 83rd FIS received its first F-104B in 1958.

The first F-104C for the USAF was accepted by the 476th TFS, 479th TFW at George AFB, California, on 15 October 1958. The first operational F-104D was accepted by the same squadron the following month.

USAF F-104A Starfighters from two squadrons at Hamilton AFB went into action for the first time from Nationalist Chinese and US bases on Formosa (Taiwan) in late 1958, following Chinese Communist aggression against

*These **F-104Cs** of the 479th **TFW** are seen at a **European** base. Though **USAF Starfighters** were never based in **Europe**, regular deployments were made during the 1960s.*

Starfighters in Vietnam

As USAF tactical aircraft faced an ever-growing threat from MiGs, the 479th TFW dispatched its 435th TFS to Da Nang in April 1965 to fly top cover for tactical operations. During the course of these the F-104 proved to be too short on range to be a useful escort fighter, a fact the North soon learned. All they had to do was wait for the F-104s to turn back before launching their own fighters in safety. On one rare occasion where the F-104 was engaged, one aircraft was shot down (by Chinese MiG-19s). The first detachment lasted until December, but resumed in May 1966 at Udorn in Thailand. During the second phase the ground-attack mission prevailed, although with a full bomb load (of just two weapons) the F-104 had a very limited range. The Starfighter took part in Operation Bolo, a successful attempt to lure the MiGs into the air. Here the F-104s failed to engage, while F-4 Phantoms scored heavily. In addition to the MiG loss, two F-104s fell to SAMs, six to AAA and six to non-combat causes. In this view (below) camouflaged 479th TFW F-104Cs crowd the Udorn ramp with T-28s and RF-101s.

***Above:** The West German training establishment underwent several unit numbering changes, the 4510th CTW later becoming the 58th TFTW (TTW from 1977). The aircraft above proudly proclaims the heritage of the 'Fighting 69th', one of the 58th's two squadrons.*

***Below:** The Armament Development & Test Center at Eglin operated 24 QF-104A supersonic target drones.*

USAF/ANG/NASA Starfighter units

USAF Air Defense Command: F-104A/B, 83rd Fighter Interceptor Sqn; 337th FIS, Hamilton AFB, California, February 1958, and Patrick AFB, Florida, (1961); 56th FIS, Wright-Patterson AFB, Ohio (1957); 319th FIS; 331st FIS; 337th FIS, Westover AFB, Massachusetts, to 1959-60; 319th, 331st and 482nd FIS, 32nd Air Division, Homestead AFB, Florida, March 1963 to December 1969; 538th FIS, Larson AFB, Washington (1958)
Tactical Air Command: F-104C/D, 434th, 435th, 436th, and 476th Tactical Fighter Squadrons (479th Tactical Fighter Wing), 831st Air Division, George AFB, California (16 October 1958 to 1965). 435th TFS to Torrejon (Spain), November 1959; 4512th, 4518th, 4443rd USAF Combat Crew Training Sqns, 4510th Combat Crew Training Wing; 4512th, 4518th, 4443rd Combat Crew Training Squadrons, 58th Tactical Fighter Training Wing, 405th Tactical Training Wing, Luke AFB, Arizona (training of West German pilots)
Air National Guard: F-104A/B, 151st Fighter Interceptor Sqn, Tennessee ANG (June 1960 to March 1963), Knoxville; 157th FIS, South Carolina ANG (February 1960 to June 1963), McEntire ANGB; 197th FIS, Arizona ANG (July 1960 to September 1962), Phoenix Sky Harbor; F-104C/D, 198th Tactical Fighter Sqn (15th Tactical Fighter Group), Puerto Rico ANG, Muniz ANGB/San Juan (summer 1967 to July 1975)
Air Research and Development Command: Air Force Flight Test Center and Air Force Test Pilots School, Edwards AFB, California: F-104A/B/C/D/G, NF-104A (three assigned September 1963)
Air Proving Ground Command: Armament Development & Test Center, Eglin AFB, Florida; 3205th Drone Squadron: QF-104A (11)
National Aeronautics and Space Administration (NASA): Dryden Flight Research Facility, Edwards AFB, California, YF-104A (55-2961/NASA 818), F-104A (56-0749; 56-1734), F-104A/G (56-0790/NASA 820), F-104B (57-1303/NASA 819), TF-104G (61-3065/27 and 37/NASA 824, 66-13628/28 and 09/NASA 825, 24+64/NASA 826), F-104N (NASA 011/811; NASA 012/812; NASA 013/813); Ames Flight Research Facility, NAS Moffett Field, California, JF-104A (56-0745), F-104B (57-1303/NASA 819)

the Republic of China island of Quemoy in the Straits of Formosa. The display of their Mach 2 capabilities recorded by PRC ground radars proved a sufficient deterrent, although in reality most of the action was over by the time the Starfighters arrived and their impact on Peking's leadership was negligible. In October 1961, when the USSR cut West German access links to Berlin, three ANG F-104A squadrons assigned to Air Defense Command were transferred to Tactical Air Command and rushed to Europe to reinforce NATO's air defences. During the 1962 Cuban missile crisis, USAF F-104Cs were deployed to bases in the southeastern US as the most effective available counter to the threat of Soviet-supplied MiG fighters operating from that island. They remained in that area until the late 1960s.

Fifteen F-104Cs of the 479th TFW were also sent to South Vietnam in March 1965 to counter North Vietnamese interference with USAF strike aircraft, after the shooting-down of two Republic F-105s by NVAF MiG-17s. Each of the 479th's three F-104 squadrons served rotation tours, which were repeated in mid-1966, when the USAF still operated some 115 Starfighters, including 40 F-104As at Homestead and Webb AFBs, and about 75 F-104Cs at George AFB. By early 1967, however, only one Starfighter squadron remained in the regular USAF inventory, and this was finally disbanded a year later. F-104B/Cs continued operating with the Air National Guard until July 1975.

***Above:** In their early service with the 479th TFW, F-104Cs wore flamboyant markings, though these disappeared as the F-104 adopted serious tasks during the Berlin and Cuba crises.*

***Left:** NASA's Dryden facility at Edwards AFB adopted the F-104 as the mainstay of its high performance test fleet, employing a number on a variety of programmes. NASA 824 was one of three ex-Luftwaffe TF-104Gs employed and is seen here in formation with NASA's long-serving NB-52A.*

International operators

Apart from the United States Air Force and European customers in NATO, five other air arms in North America, Asia and the Middle East took delivery of Starfighters.

Canada

Canadair built 200 CF-104 versions of the F-104G for the RCAF after Lockheed's prototype conversion. The first was rolled-out on 18 March 1961, before making its initial flight 10 days later. Powered by the Orenda-built J79-OEL-7 developing 10,000 lb (44.58 kN) thrust, or 15,800 lb (70.31 kN) with afterburning, the CF-104 was virtually identical to the F-104G. However, all but the two tactical recce squadrons of No. 1 Wing were intended for nuclear roles, so the Canadian Starfighters had 1,000 lb (454 kg) of additional fuel in place of the normal Vulcan cannon. These were later installed when the CF-104s relinquished their nuclear role in 1972 in favour of conventional ground-attack. RCAF Starfighter orders also included 38 Lockheed-built two-seat CF-104D trainers. Canadair further received US-funded Mutual Aid orders for another 140 Starfighters to F-104G standard, mainly for other export customers. Apart from one operational conversion unit established at Cold Lake, Alberta in late 1961 (later redesignated No. 417 Sqn), RCAF Starfighters were all committed to NATO operations through the Canadian Air Division in Europe. Air Division organisation originally comprised four Starfighter wings, with eight squadrons each with 25 aircraft; No. 427 was the first to form, with initial CF-104 deliveries to Zweibrücken in December 1962. In February 1964, 2 Wing at Gros Tenquin was disbanded and its two CF-104 squadrons transferred, No. 421 moving to 4 Wing at Baden-Söllingen and No. 430 to 3 Wing at Zweibrücken. As the RCAF's other French base, Marville, was also closed by 31 March 1967, its two CF-104 recce squadrons (439 and 441) then moved to Lahr, in Germany. Air Division strength was reduced with the disbandment in 1967-68 of Nos 434 and 444 Sqns, the remaining six CF-104 squadrons comprising four with a nuclear strike role and two for tactical reconnaissance. In May 1969, Canadian defence economies further reduced NATO commitments in Europe, including the closure of 3 Wing at Zweibrücken, which was transferred to USAFE, and the relocation of its squadrons to Baden (427) and Lahr (430). Air Division organisation in late 1969 then comprised Nos 430, 439 and 441 Sqns in 1 Wing at Lahr and 421, 422 and 427 Sqns at Baden. In the following year, however, the Canadian government decided to halve the strength of the Air Division to only three squadrons, and relinquish its nuclear strike role in favour of conventional ground-attack by 1972. 1 AirDiv was redesignated 1 Canadian Air Group, with HQ at Baden-Söllingen (seen below, with No. 4 Wing aircraft, some time prior to 1972) which, with the closure of Lahr, the disbandment of 1 Wing and of Nos 422, 427 and 430 Sqns, became the sole CF-104 base in Europe. Nos 439 and 441 Sqns replaced all but 421 Sqn in Nos 3 and 4 Wings at Baden. Of the remaining three squadrons, 421 was committed to converting to ground-attack roles, together with No. 439 Sqn, leaving only No. 441 to continue tactical recce tasks. With deliveries to the CAF of CF-188 Hornets, the last CF-104s were retired from service with 441 Sqn on 28 February 1986. Pictured top are a pair of CF-104As at CFB Trenton, Ontario, in September 1976

Pakistan

Ten F-104As (two of which are pictured, left) and two F-104Bs were initially delivered through MAP from the US from 15 September 1961 onwards as the first Starfighter exports, some reports claiming that they were re-engined with J79-GE-11A turbojets, developing another 1,000 lb (4.45 kN) of thrust with a maximum afterburner rating of 15,800 lb (70.31 kN). Two F-104As were later delivered from Taiwan as combat attrition replacements for 1965 losses during the war with India. Others were reported to have been donated to Pakistan following Jordanian assistance by the provision of the F-104As of No. 9 Sqn, RJAF, to help the PAF in the 1971 war with India, in which the Pakistanis admitted the loss of three more Starfighters. Pakistan has also been officially listed as receiving a single tactical-recce RF-104G from Lockheed production, but no further details have ever become available.

Japan

The F-104J was selected in 1960 to replace the JASDF's F-86F Sabres in a $207 million joint US/Japanese programme with local manufacture by Mitsubishi and Ishikawajima/Harima, the latter group producing J79-IHI-11A powerplants. Initial orders comprised 180 F-104J fighter-bombers plus 20 locally assembled two-seat F-104DJ trainers, with deliveries starting from Lockheed in early 1962. A further 30 F-104Js were then ordered for local production, with deliveries by 1967. Programme completion was scheduled by January 1965, with seven squadrons re-equipped. Mitsubishi assembled or built a total of 210 F-104J Starfighters at Komaki between 1 April 1962 and 2 December 1967. The first example was built by Lockheed Burbank, and first flown on July 1961, before being shipped to Japan and reassembled to fly at Komaki on 8 March 1962. The second and third examples followed a similar pattern, with 17 more F-104Js then assembled by Mitsubishi from knocked-down kits before Japanese production began, to equip seven all-weather interceptor squadrons between October 1962 and December 1967. Assembly was also undertaken by Mitsubishi from Lockheed-built kits of another 20 two-seat F-104DJ trainers between 1962 and 1964. At least 34 F-104Js and two F-104DJs (just over 15 per cent) had been written-off in accidents when the last JASDF unit (207th Sqn) began re-equipping with F-15J Eagles in 1984-85. 36-8518 (above) was the 18th F-104J off the Mitsubishi assembly line and is seen here with a second F-104J and a pair of two-seat F-104DJs. The latter had white upper wing surfaces (left) to aid conspicuity.

Jordan

A total of 36 early ex-USAF Starfighters were promised to Jordan by the US government in April 1966, for a nominal $1 million each, and an initial batch of three F-104As and three two-seat F-104Bs were airlifted to the RJAF in early 1967. Apart from one F-104A which had already crashed, these were almost immediately withdrawn to Turkey at the outbreak of the six-day Middle East war between 5 and 10 June 1967, in which a large part of the Arab air forces, including most of the RJAF's operational strength, were destroyed on the ground by initial Israeli air attacks. It was not until late 1968 that RJAF pilots and ground crews resumed Starfighter training in the US, prior to the receipt in mid-1969 of the first six of 18 ex-USAF F-104As and four F-104Bs, and these were initially flown by Pakistan air force pilots. A visit to Washington by King Hussein earlier in 1969 had resulted in President Nixon agreeing to supply Jordan with a second squadron of 18 F-104As, to be transferred from Taiwan's Nationalist Chinese air force storage following their replacement by F-104Gs, after the Jordanian monarch had pointed out that he had been offered MiG-21s by the USSR for about one-third the price of comparable Western equipment. No. 9 Sqn was sent with its F-104As to Pakistan to help out in the 1971 war with India, in which it is believed to have suffered several losses. The RJAF was reported to have operated about 20 F-104As and four Bs in two squadrons by July 1979, to be replaced by 34 Mirage F1s. One of the RJAF's ex-Air Defense Command F-104As is pictured, armed with a tip-mounted Sidewinder and carrying drop tanks.

Taiwan

Reliable reports of Taiwanese Starfighter deliveries have not so far become available, but most sources agree that an initial batch of 24 ex-USAF Lockheed F-104As and five two-seat F-104B trainers delivered in 1960-61 were followed between 1964 and 1969 by 46 Lockheed-built F-104Gs and eight two-seat TF-104Gs, plus 21 tactical-recce RF-104Gs from Canadair (RoCAF serials 4301 to 4362 identified). Another six two-seat F-104Ds were received in 1975 from former USAF ANG squadrons to supplement RoCAF Starfighter units in the sole wing at Ching Chuan Kang air base. Further batches of 64 Canadair/Lockheed F-104Gs and TF-104s, comprising 38 Gs (4363 to 4400?, including 4378, below right) and 26 TFs (4171 to 4196?, including 4179, below left), were transferred from the inventory in 1983 with the closure of the German training centre (69 TFTS) at Luke AFB. By 1987, the RoCAF had received at least 22 F-104Js and five F-104DJs, both airworthy and unairworthy, from Japan through the 'ALISAN 9' project, together with 15 F-104Gs and three TF-104Gs from the Royal Danish Air Force from the 'ALISAN 10' programme between February and April of the same year. Deliveries to Taiwan of at least 166 single-seat Starfighters and about 53 two-seaters in all, are therefore reasonably well-documented, plus possible additional and unknown quantities from Japan. All the early series F-104As, F-104Bs and F-104Ds were withdrawn from service in the early 1980s, some being transferred to Pakistan and Jordan. Others were subsequently used for drones or decoys. In 1990, the RoCAF's remaining Starfighters equipped six tactical fighter and one recce squadrons, and some continued in service until 1996, when they were finally replaced by the Ching-Kuo IDF. Their final armament included AIM-9J Sidewinder AAMs and locally developed Sky Sword I and II IR and semi-active radar homing AAMs. The last Taiwanese Starfighters of all were the RF-104Gs, which were finally replaced in 1998 by F-5Es converted to RF-5E standard.

European operators

Left: Carrying Sidewinder missiles, this F-104G belongs to one of the two Dutch squadrons that were assigned to all-weather interception duties.

Below: By far the largest user of the Starfighter was the West German air force, which was the launch customer for the F-104G version. Flying over typical German countryside is an aircraft of JBG 34, which was the last Luftwaffe wing to operate the type.

Designed as a lightweight, simple interceptor, the F-104 underwent a metamorphosis, winning major orders from European air forces and achieving recognition as a low-level attack and nuclear strike aircraft.

As the USAF became increasingly disenchanted with the F-104's appalling accident rate, Lockheed identified a requirement within NATO for a Starfighter derivative. West Germany was keen to obtain a supersonic multi-role fighter to equip the Luftwaffe and to build up its aircraft manufacturing industry. After evaluating proposals from a dozen or so rivals, a contract was signed in March 1959 for the development and licence-manufacture of the aircraft Lockheed had named the 'Super Starfighter', the F-104G ('G' for Germany). Belgium, the Netherlands and Italy selected the F-104G in what was called the 'sale of the century'. A gigantic European manufacturing programme was created, made up of Arbeitsgemeinschaft Nord (Hamburger, Weser, Focke-Wulf, Fokker and Aviolanda), ARGE Süd (Messerschmitt, Heinkel, Dornier and Siebel) and the Western Group (Avions Fairey and SABCA). Together, they built 350, 210 and 188 aircraft, respectively. Initially, the Belgians were teamed with Italy, but the Italian group was later separated (Fiat, Aerfer, Macchi, SIAI-Marchetti, Piaggio and SACA). The group assembled 229 F-104Gs and Italy later developed the F-104S.

Canada had also selected the type and built 200 as the CF-104G on its own production lines, from which Denmark and Norway received some aircraft.

A total of 100 F-104Gs and 12 TF-104Gs was used by two wings of the Belgian air force from mid-1963 to early 1983.

The Danish Starfighters served for 21 years, beginning in 1965. A total of 40 single-seat versions and 11 dual-seat aircraft from US, European and Canadian production lines were flown.

German service

Germany was the major user of the type, not only in Europe, but on a worldwide basis. The Starfighter served both with the West German air force (Luftwaffe) and the naval air arm (Marineflieger). A total of 604 F-104Gs was operated, along with 145 reconnaissance-configured RF-104Gs. Two-seat aircraft comprised 30 Lockheed-built F-104Fs, and 137 TF-104Gs.

JBG 31, the first wing to operate the Starfighter in Germany, began to receive the aircraft from July 1960. At its peak, in the mid-1970s, the aircraft equipped five Luftwaffe fighter-bomber wings, two interceptor wings, plus two reconnaissance wings. Luftwaffe Starfighters remained in operational service until October 1987.

From 1964 onwards, the Marineflieger used two wings of Starfighters. The Marineflieger received additional ex-Luftwaffe F-104Gs and RF-104Gs from 1971 as attrition replacements. The final examples were retired in 1988.

Dutch tactical units, reporting to NATO's 2nd Allied Tactical Air Force, received 75 F-104Gs, 25 RF-104Gs and 18 TF-104Gs from early 1963 onwards. The last Dutch Starfighter was retired in November 1984.

Starfighter FX-1 was the first aircraft produced for the Belgian air force. The silver scheme had given way to tactical camouflage by 1967.

Norway received Lockheed-built F/RF-104Gs (19) and TF-104Gs (4), and surplus Canadian single- (2) and two-seaters (4) to equip two squadrons. The last Starfighters were retired from Norwegian service in 1981.

A total of 18 F-104Gs and three TF-104Gs served with the Spanish air force between 1965 and 1972. The F-104G was given the local designation C.8.

Small numbers of Mutual Aid Program (MAP)-funded Starfighters were allocated to Greece and Turkey during the 1960s, to be augmented by vast numbers in the late 1970s and 1980s. Italy built F-104Gs before becoming the sole source of the BVR-capable F-104S, produced for Italy and Turkey.

Originally allocated 35 Canadair F-104Gs from 1961 MAP funding, the Hellenic air force also received four TF-104Gs from initial Lockheed deliveries, plus another 10 MAP-funded Lockheed-built F-104Gs and two TF-104Gs from USAF stocks. These machines equipped two squadrons, and Greece eventually received at least 170 Starfighters through US and NATO aid programmes, including nine F-104Gs and one TF-104G from Spain in 1972, and two TF-104Gs from West Germany in 1977. These were reportedly reduced by accident attrition to 29 F-104Gs and three TF-104Gs by early 1981. However, 10 Fiat-built F-104Gs were then transferred from the Netherlands in mid-1982, in addition to continuous supplies from West Germany from 1981 to 1988 as part of the 'Minerva' military aid programme to Greece. This eventually involved the supply of a total of 80 German Starfighters, including 38 F-104Gs and 22 RF-104Gs, plus 20 TF-104Gs. The Starfighter was retired from Greek service in March 1993.

Photographed in the early 1960s, this pair of Fiat-built F-104Gs belongs to the 9° Gruppo/4° Stormo, the first Italian Starfighter user. The natural metal scheme later gave way to camouflage, which was applied from July 1964.

Aeronautica Militare Italiana

Fiat produced 200 F-104Gs for the AMI, Germany and the Netherlands, including 125 for the Italian air force. Apart from 51 F-104G interceptor versions and 54 equipped as fighter-bombers, the AMI also received 12 TF-104G trainers from Lockheed and 16 from Aeritalia, to re-equip three interceptor, two strike-fighter and a reconnaissance squadron. F-104s entered service in 1963. Seven Lockheed TF-104G trainers were transferred from the Luftwaffe to the AMI in 1984/85.

The first two F-104S aircraft, armed with two AIM-7 Sparrow and four AIM-9 Sidewinder AAMs, were converted by Lockheed from AMI F-104Gs, flight trials starting in December 1966. Planned production for the AMI was 205, eventually to equip 10 *Gruppi*, but a further 20 were laid down for a subsequently cancelled Turkish order. Only one of these was completed, as a replacement for an aircraft that had crashed prior to delivery. In service, the F-104S was upgraded twice (as the ASA and ASA-M). It was finally retired in October 2004.

Turkish 'Stars'

Turkey was one of the first NATO operators to receive Starfighters through MAP funding, and the first of an initial batch of 34 Lockheed- and Canadair-built F-104Gs, plus a further 12 (including two RF versions) and six TF-104G trainers from Lockheed production, reached Turkey from May 1963, to equip 141 and 142 Filo, plus an OCU. The first of many NATO transfers then followed, with deliveries from Spain in 1972 of nine F-104Gs and two TF-104Gs. In late December 1974, the first six of an initial batch of 18 F-104S interceptors bought new from Italy were delivered. The F-104S order was doubled in 1975, and finally increased to 40.

Most Turkish Starfighter procurement, however, resulted from large-scale NATO transfers, including 18 F-104Gs from Belgium between 1981 and 1983 (withdrawn by 1987); 43 F-104Gs (including 22 RFs) and 10 TF-104Gs from the Netherlands from 1980 to 1984; nine RF-104Gs, three CF-104s and a single TF-104G from Norway in 1981; and, from October 1980, 170 ex-German Starfighters, including 33 TF-104Gs. Canada offered Turkey an initial batch of 20 CF-104s, later increased to 52, including six CF-104Ds. Thirty of these were overhauled before dispatch, the surviving 20 being broken down for spares. In all, therefore, it seems that Turkey received just over 400 Starfighters, although many of these were used for spares. The F-104 made its last flight in Turkish colours in September 1994.

F-104G Starfighter

West Germany, Italy and Norway were the only operators of the Starfighter in the anti-shipping role. In this role, it performed uncomplainingly with the German navy for over 20 years – being small, fast, and having a relatively smokeless engine, the Starfighter was hard to catch. In 1977, its capability was significantly enhanced by the adoption of the Kormoran anti-ship missile.

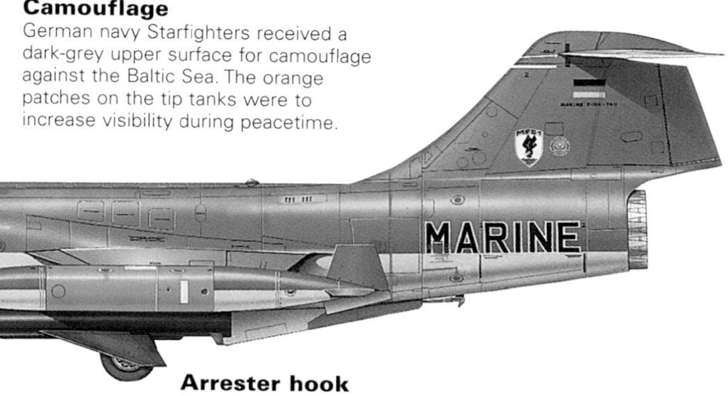

Camouflage
German navy Starfighters received a dark-grey upper surface for camouflage against the Baltic Sea. The orange patches on the tip tanks were to increase visibility during peacetime.

F-104G Starfighter 26+65
Starfighter 26+65 served until 1982 with the Marineflieger wing MFG 1, based at Schleswig in northern Germany, which was tasked with the anti-shipping mission.

Arrester hook
European Starfighters were fitted with a field arrester hook, which could be deployed to stop the aircraft running off the end of the runway in an emergency situation.

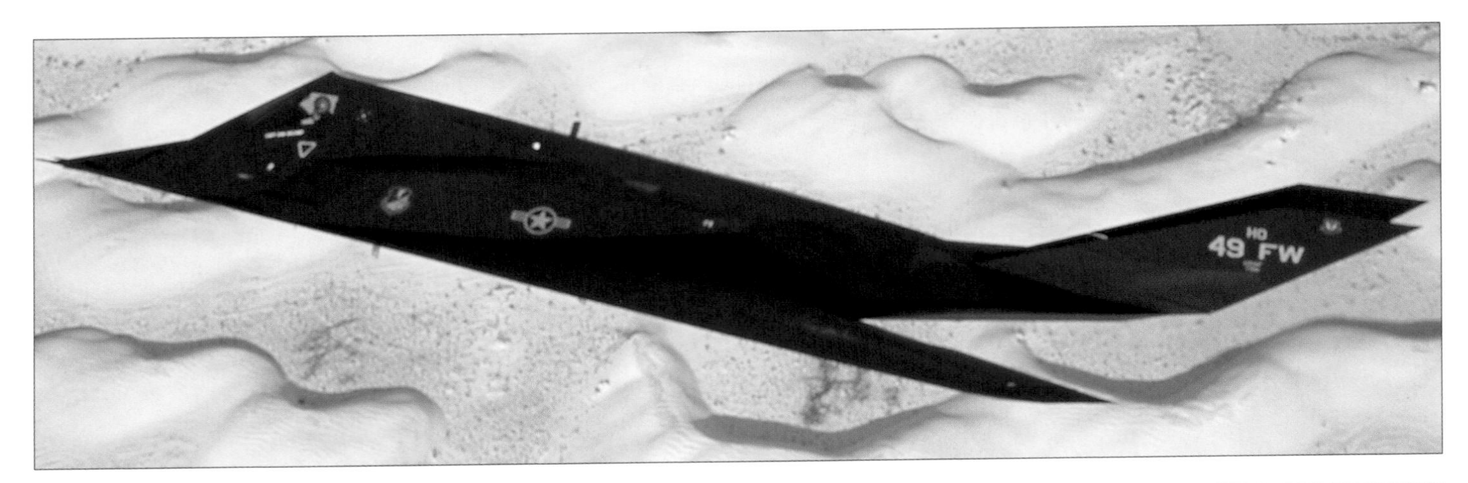

Lockheed F-117 Nighthawk

'Stealth fighter'

Above: A 49th Fighter Wing 'Black Jet' cruises serenely over the White Sands National Monument near the unit's headquarters at Holloman AFB, New Mexico.

Right: Stealth pilots are viewed as elite aviators, many having already accomplished thousands of hours on older attack types, such as F-111s, A-7s and A-10s. Many comment about the lack of visibility from the cockpit because of the F-117's heavy canopy framing.

The extraordinary shape, revolutionary radar-defeating features and a top secret, yet highly glamorous development have combined with a star appearance in Desert Storm to make the Lockheed F-117 one of the best-known warplanes in the world. It is able to penetrate hostile airspace and strike vital targets without being detected by radar defences.

The F-117 was a mystery, and to some a miracle, when revealed to the public in November 1988. Now, it is an ageing warplane with a specialised purpose.

When it emerged from a shroud of secrecy, the F-117 was hailed as marking a scientific breakthrough because of its ability to do just one thing. Today, critics are insisting that this once-revolutionary warplane is old, slow and costly, given its ability to do only that one task. But even though it has little versatility, and its retirement is now scheduled by 2009, the F-117 still performs its one mission superbly.

The F-117 is the first operational warplane to employ low observable (LO), or stealth, technology to reduce its vulnerability to radar detection. Though called a fighter, the F-117 is not intended for air-to-air combat. Its purpose is to deliver ordnance in a dense threat environment against targets of extremely high value. The F-117 emerged from a Cold War 'black' programme where it was developed in conditions of unprecedented secrecy.

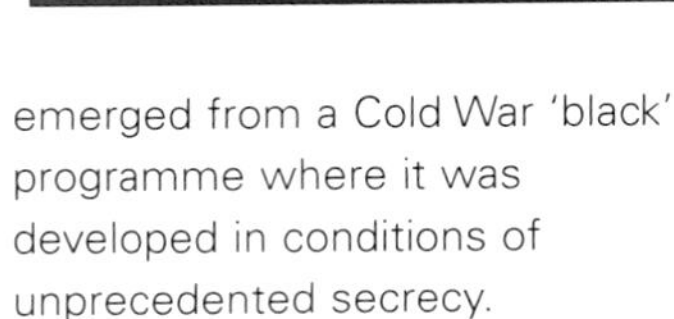

The mission of the F-117 is unique: to attack small, well-protected targets which are, in Pentagon jargon, highly leveraged. This means that their destruction will damage an enemy out of proportion to their

Viewed from directly ahead, the F-117A displays the heavily framed cockpit canopy and underneath, the twin trapezes which extend from the weapons bay for loading.

intrinsic value. A typical assignment would be to 'decapitate' an enemy's command, control, communications and intelligence (C^3I) structure by attacking it by surprise with precision-guided bombs. Other F-117 targets might be nuclear storage sites, critical bridges and tunnels, or key leadership headquarters.

The wedge-shaped, V-tailed F-117 employs radar absorbent composite materials on its external surfaces. In addition, it has angular features which contribute to its low-observable characteristics by reducing the aircraft's radar cross-section (RCS). Use of radar absorbent materials should make the aircraft appear dim to a radar while the angular shape should cause it to 'glitter' irregularly without giving any solid return signal as its aspect angle varies.

The angular shape results from a technique known as faceting, which applies computer technology to aircraft design and, in this instance, produced radical use of 'chisel-edge' leading surfaces and sharp fuselage angles, eliminating curved surfaces in order to diffuse radar returns. The skin panels of the airframe are divided into many small, perfectly flat surfaces, which reflect at a variety of angles all signals from probing hostile ground or airborne radars.

The stealth qualities of the aircraft are enhanced by engine exhaust nozzles located atop the fuselage along the wing root just ahead of the tail surfaces. The exhaust bleeds over the aft fuselage to screen the heat emissions from detection below.

Stealth pilot

The pilot of an F-117 occupies a small cockpit which features a windshield arrangement with a separate panel in front and two different-sized windows on each side. The pilot has a conventional head-up display for flight information and infra-red imagery, with an up-front control panel beneath it for radio and display mode selections. On the main panel are standard MFDs (multifunction displays) installed either side of a large monochrome CRT screen. Four protruding spikes on the aircraft's nose are air data probes for air speed and altitude sensing. The F-117 has quadruple redundant fly-by-wire flight controls.

During the 1970s, low observables technology was studied in great secrecy by the Defense Advanced Research Projects Agency (DARPA) and the USAF with a goal no less ambitious than to alter aerial warfare by producing a warplane invisible to radar. Test flights of the Have Blue proof-of-concept aircraft were followed by Project Senior Trend, which produced the similar but larger F-117.

In 1978 a decision was made to proceed with full-scale development and low-level production, making use of numerous components from other aircraft types to minimise potential risk.

Inflight refuelling is a vital element in the Nighthawk's mission if it is to strike targets at great distances. Radio-silent refuellings are regularly practised, and at night the only illumination used in such manoeuvres comes from the small light above the cockpit.

Operating under the tightest security, the aircraft flew for almost eight years before its existence was ever publicly acknowledged. The USAF finally released some limited information and a poor quality, heavily retouched, photograph in November 1988. Flying was initially done at Groom Lake, Nevada and later at Tonopah.

During Operation Just Cause in December 1989, two F-117As flew non-stop from Nevada with air refuelling to attack the Rio Hato barracks in Panama using 2,000-lb (907-kg) GBU-27A/B laser-guided bombs. The accuracy of the attack has been the subject of debate, but overall the F-117A's combat debut saw its systems working as Lockheed had intended.

The 49th FW lost its first Nighthawk squadron, the 7th FS, in late 2006, and operational service of the F-117A is due to come to an end by 2009. The F-117B version was never built. This was a much-improved new-build model with far greater bomb-carrying potential and better systems. A projected naval version, the A/F-117X, was also based on this aircraft.

Out of the black
'Stealth' operations

Above: When the veil of secrecy surrounding the F-117 was eventually lifted in 1988, it finally allowed the USAF to integrate the aircraft into regular day-to-day operations.

During the 1991 Gulf War, the F-117 Nighthawk became a media star, presenting to the world an image of laser-guided bombs falling precisely on target. At the time, few people realised that this was not the combat debut of this revolutionary aircraft.

With the entire development of the F-117 Nighthawk hidden from public view deep within the Nevada Desert, the USAF found itself in a unique position. In its possession was an aircraft that rendered practically all aerial defences ineffective, but the very existence of which still had to remain a closely guarded secret. Not only was the very nature of the fledgling operational squadron continually denied, but the radar-deflecting facets of the F-117 had to be concealed from those outside the world of 'black programmes'. These extraordinary security requirements dictated that the early operational career of the 'Stealth Fighter' would place huge demands on both logistics and, more importantly, on pilots coming to grips with learning the fine art of flying the highly demanding aircraft.

New opportunities

Having searched the ranks for suitable candidates who had a minimum of at least 1,000 hours on either the F-111, F-4 Phantom or A-10 Thunderbolt II, pilots were then interviewed.

Having the barest of details regarding their new posting, the pilots were given five minutes to decide if they were interested. Few turned down the opportunity of embarking on such a highly classified operation. The successful pilots then returned to their squadron to await further instructions, as the logistical side of the operational programme now took centre stage.

Of primary concern was the establishment of a secure base from which to fly Lockheed's new aircraft. With security now becoming difficult at the highly classified Groom Lake facility, a relocation to the Tonopah Test Range (TTR) airfield, Nevada, was begun in May 1982 and completed by August 1983.

Now designated an operational unit, rather than a test and developmental squadron, Colonel

Before 1988, all F-117 operations, including training missions, were flown under the cover of night. This caused unavoidable pilot fatigue, resulting in the early loss of three F-117s.

At a press conference on 10 November 1988, the US Assistant Secretary of Defense publicly revealed the F-117 with this poor-quality photograph. The carefully chosen image disguised many key aspects of the aircraft's design.

***Left:** A great deal of disinformation emerged concerning the true configuration and capabilities of the F-117. Misinformed press releases discussed the aircraft's poor flying qualities, while plastic kit manufacturers produced a plethora of fanciful and highly inaccurate models. The eventual revelation of the F-117 programme served only to show how successful the USAF's attempts to hide its revolutionary new weapons system had been.*

Seen during a daytime training flight, this F-117 refuels from a KC-10 Extender. An expanded and much safer training syllabus, conducted in daylight hours, replaced the earlier nocturnal sorties.

James S. Allen assumed command of the first 'stealth' unit (to be known as the 4450th Tactical Group) in May 1982. He personally took delivery of the initial aircraft on 23 August 1983.

With support facilities complete at the TTR, a host of security procedures was soon implemented, involving patrolling UH-1N helicopters and a detachment of Special Forces guards. Now the main problem facing the new pilots of the 4450th was the lack of sufficient examples of F-117s in which to gain flight experience. Despite this, the group was declared operational on 28 October 1983, having received less than a squadron of the new aircraft.

Cover story

To maintain the necessary flying hours, the 4450th Tactical Group was allocated a number of A-7Ds, although these were based at the nearby Nellis air base. The stealth pilots used the aircraft as training tools, enabling a cover story to be devised. Later, they were replaced by T-38 Talons, which were cheaper to operate.

The flight characteristics of the F-117 were found to be similar to those of the A-7D. This enabled pilots to get used to the handling characteristics of the aircraft in daytime training missions, without compromising the security of the programme. An added bonus was that, to any interested party, the 4450th could now be passed off as an A-7 test unit, until enough examples of the F-117 could be delivered. Later, the A-7s were used as chase planes during initial pilot training flights.

The F-117 was regarded by US war planners as a 'silver bullet'. In other words, only a few existed and they were to be used against high-value assets (HVAs), the Pentagon's term for the enemy's leadership structure, communications and vital transportation assets.

With its clandestine 'Stealth Fighter' operational, the USAF now had a warplane which had settled into service and was beginning to mature, although few people outside the programme knew of the F-117.

Throughout the free-spending 1980s, the 4450th Tactical Group continued to thrive. Colonel Oliver North, later involved in the Irangate scandal, devised a plan for the F-117 to be utilised against terrorist strongholds in the Middle East. A similar operation was devised against Libya's capital, Tripoli, in 1986, but a more conventional plan was eventually implemented.

In December 1989, US Forces were deployed in Operation Just Cause, the combined arms assault on Panama aimed at ousting its leader Manuel Noriega. Eager to show the potential of its 'silver bullet', the Pentagon's joint staff devised a mission that was both inventive and which would also silence the critics of the 'stealth' programme.

On the night of 19 December 1989, two F-117s were launched to support a Special Operations 'snatch' of Noriega. The 'snatch' was later called off as the aircraft approached Panamanian airspace, and the nature of the target was changed. Two more F-117s flew a bombing mission intended to 'stun and confuse' Panamanian Defence Forces (PDF) at Rio Hato, with another two F-117s flown as back-ups. Their target was a large, open field alongside a barracks housing 200 elite PDF troops, rather than the barracks itself.

The six F-117s flew from Tonopah and refuelled five times during the round trip to Panama. The two Rio Hato F-117s dropped two 2,000-lb (907-kg) GBU-27A/B bombs with BLU-109B warheads, both of which exploded several hundred feet away from their intended target. Four of the six F-117s returned to Tonopah with their bombs on board.

The Panama mission was viewed as a failure in Congress, with critics unleashing scathing attacks on the capabilities of the high-tech aircraft. Despite the press furore that followed the Just Cause missions, two years later the world's media would 'clearly see', or at least hear about, the real capability of the F-117, as demonstrated in the skies over Iraq.

The first fixed-wing aircraft to strike during Operation Desert Storm were F-117As from their base at Khamis Mushait in Saudi Arabia. Penetrating deep into Iraqi airspace virtually undetected, they hit key targets with precision.

Below: US military leaders were eager to display the accuracy of their 'new' stealth aircraft. Here, at a press conference, its capabilities are demonstrated.

A ghost at war

Spearheading the coalition air attacks on Iraqi forces in 1991 were the F-117As deployed from their base at Tonopah in the Nevada desert.

Approximately 45 aircraft, from each of the 37th TFW's three squadrons, eventually took up residence at Khamis Mushait in Saudi Arabia. On 17 January 1991, the air strikes began, with the 'Black Jets' tasked with hitting Iraq's air defence network, notably command bunkers and communications facilities. Rolling back the enemy's defences proved highly effective, enabling other aircraft to operate unhindered and forcing the Iraqis into a position from which they could not recover.

As the campaign progressed, a wealth of strategic targets fell under the bombs of the 'Black Jets', including Iraq's chemical and nuclear facilities. Other targets included airfields, bridges and key centres in Baghdad. F-117s were also credited with destroying a fleet of Tu-16 'Badger' bombers which were reportedly being prepared for a chemical bombing raid.

Mission tally

During the course of Desert Storm, 'Stealth Fighters' flew a total of 1,271 combat sorties, one third of which were flown over Baghdad. Iraq's capital city had around 3,000 AAA pieces and over 60 SAM sites, yet no hits were recorded on the F-117s. More than 2,000 bombs were dropped, all believed to be 2,000-lb (907-kg) laser-guided weapons, the GBU-27 Paveway III being the standard weapon used. F-117 pilots averaged 21 missions. All sorties were conducted at night and took an average of five hours.

Facilities at Khamis Mushait were excellent, although the considerable elevation of the runway required the fully loaded F-117s, en route to their targets, to 'top up' from the tanker after take-off. Missions flown against Baghdad were around 30 minutes duration, while those to Tikrit and Mosul were slightly longer. Accurate INS navigation took the aircraft to the target area and, once in the vicinity, the pilot would use the forward-looking infra-red system to locate and identify the target. This was followed by tracking, bomb release and use of the downward-looking infra-red turret to guide the weapon to the target. F-117As were used to hit the most strategically important and heavily defended targets, thus they had to make as much use as possible of their low observable qualities, especially while loitering above the target in order for the pilot to obtain the precise aiming point.

Most of the enemy defences only reacted once the F-117s had actually hit the targets and were on their way home, although this was not the case on 17 January, the first night of Allied air strikes. That night, a force of EF-111A Ravens and F-4G Wild Weasel electronic aircraft were escorting F-15Es, arriving at their 'jam-on point' just before the 'Stealth Fighters' entered their own target area, and sparking off intense ground fire from the Iraqi defences. This resulted in the USAF quickly altering its tactics, using the EF-111s' powerful jammers to initiate a massive AAA barrage some considerable time before the actual air strikes took place. When the final strike did happen, many of the Iraqi gunners were seriously low on ammunition and their gun barrels were overheating.

The 'Stealth' raids were conducted entirely in radio silence so that the Iraqis could not detect the location of the F-117s. And having learned the lessons of predictable flight paths during Vietnam, routes were changed as frequently as possible, as were altitudes, keeping the Iraqis on their toes.

It is possible that infra-red sensors may have detected the aircraft as they neared 'Indian' country, but the unique platypus-type exhaust outlets of the F-117 gave off a very low heat signature in comparison with other aircraft types. Furthermore, the black paint scheme proved highly effective, perhaps too much so, for friendly tanker crews sometimes had problems visually identifying F-117As.

Once the targets had been hit, the 'Stealth Fighters' would join up again for a post-strike refuelling, before making the long haul back to Khamis. Once on the ground, and having shut down the engines, the pilots would then face a long and exhaustive debriefing, followed by a well-earned day's rest. Soon, however, they would be preparing to go up again, striking deep into the heart of Iraq.

The F-117As of the 37th TFW were much valued by the USAF, being both costly and highly effective, hence they were based as far away from Iraq as possible. The location chosen was Khamis Mushait, located in the mountainous terrain of southwestern Saudi Arabia. Khamis featured huge hardened aircraft shelters, which could each accommodate two F-117s.

'Black Jets' over Baghdad

'Stealth Fighter' pilot Colonel Barry E. Horne was unanimous in his praise for the aircraft. 'We flew 45 aircraft of the 37th TFW from Tonopah, via Langley AFB in Virginia, to Khamis Mushait in Saudi Arabia. Our guiding principle was that we concentrated on high-value, heavily defended targets, which lent themselves to the use of laser-guided weapons. We'd plan to launch in daylight, late afternoon, wanting as much night over the target as possible. Some targets were close together and we'd go in a package, while others were widely spread. Being the aircraft that it is, the F-117A needed far less support on strikes. Occasionally we had EF-111A Ravens and F-4G Phantom Wild Weasels, but the whole point about the "Black Jet" was its ability to work in the face of the electronic warfare threats those aircraft are designed to counter, so our mission did not depend on them.'

Above: Differing significantly from the prototype, **Lulu Belle**, *the XP-80A's main new feature was the General Electric I-40 engine, based on a Whittle design.*

Top: The Acrojets were the first US jet aerial demonstration team, formed in 1948 by the Fighter School at Williams AFB. Their initial purpose was to show the potential of the P-80 to young pilots and those more accustomed to propeller-driven aircraft, but they were soon performing at public air shows.

Lockheed P-80 Shooting Star

America's first jet fighter

America's first production jet fighter only just missed combat in World War II, but went on to form the backbone of USAF ground-attack forces in the early part of the Korean War. The Shooting Star was used in many test programmes and then evolved into the T-33 trainer and the F-94 fighter series.

To US combat pilots of the 1940s and 1950s, the Lockheed P-80 Shooting Star was a remarkable engineering achievement and a great aircraft to fling around the sky. To critics, the P-80 took the latest scientific advances and wasted them on a mediocre airframe that retained the shape, size and wings of a propeller-driven fighter (while others were developing jets with a sleeker shape, of a smaller size and with swept-back flight surfaces).

Opinion was almost universal that the P-80 had few, if any faults – well, almost. In a hard-pressed operational setting, pilots and maintainers were furious that doors embraced the nose compartment. One flyer referred to this as a 'bad feature' because the doors had a tendency to pop open in flight when a latch came loose, rendering the P-80 almost uncontrollable. A hinge at the forward edge would have kept the doors closed in flight no matter what happened, but this remedy was never carried out. Pilots also criticised another design fault – the P-80's nose gear bay doors closed as the gear came up.

These were small complaints, however. By the time the first P-80 Shooting Stars became operational, victory was at hand and the Americans were seeing futuristic visions. Thus, in unveilings to the press at Mitchel Field, New York, and in Burbank on 1 August 1945, US Army Air Forces told the world that the Lockheed Shooting Star had the 'out-of-this-world appearance of a Buck Rogers spaceship'. By then, the P-80 was a proven aircraft, with a handful actually reaching Europe before the war ended, although not in time to fight. This was all in marked contrast to the time when the P-80 had been conceived. Then, the war was being lost and the US was in a distant third place, behind the Germans and British, in the race to develop jets.

On 18 June 1943, Clarence L. ('Kelly') Johnson visited Robert Gross, Lockheed's president, at the company's headquarters in Burbank, California. In the office, Johnson found Gross and chief engineer Hal Hibbard. 'Wright Field wants us to submit a

Apart from four aircraft that reached Europe prior to VE-Day, the first overseas P-80s were assigned to the 5th Fighter Group, under Colonel Horace Hanes. The unit received 32 Shooting Stars for its 38th Fighter Squadron at Giebelstadt, Germany, some of which can be seen here being towed through the streets.

***Right:** In the post-World War II period, the F-80 and the F-47 Thunderbolt, pictured here over the Bavarian Alps, constituted the major part of the USAF's offensive capability. Both aircraft were replaced by the F-84E Thunderjet.*

***Below:** In a show no doubt designed to impress the Soviets, the 36th Fighter Group laid on this display of F-80Bs at Fürstenfeldbruck. At least 72 aircraft can be seen, most with pilots and ground crew in attendance. The 36th FG was based at 'Fursty' from August 1948 to November 1952.*

proposal for building a plane around a British jet engine,' Johnson told the two corporate leaders. 'I've worked out some figures. I think we can promise them 180-day delivery. What do you think?'

At Johnson's behest, Lockheed established a goal of 180 days to first flight. This was an extraordinary goal. No fighter had ever been designed, developed and flown so quickly, certainly not one which used the revolutionary power of the jet engine.

Ironically, Lockheed could have started sooner. Back in 1939, Johnson's design team – later to be dubbed the 'Skunk Works' – had proposed a jet fighter. Engineers had drawn up plans on the drawing board for several versions, culminating in the model of a futuristic canard design which would have been powered by two company-designed turbojets (which existed only as a vague notion). But pre-war indifference greeted Lockheed's model. Meanwhile, isolationists were arguing that the US should stay out of 'Europe's war', and the USAAF simply had no interest in it – at least, not yet.

But in late 1943, Johnson and his staff put together their new aircraft sooner than promised – in 143 days. Johnson's team concocted an aircraft that appeared quite conventional, as if it might fly with either a jet or a reciprocating engine. In fact, the design was straightforward, but unorthodox. The XP-80 had straight wings and tail surfaces, and tricycle landing gear. The wing was a low aspect ratio, laminar-flow surface never before tested on a propeller-driven aircraft.

To their credit, factory workers were cutting metal for the P-80 before anyone at Lockheed had ever seen any kind of jet engine. The first powerplant, borrowed from Britain, became available only after the initial airframe was nearly completed.

The spinach-green XP-80, nicknamed *Lulu Belle*, was taken aloft for its first flight on 8 January 1944. By the war's end, two P-80s were in Italy, preparing for combat, two more had reached England, and 16 were flying.

It was the beginning of a revolution. In years to come, the P-80 (to be redesignated F-80 on 11 June 1948) would set numerous flying records, go to war in Korea, and inspire the F-94 fighter and T-33 trainer. As the first practical, fully operational American jet fighter, however, the Shooting Star had already secured its place in history.

An idea of the low-level environment in which the F-80s operated in Korea can be ascertained in this view of a strike south of Pyongyang on 8 May 1952. As it releases its napalm tanks on a supply building and truck park, the F-80 is engaged by a gun position concealed in an embankment. The white blob beneath the aircraft is an AA shell.

Left: Lockheed hoped to sell S-3s to West Germany and Japan; in the event the former retained its Atlantics and Japan bought Lockheed P-3 Orions.

Below: Three Viking variants were planned initially – the S-3A (nearest the camera, 179 built), the US-3A COD aircraft (centre, six converted from S-3As) and a dedicated KS-3A tanker (furthest from the camera, not proceeded with).

Lockheed S-3 Viking

Cold War sub-hunter

The US Navy's primary carrierborne, fixed-wing ASW aircraft from 1974, the S-3 Viking was re-roled in the post-Cold War era, being charged with anti-surface warfare, land-attack, tanking, and the emerging Non-Traditional Intelligence, Surveillance and Reconnaissance (NTISR) role.

Lockheed's S-3 Viking was the US Navy's carrier-based, fixed-wing ASW aircraft from the 1970s until the early 1990s and, though still in service in 2007, is now in the twilight of its career. Designed to meet the US Navy's 1964 VSX (carrier-based ASW aircraft) requirement, the first service-test YS-3A (of eight built) made its maiden flight on 21 January 1972. Conventional in design for a carrier-based warplane, the Viking is a high-wing, twin-jet aircraft with hydraulically folding wings, retractable tricycle landing gear and pressurised accommodation for its crew of four (comprising pilot, co-pilot, tactical co-ordinator and acoustic sensor operator). Based on an August 1969 contract, Lockheed manufactured the Viking in partnership with Vought, the latter company building wings, tail unit, landing gear and engine pods.

The original production S-3A variant was equipped with an AN/AYK-10 digital computer, AN/APS-116 radar and OR-89 FLIR. The heart of the Viking's ASW suite was an AN/ASQ-81 magnetic anomaly detector (MAD) sensor in a retractable tailboom. The S-3A carried 60 sonobuoys in its aft fuselage and had a ventral bomb bay and wing stations to house bombs, torpedoes or depth charges.

Service entry

The first S-3A Viking went to VS-41 'Shamrocks', the first FRS for the type, located at North Island, California, and was received in February 1974. VS-21 'Fighting Redtails', also at North Island, became the first fleet squadron to operate the type in July 1974. Lockheed built a total of 179 production S-3As, delivering the last in August 1978.

The improved S-3B variant was the result of a weapons system improvement programme launched in 1981, which retained the Viking airframe and engines but added improved acoustic processing, expanded ESM coverage, increased radar processing capabilities, a new sonobuoy receiver system, and provision for AGM-84 Harpoon anti-ship missiles. By the early 1990s nearly all existing S-3As had been upgraded to S-3B status at naval air depots.

The seventh YS-3A was modified to become the US-3A carrier onboard delivery aircraft, envisioned as a replacement for the piston-engined Grumman C-1 Trader and first flown on 2 July 1976. In all, six US-3A Vikings, stripped of ASW equipment and transformed into 'people haulers', were used to complement the turbine-powered Grumman C-2A Greyhound. Lockheed also modified the fifth YS-3A to test the aircraft as the KS-3A tanker. The dedicated tanker variant was

Seen here in Naval Air Test Center colours, the first S-3B poses for Lockheed's photographer after its first flight in 1984. An important advance was a Harpoon anti-ship missile capability.

As originally deployed, an air wing's S-3 complement numbered 10 aircraft. Subsequently reduced to six, this was then increased to eight to cover the tanking role. These VS-29 'Dragonfires' S-3As are seen aboard USS* Enterprise *sometime in the 1970s.

not produced, although operational Vikings have been adapted as part-time tankers with the same 'buddy' refuelling store.

Developed to meet the Cold War threat posed by the Soviet submarine fleet, the Viking fought in Operation Desert Storm against an enemy which possessed no submarines. The S-3A/B Viking proved an exceedingly effective conventional bomber when employed against Iraqi radar stations, anti-aircraft batteries, small vessels and other targets.

Electronic Shadow

Sixteen S-3As were converted to ES-3A Shadow standard in the early 1990s, with a variety of electronic surveillance and intercept equipment to locate and identify hostile emitters and communications stations. In mid-1998, the Navy made the decision to withdraw the ES-3A.

With the end of the Cold War, the S-3's mission emphasis shifted away from ASW and towards anti-surface warfare, land-attack and, latterly, NTISR missions. In the latter role, the S-3B demonstrated its capabilities during Operation Iraqi Freedom, equipped with underwing LANTIRN pods. In addition, with the retirement of the Navy's KA-6Ds, A-6Es and, from 2000, the ES-3A Shadows, the surviving Vikings were also expected to provide the USN with a carrier-based air-to-air refuelling facility. In 1998 the ASW mission was formally deleted; 114 S-3Bs remained in service. By 2004, four of the eight Vikings deployed in each carrier air wing were assigned a permanent tanker role, although the emergence of the F/A-18E/F has relieved the Viking of its burden as the sole carrier-based air-to-air tanker. By early 2009, the surviving S-3Bs are scheduled to be retired.

S-3B Viking

This S-3B CAG-bird of VS-24 'Scouts' is depicted as it appeared during its 1997 cruise aboard USS *John F. Kennedy* (CV-67), as part of Carrier Air Wing Eight. VS-24 was the first unit to employ the S-3B in combat, during Operation Desert Storm in 1991.

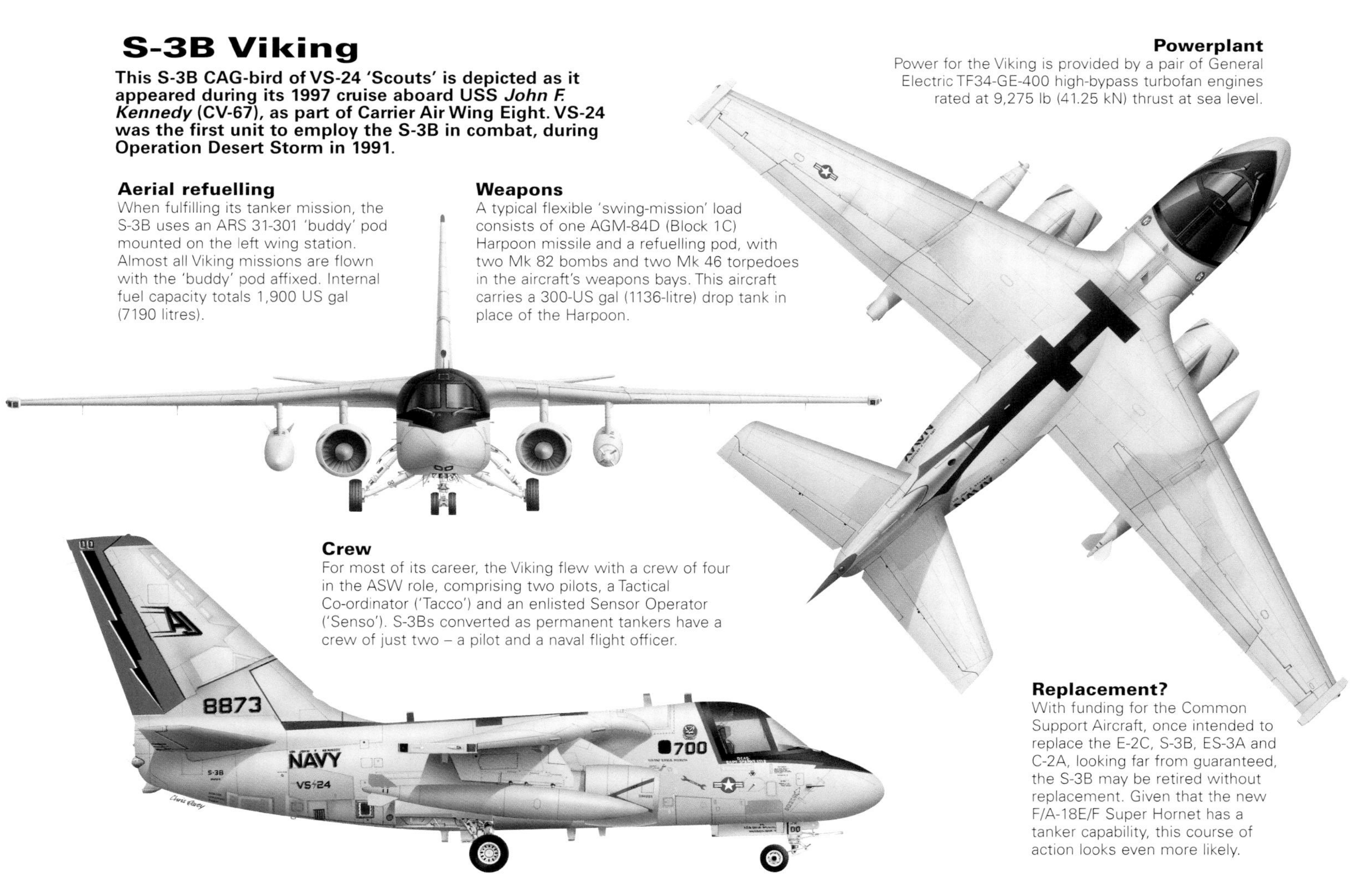

Aerial refuelling
When fulfilling its tanker mission, the S-3B uses an ARS 31-301 'buddy' pod mounted on the left wing station. Almost all Viking missions are flown with the 'buddy' pod affixed. Internal fuel capacity totals 1,900 US gal (7190 litres).

Weapons
A typical flexible 'swing-mission' load consists of one AGM-84D (Block 1C) Harpoon missile and a refuelling pod, with two Mk 82 bombs and two Mk 46 torpedoes in the aircraft's weapons bays. This aircraft carries a 300-US gal (1136-litre) drop tank in place of the Harpoon.

Powerplant
Power for the Viking is provided by a pair of General Electric TF34-GE-400 high-bypass turbofan engines rated at 9,275 lb (41.25 kN) thrust at sea level.

Crew
For most of its career, the Viking flew with a crew of four in the ASW role, comprising two pilots, a Tactical Co-ordinator ('Tacco') and an enlisted Sensor Operator ('Senso'). S-3Bs converted as permanent tankers have a crew of just two – a pilot and a naval flight officer.

Replacement?
With funding for the Common Support Aircraft, once intended to replace the E-2C, S-3B, ES-3A and C-2A, looking far from guaranteed, the S-3B may be retired without replacement. Given that the new F/A-18E/F Super Hornet has a tanker capability, this course of action looks even more likely.

Lockheed SR-71 'Blackbird'

Legendary spyplane

Almost certainly the most impressive military jet ever built, Lockheed's SR-71 is still officially the world's fastest air-breathing aircraft. Tasked with performing highly classified reconnaissance missions, the aircraft's sensor systems collected material that helped to formulate US foreign policy for more than 20 years.

The first six SR-71As were used for the flight trials programme. These were followed by the two SR-71B trainers, and then the operational aircraft, beginning with 64-17958, which was delivered to Beale on 4 June 1966. Despite a temporary halt in deliveries, due mainly to plumbing problems, aircraft arrived quickly afterwards. This machine, the fourth operational aircraft, became something of a 'hangar queen'.

For some 25 years the 9th (SRW) of the USAF flew the incredible Lockheed SR-71 'Blackbird' – the popular name was never official – on top-secret missions. During all that time, Lockheed's exotic thoroughbred was (and still is) the world's highest and fastest air-breathing machine. It was never shot down, despite hundreds of sorties over countries which were sufficiently hostile to the US to contemplate such an action – for instance China, Cuba, Egypt, Nicaragua and North Korea.

Flights over the USSR have theoretically been banned since the undertaking by President Eisenhower in 1960 following the shooting down of Gary Powers' Lockheed U-2. By then, the development of the Lockheed trio of Mach 3 aircraft (A-12, F-12 and SR-71) was well under way. The A-12 first flew in 1962, the YF-12 a year later, and the SR-71 on 22 December 1964. The programme was kept secret until February 1964, when a televised announcement was made by President Johnson.

The A-12 was conceived as a direct replacement for the U-2 in the strategic reconnaissance role. It was a lighter, single-seat forerunner of the SR-71 and was operated by the Central Intelligence Agency until the USAF 'Blackbird' became fully operational in 1968. It carried a large camera mounted behind the cockpit as well as electro-magnetic-spectrum sensors.

The YF-12 was a spin-off development of a long-range interceptor which was never ordered into production. Its Hughes radar and AIM-47 missiles later informed the AWG-9/Phoenix system for the Grumman F-14 Tomcat.

All the development flying for the A-12/YF-12 series was carried out at Groom Lake, a remote secret test site in the Nevada Desert. CIA A-12 missions were flown from here, and from Kadena AB, Okinawa. 'Blackbird' operations finally came out of the closet on 7 January 1966, when the first SR-71 was delivered to Beale AFB, California, where new, custom-built facilities awaited it.

The 'Blackbird' operated throughout its career from Beale as well as two permanent overseas detachments at Kadena (Detachment 1, 9th SRW from 1968) and Mildenhall, England (Detachment 4, 9th SRW from 1976). The type was also seen at Lockheed's Palmdale base, where 'Blackbirds' were overhauled. During the Vietnam War, they also

Two famous products of the Lockheed 'Skunk Works' fly together from Palmdale. The U-2R was the ASARS-2 development aircraft. SR-71A '17955 (nicknamed The Flower) had performed the test work on ASARS-1 for the SR-71 fleet.

Above: A scene repeated many times throughout the 1980s – an SR-71 trails its 'tiger tails' as it passes over RAF Mildenhall during an air display. The aircraft was a popular and impressive show performer and on at least one occasion, an over-ambitious pilot overstressed his Blackbird during a display.

NASA's SR-71B was used to requalify Air Force pilots for the reborn 'Blackbird' programme in the mid-1990s. Here, the two-seat trainer is eased in behind a KC-135 tanker during a training flight.

operated from Thailand and South Korea. Middle East overflights during Yom Kippur in 1973 were staged out of Seymour Johnson AFB, North Carolina.

Limited numbers

Although 32 SR-71s were built, only about 10 were in use at any one time – two each at the permanent detachments and five or six at Beale, including a pilot-training SR-71B. In addition, a single aircraft was based at Palmdale for test and development work. Eleven are known to have been written off in accidents, the others being held in storage. Aircraft were rotated in and out of storage to equalise flying hours in the fleet.

The SR-71A's unique high speed, ceiling and the rapid temperature changes that it encountered during flight made it a complex and demanding aircraft to handle. New pilots spent no fewer than 100 hours in the SR-71 simulator before progressing to the SR-71B, in which they were accompanied by an instructor pilot.

The SR-71's record for achievement is untouchable by any known aircraft on the drawing board today: 53,490 total flight hours; 17,300 missions flown (of which 3,551 were operational reconnaissance missions flown over North Korea, North Vietnam, the Middle East, South Africa, Cuba, Nicaragua and Libya); 11,008 hours flown in support of operational missions; and an unbelievable 11,675 flight hours at or above Mach 3.0.

But despite these outstanding achievements, the spiralling costs of supporting the 'Blackbird' missions was deemed too expensive by the Air Force Chief of Staff. In 1989 the retirement of the entire fleet was ordered due to high operating costs and the fact that spy satellites could provide the same reconnaissance data. Despite pleas from those within various intelligence agencies, the last Air Force flight of an SR-71 took place on 6 March 1990.

A dignified end?

While the 'Blackbird' continued on test duties with NASA, the lack of a 'quick-reaction' reconnaissance platform resulted in requests for the SR-71 to be re-introduced, utilising three examples held in flyable storage. An appeal for the SR-71 in 1997 – a result of growing tensions with North Korea over its nuclear weapons – saw the re-introduction of the 'Blackbird'. President Clinton nevertheless reversed the decision in October 1998, finally ending USAF 'Blackbird' operations for a second time, whereupon the two rejuvenated SR-71s were placed in storage at the 'Skunk Works'.

The three SR-71s used by NASA pose on the Dryden facility ramp, with Rogers Dry Lake in the background. NASA received one SR-71A and one SR-71B trainer. The first NASA pilot to qualify in the aircraft was Steve Ishmael on 25 July 1991.

Lockheed A-12

America's covert observer

In the war-torn skies of Vietnam, the A-12 provided US intelligence experts with a reconnaissance platform immune to interception.

The first operational flight undertaken by a Lockheed U-2 flown by the Central Intelligence Agency (CIA) took place on 4 July 1956.

Despite spectacular results, it was clear that the loss of an American spyplane over Soviet territory would be a political catastrophe for the US. 'Kelly' Johnson, the U-2's designer, believed that the powered glider would enjoy no more than two years' immunity to Soviet defences. This statement proved to be too severe, as the U-2 remained a unique and invaluable source of intelligence information for almost four years, until pilot Francis Gary Powers was shot down on 1 May 1960.

Research begins

Research and development of a follow-on to the U-2 began in autumn 1957, when Convair and Lockheed's 'Skunk Works' were each requested to submit a non-funded, non-contracted design for an advanced reconnaissance-gathering vehicle. On 28 August 1959, 'Kelly' Johnson was told that Lockheed's A-12 design had won the competition to build the U-2 follow-on aircraft. The next day, Lockheed was given the official go-ahead, and a project codename: Oxcart.

The first A-12 was prepared for a high-speed taxi run at its secret base deep in the Nevada Desert. Test pilot Lou Schalk accelerated down the runway and the aircraft quickly rose into the air. Schalk found the aircraft extremely difficult to handle. However, he recovered the A-12 and landed on the far side of the airfield. Two days later, he took the aircraft on its first full flight, when problems caused by the inflight shedding of the radar-absorbent material (RAM) leading edges proved to be only minor. On 30 April 1962, a year behind schedule, Schalk took the A-12 on its first 'official' flight.

Pilot recruitment

The CIA had begun the process of finding pilots for the programme before the aircraft had accomplished its first flight. Conversion flying carried on hand-in-hand with flight trials, the first CIA pilot flying the A-12 in the spring of 1963. The test programme reached a milestone on 20 July, when Mach 3 was achieved for the first time. By November 1965, the Oxcart team

***Top:** This was the first picture released (in 1982) of the A-12. The A-12 was distinguishable from the later SR-71 by having only one cockpit, a more slender nose and in lacking the SR-71's longer tailcone.*

***Below:** With the extra payload of the D-21, the M-21 became very sluggish. Eventually, when the drone's intake and exhaust covers were discarded, the ramjet was used to augment the thrust from the M-21's engines.*

The first A-12, 60-6924, is seen during refuelling trials in early 1963. The short-finned, modified KC-135A was based at Groom Lake for the duration of the tests. Tanking was a vital part of the A-12 mission. During reconnaissance flights over North Vietnam A-12s would descend to 25,000 ft (7620 m) to refuel after completing each photographic run.

was declared operational, although it would be May 1967 before the A-12 actually went into action.

'Cygnus' (as CIA pilots referred to the A-12) received its baptism of fire in the skies over southeast Asia. Four A-12s were selected for possible deployment from Kadena, Okinawa, under codename Black Shield in 1965. It was not until 22 May 1967, however, that the first A-12 left Area 51 to begin the six-hour flight to Okinawa.

On 30 May 1967, weather reconnaissance flights by the USAF deemed the conditions to be ideal for an A-12 camera run over North Vietnam as soon as possible. Early on the morning of 31 May, an A-12 left Kadena, before penetrating hostile airspace at Mach 3.2 and 80,000 ft (24390 m). The A-12 returned to Kadena after a flight of three hours 40 minutes. Several SAMs were fired, but all detonated well behind the aircraft. Recorded on film were 10 high-priority targets, including 70 of the 190 known SAM sites.

During 1967, 22 missions were performed by the A-12s, while six were flown between 1 January and 31 March 1968. Most flights were over North Vietnam, with two being made over North Korea.

In March 1968, SR-71s began arriving at Kadena to assume the reconnaissance role, signifying an end to A-12 operations.

Drone operations

A lesser-known facet of the 'Blackbird' programme was the use of the Lockheed D-21 reconnaissance drone. The programme began under 'Kelly' Johnson's Tagboard proposal.

What Johnson had in mind was something radically different from previous projects. Mindful of the U-2, Gary Powers 'aftershocks' and the inevitable political sensitivity concerning manned overflights of large expanses of 'denied territory', the 'Skunk Works', under Johnson's direction, was designing an air-launched, tri-sonic, reconnaissance vehicle.

Construction began in Building 199 at Burbank and, by June 1963, a D-21 had been mated to its mother ship. The launch platform was to be a modified A-12, designated M-21, two of which were retrofitted for the task.

Built primarily from titanium, the D-21 had a range of 1,250 nm (1,438 miles; 2315 km), cruised at Mach 3.3 and possessed an altitude capacity of 90,000 ft (27432 m). It was powered by a ramjet and, once released from the M-21 by a Launch Control Officer (LCO) sitting in what had been the aircraft's Q-bay, the drone flew its sortie independently. Programmed into the D-21's INS was the desired flight profile, allowing it to satisfactorily execute the perfect photo-recce sortie. Having completed its camera run, the drone's autopilot would bring the vehicle down to its ocean collection point. The palletised camera unit would then be ejected and allowed to parachute to the ground. As the drone continued its descent, it would be blown apart by an explosive charge. The camera unit would be retrieved by an HC-130 Hercules equipped with a Mid-Air Recovery System (MARS), and flown to a base for processing and analysis.

The first flight of this so-called 'Mother-Daughter' combination took place on 22 December 1964. Monumental problems were encountered concerning platform and systems integration. By 1966, the programme had progressed to the point where vehicle separation was to be performed. The first successful separation was completed on 3 July 1966, during the fifth of the six planned M-21/D-21 test flights.

Fatal launch

The first operational launch was to take place on 31 July 1966. Everything was progressing well, when, at Mach 3.2+ and exactly 1*g*, the LCO effected initial drone separation, after which disaster struck. A combination of factors caused the D-21 to slam down onto the aft launch pylon. The impact caused a pitch-up that was well beyond the ability of the pilot to correct. The crew ejected, but the LCO was drowned before he could be rescued.

'Kelly' Johnson was desperately upset by the loss of one of his team, and cancelled the M-21/D-21 programme. Instead, D-21s were modified to incorporate a less sensitive inlet and were launched from two B-52s for missions over China.

Unpainted, the first A-12 makes its first official flight on 30 April 1962. At the time the aircraft's J58 engines were not ready, so the first flights were made on J75 power, restricting performance. The first J58 flight (in one nacelle only) occurred on 5 October, and it was not until 15 January 1963 that the aircraft flew on J58 power alone.

*After a study into the efficiency of maintaining both the **SR-71** and **A-12** programmes, a motion was passed to 'terminate the Oxcart fleet in January 1968 (assuming an operational readiness date of September 1967 for the **SR-71**) and assign all missions to the **SR-71** fleet'. By 7 June 1968 the first Kadena-based **A-12** was on its way back to the **US** for storage.*

'Sled' in service

Lockheed's development of the A-12 resulted in the two-man SR-71 – a strategic-reconnaissance platform of unrivalled speed and ability which gathered vital intelligence, primarily from bases in Okinawa and the UK.

While working on the A-12 in spring 1962, 'Kelly' Johnson mentioned the possibility of a strike/reconnaissance variant for the USAF. By the end of April 1962, two different mock-ups were under construction, referred to as the R-12 and RS-12.

On 18 February 1963 Lockheed received authority to build six aircraft, with the understanding that 25 aircraft would be ordered by 1 July. The RS-12 and later the B-12/B-71 proposals for a strike version of the aircraft failed to win production contracts, but the USAF opted for the R-12 reconnaissance platform.

In a speech made on 24 July 1964, President Johnson revealed to the world the existence of the SR-71. Externally, the aircraft differed in shape from the A-12 by having a more elliptical nose plan. A second crew member, known as a reconnaissance systems officer (RSO), sat behind the pilot. Sensors carried by the SR-71 also differed from those of its predecessors. To enhance mission flexibility, the nose section was interchangeable, variously housing a sideways-looking airborne radar (SLAR), or an optical bar camera for horizon-to-horizon coverage. Cameras on board the SR-71 were located in palletised units which were housed in slim bays in the underside of the chine.

The prototype SR-71A was delivered from Burbank to Palmdale for final assembly on 29 October 1964. With two J58s installed, the aircraft conducted its first engine test run on 18 December 1964. On 22 December 1964, the SR-71A made its first flight.

On 18 November and 18 December 1965, the two SR-71B pilot trainers successfully completed their first flights, but the SR-71s were plagued by problems associated with the electrical system, tank-sealing and design range.

Service entry

While these problems were being worked on, the 4200th Strategic Reconnaissance Wing (SRW) was activated at Beale AFB, California, on 1 January 1965.

On 7 January 1966 the first SR-71B was delivered to Beale AFB. Three months later, on 14 April, Beale took delivery of its first SR-71A. In June 1966, the 4200th was redesignated the 9th Strategic Reconnaissance Wing, its component flying squadrons being the 1st and 99th Strategic Reconnaissance Squadrons (SRS).

On 8 March 1968, the first 'Blackbird' crew deployed to Kadena. They were soon followed by two more aircraft, and a spare crew. This marked the first overseas deployment of the SR-71 and the beginning of a

*Above: Operation El Dorado Canyon, the American reprisal raid on Libya, was flown on the night of 14/15 April 1986. Three post-strike photo-reconnaissance missions were flown by Det. 4 **SR-71s**, the first departing before the **USAF's F-111s** had returned to their bases. So important were the missions that two **SR-71s** were launched, one acting as an air-spare.*

*Left: Although most tanker support was provided by the **KC-135Q**, the **SR-71** could also refuel from the **KC-10A**. This capability was first used operationally during the 1986 Libya missions.*

When the SR-71 airframe was cold, its wing tanks did not seal properly, resulting in fuel leaking out from various joints. Ground crew therefore had to take care while operating around the aircraft, due to the toxic nature of the JP-7 fuel. However, when the aircraft was at maximum operational altitude and speed, the airframe heated up and expanded, sealing the cracks.

series of missions that would take the aircraft over Vietnam, Korea, China, Iran and the USSR.

The first operational mission from Kadena was flown some two weeks later, with a flight over Khe Sanh in Vietnam. Although fog forced the aircraft to divert to Taiwan rather than return to Kadena, the results of this sortie were outstanding.

'Habu'

While operating out of Kadena, the SR-71 was given the nickname 'Habu' (a poisonous pit viper) by the local inhabitants.

Although the majority of early 'Habu' flights from Kadena were in support of operations in Vietnam, this was not exclusively the case. On 27 September 1971, the target was the Soviet far east. Of particular interest to the US was the acquisition of signal details relating to the new SA-5 SAM system. Accordingly, one of the aircraft's Elint (electronic intelligence) sensors was modified to receive such data.

In August 1974, the Kadena deployment was designated Detachment 1 of the 9th SRW, a title it retained until it was deactivated in 1990.

The requirement to conduct operations high over the Barents Sea in an attempt to monitor the Soviet Northern Fleet came about following a request from the US Navy. The result was the deployment of the SR-71 to RAF Mildenhall, Suffolk, under Detachment 4 of the 9th SRW.

However, Det. 4's missions also took in other assignments On 12 March 1979 its mission was to obtain imagery that would allow analysts to determine the intentions of Yemen towards its Saudi Arabian neighbour. The sortie lasted 10 hours and involved tanking from five KC-135Q tankers.

By early 1980, operations from Mildenhall had become much more routine. A series of Baltic sorties in the early 1980s not only obtained invaluable intelligence at a time of high international tension, but also demonstrated US resolve to stay actively engaged in the situation by using key surveillance assets in the NATO-Warsaw Pact theatre.

During the closing stages of 1982, Det. 4's capability was doubled when two SR-71s were 'permanently' based at Mildenhall for the first time.

ASARS test

On 9 July 1983, an SR-71A deployed to Mildenhall equipped with a new Advanced Synthetic Aperature Radar System (ASARS-1). Having successfully demonstrated the radar's quantum leap in resolution, this digitised unit also had the ability to be datalinked down to ground stations, allowing near-real-time evaluation; this, it was hoped within the programme, would really provide the SR-71 with a competitive edge.

Throughout the rest of the 1980s Det. 4 continued to provide a wealth of vital surveillance material to the intelligence community; at various times over-flying Lebanon and Libya to secure it. However, on 1 October 1989 all SR-71 operations were suspended and on 22 November the programme was terminated. During a brief reactivation which began in 1995, the downloading of both ASARS and electro-optical camera imagery was successfully demonstrated, but to no avail; the programme was again shut-down, on 30 September 1999.

When legendary aircraft design engineer 'Kelly' Johnson, designed the SR-71 he provided internal serial numbers for each aircraft, the first beginning with 2001. He is reported to have said at the time that it wouldn't be until that date that the aircraft might prove vulnerable to a successful intercept. By 26 August 1981, the 'Blackbird family' had had over 1,000 SA-2s fired at it – all missed. It seems that 'Kelly's' prophesy of shoot-downs failed to take cognisance of the weaponry mustered against the programme by various politicians and groups within the ranks of his own countrymen.

Operating from Beale, most trainee SR-71 pilots took their first ride in trusty '956, seen here over the Sierra Nevada mountains.

Lockheed T-33/T2V

The 'T-birds'

Possibly a quarter of a million pilots have flown the rugged and reliable Lockheed T-33, many of whom will have taken their first step into the world of jets in this trainer masterpiece. The type will forever be remembered as the backbone of Air Training Command's massive effort during the Cold War.

Above: Never a 'star' performer, the T-33 nevertheless carved its place in aviation history by virtue of its longevity and versatility. At the heart of the T-33's success was the reliability of the J33 engine, which was derived from Frank Whittle's wartime work in the UK.

Having earlier flown P-80 Shooting Stars, the Acrostars briefly flew T-33s without tip tanks in 1952-53. The team was based at Williams AFB, Arizona, and represented Air Training Command.

The Lockheed T-33 was an unremarkable aircraft in terms of construction and performance, but it came to be built in vast numbers, and performed reliably and uncomplainingly for nearly 40 years in an era when combat aircraft were pushing back technological boundaries monthly.

At first, the US Air Force showed little interest in a two-seat derivative of its first successful jet fighter, the P-80. Undeterred, Lockheed proceeded with the development of a two-seater by itself. As the Cold War heated up, the USAF – faced with the need to train a vast number of new pilots in short order – looked to the T-33 to cover this rapidly emerging requirement.

The Lockheed engineering team added 38.6 in (98 cm) ahead of the wing and 12 in (30 cm) behind to enable a second cockpit to be accommodated, although fuel capacity had to be reduced.

The initial conversion first flew on 22 March 1948, bearing the designation TP-80C. On 11 June the type was redesignated as the TF-80C, in line with USAF doctrine, and on 5 May 1949 it was rechristened T-33A to reflect its primary training function.

Power for the Lockheed-built T-33s came from the Allison J33-A-35 turbojet, providing 4,900 lb (22.05 kN) of thrust. In most respects the T-33 differed little from the P-80 fighter from which it was derived.

The standard trainer version was the T-33A-1-LO. This had two 0.5-in (12.7-mm) machine-guns in the nose, to allow basic gunnery training. The T-33A-5-LO version was intended to serve as a navigation trainer, and did not have the gun armament.

The only other USAF version to be built as such was the RT-33A, of which 85 were taken from the T-33 production line and given a camera nose for tactical reconnaissance work. As well as these factory aircraft, many other T-33s had camera noses fitted, especially by overseas air arms.

The 'T-bird' entered service with the 3525th Flying Training Group (later Wing) at Williams AFB, Arizona, in June 1949. The T-33 was employed in the basic/advanced stages of a four-phase training syllabus introduced in late 1952. T-33s were also used for low-level navigation training, and for instrument training.

Throughout the 1950s the T-33 was the backbone of the training effort. Some idea of the size of this can be gained by the fact that in 1953 Air Training Command (ATC) narrowly missed its goal of training 10,000 pilots in a single year – virtually all of which will have sampled the T-33 at some stage of their instruction.

In 1961 the first Northrop T-38 Talon arrived with ATC. The supersonic trainer was the T-33's nominated successor in the advanced training role, and as Talon deliveries ramped up, so the cascading of T-33s to other duties accelerated.

By this time, Lockheed production had come to an end, the 5,691st aircraft emerging from the Lockheed line in August 1959. ATC relinquished its last T-33 in February 1967, but the aircraft still had many years of service to give.

ADC service

Apart from ATC, the largest USAF user was Air Defense Command, which acquired hundreds of T-33As to fulfil a variety of demands. These included the provision of fast liaison 'hacks' and target facilities.

In the target facilities role T-33s were used to simulate enemy aircraft to provide practice targets for ADC's interceptor force. ADC 'T-birds' also flew weapons controller training missions, playing the part of either incoming

Ecuador retired its AT-33s in April 1996. The first 'T-birds' had been received in 1956, with the final deliveries being made in 1988. The armed aircraft flew with Escuadrón de Combate 2312.

Seen high over Los Angeles, this aircraft is typical of the 699 T-33s received by the US Navy as the TO-2/TV-2. Yugoslavia received 52 surplus TV-2s to become the only overseas operator.

'trade' or friendly interceptors for ground-based controllers to practise the exercising of intercepts. ADC disposed of its last T-33 in 1988.

Other surplus T-33s were converted for use as drones by both the USAF and US Navy. The USN took the bulk of these, using them as targets in missile tests.

The last surviving T-33 on USAF charge was an NT-33A. This aircraft had been modified with a variable-stability system which allowed it to simulate the flight control systems of other aircraft. In this research role, the NT-33A assisted with many aircraft programmes, including the F-22, until retired in April 1997.

Having been established as the USAF's premier jet trainer, and accordingly built in vast numbers, it was no surprise that the Lockheed T-33 was also operated by a large number of foreign air arms. Virtually all of the nations that were 'friendly' with the US received the type, and a small number that weren't.

Of the 5,871 T-33As built to USAF orders, 1,058 were supplied as new to friendly nations under the Military Assistance Program. In addition, the T-33 was built under licence by Canada and Japan. As the T-33 began fading from the USAF inventory, large numbers became available for distribution among other nations, notably in Latin America.

France was the largest European user, and from 1961 put 83 of its aircraft through the T-33SF upgrade, which brought US-built T-33s and Canadair-built CT-133s to a common standard with a Hispano Suiza-built Nene, new ejection seat and new nav/comms equipment.

As many of the smaller countries intended their aircraft to be used for light attack/COIN operations, many were converted to AT-33A standard, with underwing stores pylons.

A total of 699 T-33As were diverted from USAF contracts for use by the USN and Marine Corps. They were employed as communications 'hacks', continuation trainers and for other duties. The first 26 were delivered under the TO-2 designation, although subsequent aircraft were redesignated TV-2. Several were used as drones or drone directors.

US Navy SeaStar

As a private venture, Lockheed developed a version of the T-33 aimed at naval training, including carrier landings. The L-245 featured a raised instructor's seat and a dorsal fairing, one-piece windscreen, single-point refuelling, strengthened undercarriage, larger tail surfaces, boundary-layer control flaps and leading-edge slats. Power came from a 6,100-lb (27.13-kN) thrust J33-A-24 engine.

The L-245 first flew on 16 December 1953, and led to an order for 150 aircraft under the US Navy designation T2V-1 SeaStar. In 1962, when a tri-service designation system was introduced, the T2V-1 became known as the T-1A.

Canada's Silver Stars

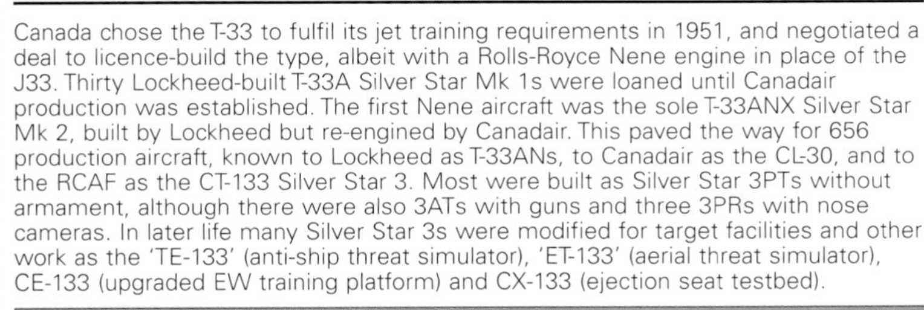

Canada chose the T-33 to fulfil its jet training requirements in 1951, and negotiated a deal to licence-build the type, albeit with a Rolls-Royce Nene engine in place of the J33. Thirty Lockheed-built T-33A Silver Star Mk 1s were loaned until Canadair production was established. The first Nene aircraft was the sole T-33ANX Silver Star Mk 2, built by Lockheed but re-engined by Canadair. This paved the way for 656 production aircraft, known to Lockheed as T-33ANs, to Canadair as the CL-30, and to the RCAF as the CT-133 Silver Star 3. Most were built as Silver Star 3PTs without armament, although there were also 3ATs with guns and three 3PRs with nose cameras. In later life many Silver Star 3s were modified for target facilities and other work as the 'TE-133' (anti-ship threat simulator), 'ET-133' (aerial threat simulator), CE-133 (upgraded EW training platform) and CX-133 (ejection seat testbed).

Lockheed U-2

High-flying spy

Above: The U-2R/U-2S has been in service since late 1967, at first augmenting and then totally supplanting the earlier U-2 versions.

Since the 1950s the mysterious shape of the Lockheed U-2 has sailed serenely over hot spots all round the Earth, recording the activity beneath it from vantage points far above the clouds. Undergoing a complete redesign in the mid-1960s to become the bigger and better U-2R, this covert observer remains one of America's key intelligence-gathering assets.

Lockheed's graceful yet purposeful U-2 first took to the air on 1 August 1955. It had been designed and built in secret for the Central Intelligence Agency, and it was used to gather photographic imagery of installations deep within the Soviet Union. Early-generation U-2s were also acquired by the US Air Force, and these were employed on reconnaissance tasks which included the collection of nuclear particles from Soviet A-bomb tests. In 1962 USAF U-2s were highly active over Cuba during the Missile Crisis.

The early U-2A to U-2G models went on to compile a remarkable service record, performing thousands of missions over and around hostile territory to provide the US with important air intelligence throughout the late 1950s and early 1960s, while also gathering a mass of scientific data on high-altitude flight, re-entry vehicle performance and nuclear fall-out. From 1964 the type was used over war-torn Vietnam.

By the mid-1960s the ranks of the early U-2 variants had been severely depleted by losses, while the intelligence requirement had increased. Lockheed had meanwhile been investigating ways of updating the design and had come up with an enlarged version, with far greater payload and range. Following a request from the CIA, the first six aircraft went to the agency, a further six following for the US Air Force.

When they first entered service, the U-2As were left unpainted. Because of the care taken in assembly by the 'Skunk Works' personnel, the aircraft were truly magnificent to see. By the early 1960s, however, aircraft operated by the the CIA had already adopted the type's better known all-black scheme.

The new U-2R aircraft entered service soon after its first flight in August 1967, and quickly showed itself to be superior in virtually all departments to the earlier variants. As well as the very considerable improvement in payload, range and operational ceiling, landing was far easier, correcting a problem that had dogged the early aircraft.

Agency aircraft

Aircraft belonging to the CIA were soon active from bases in many parts of the world,

With his U-2 in the background, this reconnaissance pilot poses with the portable air-conditioning and oxygen system which he will carry until he is connected to the aircraft's own onboard systems.

especially in Taiwan, where two aircraft were sent in 1968, to operate in Nationalist Chinese markings. This programme ended in 1974, and with it the CIA use of the aircraft, all examples then passing to the Air Force. Air Force U-2Rs saw much action during the Vietnam War, mainly from U-Tapao in Thailand. As well as missions flown in support of the operations in Vietnam, especially during the Linebacker raids, Senior Book covert missions were flown against mainland China.

By 1975 operational losses of U-2Rs had reduced the fleet down to 10 examples. Against this background, USAF and US Army officers were re-examining how reconnaissance resources should gather and distribute intelligence during future operations. Conclusions from this study resulted in the USAF announcing a programme for a 'new' tactical reconnaissance aircraft, and in 1978/79 U-2R production resumed.

In an effort to break from the aircraft's dubious past some of the 'new U-2s' were renamed TR-1s – TR standing for Tactical Reconnaissance. The remainder retained the U-2R designation, and made good the attrition suffered by the earlier batch of 12 aircraft. The first aircraft from the line was a demilitarised ER-2 for NASA's high-altitude research centre. The first TR-1A flew on 1 August 1981, with the first TR-1B trainer following on 23 February 1983. Visually, the second-batch aircraft differed little from the originals, but featured updated secondary systems such as communications. The surviving first-batch machines were later upgraded to the new standard.

European deployment

Early U-2 models had much earlier operated covertly from RAF bases within the UK, on low-profile sensitive operations. It therefore came as no surprise that a permanent U-2R unit was established at Mildenhall, Suffolk, in 1979. U-2R and SR-71 'Blackbird' operations commenced in April that year and continued until February 1983. By this time the new 17th Reconnaissance Wing at RAF Alconbury had been established to operate the TR-1A. This formation received its first aircraft on 12 February 1983 and three more examples followed in March 1985, building to an eventual total of 14.

European TR-1s were often found high over central Europe at 75,000 ft (22860 m) looking across the Warsaw Pact borders. These flights provided NATO commanders with a wealth of new intelligence material that often resulted in complete threat re-assessment.

NASA flew the first-generation U-2C (background) on many high-altitude experiments. The larger U-2R airframe offers far greater load-carrying capability and NASA procured two aircraft as ER-2s, bolstered by a third example (illustrated) which was built as a TR-1A for the USAF but was operated by NASA on long-term loan.

The final TR-1A, the last of the new-build aircraft, was accepted by the USAF on 3 October 1989. The final production total for the second-batch U-2R/TR-1/ER-2 was 37 examples, adding to the 12 U-2Rs built previously.

U-2Rs and TR-1As played a major part in Operations Desert Shield and Desert Storm. After the Gulf War, U-2Rs remained in Saudi Arabia and were one of the key elements in maintaining watch over Iraq.

In October 1991 the TR-1 designation was dropped, the entire fleet reverting to U-2R or U-2RT (later TU-2R).

Even though costs have spiralled, the U-2R fleet has been undergoing a major upgrade programme since 1994, the most significant aspect of which has been the installation of General Electric F118-GE-101 turbofans. The re-engined aircraft are redesignated U-2S or TU-2S (two-seater). In addition, the Senior Span satellite uplink system has been extended to Senior Spur standard, which allows the transmission of ASARS-2 radar imagery in addition to Sigint data. The final upgraded aircraft, featuring an all-new cockpit and enhanced avionics, emerged from overhaul in 2002, and the U-2S will continue the remarkable service record of its forebears.

Although the Cold War has ended, the U-2 fleet's commitments in the Middle East, Far East and southern Europe make it busier than ever.

U-2 operations

The U-2 provided the US intelligence community with the ideal spy platform. Alongside the USAF, the CIA played a leading role in this aerial game of espionage, flying covert missions over Russia and China.

With its sophisticated and far-reaching sensors, the U-2 was the ideal aerial platform for spying on potential aggressors. Illustrated is a Taiwanese-marked U-2R, which undertook missions over China.

Few aircraft epitomised the Cold War more than the U-2. For years it had kept watch on the Soviet Union and its allies from around their borders. The U-2 had also been heavily involved in other operations at various times, notably in Vietnam, Central America and during the Arab–Israeli conflicts. When the Cold War came to an end, the peculiar talents of the U-2 remained just as invaluable.

While the 'Skunk Works' was building the first production U-2, the Central Intelligence Agency (CIA) was selecting and training air crews. By April 1956 the first group of flight crews were declared operationally ready. The crews, along with the first two production U-2As, were flown by cargo aircraft to RAF Lakenheath, England, to prepare for their first operational mission. To preserve security, the unit was given a cover designation, Weather Reconnaissance Squadron (Provisional) 1, or WRS(P)-1.

With a handful of CIA pilots and U-2s in position at Lakenheath, President Eisenhower gave permission for the first overflights of Soviet airspace. British officials, however, objected to the origination of the flights from British soil. As a result, WRS(P)-1 moved to Wiesbaden, West Germany, and it was from here that the first overflight took place.

On 4 July 1956, a U-2A left Wiesbaden bound for Moscow and Leningrad. The flight was a complete success and the photographs obtained by the U-2 proved to be phenomenally clear. Additional overflights were scheduled and received President Eisenhower's approval.

The second CIA unit became operational at Incirlik, Turkey, in August 1956. In February 1957 WRS(P)-1 moved to Giebelstadt, West Germany, moving again to Incirlik in mid-1957. Overflights continued into 1960, and in 1958 a third unit became operational at Atsugi, Japan.

Whereas all previous overflights had been accomplished by elderly U-2A/Cs which were now reaching the limit of their capabilities, the larger, more capable, U-2R model was introduced in August 1967.

However, following the loss of Gary Powers' U-2 on 1 May 1960 – on what was scheduled to be the first overflight to travel completely across the USSR – manned overflights by US pilots had been banned. In order to circumvent this problem, the CIA ran a joint operation with Taiwan, in which Taiwanese pilots undertook missions over mainland China. Spying missions along the Chinese coast finally came to an end in August 1974.

In the meantime, CIA pilots were monitoring the ongoing conflict between Israel and its neighbours. After the UN-brokered ceasefire of August 1970, U-2s made monitoring flights along the Suez Canal, flying from Akrotiri, Cyprus. The U-2's defensive systems were tested during the missions, as Egyptian SAMs, and even Israeli fighters, threatened to attack. The flights were halted in November 1970, but resumed in April 1974 in the wake of the 'Yom Kippur' War. At the end of 1974, the CIA unit was closed down and its mission was taken over by the USAF's 100th SRW.

When it first received the U-2R in late 1968, the 100th SRW was responsible for missions over Cuba, with a single U-2R

CIA U-2s involved in overflights of hostile territory were painted overall Flat Black as camouflage against the dark-blue sky at 60,000 ft (18288 m). Spurious serials were carried on the tails.

U-2R/TR-1As played a critical part in Desert Storm, providing a regular appraisal of Iraqi force dispositions through radar imagery. This trio of ASARS-2-equipped aircraft is seen immediately after Desert Storm, on their return to the Palmdale maintenance facility.

The 9th RW is headquartered at Beale AFB, California, from where the wing supplies aircraft and personnel for the operational detachments. The unit's 1st Reconnaissance Squadron handles U-2 training, and counts four TU-2S trainers among its complement.

deployed at Barksdale AFB.

In 1969, the 100th SRW also deployed the U-2R to Bien Hoa, South Vietnam. In July 1970, the operation moved to U-Tapao, Thailand, by which time the U-2 had a Comint sensor and datalink, and Sigint soon became the main activity.

The U-2's Sigint systems were continuously improved over the years and antennae and receivers multiplied. When the US withdrew its U-2s from Thailand in April 1976, the 100th SRW's U-2 mission moved to Beale in July.

One month later, SAC made its first U-2R deployment to NATO, operating from RAF Mildenhall.

The U-2 production line was soon reopened and a new designation TR-1 was used. Meanwhile, Det. 4 of the 9th SRW was established at Mildenhall in April 1979. Late in 1979, the 9th SRW deployed its first Senior Glass aircraft to Europe, this combining the Senior Ruby Elint system with the Senior Spear Comint system.

The Senior Span configuration – using a satellite datalink to transmit intelligence from the Senior Glass Sigint suite – has seen extensive use in recent operations, beginning with Bosnia.

The Sigint mission was flown from Mildenhall until February 1982, when the newly activated 17th RW took it over from nearby Alconbury. The 95th RS was the operating squadron, receiving its first TR-1A on 12 February 1983.

In March 1985, the 17th RW received the long-awaited ASARS-2 (Advanced Synthetic Aperture Radar System), a datalinked imaging sensor which can operate round-the-clock, in all weathers. In July 1985, the first operational ASARS-2 sortie was flown. The last of the new-build TR-1As was delivered to Alconbury early in 1990. In addition to the TR-1As, eight black-budget U-2Rs were built and three TR-1s 'converted' as U-2Rs.

After a lengthy period of development, the first deployments with a fully configured Senior Span U-2R were made to Patrick AFB and Suwon AB, South Korea. In March 1989, the first deployment to Europe was made. Senior Span adds a satellite uplink pod to allow real-time global transfer of gathered Sigint data.

Gulf War missions

One of the first responses by the US to the invasion of Kuwait by Iraq in 1990 was the dispatch of U-2R/TR-1As to Saudi Arabia. During Desert Shield, five aircraft maintained a constant vigil of Iraq, and, when war broke out, the U-2s flew 260 missions.

Since the end of the 1991 Gulf War, U-2Rs have continued to operate in the theatre, and have maintained a presence over both Iraq and Afghanistan.

The 9th Reconnaissance Wing also continues long-standing detachments in Korea and Cyprus. Another major area of operations has been the former Yugoslavia. When the crisis first erupted, 95th RS U-2Rs began flying missions from Alconbury. This detachment then moved to Fairford and, from December 1995, flew from Istres in France. Single-seat U-2s now share a common U-2S designation following their re-engining, and the fleet of 35 aircraft (including four two-seat TU-2S training aircraft and two NASA ER-2s) is planned to remain in active service until at least 2011.

Lockheed Martin F-16 Fighting Falcon

The Netherlands is a major European F-16 operator and, with a host of other NATO Allies, looks set to employ its upgraded F-16s well into the 21st century.

The 'Viper'

Conceived and still marketed as the ultimate air combat machine unequalled in a dogfight, the General Dynamics/Lockheed Martin F-16 Fighting Falcon has more often been used in the fighter-bomber role.

At its conception, the F-16 was radically different from other aircraft. It was a cheap, simple, unsophisticated, single-engine, single-seat fighter design at a time when fashion dictated expensive, all-purpose, two-seat twin-engined warplanes. But when it left the drawing boards and metal was cut, the F-16 went from being a lightweight fighter to being a robust, multi-role warplane.

There were many reasons for the change – a bantam fighter was never the right solution for a nation which often deploys its forces halfway around the world – but most importantly, the US Air Force felt, initially at least, that its F-15 Eagle was too expensive and important for close air support, battlefield interdiction, and ground-attack duties. Supporters of the F-15 resisted altering their aircraft with the cry 'not a pound for air-to-ground', and the F-16 was made bigger and heavier and given the bulk of the air-to-ground portfolio.

The F-16 is easily recognised by its low-slung engine air intake and by the 'blended' approach that merges the wing with the fuselage. Its external appearance was thought odd when it first appeared, but with more than 4,000 F-16s built, it is now taken for granted. Another innovation of the F-16 – more commonly known to its pilots as the 'Viper' – was the fact that it was one of the first warplanes to introduce a 'fly by wire' flight control system, in which a computer operates the flight controls.

Expanding roles

Many continue to use the F-16 Fighting Falcon as a dogfighter. It has an impressive thrust-to-weight ratio and is extremely manoeuvrable at close quarters. With the incredible visibility afforded by its canopy and the pilot's high-up posture, and with its stability as a gun platform, the F-16 can take on almost any fighter in the world today and win. However, its fly-by-wire control system imposes finite hard limits, preventing the kind of post-stall 'ragged corner of the envelope' manoeuvring which can be performed by the latest Russian superfighters, or by the

Fast, agile and able to deliver a respectable weapon load, the F-16, once envisaged as a pure dogfighter, has developed a number of specialised roles. European air arms – an aircraft of the Danish air force is illustrated – were consequently quick to adopt the type.

Above: Envisaged as a cheap, lightweight fighter intended essentially for daylight missions, the F-16 has emerged as a considerably more sophisticated warplane, with ever-increasing night and bad-weather capability.

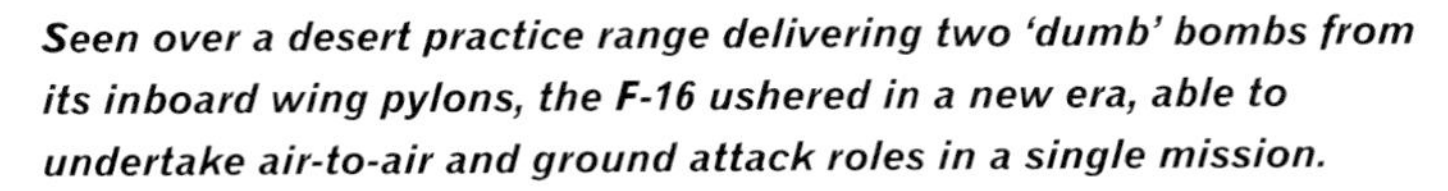

Seen over a desert practice range delivering two 'dumb' bombs from its inboard wing pylons, the F-16 ushered in a new era, able to undertake air-to-air and ground attack roles in a single mission.

thrust-vectoring F-22 Raptor. The earliest F-16 models also lack an IRST (infra-red search and track) capability and helmet-mounted sight, and still rely on the aged Sidewinder missile and a cannon with arguably too small a calibre. However, later variants and upgrades add both the AIM-120 AMRAAM for BVR engagements and the Joint Helmet Mounted Cueing System (JHMCS) for off-boresight targeting.

As a fighter-bomber, the F-16 excels. Cheap enough to deploy in large numbers and supportable enough to sustain an intensive sortie rate, the F-16 carries a remarkable warload (for an aircraft of its size) and, moreover, has been integrated with a huge variety of offensive weapons, sensors and systems, enabling it to perform a wide range of air-to-surface tasks over land and sea.

An ideal tactical fighter aircraft for contingency operations, capable of performing almost any mission, the Fighting Falcon has matured into a 'jack of all trades' – much more useful than being a master of only one.

Bird of peace

Recent world events have seen the F-16 become an airborne peace negotiator for the West, with units being deployed to both the Afghan and Gulf theatres. Having proved its offensive capabilities here through the attacking of ground targets, the F-16s remain on guard, ensuring that future resolutions and agreements are rigidly enforced.

Despite its small size and often muted lack of range, the F-16 remains a potent combat aircraft. Its sheer worldwide sales and the various mid-life update packages currently being offered to improve earlier models will enable the F-16 to undertake any combat mission in an increasingly hostile air combat environment.

Pakistani F-16s have seen action on the border with Afghanistan, claiming Afghan and Soviet air force warplanes during border scuffles. In one instance, a Soviet Su-25 'Frogfoot' was shot down.

In 1982, it was announced that the USAF's Thunderbirds flight demonstration team would trade in its T-38 Talons for F-16 Fighting Falcons. Only slight modifications were made to the aircraft, one of which was the removal of the internal gun.

F-16A/B and ADF

By opting to purchase F-16As, the initial four European operators were now equipped with a fighter which could outfly and beat the latest generation of Soviet fighters.

Having proved to be an extremely capable aircraft during testing, the Fighting Falcon became one of the West's leading fighters. Early variants have since achieved record-breaking sales to the USAF and foreign operators.

General Dynamics' (now Lockheed Martin's) F-16 continues to undergo constant evolution. A complicated series of modifications has led to a number of distinct variants and blocks within variants, all with their own unique capabilities and recognition features.

General Dynamics built eight full-scale development (FSD) F-16A/B airframes. The first FSD F-16A flew on 8 December 1976, while the first two-seat FSD F-16B flew on 8 August 1977. These FSD machines could be identified by their black radomes and black RWR (radar warning receivers) on either side of the fuselage. The FSD F-16 introduced AN/APG-66 radar, and increased fuselage length and fin height. As with all subsequent variants, the addition of a second seat to produce the two FSD F-16Bs did not change the aircraft's dimensions or weight, and added no aerodynamic drag. Some 1,500 lb (580 kg) of fuel tankage was lost, however.

Most of the FSD aircraft served useful test roles, with the third and fifth FSD F-16As being modified to F-16XL standard.

The F-16A/B Block 1 retained the black radome and RWR covers. Power was provided by the Pratt & Whitney F100-PW-200 turbofan engine.

Designation system

A complicated system of F-16 identification was created at an early stage. First, a change in model letter suffix is used to distinguish a single-seat F-16A from a two-seat F-16B. Thus, the first batch of F-16As and F-16Bs are both Block 1 aircraft.

Surviving F-16A/B Block 1 Fighting Falcons, together with Block 5s, were retrofitted with minor equipment changes and brought to F-16A/B Block 10 standard from 1982 to 1984.

F-16A/B Block 5 aircraft introduced the grey radome and nose RWR cover which became standard. Powerplant is the P&W F100-PW-200 turbofan.

Block 10 aircraft introduced minor internal changes.

Above: Entering testing alongside the batch of single-seat F-16s were a limited number of two-seaters. A distinguishing feature of early Fighting Falcons was their all-black radomes. One role envisaged for the two-seat F-16B was defence suppression, more widely known as 'Wild Weasel' missions.

Large numbers of F-16As were supplied to four European nations – Belgium, Denmark, the Netherlands and Norway – in what was often referred to as the 'sale of the century'. A USAF F-16 formates with F-16As from each of these air arms.

As well as standard F-16s, the ANG received two specialised variants. The first, intended for the ground-attack role, carried the GPU-5/A gun pod. The second, more specialised, variant was the F-16 ADF (illustrated), dedicated to North American air defence.

Twenty-four F-16A/B Block 10s were modified for the close air support role with the GPU-5/A centreline pod. This housed a GAU-13/A four-barrelled cannon. The gun pod was never satisfactorily integrated with the aircraft, and the gun pod-capable aircraft went into storage.

F-16A/B Block 15 aircraft introduced the enlarged horizontal stabiliser, which reduces take-off rotation angle and allows flight at higher angles of attack. Block 15 machines carry two parallel RWR antennas beneath the radome and no blade antenna under the intake.

Minor changes to the AN/APG-66 radar provide limited 'track-while-scan' capability. A Have Quick UHF secure voice radio system was also introduced, along with a new cockpit layout. Netherlands Block 15 F-16A(R) aircraft carried the Orpheus day/night reconnaissance pod.

Block 15 Operational Capability Upgrade (OCU) aircraft introduced structural reinforcement and the enlarged HUD found on F-16C/Ds. The programme updates radar and software, fire control and stores management computers and adds provision for AN/ALQ-131 jamming pods. Upgrading to the more reliable, 26,660-lb (118.32-kN) thrust F100-PW-220E is also facilitated.

Aircraft subject to the Block 15 Mid-Life Update (MLU) are refurbished with a cockpit similar to that of the F-16C/D Block 50/52. They are equipped with AN/APG-66(V)2A radar, a GPS navigation system, and other features including a wide-angle HUD, night vision goggle compatibility, a modular mission computer replacing the existing three, and a digital terrain system. Most recipients of this upgrade are offered a helmet-mounted display and AN/APX-111 IFF.

Block 20 for Taiwan

The F-16A/B Block 20 designation applies only to the 120 F100-powered F-16As and 30 F-16Bs built for Taiwan. Taiwan's aircraft have the improved AN/APG-66(V)2 radar of the MLU aircraft, but employ different IFF and use the AN/ALQ-183 ECM pod.

The US Air Force announced in October 1986 the conversion of 270 (later changed to 241) F-16A/B Block 15 aircraft to ADF standard. The Cold War drove military plans, which called for 14 Air National Guard units to receive the ADF.

The ADF conversion was centred primarily on upgrading the existing AN/APG-66 radar to improve small target detection and to provide continuous-wave illumination (thus giving the ability to launch AIM-7 Sparrow BVR missiles). Further modifications included a night identification light in the port forward fuselage, advanced IFF, high-frequency single side-band radio, improved ECCM and provision for GPS and AIM-120 missile datalink.

Actual conversion of the F-16 ADFs was completed in early 1992. Changes brought about by the collapse of the Soviet Union led to a wave of drastic military cuts throughout the US armed forces. Among the ranks of the USAF, the ADF-equipped squadrons were to suffer heavily. The large quantities of surplus ADF airframes resulted in the aircraft being heavily marketed to export customers. First among the foreign operators to acquire the interceptor was Portugal.

Portuguese F-16 ADFs have a primary air defence tasking, but can be armed with AGM-65 Mavericks for secondary ground-attack duties. Clearly visible is the bulged fin base housing the relocated rudder actuators.

F-16A Block 15 Fighting Falcon

This F-16A wears the characteristic markings of Venezuela. Twenty-four F-16As were delivered to the two squadrons of Grupo de Caza 16 at Maracay, wearing scrambled serials to confuse observers. Air defence is their main mission, although air-to-ground operations are also important, hence the camouflage.

Wing
The F-16 wing structure has 11 spars, with five ribs and the upper and lower and load-bearing skins. By blending into the fuselage the wing root can be stronger, with less structural weight. The wing has a 40° sweepback on the leading edge, and is of NACA 64A-204 section.

Nosewheel
The F-16's nosewheel is located aft of the intake to avoid foreign objects being thrown up into the engine, any such damage caused in this way being of concern with a large, low-slung large intake. The nosewheel rotates through 90 degrees during retraction to lie flat under the intake trunk.

Along with its improved capabilities came a host of new roles for the F-16. None was more important than that of SEAD. For this role, these PACAF examples are each fitted with two AGM-88 HARMs on their inner pylons.

F-16C to F

The later variants

The F-16 has far outgrown its lightweight fighter origins and has become today's benchmark multi-role fighter. Radical revisions of the basic design have introduced a host of new capabilities that were out of the F-16's reach as recently as the last decade.

The 86th TFW at Ramstein AB, West Germany, became the first US overseas base to operate the F-16C and D (illustrated), in December 1985. The aircraft were tasked with fighter and day attack missions until the wing moved to Aviano in support of NATO's 4th ATAF.

The F-16C first flew on 19 June 1984. F-16C and two-seat F-16D models are distinguished by an enlarged base or 'island' leading up to the vertical fin, from which protrudes a small blade antenna. This space was intended for the internal airborne self-protection jammer, which the USAF abandoned in favour of the continuing use of external ECM pods.

Compared with earlier versions, the F-16C/D gives the pilot a new HUD, at the base of which is a function keyboard control (located in a console to his/her left in earlier variants). The pilot also has an improved data display, with key items of information located at 'design eye' level for HOTAS flying. F-16C/Ds employ the AN/APG-88 multi-mode radar with-increased range, sharper resolution and expanded operating modes, and have a weapon interface for the AGM-65 Maverick and AMRAAM missiles.

F-16C single-seat and F-16D two-seat fighters introduced progressive changes, some installed at the factory and others as part of the Multi-Stage Improvement Programme (MSIP) (avionics and cockpit and airframe changes) and MSIP III (further systems installation), aimed at enhancing the F-16's ability to fly and fight at night.

F-16C/D aircraft retain the unique low-slung intake configuration of earlier Fighting Falcon variants. They have fuselage-wing 'blending', fly-by-wire controls and a blown polycarbonate canopy which, in these later versions, has a gold tint due to a lining of radar-reflecting materials. F-16C/D models also keep the M61A1 Vulcan 20-mm cannon and retain the ability to carry up to 16,700 lb (7575 kg) of ordnance, including most bombs and missiles in the USAF inventory. Block 25 aircraft entered production in July 1984 and totalled 319 – 289 F-16Cs and 30 F-16Ds. With Block 30/32 came the reconfigured engine bay, with options for the GE F110-GE-100 (Block 30), offering 28,984 lb st (128.9 kN), or P&W F100-PW-220 (Block 32), offering 28,840 lb st (106.05 kN).

The F-16C Block 40 is also powered by the General Electric F110-GE-100, while F-16C Block 42 aircraft are fitted with the Pratt & Whitney F100-PW-220.

The change to -220 power in Block 32/42 aircraft brought a need to alter the contours of the F-16's air intake to accommodate

Navy aggressor

The decision by the US Navy to acquire Fighting Falcons arose from the desire to match the expanding capabilities of the new generation of Soviet warplanes in the adversary arena. Basically similar to the USAF F-16C, the Navy F-16Ns were powered by a GE F110 turbofan. To improve performance, the aircraft had their stores pylons and M61cannon deleted. However, unforeseen fatigue-induced problems, associated with DACT, resulted in the entire fleet being grounded, and eventually retired in 1991.

In June 1988 Egypt signed a deal for 41 F110-powered Block 40s, to join the 82 earlier-model F-16s already in service. Block 40 deliveries began in October 1991, followed by 52 additional aircraft in 1994/95. Another batch of 21 single-seat Block 40s was ordered in May 1996 and yet another, for 24 machines, in 1999.

Modular Reconnaissance Pod

In an effort to increase the capabilities of its early model F-16s, Denmark launched a development programme to find a new tactical reconnaissance system. The result was the Per Udsen Modular Reconnaissance Pod (MRP), which can house a variety of sensors. The MRP has been certified for service, and is in service with the Belgian (as seen here), Danish and Dutch air forces.

the larger amount of air ingested. Because the change was not made initially, early F-16C/D Block 30s are 'small inlet' aircraft, the wider air intake having become standard for GE power on 'big inlet' models after delivery began.

In addition, Block 30/32 aircraft have the ability to carry AGM-88 HARM missiles, and AIM-120 AMRAAM. Avionics hardware changes were also introduced to the Block 30/32, which totals 501 aircraft, comprising 446 F-16Cs and 55 F-16Ds.

F-16C/D Block 40/42

Block 40/42 'Night Falcons' began to come off the production line in December 1988. This version introduced LANTIRN navigation and targeting pods, a GPS navigation receiver, AGM-88 HARM II, AN/APG-68(V) radar, digital flight controls, automatic terrain-following and, as a consequence, increased take-off weight. Greater structural strength raises the Block 40/42's 9*g* capability from 26,000 lb (12201 kg) to 28,500 lb (12928 kg). The heavier all-up weight and the need to accommodate LANTIRN resulted in larger landing gear behind bulged landing gear doors and relocated landing lights.

Block 40/42 aircraft have been delivered to the USAF, Israel, Egypt, Turkey and Bahrain. A Block 42 F-16D equipped with AMRAAMs became the first USAF F-16 to score an air-to-air victory by downing an Iraqi MiG-25 on 27 December 1992.

In December 1991 General Dynamics began delivering F-16C/D Block 50 and 52 aircraft. The first flight date for the Block 50 was 22 October 1991. The first Block 50s went to the 388th Fighter Wing at Hill AFB, Utah, in 1992, followed by delivery to USAFE's 52nd FW. Block 50/52 Falcons introduced the AN/APG-68(V)5 radar with improved avionics computer. Other additions to Block 50/52 included an AN/ALE-47 chaff/flare dispenser, ALR-56M advanced RWR, Have Quick IIA radio, anti-jam VHF, full HARM integration and wide-angle HUD.

These F-16s are powered by the Improved Performance Engine (IPE) versions of GE and P&W engines, the 29,588-lb st (131.6-kN) F110-GE-129 and 29,100-lb st (129.4-kN) F100-PW-229, respectively. Problems arose with developmental test aircraft for the Block 52 programme in July 1991, and these had to be refitted with older F100 variants until the P&W IPE's fourth fan stage could be redesigned. Since that time, both P&W and General Electric have also offered engines in the 32,000-lb (142.32-kN) thrust class.

Around 100 USAF F-16C/D Block 50/52 aircraft were raised to Block 50/52D standard, with provision for the AN/ASQ-213 HARM Targeting System pod carried under the starboard side of the intake. This provides the F-16 with a limited 'Wild Weasel' defence-suppression capability.

The latest production version of the F-16C/D is the Advanced Block 50/52 with upgraded AN/APG-68(V)9 radar, night vision goggles and JHMCS, among other improvements. The first customer was Greece, with deliveries beginning in April 2003. Israel committed to a somewhat similar two-seat machine, as the F-16I, initially ordering 50 aircraft, before also taking up 52 of 60 options.

Block 60 and beyond

In an effort to increase the long-range striking ability of the F-16, Lockheed Martin developed the Block 60 variant with AN/APG-80 multi-mode agile beam radar, revised cockpit, advanced ECM and internal FLIR. The UAE emerged as the first customer for the radically upgraded F-16E/F Block 60, with the first of 80 aircraft delivered in July 2005.

Above: Greek F-16s are unusually configured. Hellenic air force Block 50 aircraft are the only F-16Cs with a searchlight for night interception, located on the starboard front fuselage.

Left: The Block 60 configuration integrates conformal fuel tanks with a mass of new electronic systems. This version forms the basis of the UAE's 80-aircraft F-16E/F order. This advanced development is known to Lockheed as the Desert Falcon, of which the initial two-seat F-16F is illustrated. A first flight was made on 6 December 2003.

Left: In 1983, the 'Swamp Foxes' – 157th FS, 169th FW, South Carolina ANG – became the first Air National Guard unit to fly the F-16. During Operation Desert Storm the unit flew 1,750 attack missions. The 'Swamp Foxes' now fly the latest USAF variant of the 'Viper', the F-16C Block 52. The aircraft illustrated is armed with AMRAAMs on its wingtip and underwing pylons.

Below: Early 1979 saw the first F-16s entering service, the USAF's Hill-based 388th TFW pipping the Belgians and Dutch to the post. Hill became the USAF's 'F-16 capital' as the co-located Ogden Air Logistics Center was picked as the central maintenance depot for the type.

US operators

By far the largest operator of the Fighting Falcon is the USAF, which has flown almost every variant of the aircraft. The type remains one of the most important aircraft in the US inventory. Current in-service versions include highly capable Block 50/52 examples which fulfil the 'Wild Weasel' anti-radar role.

The F-16 Fighting Falcon is the most numerous warplane in the USAF inventory. LANTIRN-equipped F-16C Block 40/42 fighter-bombers equip the bulk of the active force's fighter wings, while advanced Block 50/52 examples undertake the suppression of enemy air defences (SEAD) role with the unofficial designation F-16CJ. A series of OCUs (operational capability upgrades) continues to enhance the performance of the Falcons already in US service. F-16C/Ds serve in Air National Guard units, while Block 30/32 F-16C versions equip a handful of Reserve units.

Early service

The F-16 entered service with the USAF as a cheaper alternative to McDonnell Douglas's highly capable, but extremely expensive, F-15 Eagle. Lightweight and extremely agile, the diminutive F-16 came as a surprise to many former USAF F-4 pilots, who initially viewed the aircraft with some scepticism. Such doubts were soon erased once the capabilities and reliability of the aircraft became apparent. Early USAF plans called for the procurement of 1,388 aircraft, but this large number of airframes was a constant source of argument, with USAF officials using the fighter's multi-role capability to justify such a large procurement programme. Regular USAF pilots viewed the F-16 as a lightweight dogfighter, however, and it seemed that the F-16 was now in danger of becoming a costly, complex machine, being required to deliver bombs and rockets on demanding CAS missions.

Delivery of operational aircraft to front-line units began in January 1979 with the 388th TFW at Hill AFB, Utah. The 56th TFW at MacDill AFB, Florida – one of the USAF's Replacement Training Units (RTUs) for the F-16 – was next to re-equip.

Overseas operations

The first US unit to operate the Fighting Falcon overseas was the 8th Tactical Fighter Wing (TFW) 'Wolfpack'. Based at Kunsan Air Base in South Korea, the 8th TFW was at the forefront of the Cold War in the Korean peninsula. In what was viewed as a 'face-off' against North Korean expansion, 'Wolfpack' F-16s patrolled the borders, and constituted the USAF's strike capability during an uneasy peace that remains to this day. Early A/B models were replaced with more capable C/D variants and at present, two USAF F-16C/D squadrons are active at Kunsan: the 35th FS 'Phantoms' and the 80th FS 'Juvats'.

Among the best-known USAF F-16s were those attached to the Adversary Tactics Division of the 414th Combat Training Squadron (Red Flag), based at Nellis AFB. Better known as the 'Aggressors', the squadron's F-16s simulated enemy aircraft during Red Flag exercises.

Left: The adoption of the F-16 by the Thunderbirds Aerial Demonstration Team gave the team a powerful and agile mount. This, together with unrivalled visibility from the cockpit, makes the F-16 a perfect vehicle for advanced formation-flying.

With the Cold War continuing through the 1980s, European deployment of the F-16 was viewed by US generals as a priority. In July 1982 the first such unit, the 50th TFW at Hahn AB, West Germany, replaced its F-4E Phantom IIs with F-16A/Bs. Other units followed, but with improved C/D aircraft. On 21 December 1985 the 86th TFW at Ramstein AB, West Germany, commenced operations with the F-16C, allowing fighter and day attack missions to be flown.

By far the most capable Fighting Falcons operated by the USAFE, however, are those assigned to the SEAD role. Having replaced the 'Wild Weasel' F-4G Phantom II, the F-16C/Ds of the 52nd Tactical Fighter Wing became operational on 4 July 1987.

Weekend warriors

As the F-16 was being introduced to regular front-line USAF squadrons, a shift in defence policy by the Pentagon allowed America's ANG units to receive the latest aircraft at the same time as their full-time counterparts. Having long suffered the stigma of operating second-hand, 'pass-me-down' airframes, the ANG received its first brand-new F-16s in early 1986, this distinction going to the 162nd Tactical Fighter Group of the Arizona ANG. A succession of units went on to receive the Fighting Falcon, in the process dispensing with their veteran A-37s and A-7 Corsair IIs. Indeed, during Operation Desert Storm two ANG F-16 units earned a lasting place in history. In particular, Fighting Falcons from New York's 174th TFW struck numerous Iraqi ground targets using cluster bombs and AGM-65 Maverick guided missiles.

Due to the sheer numbers in service with the USAF, it is inevitable that Fighting Falcons have been at the forefront of USAF combat operations. As well as participating in successive Desert Storm and Iraqi Freedom operations in the Persian Gulf, US F-16s have been a key component of US peacekeeping policy which has seen the aircraft deployed to Italy for operations over Bosnia, and to Saudi Arabia and Turkey for operations over Iraq. In addition, USAF F-16s have maintained a regular policing presence in Afghanistan.

Although intended primarily as an attack aircraft with the USAF, dogfighting being left to the F-15 Eagle, US F-16s have achieved five air-to-air kills, four over the former Yugoslavia. By far the most well-known of these was Major Bob 'Wilbur' Wright's triple-kill of Serbian Galebs on 28 February 1994. Taking just three minutes, the engagement served to prove the capabilities of an aircraft that will remain a vital element of the USAF in the foreseeable future.

Several F-16s served with the 6510th Test Wing (AFSC) at Edwards AFB, California. The aircraft acted as chase-planes, as well as undertaking a number of test roles themselves. They also provided future USAF test pilots with fast-jet experience.

European operators

***Left:* Regarded as the backbone of NATO's European fighter force, the F-16 Fighting Falcon is in service with a host of operators, fulfiling the interceptor (illustrated by this Turkish air force example) and ground-attack roles. To remain effective, many European air arms have rotated their early-model 'Vipers' through a Mid-Life Update (MLU) programme which will allow the aircraft to remain viable well into the 21st century.**

Turkey

In September 1983 Turkey announced plans to buy 156 F-16s (132 F-16Cs and 24 F-16Ds) in Block 30 and 40 configurations. All but the first eight aircraft were assembled in Turkey by Tusas Aerospace Industries (TAI), and deliveries started in October 1987. From the 44th aircraft, the TAI line standardised on Block 40. TAI has also built 46 F-16C/D Block 40s for the Egyptian air force under the Peace Vector programme. In March 1992, Turkey placed a follow-on order for 80 F-16 Block 50s (including 20 two-seaters), with deliveries continuing into 1999. Turkey's aircraft have been equipped with LANTIRN pods and carry Israeli-developed 600-US gal (2271-litre) drop tanks. Turkish F-16Cs have been participants in NATO air operations over Bosnia.

Belgium

Belgium was one of the four NATO start-up partners (with Denmark, the Netherlands and Norway) to operate the F-16. In February 1978, the first European F-16 assembly line was opened at SABCA/Sonaca in Belgium. Belgium took delivery on 29 January 1979 of the first locally manufactured F-16 out of the country's original order for 116 (96 F-16As/20 F-16Bs). Belgium tested the F-16A with the French Magic 2 infra-red missile and in February 1983, the country announced plans to purchase an additional 44 F-16s (40 F-16As, four F-16Bs). By the mid-1980s, the Belgian air force was looking at ways of improving its F-16A/Bs in response to the increasing Soviet threat. Accordingly, it joined the F-16 Mid-Life Update (MLU) programme, some 84 F-16As and six F-16Bs of Belgium's Block 10 and 15 aircraft being upgraded to virtually the standard of the latest Block 50 F-16s. Initial deliveries of the MLU F-16s saw the first of the squadrons become operational on the 'new' aircraft in late 1999. To supplement the upgrade, AIM-120Bs and AGM-65 Mavericks were also ordered. Despite the crippling cost reductions of the early 1990s that saw air force flying hours reduced to below NATO's minimum, five squadrons (including an OCU) remain active, with a total of 72 aircraft on strength. Surplus airframes have been sold to Jordan, which took 14 examples. The Belgian air force has had a long tradition of decorating its aircraft in honour of special anniversaries. Illustrated is an F-16 from 1st Wing, Beauvechain, 350 Sm/Esc, marked in celebration of the unit's 45th anniversary.

Denmark

Denmark was a member of the quartet that brought the F-16 Fighting Falcon to Europe. Denmark's first 58 'Vipers' (46 F-16As and 12 F-16Bs) came from the SABCA line in Belgium, beginning with the delivery of an F-16B on 18 January 1980. These F-16A/B Block 1 aircraft were later upgraded to F-16A/B Block 10 standard by the local Aalborg workshop in the Pacer Loft I programme. In August 1984 Denmark ordered 12 follow-up F-16s (eight F-16As and four F-16Bs), built by Fokker in the Netherlands. Denmark participated in the five-nation NATO F-16 MLU programme and upgraded a total of 61 airframes (48 F-16As and 13 F-16Bs). At present Denmark's two (reduced from four) F-16 squadrons fulfil both an air interception and ground-attack role. Following the retirement of the RF 35 Draken, which left Denmark without any national airborne recce capability, Red Baron reconnaissance pods were subsequently fitted to the undersides of F-16s as a short-term measure. However, in 1994, the Royal Danish Air Force initiated the development of the Per Udsen Modular Reconnaissance Pod (MRP), which can house a variety of sensors. Such is the importance attached to this role that one reconnaissance-equipped F-16 is maintained on 24-hour alert.

Netherlands

The primary Cold War role of the Netherlands air force (KLu) F-16s was that of close support within NATO's 2nd Allied Tactical Air Force (2 ATAF). Their secondary role was one of air superiority over the battlefield and within the region allotted to the Netherlands in NATO. In May 1979, the first Dutch-assembled F-16 from the the second European assembly line (after Belgium) made its maiden flight. Quickly following in March 1980 was an order for 213 aircraft, followed in 1989 by an attrition batch of 10 F-16As. A further 51 F-16A/B Block 15 aircraft followed. Six front-line squadrons, one training unit and one test squadron are equipped with the aircraft, making the Netherlands the most significant European operator. The KLu upgraded its F-16s by way of the MLU programme which resulted in 138 (reduced from 170) of the original 213 F-16A/Bs being upgraded to F-16AM/BM standard.

Portugal

The Peace Atlantis programme brought the F-16 to Portugal in July 1994. With a delivery consisting of 17 Block 15 F-16As and three F-16Bs, the first four aircraft were delivered to Esq 201, BA5 Monte Real. Powered by F100-PW-220Es, these aircraft have a primary air defence role (with AIM-7Fs), but have also been armed with AGM-65s and deployed to Aviano for NATO peacekeeping tasks. A follow-up order for 25 exUSAF F-16A/Bs (including four two-seaters) was made in 1996 with deliveries completed in 1999. A total of 20 of these latter aircraft has undergone the MLU.

Norway

Norway employs its F-16s primarily in a defensive role, with Nordic geography dictating an important anti-shipping task. On 12 December 1979 the first Fighting Falcon for the air force completed its maiden flight. Norway acquired 72 F-16A/Bs (60 F-16As and 12 F-16Bs), although six further examples followed as attrition replacements. Norwegian F-16s are equipped with tail-mounted braking parachutes and an identification spotlight. Three (reduced from four) squadrons are equipped with F-16s.

Italy

In preparation for the retirement of the F-104S and pending the full introduction of the EF2000, the AMI took out a lease in March 2001 covering the supply of 34 F-16A/Bs (including four two-seaters) from US stocks. Most of these aircraft are Block 15 ADFs, and four spare airframes were also provided. Delivered between July 2003 and March 2004, the aircraft replace 24 Tornado F.Mk 3s leased from the RAF as a previous stop-gap until 2003. Operating units are 23° Gruppo, 5° Stormo at Cervia, and 10° Gruppo and 18° Gruppo of 37° Stormo at Trapani.

Poland

As the first ex-Warsaw Pact 'Viper' operator, Poland signed a contract for 48 Advanced Block 52 F-16C/Ds (including 12 two-seaters) in April 2003. Polish F-16s are among the most capable within NATO, with JHMCS, Sniper ER targeting pods, AIM-9X and AIM-120C AAMs, and AGM-154 JSOW and JDAM air-to-ground weapons. Onboard equipment includes AN/APG-68(V)9 radar and the AN/ALQ-211(V)4 EW suite. The first operating unit is 3 ELT at Poznan, where the first batch of deliveries arrived in November 2006. This will be followed by 6 ELT at the same base, and 10 ELT at Lask by 2009.

Greece

Greece ordered 40 F-16C/D Block 30s in January 1987, and deliveries started in November 1988. A follow-on order for 40 Block 50s with GE engines, including eight two-seaters, was placed in April 1993. The first four aircraft arrived in-country on 28 July 1997. Greece ordered a further 60 Fighting Falcons in April 1999. This third order consisted of the Advanced Block 52 version, with 60 aircraft in a 50:50 mix of F-16C and D models. Greece ordered LANTIRN for its Block 50/52s, and the aircraft have the Northrop Grumman ASPIS EW suite. The F-16s are operated by 110 Wing at Lárisa, which is divided into two front-line squadrons, 337 and 346 Miras; the 111 Wing (330, 341 and 347 Miras plus a training unit) at Néa Anghialos; 115 Wing (340 and 343 Miras) at Soúda; and a Weapons and Tactics School as part of 117 Wing at Andravída.

F-16C Block 50

Receiving its first aircraft under the Peace Xenia programme, Greece became the 14th nation to adopt the F-16 when it first ordered 40 F-16C/D Block 30s. These were then followed from 1997 by 40 Block 50 F-16C/D s under the Peace Xenia II programme, and by 60 F-16C/D Advanced Block 52s from 2002.

Engine
As with all Block 50 aircraft, a GE F110-GE-129 Improved Performance Engine is fitted to Greek examples, offering a 30 per cent increase in thrust over Block 30 Fighting Falcons.

Falcon camouflage
Unlike the majority of F-16 operators, Greece dispensed with the traditional USAF scheme, opting instead for a complex two-tone blue/grey scheme.

The tailfin marking on this F-16A Netz is that of No. 140 'Golden Eagle' Squadron, which employs the Fighting Falcon on air defence duties from its base at Nevatim.

Israeli F-16s

Operational service

Entering combat shortly after delivery, the F-16s of the Israeli air force have earned themselves a remarkable operational record in the Middle East. Intense security surrounds their achievements.

Seen on a test flight in the US, '598' is one of the Block 40 aircraft delivered during the early 1990s. Before delivery, each aircraft is thoroughly flight-tested at Fort Worth.

Israel is one of the world's smallest countries, but its armed forces are large, well-equipped and perhaps the most skilled and professional in the world. Seen as being at the cutting edge of Israel's aggressive defensive policy is the Chel Ha'Avir (Israeli Defence Force/Air Force, or IDF/AF). Surrounded by neighbours who would be eager to see its demise, Israel was keen to secure the best arms that money could buy. It was a loyal customer of the Dassault Mirage series through the 1970s, but the Peace Agreements during the 1980s – particularly the signing of the Camp David Peace Treaty with Egypt – allowed the IDF/AF to once more become an accepted arms customer of the United States.

High on the list of priorities was a suitable replacement for the ageing Mirage IIIs and A-4 Skyhawks. With US officials impressed by the arrival of peace between Middle Eastern nations, President Carter agreed in 1980 to supply Israel with 75 Block 10 F-16 Fighting Falcons (67 F-16As, eight F-16Bs) under the Peace Marble programme; these were the first Fighting Falcons to be delivered to any customer within the Middle East.

Before the initial delivery was completed, the Fighting Falcons were, in 1982, receiving their baptism of fire over the Bekaa Valley, notching up an impressive tally of 44 aerial victories over Syrian MiGs. One year earlier, F-16s had been used on a deep penetration strike into Iraq to destroy the Osirak nuclear reactor then under construction. Having proved their worth in combat, Israel requested, and received, more F-16s in October 1987. These comprised the improved Block 30 models (51 F-16Cs and 24 F-16Ds) equipped with a sophisticated AN/APG-88 pulse-Doppler multi-mode radar and General Electric's more powerful F110-GE-100 turbofan.

Israeli officials have been reluctant to release detailed information concerning Fighting Falcon units, but what is known is that at present 10 front-line squadrons are equipped with F-16s of various marks and the fleet has undergone a major upgrade programme which saw the introduction of an export version of the LANTIRN pod, known as Sharpshooter, and featuring only the targeting mode. Sharpshooter was in turn followed by a locally developed navigation and targeting pod, the Rafael Litening IR

Israeli lightning

Israel's Block 40 deliveries covered 30 examples each of the F-16C and F-16D, which are known locally as the Barak (lightning). The Block 40 aircraft retain the F110-GE-100 turbofan, and the first examples were received in July 1991.

Between August 1994 and March 1995, a further 36 F-16As and 14 F-16Bs were delivered to the IDF/AF from USAF stocks, as a result of Israel's agreement not to become involved in the fighting during Operation Desert Storm. Since their introduction, a host of indigenous modifications have been made to the airframes, which has resulted in some F-16Ds being fitted with an enlarged dorsal spine containing indigenous EW equipment, including the Elisra SPS 3000 self-protection jamming system. The F-16D has also served as a testbed for the indigenous IMI Star-1 anti-radiation missile, which, if successful, will join the IMI Runway Attack Munition in the IDF/AF inventory.

Air-to-air weapons options for the Israeli fleet include the full range of locally developed Rafael AAMs, including the Python 3 (introduced from 1991) and the Python 4 from 1997. The latest Python 5 was deployed during the fighting in Lebanon in 2006, and scored its first kill against a Hezbollah drone. For precision attack missions, the latest IDF/AF Fighting Falcon store is the 2,000-lb (907-kg) Rafael Spice PGM, which combines electro-optical guidance with a GPS unit and datalink.

The latest IDF/AF F-16 model is essentially the Israeli version of the Advanced Block 52, and is better known as the F-16I. A total of 102 of these F110-powered all-weather strike aircraft was ordered, with the first example being delivered in February 2004. The F-16I features conformal fuel tanks and the AN/APG-68(V)9 synthetic aperture radar. In addition, a wide range of locally developed avionics and

Marked as '253' to indicate the initial operating squadron, this is the first F-16I Sufa, rolled out at Forth Worth on 14 November 2003. The variant made its first flight on 23 December 2003.

electronics equipment is incorporated, including the mission computer, stores management system, integrated EW suite (including radar and missile approach warning systems and jammers), cockpit displays and HUD, and the pilot's Dash IV helmet-mounted sight. While previous Israeli F-16s have been integrated with the Sharpshooter and Litening IR pods, the F-16I is compatible with the latest Litening II pod, developed locally by Rafael. The initial operator of the F-16I was No. 253 Squadron.

Front-line IDF/AF Fighting Falcon operators are concentrated around wings located at Ramat David air base in the northern half of Israel; Hatzor air base, just to the south of Tel Aviv; Ramon air base in the heart of the Negev Desert; and at Nevatim air base, in the northern Negev.

Ramat David is home to Nos 109, 110 and 117 Squadrons, which are equipped with the multi-role Block 30 F-16C/D.

Hatzor supports a further two Fighting Falcon units, Nos 101 and 105 Squadrons, equipped with Block 40 F-16C/Ds.

Ramon has three active units, Nos 107, 119 and 253 Squadrons. These have all now received the F-16I. However, some sources indicate that No. 107 Squadron has relocated with its F-16Is to Hatzerim, in the northern Negev.

Finally, Nevatim is home to two units tasked with air defence, Nos 116 and 140 Squadrons, both equipped with the older Block 15 F-16A/B. A third unit with a primary air-to-air mission was No. 144 Squadron, which moved from Nevatim to Hatzor, before being disbanded in October 2005.

Other operating units

Second-line IDF/AF operators include an F-16 aggressor unit, No. 115 Squadron, which flies early-model F-16A/Bs from Ovda, and the Flight Test Centre at Tel Nof, which operates a variety of different F-16 versions.

Israeli F-16s were heavily committed during the conflict in Lebanon in 2006, and it is safe to assume that the Fighting Falcon units of the IDF/AF will play a major role in shaping the future of Israel's political position within the Middle East.

F-16D Block 40 Barak

Israel has the most diverse 'mix' of Fighting Falcons of any operator today, ranging from early F-16A Block 10 'small-tail' aircraft to the example illustrated below, which is an F-16D Block 40 Barak. The initial batch of Fighting Falcons (F-16A/Bs) were named Netz (hawk), while the 'second-generation' F-16C/D is the Barak (lightning). The latest F-16I with conformal tanks carries the local name Sufa (storm).

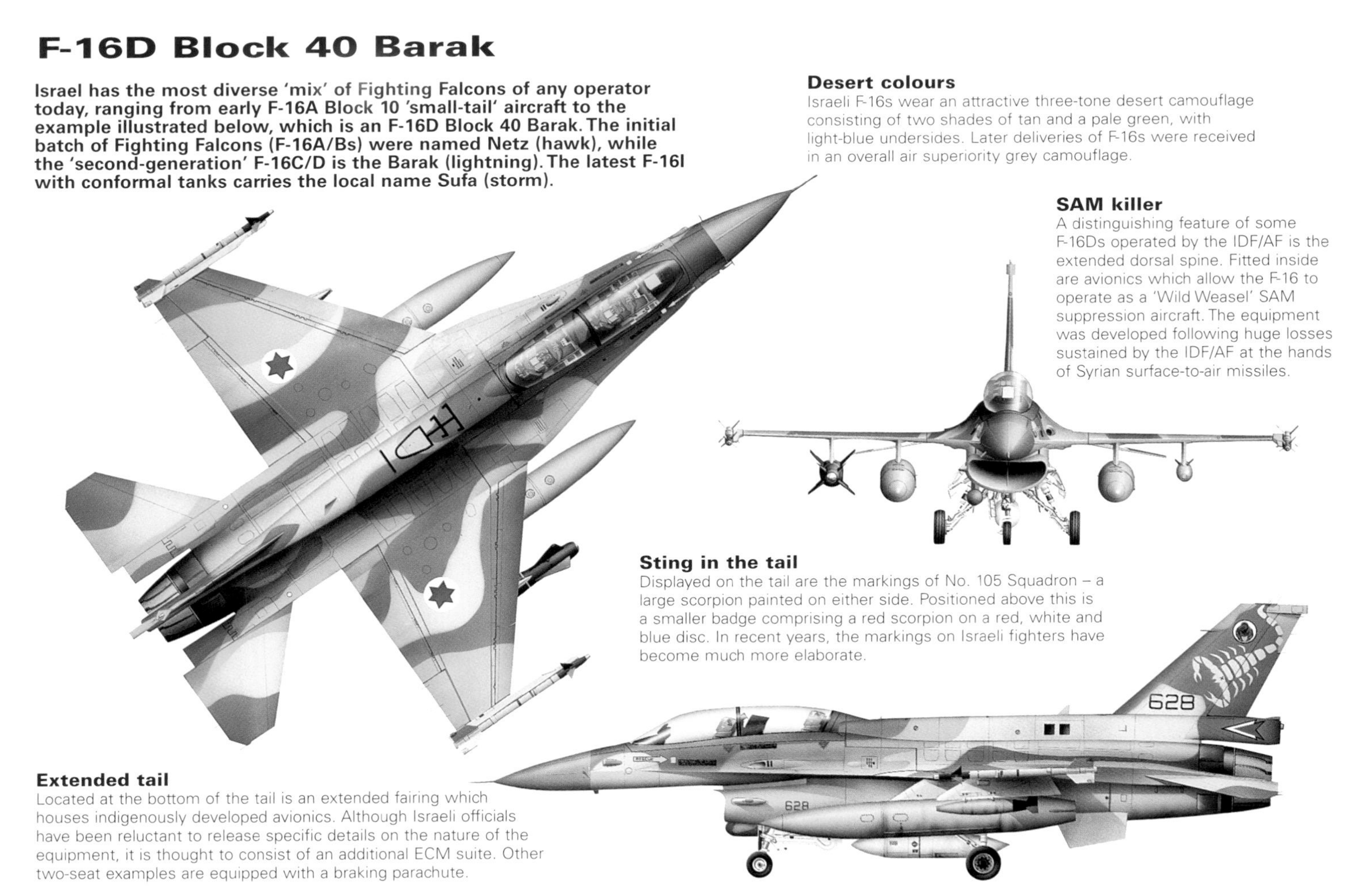

Desert colours
Israeli F-16s wear an attractive three-tone desert camouflage consisting of two shades of tan and a pale green, with light-blue undersides. Later deliveries of F-16s were received in an overall air superiority grey camouflage.

SAM killer
A distinguishing feature of some F-16Ds operated by the IDF/AF is the extended dorsal spine. Fitted inside are avionics which allow the F-16 to operate as a 'Wild Weasel' SAM suppression aircraft. The equipment was developed following huge losses sustained by the IDF/AF at the hands of Syrian surface-to-air missiles.

Sting in the tail
Displayed on the tail are the markings of No. 105 Squadron – a large scorpion painted on either side. Positioned above this is a smaller badge comprising a red scorpion on a red, white and blue disc. In recent years, the markings on Israeli fighters have become much more elaborate.

Extended tail
Located at the bottom of the tail is an extended fairing which houses indigenously developed avionics. Although Israeli officials have been reluctant to release specific details on the nature of the equipment, it is thought to consist of an additional ECM suite. Other two-seat examples are equipped with a braking parachute.

The USAF has an eventual requirement for 381 F-22As, although this figure is almost certain to be drastically reduced as a result of budget constraints. Together with a smaller procurement – a Raptor force in the region of 180 aircraft is possible – the fleet will also take on a greater variety of roles, including precision attack.

Lockheed Martin F-22 Raptor

America's cutting edge

F-15 Eagles may have ruled the skies in the past, but today the aircraft is ready for replacement, especially if it is to face competition from the latest Russian types. The USAF's next-generation air dominance fighter is the Lockheed Martin F-22 Raptor.

The ATF programme was conceived in 1981. By 1985, Lockheed had produced a fanciful and misleading artist's impression of what would eventually become the F-22.

In late April 1991 the USAF chose Lockheed/Boeing/ General Dynamics to develop its proposal of the Advanced Tactical Fighter (ATF) over rival Northrop/McDonnell Douglas's YF-23. As a replacement for the Eagle, the ATF represents the single biggest advance in fighter performance since the first jets. It combines 'stealth' with a huge increase in supersonic endurance and manoeuvrability, and it is the first military jet to reflect the revolution in computer technology in its basic design and onboard electronics. Lockheed Martin encountered numerous design problems in its development of the YF-22, leading to significant visible changes from the original artist's impression of the aircraft. It was 29 August 1990, some three years after construction had begun on the earliest prototype, that the first aircraft (N22YF) was unveiled at Lockheed's Palmdale facility in California.

Restrained by heavy chains, the Pratt & Whitney YF119-powered YF-22 is seen here undergoing afterburner trials during one of the many static tests conducted during the programme.

This first prototype flew for the first time on 29 September 1990, while a second aircraft (N22XF) followed it into the air on 30 October. Each prototype received a different powerplant, both of which were still under evaluation by the USAF. Pratt & Whitney's YF119 turbofan proved to be more reliable than General Electric's similar YF120.

Following an extended flight-testing period, to allow for final engineering adjustments, the USAF announced on 23 April 1991 that the YF119/YF-22 combination had been selected and issued a contract for 11 (later reduced to nine) Engineering and Manufacturing Development (EMD) flying prototypes on 2 August (including two tandem-seat F-22Bs, which were in the event completed as F-22A single-seat aircraft), plus one static and one fatigue test airframe.

As construction began on the first two F-22A Raptors, an

***Above:* Designed from the outset for 'supercruise' performance, the F-22A is powered by a pair of 35,000-lb (156-kN) Pratt and Whitney F119 turbofans with two-dimensional thrust-vectoring (+/-20°) nozzles for improved manoeuvrability and flight performance.**

In general, no external weapons are carried on the Raptor in an effort to retain the aircraft's 'stealth' characteristics. Instead, four weapons bays (two in the engine intake sides and two under the fuselage) house AAMs and/or precision-guided bombs.

expansion of the aircraft's role was proposed. This saw the addition of air-to-ground attack missions, the aircraft being armed with precision-guided munitions (PGMs), and as a result the Raptor was designated as the F/A-22 between September 2002 and December 2005.

The first pre-production aircraft (91-4001) made its maiden flight on 7 September 1997. The F-22A incorporates noticeable design changes over the prototypes, among the most prominent being the broader undernose fairing and repositioned intakes. A second Raptor took to the air on 29 July 1998, and there were 18 development and pre-production F-22A aircraft flying by late 2003. In the meantime, development work continued on both the Raptor's radical AN/APG-77 radar, which was flown on a Boeing 757 testbed, and the AN/ALR-94 integrated EW system.

On 26 September 2003 a first F-22A was delivered to an operational USAF unit, the 43rd Fighter Squadron of the 325th Fighter Wing at Tyndall AFB, Florida. By the end of 2004, the 43rd FS had received a total of 13 aircraft, and by the second quarter of 2004, the squadron was operating with its full complement of 23 Raptors.

Front-line Raptors

The role of the 43rd FS is pilot training, and on 12 May 2005 the first front-line USAF Raptor unit began to receive its first equipment. This squadron is the 27th FS, 1st FW at Langley, Virginia, and the unit achieved initial operational capability on 15 December 2005.

Following the re-equipment of the 1st FW, next in line to receive the Raptor is the 3rd FW at Elmendorf AFB, Alaska, which will have two F-22A squadrons on strength from 2009. Although future acquisition is subject to funding pressures, with the F-22A, the USAF will maintain its lead in the field of air superiority well into the 21st century.

***Below:* The Raptor sets entirely new standards in the realm of air dominance fighters, the pilot having unrivalled 'information superiority' thanks to the active electronically scanned array (AESA) AN/APG-77 radar with a range of around 125 miles (201 km).**

***Above:* A 27th FS F-22A takes on fuel from a KC-135 Stratotanker over Iwo Jima, in February 2007. At the time, the Raptor was completing its first overseas deployment, to Kadena AB, Okinawa.**

Complete with arrester hook, the X-35C was the demonstrator for the US Navy's CV carrierborne JSF version. Although the larger surfaces altered the aerodynamics when compared with the X-35A, Lockheed Martin engineers 'tweaked' the flight control system so that the two aircraft felt very similar in the cockpit.

Lockheed Martin F-35

Lightning II

Although the threat of cancellation has long hung over it, the US Joint Strike Fighter programme is the most important military aircraft venture in the world. Lockheed Martin's F-35 Lightning II is based on the original X-35 JSF technology demonstrator.

Lockheed Martin's F-35 aircraft employs a host of features which make it a generation ahead of previous fighters. Furthermore, advances in technology allow the F-35 to offer F-22 'stealth' characteristics and avionics at F-16 prices, with unprecedented predicted savings in maintenance.

In November 1996 Lockheed Martin and Boeing were awarded contracts to develop their JSF proposals further. Part of the contract involved the construction of two Concept Demonstration Aircraft (CDAs) with which to prove the technologies the teams aimed to employ in their Preferred Weapon System Concept (PWSC) proposals. Based on the PWSC submission, actual data from the CDAs, computer predictions and a host of supporting proposals, the Pentagon then 'down-selected' the Lockheed Martin team on 26 October 2001, the company then proceeding with the System Development and Demonstration (SDD) phase.

Lockheed had been a front-runner in pre-JSF competitions (CALF, JAST) and continued to refine its design throughout. As its name implies, JSF is a multi-service programme which will provide a land-based fighter for the USAF, carrierborne aircraft for the US Navy and, most technically difficult, a STOVL platform for the USMC, RAF and Royal Navy. Demonstrating the necessary attributes for these differing requirements with two CDAs meant that one would have to 'double-up' its tasks.

X-35 configuration

Owing to the nature of Lockheed Martin's overall design concept, it was natural to build a conventional take-off and landing (CTOL) demonstrator – which was designated X-35A – to display the 'up and away' performance of the design, before fitting it with the STOVL equipment to become the X-35B. The second aircraft (X-35C) was built to test elements of the carrierborne (CV) variant, although it was constructed with the ability to accommodate the STOVL lift-fan as an insurance measure should the first aircraft be lost.

Lockheed Martin's X-35 was much closer in configuration to the final design than the rival Boeing CDAs. The X-35 resembled a scaled-down F-22, with twin, outward-canted fins, all-moving tailerons set well back, angular intakes and a stealthy, chined nose. Power in the CTOL/CV versions was provided by a single Pratt & Whitney F119-611C turbofan. An unusual feature of the X-35 was the diverterless intakes, which had a bulge on the fuselage side to spill a turbulent boundary layer either side of the intake lip. The intake was serpentine to trap radar energy,

In preparation for a first flight, test pilot Tom Morgenfeld runs up the F119-611C engine of the X-35A to full power. The production-standard version of this engine for the F-35 is the P&W F135.

The USAF has a stated requirement for 1,763 JSFs, most of which will replace the F-16 (right), with which the now-retired X-35A is seen here. Other JSFs will replace A-10s as the USAF moves to a two-fighter force.

and there was a radar blocker downstream. On the F-35 production aircraft, weapons can be housed in bays in the underside, and standard weaponry consists of two AIM-120 AMRAAMs and two GBU-31 JDAMs. Additional weapons can be carried externally, although these greatly increase the radar cross-section.

The X-35A CTOL demonstrator took off for the first time on 24 October 2000. Built in the famous 'Skunk Works' at Palmdale, the aircraft transferred to Edwards to undertake an intensive period of trials which involved high-speed manoeuvring, inflight refuelling and supersonic flight. The X-35A completed its test programme on 22 November 2000, having logged 27 flights. It then returned to Palmdale for conversion into the STOVL X-35B.

CV demonstrator

On 16 December 2000, the X-35C was taken aloft for the first time. This aircraft represented the carrier variant intended for the US Navy. In order to cope with the demanding approach handling requirements, the CV version has substantially larger wings and tails. In order to preserve the commonality of the basic design, Lockheed Martin achieved this by 'picture-framing' – that is, adding area around the basic CTOL design's surfaces without dramatically affecting the internal structure. The team accepted a slight reduction in permissible *g* loads (from +9 to +7.33) but this was still within the US Navy's requirements.

The primary aim of the X-35C test programme was to validate the aircraft's low-speed handling qualities. A series of mock carrier approaches were made on a dummy deck at Edwards, before the X-35C went to the Navy's test establishment at Patuxent River, Maryland. An exhaustive series of mock FCLPs (Field Carrier Landing Practices) proved the X-35C's excellent handling on the approach at sea level, and involved many 'off-nominal' scenarios during which the aircraft's ability to recover rapidly and safely were tested.

X-35C testing came to an end on 11 March 2001, by which time it had racked up 73 flights. Apart from the 250 FCLPs flown, it also found time to continue some of the X-35A's 'up and away' testing, and flew supersonically. It also validated refuelling procedures with the KC-10 Extender.

Many of the systems for the production F-35 are being tested on Northrop Grumman's BAC One-Eleven trials aircraft. This also has a trial installation of the F-35 cockpit, which has a single contiguous projected display stretching across the full width of the instrument panel. There is no head-up display, all relevant information being displayed on the pilot's helmet visor. Both X-35 demonstrators featured a more conventional cockpit and were fitted with standard HUDs.

On its 10th flight the X-35A demonstrated aerial refuelling, hooking up to a 412th Test Wing NKC-135E. Both X-35s had USAF-style boom receptacles, whereas Boeing's CDAs were fitted with Navy-style probes.

While commonality between variants was a key goal of the Lockheed Martin teams, there are notable differences between them. Apart from the 'picture-framing', the CV version of the F-35 also has much stronger undercarriage and folding wings. Both CV and CTOL aircraft have larger weapons bays to take the 2,000-lb GBU-31 JDAM (the STOVL F-35B is envisaged only with the 1,000-lb GBU-32).

The SDD phase called for 15 instrumented flying aircraft (six CTOL F-35As for the USAF, four US Navy F-35C CV variants and five USMC/UK F-35B STOVL versions), plus eight ground-test airframes. The first of the flying SDD aircraft, an F-35A – by now named Lightning II – made its maiden flight on 15 December 2006. Deliveries of a planned total of 2,593 aircraft for the US and UK are due to begin in 2009.

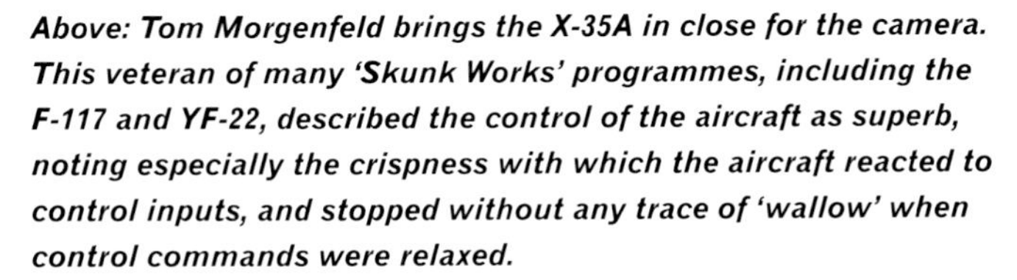

Above: Tom Morgenfeld brings the X-35A in close for the camera. This veteran of many 'Skunk Works' programmes, including the F-117 and YF-22, described the control of the aircraft as superb, noting especially the crispness with which the aircraft reacted to control inputs, and stopped without any trace of 'wallow' when control commands were relaxed.

Left: The initial F-35A touches down after its successful first flight on 16 December 2006. The flags on the intake side indicate the international partners that had, at the time, committed to the JSF project to varying degrees: the UK, Italy, Netherlands, Turkey, Canada, Denmark, Norway and Australia.

STOVL F-35B

For both JSF teams, the STOVL (Short Take-off, Vertical Landing) configuration intended for the US Marine Corps and the UK was the hardest challenge. Lockheed Martin chose an unproven lift-fan arrangement for its X-35B demonstrator, which emerged as the successful 'productionised' F-35B.

***Top and above:** Lockheed Martin's **STOVL** concept employs a large number of moving parts which must function correctly. As well as the doors which open on the aircraft's spine and undersides, these photographs highlight the vectoring engine nozzle, which is angled slightly downwards in the top photograph, and nearly vertically in the lower picture. The thrust from the cold air fan in the front fuselage is also vectored.*

It is interesting to note that the three pre-1996 JSF competitors had chosen three different propulsion concepts for their STOVL aircraft. Boeing employed the direct-lift concept, as proven in the Harrier family, while the rejected Northrop/McDonnell Douglas design employed the lift-plus-lift/cruise concept. Lockheed Martin opted for a completely different tack, and one which had not hitherto been employed – the lift fan.

This concept uses the vectored thrust from the engine combined with that from a cold air fan, itself driven by power from the engine. The main disadvantage of this scheme is that when not used for STOVL flight the lift fan becomes 'dead' weight. In the Lockheed Martin design, though, there are hidden benefits. The space occupied by the lift fan in the STOVL version can be used for fuel in the CV (US Navy) and CTOL (USAF) variants. Both services have greater range requirements than the USMC.

Lift-fan concept

However, the lift fan also has two major advantages over the direct-lift concept employed by Boeing on its rival X-32B: firstly, it greatly improves the thrust recovery from the engine, and secondly it avoids many of the problems caused by hot exhaust gases re-entering the engine.

Lockheed Martin designers calculated that the lift fan would blow a cushion of cold air under the hovering aircraft, preventing most hot exhaust gases, which could seriously degrade engine performance, from reaching the intakes: in hover tests intake temperatures rose just 5°F (3°C).

In Lockheed Martin's JSF proposal the STOVL version was aerodynamically similar to the CTOL USAF aircraft, for which the X-35A acted as the flying testbed. When its programme of demonstrating 'up-and-away' performance came to an end on 22 November 2000, the X-35A returned to the 'Skunk Works' at Palmdale to be fitted with the STOVL lift-fan arrangement and to re-emerge as the X-35B.

Essentially the lift fan is a large-diameter two-stage counter-rotating fan mounted in a bay behind the cockpit. Doors open in the forward spine to admit cold air for the fan, while doors open below to allow the accelerated air through. This air can be vectored to allow a smooth transition from pure jetborne flight (i.e. hovering) to wingborne flight. In the X-35B the air is blown through a vectoring D-section nozzle, but in the F-35B production version this is to be replaced by a cascade of moveable vanes.

Power for the fan comes via a drive shaft from the compressor face of the engine, which has a clutch (using a form of carbon brake technology) to provide controllable torque power to the shaft. The shaft ends in a single gear, which drives the two stages of the fan. At full power the lift fan provides around 18,000 lb (80 kN) of thrust.

Of course, this thrust is provided at the front of the aircraft, and to balance it the normal engine exhaust is vectored

On 24 June 2001, the X-35B completed its first sustained hover: 35 seconds at 25 ft (7.6 m) altitude. During its flight test programme it made 18 vertical take-offs and 27 hover landings.

downwards through a three-section articulating exhaust nozzle. The nozzle can be swivelled to 15° beyond the vertical to allow the aircraft to move backwards while hovering. Pratt & Whitney's engine for the X-35B is the F119-611S, known as the F135 in production form. The amount of thrust from the engine, and from the lift fan, can be controlled either simultaneously or differentially to control pitch and climb/descent rates.

Additional air is drawn from the engine's fan to two 'roll posts' under the aircraft's wings. The flow to these outlets is variable, providing roll control in the hover. Together, the four nozzles provide around 40,000 lb (178 kN) of thrust.

STOVL conversion

When the F-35B transitions from wingborne to jetborne flight, a complex sequence takes place, although the transition appears seamless to the pilot thanks to computer control. Four sets of doors open: two sets cover the inlet and outlet for the lift fan, one set covers an auxiliary intake for the engine mounted immediately aft of the lift fan upper doors, and another set opens under the rear fuselage to allow the main nozzle to swivel downwards. All these doors have to fit precisely to preserve the aircraft's 'stealth' characteristics.

Flight profile

For take-off a short roll is standard practice, the propulsion system set in STOVL mode, but with the thrust angled obliquely backwards. The aircraft lifts off after about 500 ft (152 m) of runway, then climbs and accelerates away to full wingborne flight. The propulsion system is configured and reconfigured automatically during the process.

With the X-35B complete, Lockheed Martin moved cautiously to a first flight. Unlike Boeing, which chose a 'fly, then hover' approach, LM elected to begin flight tests with vertical take-offs. Tests first got under way over a hover pit. This allowed the aircraft to mimic hovering without leaving the ground. The hover pit outlet doors could be opened or closed to simulate hovering in and out of ground effect. Initial trials began with the X-35B firmly rooted to the grate.

Further hover testing without the restraints culminated with the first full hover on 23 June 2001. After additional hovering flights, the X-35B took off conventionally on 3 July for the trip to Edwards, from where the remainder of the flight test programme took place. During the tests the X-35B was successfully hover-landed at 34,000 lb (15422 kg), twice the weight of a 'legacy' STOVL aircraft such as the AV-8B Harrier II.

While hovering and wingborne flight had been mastered, the big test came on 9 July 2001, when the first airborne transition from STOVL to CTOL mode was undertaken. On 16 July the aircraft was brought in from wingborne flight to a vertical landing.

On 20 July the Lockheed Martin team achieved its primary goal – 'Mission X'. This demonstrated the standard *modus operandi* of the aircraft, beginning with a STOVL-mode short running take-off, transition to CTOL mode for a supersonic dash, and then transition to STOVL for a vertical landing. On 30 July the X-35B completed its flight programme with all goals achieved. In the middle of August the final bids and test data were submitted to the programme office and, in October 2001, Lockheed Martin was awarded the EMD contract.

A first F-35B production aircraft was expected to fly in the third quarter of 2007, to be followed by the first F-35C CV version in early 2009. In addition to firm backing from the USMC, RAF and Royal Navy, the F-35B STOVL version has also attracted interest from the USAF and from a number of foreign nations (including Australia, Italy and Taiwan), and the F-35C may yet rival the CTOL F-35A in terms of export sales.

Above: Driven by a shaft from the engine, the lift fan provides nearly half the thrust in the hover. Behind are auxiliary engine intake doors, required to provide the necessary mass flow.

Left: The moment of truth – test pilot Simon Hargreaves lifts the X-35B into the air for its first free flight on 23 June 2001. Previously, the aircraft had been tested with physical or weight restraints.

52-1418 was the first of 403 B-57s of all variants built by the Glenn L. Martin Company between 1953 and 1957. '418 was one of eight B-57As – effectively US-built Canberra B.Mk 2s.

Martin B-57 Canberra

The USAF 'buys British'

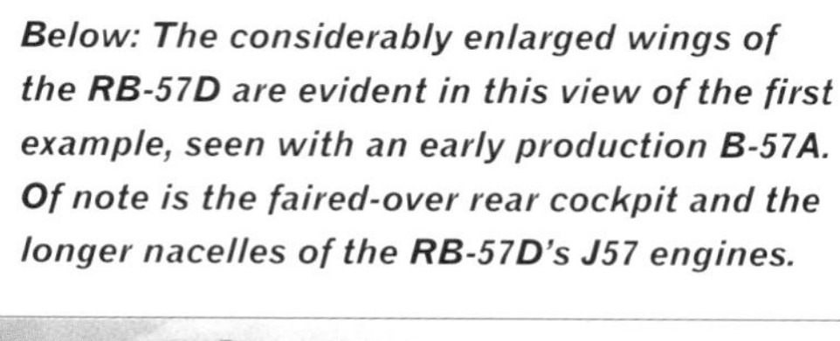

Below: The considerably enlarged wings of the RB-57D are evident in this view of the first example, seen with an early production B-57A. Of note is the faired-over rear cockpit and the longer nacelles of the RB-57D's J57 engines.

With its sudden involvement in Korea in 1950, the USAF urgently needed a replacement for the B-26 Invader in the night intruder role. It stipulated that the new tactical bomber should be based on an existing design, and ultimately selected the Canberra.

Before a decision was made about a B-26 replacement, a shortlist was drawn up, comprising North American's B-45 Tornado (in service with TAC) and AJ Savage (used by the US Navy), plus three types yet to enter service – the Avro Canada CF-100, English Electric Canberra and Martin's XB-51. A 'fly-off' contest was arranged for late 1950.

Interim type?

In the meantime, however, the USAF concluded that both the Canberra and XB-51 were suitable for the requirement. The USAF committee suggested that enough Canberras be purchased to equip two bomb groups until the XB-51 became available. Negotiations with English Electric for 300 aircraft took place and Martin was eventually licensed to build the aircraft, known as B-57s.

Despite this behind-the-scenes activity the fly-off went ahead, in February 1951. The Canberra was announced the winner in March and an order was placed with Martin for 250 B-57A night interdiction bombers. The B-57A was based on the Canberra B.Mk 2, but powered by Armstrong Siddeley Sapphire turbojets, built by Wright as J65s.

The earlier plan to order the XB-51 as an eventual B-57 replacement was ultimately rejected by the USAF, who saw that the Canberra would ably fill their requirements.

In the event, design changes requested by the USAF, the crash of one of two Canberra Mk 2 pattern aircraft, and delays in engine production all contributed to lengthy delays. The first B-57A took to the air on 20 July 1953 and was followed by another

B-57Bs of the 345th Bomb Group (Tactical) break for the camera. The 345th, based at Langley AFB, was the first of four tactical bomb groups to receive B-models from 1955.

***Right:* A 'Patricia Lynn' RB-57E rests in a revetment at the type's base of Tan Son Nhut AB, South Vietnam. The elongated nose, housing two cameras, was a distinguishing feature of this variant.**

***Below:* Clouds of smoke pour from a cartridge starter aboard 53-3888, a B-57B based at Bien Hoa, South Vietnam, in 1965. '888 was to be the first USAF jet bomber to drop live ordnance on an enemy when it bombed Viet Cong positions east of Saigon on 19 February.**

seven examples. Apart from its J65 engines, the B-57A boasted a number of features not found on the Canberra Mk 2, including eight wing-mounted machine-guns.

As B-57A production gathered pace, concern that the pilot's visibility was inadequate for ground-attack work led to the design of a new tandem two-seat cockpit with a single canopy. Another improvement for the intruder role was the addition of fuselage air brakes and, from the 91st aircraft, four 20-mm cannon in place of the machine-guns.

After eight B-57As and 67 camera-equipped RB-57As had been completed, the new model, designated B-57B, entered production and became the principal B-57 variant. In all, 202 were built and were followed by 38 B-57C conversion trainers.

The RB-57A version, with a camera bay aft of the bomb bay, equipped three USAF wings from 1954. Ten RB-57As were re-equipped with uprated J65-W-7 engines and were lightened to increase service ceiling. Eventually redesignated RB-57A-1, these were split between USAFE and FEAF units. Two other machines became RB-57A-2s in 1957, with high-altitude radar installed. A third aircraft, known as 'Switch Blade', was equipped for flights along the Iron Curtain and along the borders of North Korea and China.

The next batches were 20 RB-57Ds, with long-span wings, and 68 B-57Es. The latter was a target-towing variant, based on the B-57C. These were the last production Martin-built Canberras, bringing total production to 403.

The first Canberras entered USAF service in 1954, when TAC's 363rd Tactical Reconnaissance Wing at Shaw AFB, South Carolina, received RB-57As. The following year, four tactical bomb groups began to receive B-57B intruders.

It was the 13th Bomb Squadron, 3rd BG that first took the B-57 into combat, in Vietnam in early 1965. B-57s served in southeast Asia until 1971, concentrating on night interdiction missions. This role led to the development of the B-57G dedicated night intruder under the 'Tropic Moon III' project in 1969.

Vietnam reconnaissance

The war in southeast Asia also spurred development of the RB-57E 'Patricia Lynn'. These were the first jets introduced into the air war in Vietnam, in 1963, and spent eight years in the theatre – longer than any other jet type during the war. The six RB-57Es were equipped with up to three cameras and an infra-red scanner in a redesigned nose.

Post-Vietnam, numerous B-57s were passed to the ANG, which had received RB-57As as early as 1958. The B-57 was retired in 1981.

Two other air arms operated B-57 bombers. South Vietnam flew a handful of B-57Bs in 1965-66, while Pakistan took delivery of 22 B-57Bs and three B-57Cs in 1959. Pakistan's aircraft saw combat in the 1965 and 1971 wars with India.

The most radically altered of the RB-57s were the RB-57Ds and Fs. Built for SAC, the 20 RB-57Ds utilised a B-57B fuselage mated to a new wing with nearly twice the span of the standard wing, and had new Pratt & Whitney J57 engines. The first six RB-57Ds entered service in 1956 with the 6021st Reconnaissance Squadron at Yokota AB, Japan.

The second batch of RB-57Ds totalled seven aircraft. Four of these were equipped with inflight refuelling capability. The single RB-57D-1 featured a large nose-mounted radar in a bulbous radome and SLAR. The balance of the D-models were RB-57D-2s. These six machines were two-seaters, with nose-mounted radar.

General Dynamics was chosen to design a 'super D' with which to replace the first 'long-wing' aircraft. Twenty-one were converted and sported massive, 122-ft (37.2-m) wings and two P&W TF33 turbofans. The first of these RB-57Fs entered USAF service in 1964. The final four RB-57Fs were also dedicated spyplanes operated by USAFE and FEAF units. However, most Fs were used by the Air Weather Service and were redesignated WB-57F. Two examples remained in NASA service in 2007.

WB-57F 63-13290 started life as B-57B 52-1562 and was the fifth conversion to RB-57F standard. Fifteen of the 21 aircraft produced were configured, at least initially, for air sampling operations with the 58th Weather Reconnaissance Squadron. These machines were eventually redesignated WB-57F and carried various types of equipment, including podded air samplers on the wings.

McDonnell F-101 Voodoo

The 'One-Oh-Wonder'

The 'Happy Hooligans' were the 178th Fighter Interception Squadron, North Dakota ANG, which flew F-101B/Fs between 1969 and 1978. The last ANG Voodoos were retired in 1982.

Development of the McDonnell Voodoo was particularly long, the type being subject to more changes in policy and planning than any of its contemporaries in the so-called 'Century Series'.

Had the initial late 1940s proposal for a penetration/escort fighter gone ahead, the Voodoo would have been known as the F-88, two prototypes of which were ordered by the USAAF in 1946.

The first prototype flew in 1948, but nearly two years were to elapse before it was joined by the second machine, with considerably better performance as a result of its afterburning Westinghouse J43 engines. In the event, the XF-88 had only a brief flying career, as the project was cancelled in August 1950.

In January 1951 SAC laid down criteria for a more suitable escort fighter and the USAF agreed to examine proposals. McDonnell's submitted concept, based on the F-88, found favour, but some months were to pass before the USAF decided to proceed, releasing funds in October 1951.

The initial production run was intended to be kept to a minimum number for testing. In the event, no pre-production Voodoos reached the combat inventory. In November 1951, it was revealed that the new fighter would be known as the F-101.

McDonnell accepted an initial contract on 15 January 1952, but the project was slowed by the Korean War armistice and the USAF's decision to delay the release of funding. In October, the production-hold order was rescinded, and by the end of the year a further three F-101s had joined the flight-test programme, the USAF specifying that operational capability should be achieved by early 1957.

Early trials revealed serious deficiencies. These centred around the P&W J57-P-13 turbojets which were prone to compressor stalls; and poor longitudinal stability qualities, with a tendency to pitch up. Another production-hold order came into effect in May 1956. By then, 29 aircraft were engaged in test work, but this stoppage was of relatively short duration.

The original production proposal called for the construction of the first 33 machines with a stress factor of 6.33 *g*, with subsequent Voodoos capable of absorbing 7.33 *g*. Eventually, the USAF accepted the 6.33-*g* aircraft as the F-101A, while the 7.33-*g* examples became F-101Cs.

1956 was spent incorporating design changes and production line improvements, including the installation of an active inhibitor to solve the pitch-up problem, clearing the way for USAF production authorisation for operational service, final restraints being lifted in November 1956.

Voodoos for TAC

By now, changes in SAC philosophy had prompted the decision to dispose of its fighter force in 1957. Thus, TAC assumed responsibility for the F-101. Despite TAC reluctance, production continued and the F-101A entered service with the 27th Strategic Fighter Wing at Bergstrom AFB, Texas, in May 1957. Ultimately, only 50 of the 77 F-101As produced saw front-line service, but the problem of just what was the best use to make of the F-101As was solved in 1958/59 with their transfer to USAFE's 81st TFW at RAF Bentwaters and Woodbridge in the UK, the type's long range and nuclear capability providing a significant boost to the forces at the disposal of NATO.

The XF-88 made its maiden flight on 20 October 1948 at Muroc Dry Lake, California. In 1953 the aircraft flew in XF-88B configuration, fitted with a supersonic propeller.

The only other tactical fighter variant was the F-101C, which featured the stronger 7.33-*g* structure. Production began in early 1956, although doubts about the value of the Voodoo as a tactical fighter were confirmed in December 1956 when it was revealed that a combined total of only 124 F-101A and F-101C aircraft would be built. The new variant initially joined the 27th TFW, with effect from September 1957, and soon found its way to Europe, where it also served with the 81st TFW, enjoying a front-line career which ended in 1966.

A substantial number of the surviving F-101A/Cs was reconfigured for reconnaissance duties with the ANG. After the installation of a battery of cameras in a redesigned nose, modified F-101As were known as RF-101Gs, while F-101Cs became RF-101Hs, the two models remaining active until 1973.

In the meantime, work on a new-build reconnaissance model had proceeded steadily from 1951, rewarded by a contract in 1953 that covered the production of two YRF-101A prototypes. The first prototype was airborne in May 1954.

Production-configured RF-101As appeared in summer 1956, however, aircraft production outstripped the development of mission equipment, and early specimens represented only a minimal advance over the RF-84F. Nevertheless, the RF-101A entered service with the 363rd Tactical Reconnaissance Wing in May 1957, the unit initially receiving most of the 35 aircraft produced by October 1957.

Built in greater numbers than the rest of the single-seat Voodoos combined, the RF-101C was the definitive reconnaissance model. The RF-101C benefited from the 7.33-*g* structure and by December 1956 orders stood at 166 aircraft. First flying in July 1957, the RF-101C was rapidly introduced into service with the 432nd TRG. Overseas deployment followed, aircraft joining USAFE and PACAF during 1958.

Vietnam service

The RF-101C suffered from a range of problems, but when the systems were working satisfactorily it was an excellent reconnaissance platform that proved its worth in southeast Asia, detachments being active there from 1961. The advent of the RF-4C helped to bring about the RF-101C's withdrawal, which took place during 1969/70, survivors being passed on to the ANG, with which they served until January 1979.

The final and most numerous variant of the Voodoo was the F-101B, a total of 480 being built. About one-quarter were fitted with dual controls, these aircraft being known initially as TF-101Bs, although they were subsequently redesignated as F-101Fs. A two-seater derivative optimised for air defence duties, the F-101B was produced mainly as a form of insurance in case the so-called 'ultimate' F-106 interceptor failed to satisfy USAF requirements.

The initial interceptor proposal by Air Defense Command was made during October 1952 but was quickly rejected. ADC raised the suggestion again some six months later, recommending the F-101's use as a long-range interceptor and in areas where existing radar coverage was poor. On this occasion, USAF headquarters was more enthusiastic.

Study of various proposals resulted in the F-101 being judged most suitable in June 1954, and in early 1955 McDonnell received an initial contract for 28 specimens (soon raised to 96). The first F-101B, with accommodation for a radar intercept officer in the rear cockpit, made its maiden flight on 27 March 1957.

Around one-fifth of the F-101Bs in use from 1959 to 1969 were lost through attrition, a figure resulting from a high degree of design flaws. This was the most numerous Voodoo variant, with 480 produced.

Trials were completed in mid-March 1959, some two months after the F-101B had entered operational service with the 60th FIS at Otis. Problems abounded, but by December 1960 no fewer than 17 squadrons had converted to the Voodoo.

Phase-out from the front-line ADC force, when it came, was fairly swift, being accomplished between 1968 and 1971, although the aircraft continued to serve with the ANG until 1982.

The last of these aircraft in service were those of Nos 409, 410, 414, 416 and 425 Squadrons, Canadian Armed Forces. CF-101B was the Canadian designation for the F-101B, supplied in two batches. A first batch of 66 Voodoos – 56 F-101Bs, and 10 dual-control F-101Bs (known to the Canadians as CF-101Fs) – was delivered to the RCAF between 1961 and 1962. In 1970/71, the surviving CF-101Bs were swapped for 56 ex-USAF Voodoos. They continued in their NORAD-dedicated air defence role until, one by one, the units began to hand in their CF-101s. The last of the CF-101Bs hung on with No. 414 Squadron until 1984.

RF-101Cs were delivered to the 432nd TRG at Shaw from the end of 1957. A year later, the RF-101s were put under the control of the 363rd TRW, in whose markings this aircraft is seen. The Shaw wing flew 82 combat reconnaissance flights during the Cuban missile crisis.

Canada's dual-control aircraft were known as CF-101Fs; this is a No. 425 Squadron example. Both the F-101F and CF-101F had only basic controls in the rear cockpit, with no controls for the flaps, afterburner or landing gear.

*Charleston, South Carolina, is the backdrop for this stunning view of a 437th Airlift Wing **C-17 Globemaster III** in flight. The first production **C-17s** went to **Charleston AFB** from 1993.*

McDonnell Douglas (Boeing)

Globemaster III

The C-17 Globemaster III is today the most important transport aircraft for the US Air Force, this giant cargo craft being able to haul military equipment rapidly and easily to distant troublespots.

The US Air Force's 21st-century airlifter, the C-17 Globemaster III has made one of the most remarkable turnarounds in aviation history.

In the late 1980s, the C-17 was behind schedule and over budget, and the programme to develop the new transport was so poorly managed that several USAF officers had to be disciplined. Since then, the production effort by Boeing (formerly Douglas) has won industry awards, the C-17 is flying with three active-duty USAF airlift wings, and the type has appeared at every crisis spot from Korea to Kosovo.

The C-17 is a high-wing, four-engined, T-tailed transport. It boasts an ergonomic flight deck with digital displays; the two pilots sit side-by-side and the aircraft is flown with a control stick instead of the yoke traditionally used on transports. It was the first cargo aircraft with a HUD. The airlifter's 168-ft (51.08-m) wing is swept at 25° with a supercritical aerofoil and has winglets for fuel efficiency.

The four Pratt & Whitney F117-PW-100 turbofan engines are rated at a remarkable 41,847-lb (188.3-kN) thrust each, and are located ahead of, and below, the C-17's wings on cantilevered pylons.

Airlift virtuoso

USAF active-duty C-17s serve with the 437th Airlift Wing at Charleston AFB, South Carolina; the 62nd AW at McChord AFB, Washington; and the 305th Air Mobility Wing at McGuire AFB, New Jersey. The USAF was long expected to acquire 120 Globemaster IIIs at a sticker price of around $1 million per aircraft. However, USAF orders had risen to 190 by 2007, keeping the Long Beach, California, production line open until at least mid-2009.

The C-17 prototype made its maiden flight on 15 September 1991. At the time, misfortunes were rife. The first flight was more than a year behind schedule. Worse, a new problem emerged in October 1991: a static test C-17 had a wing structural failure in tests, but minor changes eventually resolved this problem.

The C-17 test programme was carried out with remarkable efficiency. Unlike the development programme which preceded it, the flight test programme met cost and scheduling milestones. When aircraft P-3 made its first flight on 7 September 1992, Douglas obtained permission to land on the Edwards dry lake bed for the first time. Landing on the rough

*Below: **US** 82nd Airborne Division Paratroopers in action. The **C-17** required minor changes to its doors before being cleared for airdrop operations.*

Above: Globemaster ZZ172 is pictured at Brize Norton in July 2001. The aircraft had arrived at the station in June. Like all US-built military aircraft, the RAF's C-17s are allocated US serial numbers.

Below: At Rhein-Main Air Base in Frankfurt, Germany, in 1995, a pair of C-17A Globemaster IIIs of the 437th Airlift Wing carry out a humanitarian mission to Bosnia in Operation Joint Endeavor.

surface proved to be no problem at all. Soon afterwards, an M60 main battle tank became the first tracked vehicle to be loaded on to a C-17. Various loads of vehicles and armour have since been carried by the aircraft.

The first production C-17, known as P-1, made its maiden flight on 19 May 1992. Charleston's 17th Airlift Squadron, part of the 437th AW, received its first aircraft on 14 June 1993.

The Globemaster III name, honouring the earlier C-74 and C-124 manufactured by Douglas, was applied to the C-17 in February 1993.

The delays and difficulties in the early C-17 programme gave way to dramatic improvements partly because Operation Desert Shield, in 1990, demonstrated the urgent nature of the strategic airlift role, and partly because Douglas management ordered thorough housekeeping and reorganisation. The manufacturer, which was then part of McDonnell Douglas, has now become part of Boeing.

With testing, development, and production back on the right track, the C-17 began in the 1990s to demonstrate its enormous value as a key tool in the Pentagon's warfighting plans. The USAF's only other big lifter, the C-5 Galaxy, has been plagued by reliability problems and has had a 'mission-capable rate' as low as 50 per cent. Mission-capable rates for the C-17 fleet have now hit the 92 per cent mark. The C-17 is among the few airlifters that can operate easily, and reverse, on unpaved airstrips.

During Operation Allied Force – the war over Kosovo in 1999 – NATO forces relied heavily on the poorly equipped airport at Tirana, Albania. The C-17 proved to be the only airlifter that could consistently haul outsized loads into Tirana, where the US Army's Apache attack helicopter force was mustered.

The first of eight airframes for the ANG was delivered to Jackson, Mississippi, in December 2003. The Air Force Reserve Command has also received eight aircraft, these going to March AFB, California, from August 2005. Since February 2006, the C-17 has had a presence with PACAF, with a two-aircraft detachment at Hickam AFB, Hawaii. Training for the USAF C-17 community (and export operators) is conducted on eight aircraft operated at Altus AFB, Oklahoma.

Globemaster exports

As the first export customer, the RAF's four C-17s were ordered as a 'stop-gap' measure until the arrival of the Airbus A400M. The UK's urgent need for an interim strategic airlifter necessitated a short-term fix, and Boeing immediately tendered the C-17 to meet the requirement, the Globemaster emerging as by far the most suitable aircraft. The aircraft are four new-build, extended-range Lot 12 C-17As, that incorporate an additional fuel tank in the previously 'dry' bay in the wing centre-section. The aircraft are operated by No. 99 Squadron at RAF Brize Norton, the first aircraft being handed over to the RAF in May 2001.

The first deployment to an operational theatre was made in August 2001 when an initial C-17 flight delivered Lynx helicopters, their crews and support equipment to Macedonia as part of the UN peacekeeping operations. The RAF has since expressed its intent to purchase the aircraft when the lease expires, and to acquire a fifth example in 2010/11.

In November 2006, the Royal Australian Air Force received the first C-17A from a four-aircraft order announced in March 2006 and worth some US$2.2 billion. These will be operated by No. 36 Squadron at RAAF Amberley, and are equipped to Block 17 standard, incorporating improved avionics and software.

The latest customer is Canada, which signed up for four C-17As in February 2007, with the first deliveries to 8 Wing at Trenton, Ontario, planned to begin before the end of the year.

Night or day, the C-17 is easier to load and unload during a crisis, thanks to a computerised system that enables a single loadmaster to handle and stow a full load of cargo.

McDonnell Douglas F-4 Phantom II

'Phabulous Phantom'

Above: In 1988 the Missouri ANG (based across the runway from the McDonnell factory) painted this F-4E for the Phantom's 30th anniversary. The aircraft (68-338) was a double MiG-killer.

For two decades the two-seat F-4 Phantom was unchallenged as the Western world's top fighter, yet its origins lay in a single-seat attack-dedicated loser, rejected by those who would later rely on it as the backbone of their air power.

What we now know as the F-4 Phantom II can be traced back to McDonnell losing out in a fighter competition to the Vought F8U Crusader. Stung by this setback, McDonnell's design team attempted to come up with an aircraft that the US Navy would want. The result was a privately funded long-range attacker, designated F3H-G by the company. Navy interest was sufficient for McDonnell to be awarded a two-aircraft prototype contract, the aircraft to be designated AH-1.

During the course of its development the AH-1 was re-roled as a fleet defence fighter, resulting in a designation change to F4H-1. In the process it gained a second seat for a radar operator. Also under development at the time was the single-seat Vought XF8U-3 Crusader III. The F4H-1 first flew on 27 May 1958, with Bob Little at the controls. In the ensuing competition with the Crusader III, the F4H-1 triumphed with ease, although the Vought aircraft was faster and showed greater potential as an air-to-air fighter. Nevertheless, the F4H-1, even at this stage, showed enormous versatility, an asset that was to make it the yardstick for fighters in the 1960s and 1970s as the world's air forces moved to true multi-role capability.

McDonnell test pilot Bob Little poses next to the first F4H-1. Although the team knew they had a potentially brilliant aircraft on their hands, they could hardly have expected the huge success that the Phantom would enjoy.

Record-breaker

No mean performer itself, the F4H-1 set numerous records in the first years of its existence and, by the time it entered operational service with the US Navy in July 1961, it was by far the best fighter in the world. Never intended to win any beauty prizes, the Phantom II (redesignated F-4 in 1962) nevertheless offered huge combat capability. Its two J79 engines provided superb performance and twin-engined safety, and its unusual wing/tailplane configuration conferred good manoeuvrability in all speed regimes, while keeping carrier approach speeds within acceptable limits. The weapon

Above: The unmistakable bulk of the F-4 in classic pose aboard USS **Nimitz.** *The aircraft is from the USMC's VMFA-333 (nicknamed the 'Shamrocks' or 'Triple Trey') during a rare cruise afloat.*

Below: The Phantom became the best-known and most numerous aircraft of the Vietnam War, serving with the US Air Force, Marines and Navy. Here an F-4B of VF-96 rockets Viet Cong positions in South Vietnam early in the war.

***Above:* Procured primarily for the strike/attack and reconnaissance roles, the RAF's Phantom FGR.Mk 2s were later re-roled for air defence missions. This example from No. 29 Squadron carries four Sidewinders, four Sky Flash missiles and an SUU-23 gun pod.**

***Right:* Carrying cameras and other sensors in its redesigned nose, the RF-4C was an excellent low-/medium-level tactical reconnaissance platform, blessed with blistering speed down low.**

system was extraordinary for its time: a long-reaching radar in the nose fed data to a central fire-control computer, allowing the four Sparrow missiles to be launched at maximum range. Four Sidewinders (or Falcons) backed up the primary armament.

Navy Phantoms served from carriers until eventually replaced by F-14 Tomcats and F/A-18 Hornets. Major variants were the F-4B, F-4J (new fire-control system, stabilator slats and drooping ailerons), F-4N (updated F-4Bs with new avionics), and F-4S (updated F-4Js with manoeuvring slats). The type saw extensive Vietnam service and remained in the fleet until 1986.

Early Navy experience of the Phantom convinced the US Air Force that here was a true classic. Accordingly, the Air Force bought a minimum-change version (F-110A, later F-4C) to equip its multi-role fighter units. F-4Ds followed, these being better equipped for air-to-ground operations, although they retained a considerable air-to-air prowess. Both variants also saw extensive action in southeast Asia, as did the F-4E, the first variant to introduce an internal cannon. F-4Es became the USAF's standard fighter until large-scale replacement by F-16 Fighting Falcons began.

Reconnaissance mission

From an early point the Phantom was considered for the tactical reconnaissance role, resulting in the RF-4B for the Marine Corps and RF-4C for the USAF. Both variants provided long service, the RF-4Cs surviving long enough to fly combat missions in the 1991 Gulf War. Another specialised role was that of defence suppression, modified F-4Cs seeing action during the last months of the war in Vietnam before the definitive F-4G was introduced to service in 1978. The F-4G Wild Weasel V was the last variant in front-line US service, its swansong taking place during Desert Storm.

Naturally, the F-4 was widely exported. The first overseas customer was the Royal Navy, which ordered a much-modified aircraft powered by the Rolls-Royce Spey turbofan. The RAF also purchased Spey-powered aircraft, and these were initially used for ground-attack duties in Europe, including standing nuclear alert alongside their USAF brethren. Other customers followed soon after, including Australia (pending delivery of F-111s), Egypt, West Germany (with F-4Fs), Greece, Iran (whose aircraft saw much action in the Iran-Iraq War), Israel, Japan (which built the type under licence), South Korea, Spain and Turkey.

While US Phantoms slugged it out with North Vietnamese MiGs and SAMs, Israel's Phantom force saw intensive action against Egyptian and Syrian forces. During the Yom Kippur War of 1973, the F-4E was Israel's principal fighter, scoring many confirmed kills over Egyptian and Syrian MiGs, albeit at some cost.

The Phantom is still in front-line service with a handful of overseas customers. Upgrade programmes have added new avionics and weapons to keep the old warhorse a viable proposition over today's battlefield.

Israel's F-4s saw action from as soon as they were delivered in 1969. This trio is from No. 107 'Knights of the Orange Tail' Squadron.

US Navy and Marine Corps variants

F-4A (F4H-1/F4H-1F)

Following on from the two Phantom prototypes were 45 aircraft initially designated F4H-1, but later redesignated F4H-1F. In September 1962 they became F-4As. As the first 21 aircraft were considered as pre-production aircraft, configurations varied wildly. The first aircraft retained the small radome and low canopy of the prototypes but, from aircraft no. 19, the enlarged canopy and large radome were introduced. Powerplant was the J79-GE-2A or J79-GE-8 in late aircraft, as exemplified by the aircraft shown here, the eighth from last F-4A. None was issued to a front-line squadron, most seeing service with test or training units.

RF-4B (F4H-1P)

The RF-4B followed the USAF's RF-4C, and was generally similar in appearance. It was procured for the Marine Corps, which required an organic tactical reconnaissance capability (the Navy deemed it had sufficient recce assets in the RA-5C and RF-8A/G). First flying on 12 March 1965 with Irving Burrows at the controls, the RF-4B was based on the F-4B airframe with a recce nose housing cameras, IR linescan and a SLAR. The last 12 (of 46 total) had the thick wing of the F-4J. The final three had the rounded undernose bulge seen on many RF-4Cs (below). The Marine photo-Phantom went into service with VMCJ-2 and VMCJ-3, both of which provided aircraft for VMCJ-1 (above) operating in Vietnam, beginning in 1966. RF-4Bs occasionally operated from carriers in small detachments and were progressively updated. In 1975 all RF-4Bs were concentrated in VMFP-3 at El Toro, where the type was retired in August 1990.

F-4B (F4H-1)

Initially procured under the F4H-1 designation (with surviving earlier aircraft being retrospectively christened F4H-1F), the F-4B (after September 1962) was the first definitive production version and accounted for 649 aircraft, the first of which was flown on 25 March 1961 by Thomas Harris. The first F-4Bs were virtually identical to the last of the F-4As but were regarded as being in full operational configuration, with AN/APQ-72 radar, AN/AJB-3 nuclear bombing system, AN/ASA-32 Automatic Flight Control System and a full set of hardpoints. Power came from the J79-GE-8 or -8A, and the AN/APR-30 radar homing and warning system (RHAWS) appeared from the 19th F-4B (and was retrofitted to earlier machines). Deliveries to the US Navy began in the spring of 1961, the first unit to receive the F-4B being VF-121 'Pacemakers' at Miramar, which acted as the West Coast training unit. The East Coast unit, VF-101 'Grim Reapers', followed soon after. The Atlantic Fleet's VF-74 'Bedevilers' was the first front-line unit, deploying aboard the Navy's showpiece carrier USS *Forrestal*. It was F-4Bs that recorded the Phantom's first combat action on 5 August 1964 in the Gulf of Tonkin Incident, and again an F-4B scored the Phantom's first air-to-air kill on 9 April 1965 when a VF-96 aircraft shot down a Chinese MiG-17. F-4Bs had a long service career with both the Navy and Marine Corps, the last being retired from the Marine Reserve in January 1978. Many were converted to F-4N or for special purposes as NF-4Bs (test) or QF-4Bs (drone).

F-4G

Twelve conversions of F-4Bs were made to F-4G status, this variant featuring an AN/ASW-13 datalink which was intended to allow automatic control of the aircraft for airborne intercepts, and hands-off landings. The latter function required the aircraft to have a retractable radar reflector ahead of the nosewheel. Ten of the aircraft saw service in Vietnam, with VF-213, from October 1965. During this cruise they acquired experimental dark-green camouflage. The aircraft were 'de-modded' to F-4B status in 1966/67, although some elements of the system were incorporated into the F-4B and F-4J.

Left: Visible just ahead of the nosewheel door of this F-4G is the retractable radar reflector which, combined with the shipboard AN/SPN-10 radar, allowed the variant to make automatic carrier landings.

***This illustration shows one of the VF-213 F-4Gs during its 1965/66 combat cruise in USS* Kitty Hawk.**

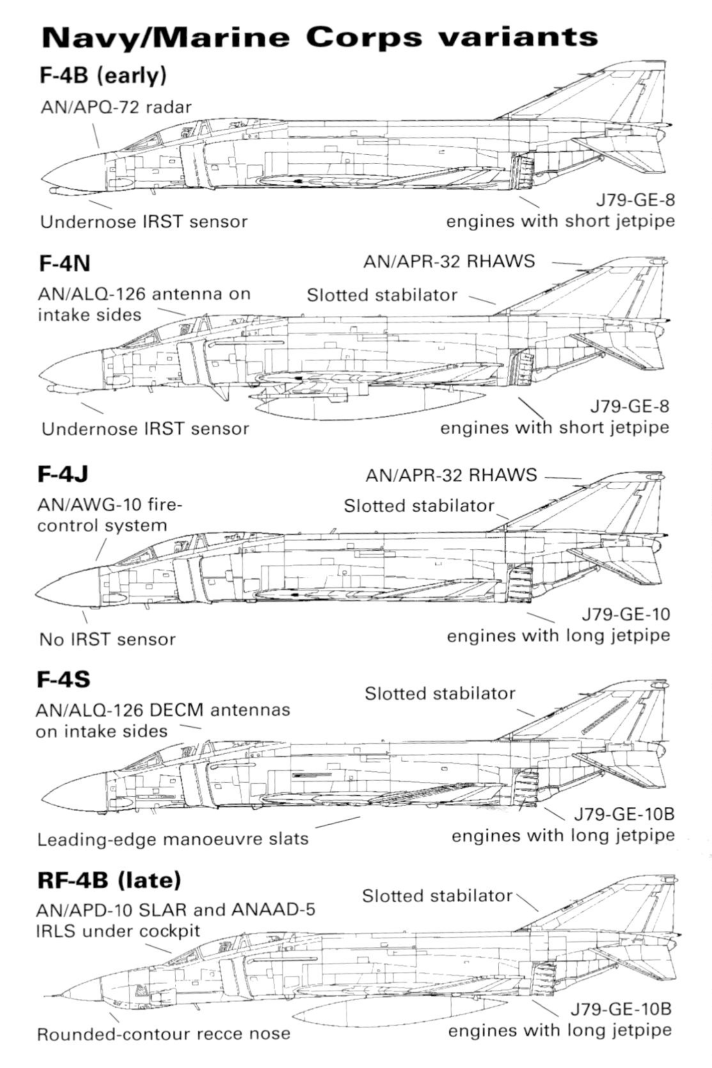

F-4J

The second of the major Navy/Marine production versions, the F-4J introduced a host of new features. J79-GE-10 engines were fitted, characterised by longer jetpipes, while a slotted stabilator was installed to provide greater down-force on launch, and drooping ailerons used to reduce approach speed. The undercarriage was strengthened and enlarged, requiring bulges above and below the wings to accommodate the larger units. In avionics terms, the F-4J introduced the AN/AWG-10 fire-control system with AN/APG-59 radar among other items, including a one-way datalink. The undernose IRST was dispensed with, and the RHAWS upgraded to AN/APR-32 standard, with neater antenna installations. During the F-4J's career there were several upgrade programmes, notably that which added AN/ALQ-126 ECM in fairings on the intake sides. 522 were built, the first flying on 27 May 1966. Deliveries began in December 1966 (to VF-101) and the variant was soon in action in Vietnam. Fifteen surplus aircraft were purchased by the RAF as the F-4J(UK). Others were converted to F-4S standard.

F-4N

Under Project Bee Line the US Navy upgraded 228 F-4Bs to F-4N standard, the first conversion flying on 4 June 1972. The programme extended the aircraft's structural life and modified the avionics, including a new mission computer and the addition of AN/ALQ-126 Deceptive ECM antennas on the intake sides. As the aircraft retained the undernose IRST and J79-GE-8 engines of its F-4B origins, this was the best recognition feature for the F-4N. During Bee Line, the aircraft all received the slotted stabilator of the F-4J (some F-4Bs already had this) and had their inboard leading-edge flaps locked shut, as this had proven to give greater lift and stabilator authority. Redeliveries began in 1973, and the F-4N remained in service until the mid-1980s. Shown below are aircraft from VMFA-321.

Special-purpose variants

In addition to the main fighter variants, there have been several special-purpose conversions. One F-4B became an EF-4B for use as an electronic warfare aggressor with VAQ-33, the squadron later employing two EF-4J conversions. Two F-4Bs were used for trials as NF-4Bs, while an F-4B previously converted to YF-4J (prototype F-4J) standard later served as an ejection seat testbed. Considerable numbers of Phantoms have been converted to drone status for missile and other tests under the QF-4B and QF-4N designations, joined by a single prototype QF-4S. At least one F-4J was converted to DF-4J standard to act as a drone controller at NAS Point Mugu. Seven F-4Js were modified for use by the Blue Angels formation display team, but the survivors were subsequently returned to operational standard.

Point Mugu is home to much of the Navy's missile test programme. Seen at the base are a DF-4J drone controller (left) and a QF-4N drone (below).

F-4S

Spurred by the success of Bee Line, the Navy decided to follow up with a structural/avionics upgrade for the F-4J, resulting in the F-4S. The first of 248 conversions flew on 22 July 1977. Apart from the provision of digital AN/AWG-10B fire-control system and smokeless J79-GE-10B engines, the principal change was the addition of two-position leading-edge manoeuvre slats, which greatly enhanced turn performance. The last F-4S retired from Marine service (with VMF-112) in early 1992.

US Air Force
Variants

Although at first reluctant to operate an aircraft initially designed for the US Navy, the USAF was unable to ignore the outstanding capabilities offered by the Phantom. At first, USAF F-4s carried minimal modifications compared to USN machines, but the Air Force eventually developed its own highly capable variants to fulfil a multitude of roles.

RF-4C

The RF-4C was based on the airframe of the F-4C, although extra equipment reduced its internal fuel capacity. All RF-4Cs retained nuclear capability and late-service aircraft were often fitted with Sidewinders for self-defence. The F-4C's AN/APQ-72 radar was replaced by the much smaller Texas Instruments AN/APQ-99 for mapping, and terrain collision avoidance. Intended for day and night photographic reconnaissance, the RF-4C was fitted with two pairs of photoflash ejectors on the upper rear fuselage. The RF-4C could carry a single forward oblique camera, or vertical camera; behind this was a low-altitude camera although this was often replaced with a trio of vertical, left and right oblique models. A number of other cameras was employed by the RF-4C, including a giant LOROP (Long-Range Oblique Photography) example which was carried in a centreline pod. Initial plans called for the RF-4C to equip 14 squadrons, with the first activated in 1965. The first production RF-4C went to the 33rd TRTS, a training squadron, at Shaw AFB, South Carolina, on 24 September 1964. The first operational squadron, the 16th TRS at Shaw, AFB, was deemed combat-ready in August 1965 and deployed to Vietnam in October 1965. A small number of USAF and ANG RF-4Cs participated in Desert Storm. The RF-4C was in production for longer than any other variant except the F-4E. The last USAF unit was the 192nd RS, ANG, which finally retired its examples on 27 September 1995, delivering six of its RF-4Cs to Spain.

F-4C

The USAF's Specific Operational Requirement requested an aircraft based on the USN F-4B, but with added ground-attack capability and dual controls for a second pilot (in the back seat). Certain naval features were retained on the aircraft such as folding wings, catapult and arrester hooks. The General Electric J79-GE-15 turbojet engines were kept, as was the self-contained cartridge starter. US Navy high-pressure tyres were replaced with larger lower-pressure examples, and a USAF-style inflight-refuelling receptacle was installed in the dorsal spine. The rear cockpit had new consoles and the AN/APQ-72 radar of the F-4B was modified to AN/APQ-100 standard to enhance the F-4C's ground-attack capability. Provision was made for all USAF tactical stores. Some 27 F4H-1s (F-4Bs) were delivered to the 4453rd Combat Crew Training Wing at MacDill AFB, Florida, in preparation for the arrival of the F-4C, the first examples of which were passed on to the 12th TFW. The USAF's first two MiG kills of the Vietnam War were accomplished by F-4Cs, which were to bear the brunt of the fighting in the early years of the conflict. Following their withdrawal from USAF service, refurbished examples were delivered to Spain in 197172 to serve with Nos 121 and 122 Squadrons. Each squadron also operated two ex-USAF RF-4Cs. The Spanish F-4Cs were withdrawn from front-line use following the introduction of the F/A-18 Hornet.

F-4D

Although externally identical to the F-4C which preceded it into USAF service, the F-4D was, in fact, very different. It was the first purpose-designed USAF Phantom variant, incorporating all the modifications required by the USAF. Retaining the basic airframe and engines of the F-4C, the F-4D had the same fuel tankage as the RF-4C. The major differences concerned the avionics, the AN/APQ-100 radar being replaced by the smaller, lighter AN/APQ-109 as part of the AN/APA-65 radar set, which introduced an air-to-ground ranging mode. Externally, the nose remained unchanged. Delivery of F-4Ds began in March 1966, initially to the 36th TFW at Bitburg, West Germany, followed by the 4th TFW at Seymour Johnson AFB, North Carolina. The F-4Ds began replacing F-4Cs in Vietnam from the spring of 1967. The AIM-7 Sparrow capability of earlier Phantoms was retained although the AIM-9 Sidewinder was initially deleted pending the introduction of the AIM-4D Falcon AAM. Sidewinder capability was soon re-introduced, however, following the cancellation of the AIM-4D. Some 793 examples of the F-4D were delivered in total, with 36 examples going to the RoKAF (South Korea). A second customer for the type was Iran. Both Iran and South Korea retained operational F-4Ds into the 21st century, with the final 14 Iranian examples the subject of a number of local upgrade and life-extension projects .

The F-4D remained in service with AFRes units long enough to receive 'Lizard' camouflage during the late 1980s. This example served with the 89th TFS/906th TFG at Wright-Patterson AFB, Ohio.

US Air Force variants

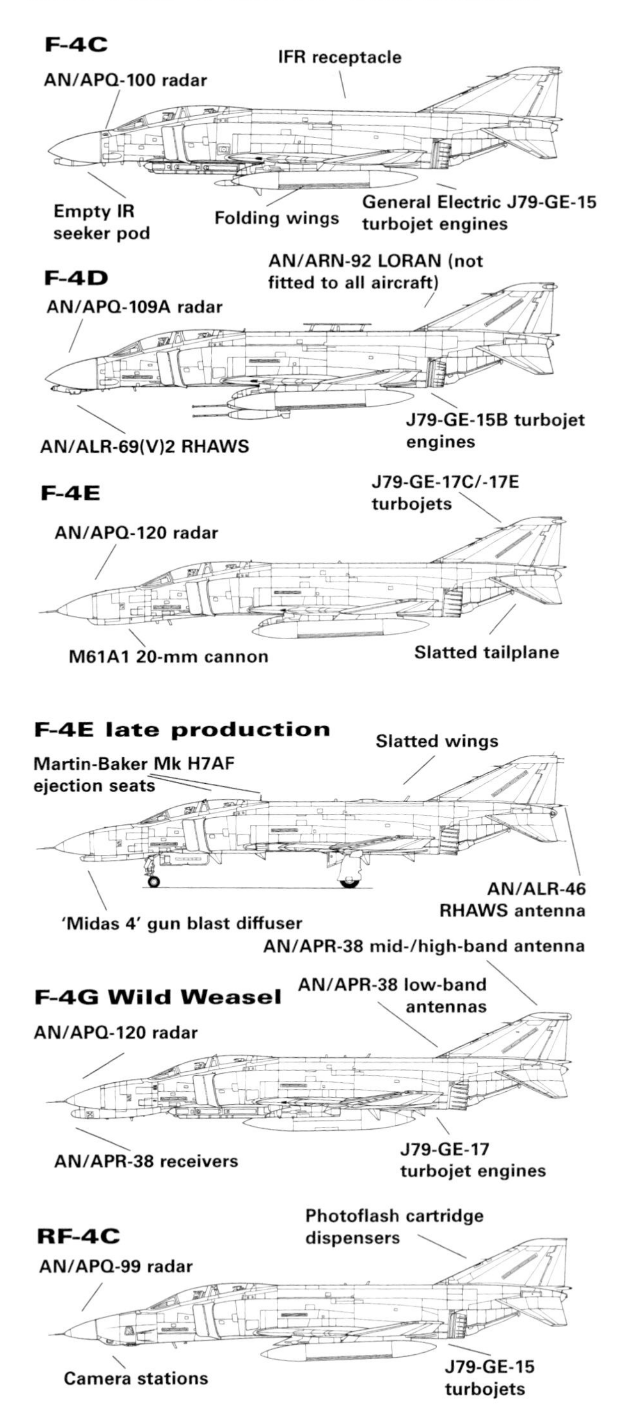

Special-purpose variants

The widespread use of the Phantom within the ranks of the USAF meant that modified examples were employed for a variety of test and evaluation duties, as well as being converted to target drones. One of the most famous test F-4s was aircraft 62-12200 (illustrated below). Built as a Navy F-4B, the aircraft was later converted to serve as the USAF RF-4C prototype. Following the completion of this trials work, 12200 was selected to serve as a fly-by-wire (FBW) control system testbed. Known as the PACT (Precision Aircraft Control Technology) demonstrator, the F-4 Phantom (FBW) made its first flight on 29 April 1972. Lead ballast was added to the rear fuselage to destabilise the aircraft in pitch and the aircraft helped to pave the way for fly-by-wire controls.

F-4E

Combat deployment of the F-4Cs and F-4Ds in southeast Asia from 1965 and May 1967, respectively, revealed shortcomings in these variants and in the very concept of a gunless fighter. Tests were carried out with an internal nose-mounted M61 cannon on an RF-4C, which at first attracted little interest. Then, McDD proposed an improved variant, the F-4E, which first flew on 30 June 1967, and entered service in 1968. It became the most numerous version built, with 1,397 examples manufactured. It was distinguishable from other variants by its internal centreline 20-mm M61A1 Vulcan cannon, with 640 rounds in an undernose fairing. A new AN/APQ-120 solid-state radar fire-control system was housed in a longer nose. Also introduced was a seventh fuselage fuel cell and slots to increase tailplane authority, while powered wing-folding was removed. Later modifications saw the introduction of a leading-edge TISEO electro-optical sensor, and full air-to-air capability was retained with AIM-7 and AIM-9 AAMs. USAF examples were finally retired in late 1992, although at the start of the 21st century the F-4E remained in front-line service with Germany (as the F-4F), Iran, South Korea and Japan.

F-4Es served with the USAF in a variety of roles. One of the most public was with the Thunderbirds Aerial Demonstration Team (right). Late model F-4Es featured slatted outer wings (below).

F-4G

Mindful of the success of the F-105G in the Wild Weasel role, the USAF decided to allocate its new F-4 to this role, also. The F-4E's cannon was deleted, and an AN/APR-38 radar and missile detection and launch homing system was installed. Westinghouse ECM underwing pods were used in conjunction with AGM-45 Shrike (later AGM-88 HARM) anti-radiation missiles for the destruction of SAM radars. All the 116 F-4Gs produced were rebuilds of existing F-4Es and, apart from the totally new avionics, the only other significant change was that made to the J79-17 engines which were modified to minimise smoke production. Self-defence weaponry was confined to a pair of AIM-7 AAMs in the rear fuselage recesses. During Desert Storm, F-4Gs played a leading part in the aerial campaign, with aircraft from the 35th TFW scything a path through Iraqi air defences with HARM missiles. Despite the succession of upgrades made to the F-4Gs in later years, the aircraft was replaced within the USAF by Block 50/52 F-16Cs.

Export variants

Based on aircraft used by the US Navy, Marines and Air Force, some Phantom variants were developed exclusively for export customers. The United Kingdom, Germany and Japan all had versions tailored to their own requirements.

Royal Air Force Phantom FGR.Mk 2 and F-4J(UK)

Following two prototype YF-4Ms, the RAF acquired 116 production-standard F-4M Phantom FGR.Mk 2s, following the cancellation of the Hawker Siddeley P.1154 V/STOL strike/attack aircraft. Phantoms entered service first in the interdiction/strike and reconnaissance roles, carrying a wide array of stores including nuclear munitions. During the mid-1970s, when the Phantom was being replaced by the SEPECAT Jaguar in the ground-attack role in RAF Germany squadrons, the aircraft in turn replaced the Lightning in the air defence role. Phantom FGR.Mk 2s served with Nos 2, 6 (the first RAF Phantom squadron), 14, 17, 19, 23, 29, 31, 41, 43, 54, 56, 64 (as a shadow squadron for 228 OCU), 74, 92 and 111 Squadrons, as well as No. 1435 Flight in the Falkland Islands. The strain on the fleet caused by basing Phantoms in the Falklands resulted in the RAF acquiring 15 surplus USN/USMC F-4Js, which served with No. 74 Sqn from August 1984 until September 1992. Only No. 56 Sqn – known as the 'Firebirds' – lasted longer, ceasing F-4 operations at the end of that year, bringing to a close RAF Phantom operations.

Luftwaffe F-4F Phantom

The F-4F was a lightweight simplified F-4E for the Luftwaffe; that service ordered 175 aircraft to bridge the gap between the F-104 Starfighter and the Tornado. Ten F-4Es were also acquired for training purposes, but remained in the US. The first F-4F was delivered on 5 September 1973, the type serving initially in two fighter-bomber wings and two interceptor wings. With the introduction of the Panavia Tornado in the early 1980s, the Phantom wings became dual-roled, but concentrated on air defence duties from 1988 onwards. In 2007, F-4Fs equipped JG 71 'Richthofen' at Wittmundhafen and JG 74 at Neuberg. The Taktische Ausbildungseinhiet Holloman in New Mexico was disbanded in late 2004.

Fleet Air Arm Phantom FG.Mk 1

Fifty F-4K Phantom FG.Mk 1s were ordered for the Royal Navy's Fleet Air Arm in July 1964. The use of Rolls-Royce Spey engines in British Phantoms dramatically increased the unit price of the aircraft and, while increasing range, decreased maximum speed, height and performance at altitude. The premature retirement of HMS *Victorious* and the prohibitive cost of refitting HMS *Eagle* left HMS *Ark Royal* as the only suitable carrier for the Phantom. Thus, half the order was diverted to the RAF, equipping No. 43 Squadron at Leuchars. In the Navy, the aircraft served with No. 700P Sqn at Yeovilton from April 1968 to March 1969 on trials work, No. 767 Sqn for type conversion during January 1969 to July 1972, also at Yeovilton, and operationally with No. 892 Sqn from March 1969, on various cruises on HMS *Ark Royal*, to the end of 1978. After 1978 the aircraft passed to the RAF and No. 111 Squadron.

Japanese Air Self Defence Force F-4EJ Phantom

The Japanese F-4EJ version was optimised for the air defence mission via deletion of the F-4E's bombing system and provision for air-to-ground ordnance. A total of 140 aircraft was received by the Japanese Air Self-Defence Force (JASDF) from the McDonnell Douglas and Mitsubishi production lines, including the very last Phantom built, 17-8440, which was handed over in May 1981. Upon entering service the aircraft joined six squadrons: the 301st to 306th Hikotai. A programme from 1990 replaced the AN/APQ-120 radar with the AN/APG-66J and extended the airframe life from 3,000 to 5,000 hours, producing the F-4EJ Kai (meaning 'extra' or 'plus'). Pending replacement by an all-new type, the F-4EJ Kai serves alongside F-15EJs in the interception role. The final F-4EJ Kai operators are the 8th Hikotai at Misawa, the 301st Hikotai at Nyutabaru, and the 302nd Hikotai at Naha.

Foreign variants

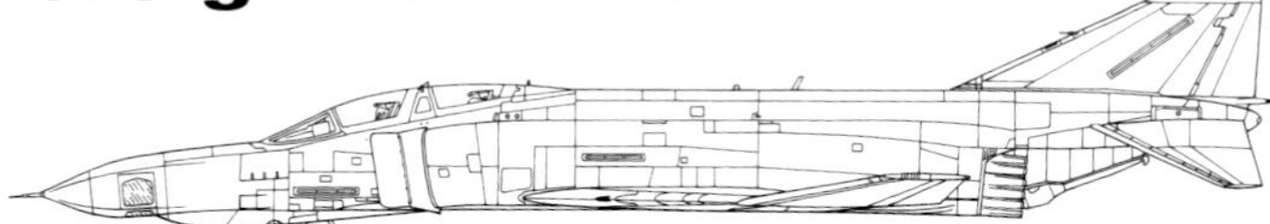

F-4E(Special) or F-4E(S)
Three Phantoms were converted to house the enormous HIAC-1 LOROP camera and passed to Israel. The nose featured slab-like sides and large camera windows.

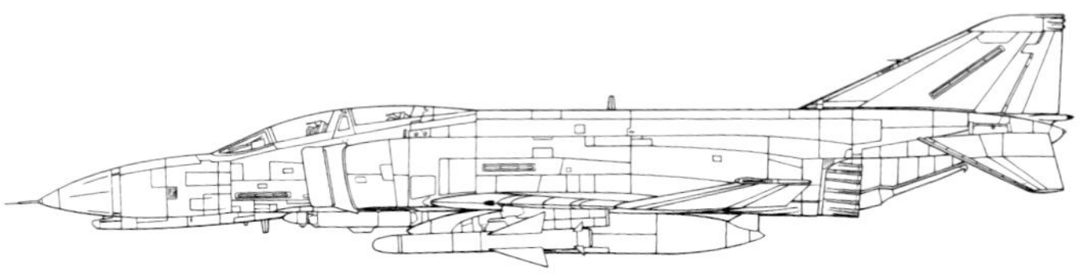

JASDF F-4EJ Kai
Almost identical to the F-4EJ, the upgraded F-4EJ Kai features tiny strengthening ribs on the outside of the radome, which houses the new AN/APG-66 radar.

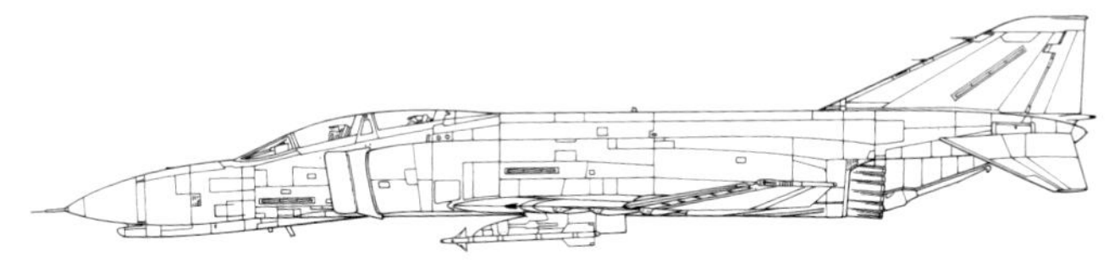

Luftwaffe F-4F
Differences between the F-4E and the German F-4F are not readily noticeable on the exterior of the aircraft, which was lighter and lacked Sparrow missile equipment.

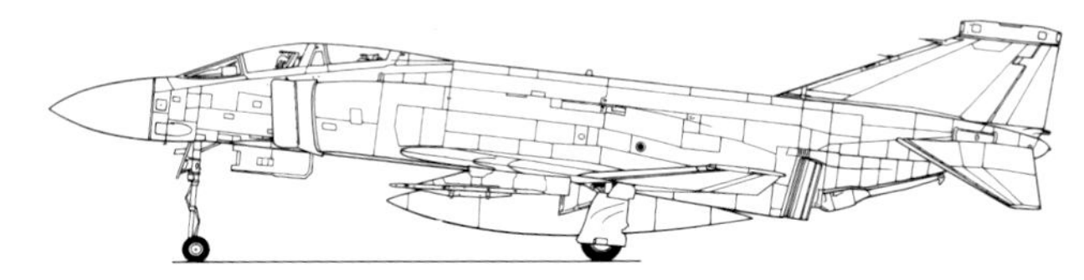

FAA carrier-compatible F-4K Phantom FG.Mk 1
Based on the F-4J, the F-4K had a folding radar and radome, extended nose wheel leg, a strengthened arrester hook and Spey 202/203 engines installed.

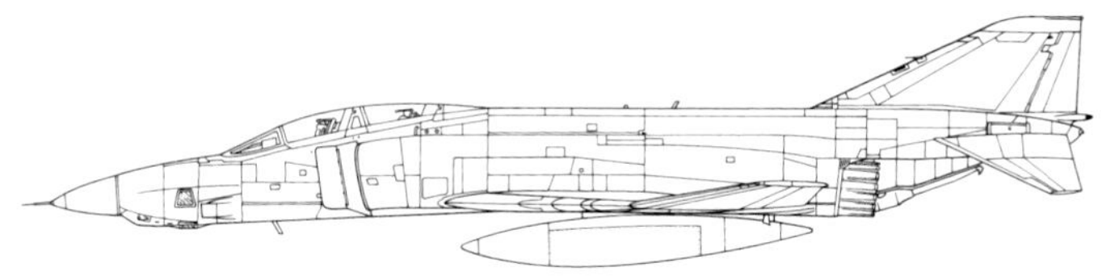

International Export RF-4E
The RF-4E mated the airframe and J79-GE-17 engines of the original (unslatted) F-4E with the RF-4C's nose. This Luftwaffe RF-4E has a SLAR in the fuel tank body.

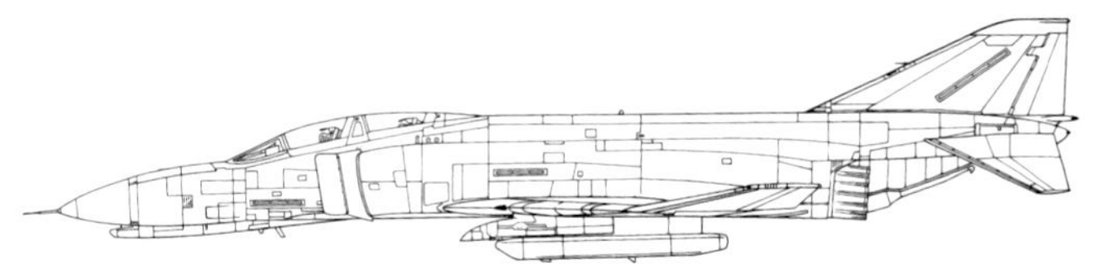

JASDF RF-4EJ Kai (converted F-4EJ)
The nose of the F-4EJ converted to the reconnaissance role looks very different to that of aircraft originally built as RF-4EJs (see photograph at bottom of this page).

Export Reconnaissance Phantoms

First flown on 15 September 1970, the RF-4E was produced to a German specification for an RF-84F replacement. First introduced into service with AG 51 at Bremgarten, followed by AG 52 at Leck, a total of 88 aircraft were produced for the Luftwaffe. They were given a ground-attack capability from 1978 onwards, which they maintained until 1988. Four other nations also acquired RF-4Es from the production line, of which Iran was the second largest customer. A total of 27 aircraft were delivered to Iran prior to the Islamic revolution; 11 others were withheld. It is thought that most of the surviving RF-4Es in Iran were cannibalised for spares to keep the 'fighting Phantoms' airworthy. Israel received six RF-4Es and three RF-4E(S)s equipped with the HIAC-1 camera, requiring modified nose contours. Eight and six FY 1977 aircraft were delivered to Turkey and Greece, respectively. Surviving Turkish RF-4Es, new-built and ex-Luftwaffe, fly with 113 Filo at Eskisehir, while the Greek aircraft fly with 348 MTA at Lárisa.

Japanese Reconnaissance Phantoms

Most Japanese Phantoms were built by Mitsubishi, but all the original reconnaissance-tasked RF-4EJs were assembled by McDonnell Douglas. Fourteen aircraft were produced and they differ from USAF RF-4Cs only in the deletion of some US-supplied electronics and replacement by Japanese equipment. All aircraft equipped the 501st Hikotai at Hyakuri following delivery. After being upgraded in the early 1990s, RF-4EJs were designated RF-4EJ Kais. At least two of the original batch have been lost in accidents. A shortfall in reconnaissance assets was subsequently overcome by the conversion of 17 F-4EJs to RF-4EJ Kai standard. The converted aircraft retain a limited combat capability, including the internal gun, and have no structural modifications. RF-4Es were delivered in a pale (gull) grey but later received a striking brown and two-tone green camouflage scheme. Surviving aircraft remain with the original operator, the 501st Hikotai at Hyakuri, alongside F-15J/DJs.

The second Atlantic Fleet deployable squadron to receive F-4Bs was VF-102 'Diamondbacks'. Here three of its aircraft are seen aboard USS *Independence*.

US operators

Once the backbone of the US Navy and USAF, Phantoms served in every theatre, fulfilling the roles of fighter, bomber and reconnaissance platform. Having provided sterling service during the air war over Vietnam, in the twilight of their career F-4s undertook one further war in the Persian Gulf.

The Phantom was first deployed aboard a carrier in February 1962, when F4H-1s of VF-102 operated from USS *Enterprise*. At the time of the Gulf of Tonkin incident in August 1964, 13 of 31 Navy-deployable fighter squadrons were equipped with F-4Bs, one had a mix of F-4Bs and F-4Gs, and one was converting to F-4Bs. In addition, two RAG squadrons flew a mix of F-4As and F-4Bs.

During the war in southeast Asia, 22 Navy squadrons and a Marine squadron made 84 war cruises to the Gulf of Tonkin (including 51 with F-4Bs, one with F-4Gs and 32 with F-4Js). They claimed 41 confirmed aerial kills, but 71 of their F-4s were lost in combat (five to enemy aircraft, 13 to SAMs and 53 to AAA) and 54 were lost in operational accidents during wartime deployments.

By the time US combat operations in southeast Asia ended, Tomcats had begun supplementing F-4s in deployable squadrons. The process continued until the end of 1983, when VF-21 and VF-154 became the last squadrons to trade F-4Ns for F-14As. Finally, the last two deployable squadrons, VF-151 and VF-161, transitioned from the F-4S to the F/A-18A in 1986.

With reserve units, F-4Bs were first assigned in the spring of 1969 to VF-22L1, a squadron belonging to the Naval Air Reserve Training Command. However, VF-22L1 only had a brief existence as the Naval Air Reserve was reorganised in April 1970. Phantoms were then operated by four reserve squadrons, with the last F-4s being those of VF-202, which transitioned from the F-4S to the F-14A in 1987.

The Marine Corps received its first F4H-1s in June 1962, when VMF(AW)-314 transitioned. USMC

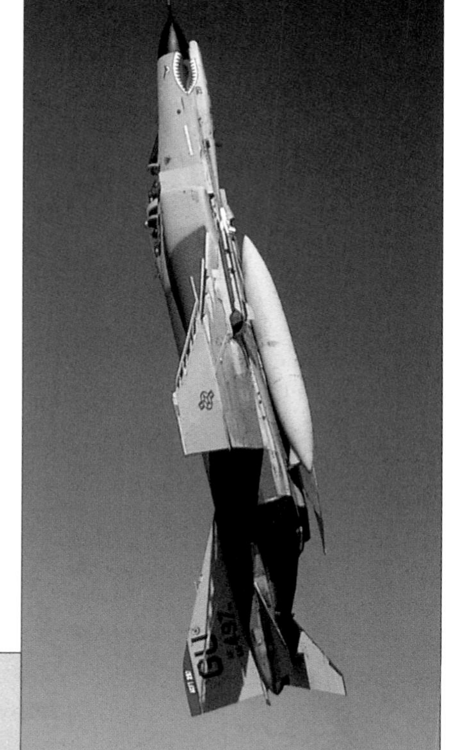

*Right: Illustrated here in the final colour scheme utilised by the **USAF**, the **F-4E** was the definitive fighter **Phantom**. At the request of pilots, the **F-4E** carried an **M61A1 20-mm cannon** in a fairing under the nose.*

VF-114 'Aardvarks' claimed the distinction of being the first deployable Pacific Fleet Phantom squadron in 1962 and subsequently converted to the F-4J (pictured) in 1970.

RF-4Bs served with three composite squadrons and a reconnaissance squadron, and fighter versions (F-4B, F-4J, F-4N and F-4S) equipped 15 fighter attack squadrons, two training units and four reserve squadrons.

Beginning in April 1965, when F-4Bs landed at Da Nang, Marine Phantoms took an active part in the Vietnam War from bases in Vietnam and Thailand and from the deck of the USS *America*. Seventy-two fighters and three RF-4Bs were lost in combat, and four other USMC Phantoms were lost in operational accidents.

Post-Vietnam, Phantoms remained the only fighters in service with the Fleet Marine Force (FMF) until the advent of the F/A-18 Hornet in 1983. The 12 FMF squadrons went on regular six-month rotational deployments to Japan and made a few carrier deployments.

The last active-duty USMC Phantom unit was the Hawaii-based VMFA-235 'Death Angels', which transitioned to the F/A-18A Hornet in 1989. On 18 January 1992 a ceremony at NAS Dallas, which marked the retirement of the F-4S by reserve unit VMFA-112 'Cowboys', also meant that the F-4 had passed from the US Sea Service inventory, after almost 32 years of service.

USAF service

Few aircraft have made such an impact on the USAF's inventory as the Phantom. First delivered to TAC on 24 January 1962, under the designation F-110A (the designation was later changed to F-4C), the two initial aircraft were, in fact, borrowed Navy F4H-1s.

Phantoms became the backbone of USAF strike operations over Vietnam, fulfilling both air-to-air and air-to-ground roles. This F-4D is armed with GBU-10 Paveway laser-guided bombs. Such weapons were used to destroy the Paul Doumer bridge, a main supply route for the NVA.

The desire to quickly put the Phantom into front-line service with USAF squadrons saw that a further 29 Navy F-4Bs were borrowed pending the delivery of the USAF's own F-4Cs. Two wings (the 12th and 15th TFWs) were quickly established, being equipped at Macdill AFB, Florida.

USAF Phantoms had been in service for little more than two years when F-4Cs of the 555th TFS deployed to Naha AB, Okinawa, in December 1964 in response to the escalating war in Vietnam. While carrier-based Navy F-4s were already engaged in combat operations against North Vietnam, USAF examples mainly undertook interdiction missions in the early years of the campaign.

Following steady improvements to the aircraft, a purpose-built USAF model entered service in March 1966. Although externally almost identical to the F-4C, the D model incorporated all the specific modifications required by the USAF. The D began replacing the C over Vietnam from spring 1967.

The Phantom became a legend during its combat service in Vietnam. Typical USAF strike missions often saw photo-equipped RF-4Cs flying pre-strike recce sorties, prior to F-4C/Ds attacking the target under a protective umbrella of CAP F-4Ds. Following the attack, post-strike reconnaissance would be performed by the same RF-4Cs. USAF pilots accomplished a highly distinguished combat record with the aircraft. By far the greatest USAF F-4 pilot in terms of MiG kills was Capt. Steve Ritchie, who downed four MiG-21s.

In Europe, the Phantom was again to prove how vital an aircraft it was within the USAF. No fewer than six wings were equipped with the aircraft, which served through to 1994 when the final F-4Gs were withdrawn at Spangdahlem AB, Germany.

A major change in the structure of the Air National Guard and Air Force Reserve in the 1970s resulted in new-build Phantoms reaching the Reserve. The first unit was the 170th TFS/183rd TFG at Springfield, Illinois, with F-4Cs.

Towards the end of their career, F-4s were in action again, with F-4Gs of the 35th and 52nd TFWs in combat over the deserts of Iraq in 1991. Other Phantom variants in the conflict were the RF-4Cs of the Alabama ANG. This was, however, to be the last war for the USAF Phantom which, after its return, was steadily withdrawn from service.

By the mid-1990s there were few US Phantom operators remaining. RF-4Cs of the 192nd RS, ANG, were finally retired on 27 September 1995, while those F-4Gs serving with the 190th FS were withdrawn from service in early 1996.

A pair of F-4Bs of VMFA-513 'Flying Nightmares' demonstrate the type's prodigious load-carrying ability shortly after entering service with the squadron in 1963.

Above: An F-4F of the Luftwaffe's Jagdbombergeschwader (JBG) 35, with high-conspicuity Dayglo orange panels applied over the basic early grey and green camouflage scheme.

Left: Like its contemporary, the Buccaneer, the McDonnell Douglas F-4 Phantom II was an aircraft which the RAF originally did not want; rather, it was foisted on the service by political events. However, it went on to be the stalwart of the air force for over 20 years, respected by its crews and foes alike for its exceptional weapon system, good performance and undeniable strength.

Export operators

Although it was perhaps considered most important in Britain, Germany and Japan, the Phantom was also purchased on a large scale to fulfil a multitude of roles with other countries. Iran and Israel took their F-4s into combat, adding to the reputation already forged by the aircraft with US forces over Vietnam.

The Royal Navy became the Phantom's first overseas customer as the result of not being able to agree with the RAF on a joint specification for the proposed P.1154 V/STOL strike/attack aircraft. The RN therefore decided to order the F-4K and the first examples arrived at Yeovilton in April 1968. The aircraft were designated FG.Mk 1 and they went on to equip three units. The Phantoms had a relatively short career with the Royal Navy, serving until 1978, when the surviving examples were transferred to the Royal Air Force.

With the cancellation of the P.1154, the RAF followed the RN's example by purchasing the F-4. McDonnell proposed the F-4M for RAF service and, in 1965, it was announced that the RAF would purchase 200 of what it would name the Phantom FGR.Mk 2. However, this figure would be reduced to 150, of which the final 32 examples were not taken up.

The first RAF Phantom arrived in Britain in 1968, with the type entering operational service the following year. Early squadrons were initially based in the UK, but the main concentration of Phantoms was in RAF Germany.

A change in tasking began in spring 1974, when No. 54 Squadron re-equipped with Jaguars and passed its Phantoms to No. 111 for air defence. Further Germany-based squadrons began to adopt the Jaguar, and the change to air defence for the Phantom was accompanied by the addition of RWRs and Medium Sea Grey camouflage.

Phantom ranks were thinned in the late 1980s by the conversion of squadrons to the Tornado F.Mk 3. In 1991 BAe performed the last Phantom overhaul while, in the second half of the year, RAF Germany said goodbye to its air defence Phantoms.

Luftwaffe service

West Germany became a major Phantom operator. The initial two wings to be equipped were reconnaissance units, which received RF-4Es from 1971. The Luftwaffe then purchased 175 F-4Fs, with the first unit being declared combat-ready in May 1976. These aircraft were originally segregated into two fighter-bomber wings and two interceptor wings, but with the full service entry of the Tornado, they concentrated solely on air defence duties from 1988.

Luftwaffe Phantoms were subject to a series of upgrades, the most significant being the ICE (Improved Combat Efficiency), conferring BVR look-down/shoot-down capabilities. This programme was completed between 1983 and 1997, and will enable the Luftwaffe's F-4Fs to remain in service until 2012.

The Japanese Air Self-Defence Force acquired its first F-4EJs in July 1971. These aircraft were US-built, but from May 1972, Mitsubishi built the Phantom itself. In addition, 14 RF-4EJs were supplied from US production, their delivery taking place between 1974 and 1975. Originally, six squadrons of the Air Defence Command received F-4EJs within the Northern, Central and Western Air Defence Forces, plus the Southwest Composite Air Wing.

In later years, the F-4EJ was supplemented and then gradually replaced by the F-15J, also built by Mitsubishi. Today there are only three F-4EJ units. RF-4s provide the JASDF with its only tactical reconnaissance ability and a mixture of RF-4Es and RF-4EJs is operated.

A reluctant and short-term Phantom operator, the RAAF leased 24 USAF F-4Es and RF-4Es when its acquisition of 24 F-111Cs went seriously awry. As an interim measure, Australia's

***Left:* Israeli Phantoms gave invaluable service. Only at the end of the 1990s did the last F-4E-2000 upgraded airframes begin to be retired in favour of the F-15I Ra'am.**

***Below:* Greece received eight RF-4Es between June 1978 and April 1979. Five surviving aircraft from this original order served on until 1992, when they were replaced by 29 ex-Luftwaffe RF-4Es. One of the original aircraft is illustrated.**

factory-fresh Phantoms were leased, with the first five aircraft arriving at in September 1970. The Phantoms served with two squadrons, undertaking air interception and ground attack duties. After work on the F-111 recommenced in December 1971, the F-4s were returned to the US, from October 1972.

Middle East Phantoms

As a result of a major switch in political leaning from Moscow to the US in the late 1970s, Egypt was supplied with 35 ex-USAF F-4Es. Delivered under the codename Peace Pharaoh, the first 18 aircraft arrived in Egypt in September 1979. Operating with two squadrons at Cairo West, the Phantoms were flown back to the US in 1982 for a major overhaul. Upon their return to Cairo West, serviceability still remained poor but the Phantoms were given one last chance in mid-1983 when a US-led maintenance team boosted serviceability to 80 per cent. In 1983 the remaining 33 Phantoms were supplemented by an additional seven aircraft, to bring the Egyptian F-4 fleet to a total of 40 aircraft.

Iran ordered 32 F-4Ds in 1966 and these entered service with two interceptor squadrons at Mehrabad in 1968. Four years later, orders for a total of 177 F-4Es and 28 RF-4Es were placed, deliveries occurring between 1974 and 1977. Iran had now become the second-largest overseas operator of the type. A further eight squadrons were equipped, but, following the Islamic revolution, technical support for the F-4 fleet was halted. Despite attrition during the long-running war with Iraq, local upgrading has improved radar detection range and added several new weapons.

Israeli Phantoms were the most battle-proven of any export operator. First delivered in 1969, the aircraft were soon undertaking combat missions. By 1973 around 180 F-4Es and 12 RF-4Es had been delivered for service with six squadrons – over 33 Phantoms were lost during the 1973 war. Israel undertook extensive refurbishment of its fleet and also received further deliveries of new-build and ex-USAF aircraft between 1974 and 1976. In the mid-1980s, the IDF/AF instigated an ambitious programme to upgrade 130 of its F-4E and RF-4E aircraft, adding airframe reinforcements, new avionics and multi-mode radar.

Greece maintained five Phantom squadrons, originally supplied with both new production and second-hand aircraft. The aircraft were first acquired in 1974 under a 36-aircraft contract for F-4Es, codenamed Peace Icarus. Greek acquisitions continued with a subsequent order for 18 F-4Es and eight RF-4Es for delivery between 1978 and 1979. A further 28 F-4Es were delivered during late 1991. A total of 70 F-4Es underwent a local Service-Life Extension Programme (SLEP) and were then upgraded to a similar standard as the F-4F ICE.

A batch of 36 second-hand F-4Cs was first delivered to Spain under the Mutual Defence Aid Program. Designated C.12 in Spanish service, the F-4 entered service in 1971. As the F/A-18 arrived, withdrawal of the F-4C began in 1979. However, eight ex-USAF RF-4Cs were delivered in January 1988 and currently serve in the reconnaissance role.

Turkey's first batch of 40 F-4Es was received in 1973. A follow-on order in 1977 comprised 32 more F-4Es and eight RF-4Es. Several batches of former USAF F-4Es were subsequently obtained. A two-part IAI upgrade programme has provided structural upgrading and the fitting of a new avionics. IAI upgraded 26 F-4Es in Israel and supplied kits for another 28 F-4Es, for local upgrading.

Far East service

The Republic of Korea Air Force ordered an initial 18 F-4Ds in 1968. The first six arrived in Seoul in August 1969. A further 18 F-4Ds arrived in 1972. Deliveries during 1987/88 added a further 24 examples to the RoKAF fleet. In common with most operators, South Korea enhanced its fleet with the F-4E in 1978. The 37 F-4Es delivered were all new-build examples and were acquired alongside 12 RF-4Cs.

F-4EJ Kai

The 306th Hikotai at Komatsu was the last Japanese Phantom unit to re-equip with the F-4EJ Kai, receiving its 22 aircraft between August 1989 and March 1991. This aircraft was painted up to commemorate the unit's 10th anniversary on 30 June 1991. The unit has since been re-equipped with the F-15J.

Conversion programme
Ninety-six of Japan's surviving 125 F-4EJs were converted to F-4EJ Kai configuration and 17 more were converted to recce duties. The F-4EJ Kai prototype made its maiden flight on 17 July 1984 and full conversions began to be redelivered from 24 November 1990.

McDonnell Douglas (Boeing) F-15 Eagle

US superfighter

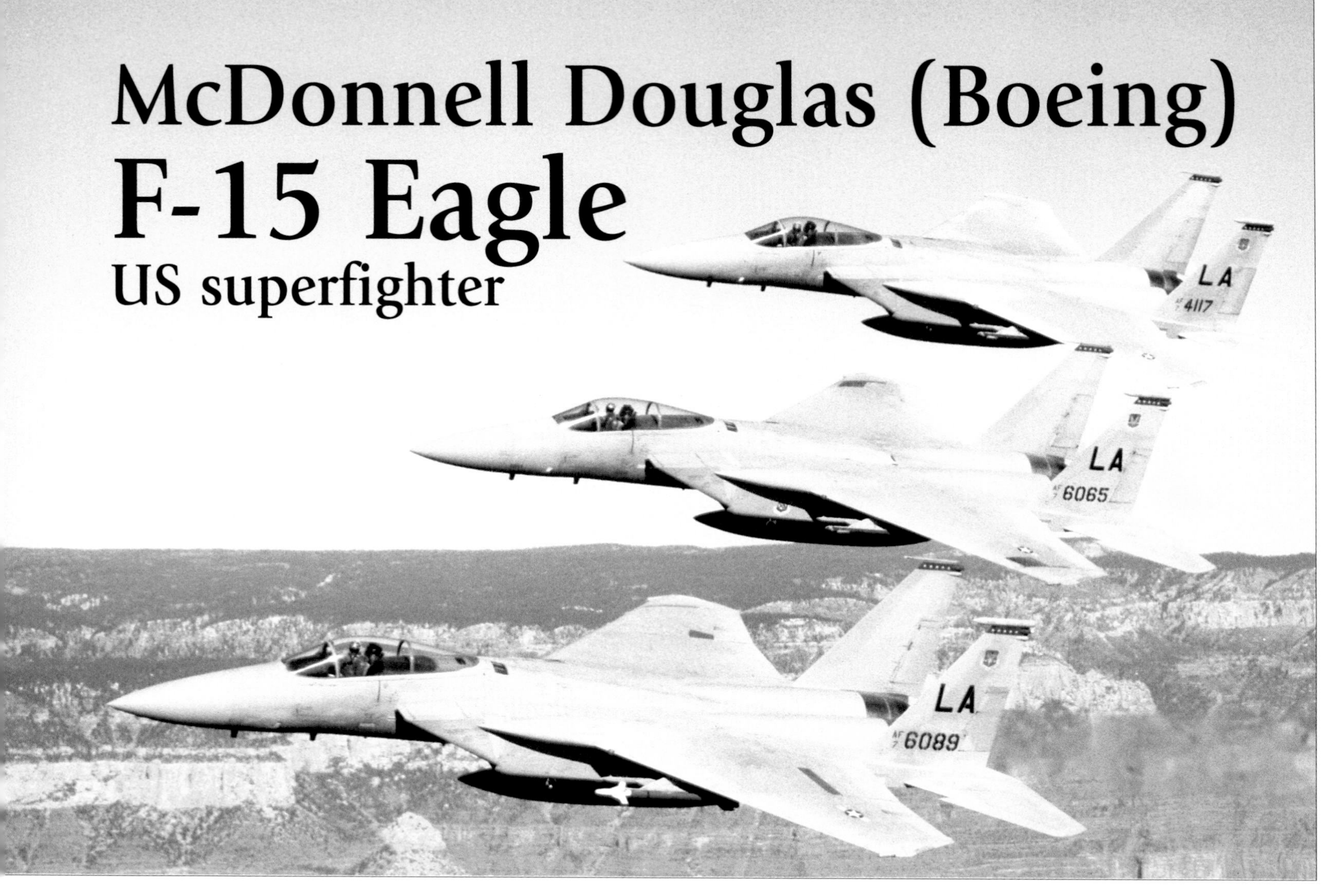

Based at Luke AFB, Arizona, with access to large tracts of relatively empty airspace, the 58th Tactical Training Wing was the first recipient of the F-15. Renumbered as the 405th TTW in August 1979, the unit continued to train F-15A/B crews until 1988.

Developed as a fighter with a wide margin of performance and technological superiority over its rivals, the F-15 held the position of being the world's premier fighter for more than 20 years. It has also been developed into a successful strike platform.

The history of the F-15 dates back to the late 1960s, when a far-reaching specification known as F-X was laid down by the US Air Force. This, in essence, required the basic F-4 weapons load (four Sparrows, four Sidewinders plus a 20-mm Vulcan cannon) to be repackaged into an aircraft optimised for air combat. The eventual result was the F-15 Eagle, which marked a major advance in virtually all areas.

Range and manoeuvrability were markedly improved, while the aircraft's AN/APG-63 radar ushered in a new era of look-down/shoot-down capability. The cockpit was designed to enable the single pilot to extract the maximum fighting capability from the impressive systems, utilising then-novel concepts such as a head-up display and HOTAS controls. The airframe was stressed for sustained high-*g* turning, while the F100 turbofans were fuel-efficient yet awesomely powerful. From the F-15C/D model onwards, the pilot could in theory also slam the throttles from idle to full without fear of compressor stall (although, in reality, the F100 proved very troublesome in the early days of the F-15). Similarly, the F-15 had a 'carefree' handling system which automatically limited control inputs from the pilot at the outer edges of the flight envelope to prevent departures.

Reaching service status in November 1974, the F-15A (and the equivalent F-15B two-seater) immediately demonstrated a dramatic improvement in combat power over the F-4E Phantom which was, at the time, the USAF's mainstream fighter. In January 1976 the 1st TFW became the first front-line unit to be declared operational. Other USAF units swiftly followed, both at home and overseas.

Multi-role fighter

In USAF service the F-15's repertoire was rapidly expanded to embrace all areas of the fighter role. Its rapid-reaction time, excellent radar and high speed/climb performance allowed it to perform the dedicated interceptor role with ease, and F-15s stood 'Zulu' ground alert in Korea and West Germany, as well as back home. Occupying most F-15s was, and is, the air superiority role, flying sweep, CAP and escort roles.

Israel became the first export customer for the F-15, receiving its first aircraft in December 1976. Israeli F-15A/Bs (locally named Baz) were soon in action against Syrian aircraft, achieving several successes. In 1982 Israeli Eagles scored around 40 kills for no loss during the hectic air fighting against Syrian MiGs over the Beka'a Valley.

Continuing development of the Eagle saw the introduction of the F-15C/D in 1980, initial deliveries of which went to units in West Germany and Okinawa. The C/D introduced several new features,

***Left:* The shortest-lived Eagle operator was the 5th FIS 'Spittin' Kittens', which was tasked with CONUS air defence missions from Minot AFB, North Dakota, from April 1985 to July 1988. The first three CONUS-based F-15 interceptor units had previously flown Convair F-106 Delta Darts.**

***Below:* The strategic importance of Alaska was emphasised by the equipment of a single squadron (43rd TFS) of the 21st Composite Wing with F-15A/Bs.**

Problems were initially encountered with the Eagle's Pratt & Whitney F100-PW-100 engine, and the X-band Hughes AN/APG-63 coherent pulse-Doppler radar, both of which had been designed specifically for the F-15. These were overcome during the early part of the Eagle's service career.

The F-15A has a sophisticated avionics system, with the main radar being supplemented by an AN/ALR-56 RWR, and an AN/ALQ-128 EW warning system. These are backed up by an AN/ALQ-135 countermeasures set. Lessons learned in Vietnam proved that good pilot visibility was essential, and to this end the F-15 pilot sits high up and well forward on an ACES II ejection seat (replacing the earlier McDonnell Douglas Escapac IC-7) under a blown canopy, with excellent all-round view. The cockpit itself is well laid out, but is equipped only with analogue instruments, with no CRT multi-function displays. A HUD and a variety of control-column and throttle-mounted controls give hands-on throttle and stick (HOTAS) operation of all important systems. The Eagle was designed to fight primarily in the HOTAS mode, the pilot receiving all necessary information from his HUD and being able to cue his or her weapons system without having to look down into the cockpit.

Developed alongside the 'A' model was the TF-15A two-seat trainer. It is fully mission capable, but lacks the AN/ALQ-135 ECM and is 800 lb (364 kg) heavier than the single-seater. In 1978 the TF-15A was re-designated as the F-15B in recognition of its combat-capable status.

Enhanced Eagles

In the 1990s, with relatively few 'new-build' aircraft being ordered apart from the F-22 Raptor, the USAF began improving its F-15A/B fighters through a Multi-Stage Improvement Program (MSIP). This programme replaced the troublesome F100-PW-100 turbofans with the slightly less powerful but more reliable -220 engines of all but the earliest production F-15Cs. It also includes new avionics and digital central computers which replace the original analogue computers.

F-15A/B Eagles emerging from the MSIP differ visually from F-15C/D models by lacking the radar warning receiver antenna located next to the horizontal stabiliser. They also lack the 2,000 lb (907 kg) of extra fuel carried by the F-15C. MSIP F-15A/B aircraft replaced non-MSIP F-15C/D models beginning with the 32nd TFS in 1992.

Home Guard

As the Eagle entered service with front-line USAF units, seven ANG units started to receive F-15A/B models, the first being the 199th FIS, Hickam AFB, Hawaii, which replaced its F-4C Phantoms in the summer of 1987. Following the introduction of the improved F-15C into regular USAF units further ANG units went on to receive early Eagle variants, signifying the final withdrawal of the F-4 Phantom from the interceptor role with the US Air Force.

After replacement in the front line by F-15C/Ds, F-15A/Bs were 'cascaded' to Air National Guard units such as the 122nd Tactical Fighter Squadron, Louisiana ANG, as illustrated here.

F-15C/D: Improved Eagle

Above: The F-15Cs of the 18th Fighter Wing, USAF, at Kadena AB, Japan, periodically stand alert duty in Korea, as a result of the Okinawa-based unit's proximity to the strategically important Korean peninsula.

In order for the F-15 to retain its mantle of 'the world's premier fighter', McDonnell Douglas began work on a second-generation design, which would measurably improve the Eagle's performance.

All areas of the F-15 design were looked at and improved where necessary, although the resulting F-15C/D is externally similar to the preceding F-15A/B. Internal space was found for an additional 2,000 lb (907 kg) of fuel, while the F-15C/D was the first operational model to be able to carry conformal fuel tanks (CFTs). The ability to carry a load of over 43,000 lb (19505 kg) of fuel meant that the Eagle could self-deploy to an air base in the Persian Gulf, with either two stops or inflight refuellings.

The first F-15C flew on 26 February 1979, followed by the first F-15D two-seater on 19 June. Initial production C/Ds were powered by the same F100-PW-100 engines which had powered the A/B, but from November 1985 the considerably more reliable F100-PW-220 was introduced.

Avionics systems were also improved, the first F-15C/Ds emerging with the improved AN/APG-63PSP (programmable signal processor) radar and better ECM equipment. From 1989 the AN/APG-70 radar (a much-modified AN/APG-63) was incorporated. Using the same antenna, the AN/APG-70 had new signal processor systems nearly five times quicker than those of the AN/APG-63, while able to handle much larger volumes. C- and D-model Eagles were rapidly delivered to front-line fighter units around the world, and by the time the last of the second-generation F-15s had been delivered to the USAF, some 408 F-15Cs and 62 F-15Ds had been produced.

A Bitburg-based F-15C of the 36th TFW suffers a 'flame out' during a take-off in June 1989. During Operation Desert Storm, the wing deployed its 53rd TFS to Saudi Arabia and its 525th TFS to Turkey.

Middle East Eagles

When the American C/D-model Eagles came on the scene, Israel was already interested in a further F-15 procurement. Project Peace Fox III delivered 18 F-15Cs and eight F-15Ds from the FY1980 and 1983 Eagle production runs. In IDF/AF service, the F-15C/D acquired the name Akef (buzzard). Later, five additional F-15Ds were delivered from FY90 production under Peace Fox IV, these probably being based on the F-15E airframe rather than the F-15D, as the latter was no longer in production. The aircraft were delivered to the IDF/AF's No. 106 Squadron, alongside the A/B-equipped No. 133 Squadron at Tel Nof. Like the earlier A/B models, they are equipped with locally produced EW equipment. Weapons include the Python series of AAMs, which have largely replaced the AIM-9.

Front-line Japanese Eagles wear a standard air superiority camouflage, consisting of two shades of grey. The first half of the six-digit serial system corresponds to the procurement year (5: 1985), aircraft class (2: twin-engined), and basic role (8: all-weather fighter); the last three digits refer to the individual aircraft number in sequence.

***Right:** The **F-15** is a big fighter by any standards, but this size is emphasised when compared to the **RAF's** diminutive **Hawk**. The 'tennis court' wing is lightly loaded, combining with a high thrust-to-weight ratio to provide good manoeuvrability.*

*Israel's **F-15C/D Akefs** were initially operated by **No. 106 Squadron** at **Tel Nof**. This aircraft combines a **Python 3** on the outer launch rail with an **AIM-9** on the inner. Locally built **EW** technology replaces some equipment, including the **ALQ-128 RWR**.*

In the 1970s, the Royal Saudi Air Force (RSAF) began to consider procuring an interceptor to replace its BAC Lightnings. The details of the Eagle purchase became part of the contents of the Camp David Peace Accords between Israel, Egypt and the US, stating that only 60 of the Eagle airframes would be allowed on Saudi territory at any time. Since the RSAF order was for 62 C/D-model F-15s, two were to be held back as attrition replacements.

Procured under Project Peace Sun, the initial RSAF F-15s were ordered from the FY80 and 81 production runs. In 1991, a further order of 12 attrition aircraft was contracted under Peace Sun VI, and these were delivered from February 1992. They quickly showed their teeth when, on 5 June 1984, two RSAF F-15s shot down a pair of Iranian F-4s over the Persian Gulf. By 1990 three RSAF Eagle squadrons were in service: No. 5 at Taif, No. 6 at Khamis Mushait and No. 13 at Dhahran. By this time, the restriction of only allowing 60 RSAF F-15s had been dropped, and two dozen additional F-15Cs and F-15Ds were rushed to the RSAF during the 1990/91 Persian Gulf crisis, forming No. 42 Squadron at Dhahran. During the Gulf War, the RSAF's finest moment came when a pair of Eagles shot down a pair of Exocet-carrying Iraqi Mirage F1s.

F-15J/DJ

The second overseas customer for the Eagle was the Japanese Air Self-Defence Force (JASDF), which evaluated the F-15 in 1975. The JASDF versions of the Eagle (the F-15J is the single-seat version, and the F-15DJ a two-seat fighter trainer) were co-produced by Mitsubishi, but were functionally almost identical to early-production C/Ds in USAF service. Initially, the procurement, run under Project Peace Eagle, was for 123 aircraft, but by early 1998 totalled 213 (169 F-15Js and 44 F-15DJs).

Initial F-15J production was undertaken at St Louis, where two aircraft were built, the first undertaking its maiden flight in June 1980. The next eight F-15Js were supplied to Mitsubishi as kits for final assembly in Japan, the first of these flying on 26 August 1981. Subsequent F-15J production was by Mitsubishi. All F-15DJ production from FY1988 onwards was by Mitsubishi (this coincided with MDC production conversion to the F-15E). F-15Js began entering service (with 202 Hikotai) in 1981.

The JASDF has conducted a major mid-life upgrade of the F-15J/DJ fleet. This includes installation of F100-IHI-220E engines (licence-produced versions of the F100-PW-220) and an upgraded radar designated AN/APG-63U. In addition, the indigenously-designed AAM-4 air-to-air missile has been incorporated.

*The **F-15's** cockpit was designed to minimise the amount of time the pilot had to spend with his or her 'head down' during combat. Consequently, the cockpit is dominated by a large head-up display, presenting the pilot with vital combat information.*

F-15 strike variants

Turning the West's best air-to-air fighter into a nocturnal mud-mover was an idea opposed by many. However, today's F-15E and its successors are without doubt the most capable strike/attack platforms in the world, while retaining the Eagle's air combat prowess.

All F-15s were built with air-to-ground capability, and wired for the carriage of air-to-ground ordnance. They were originally intended as dual-role aircraft, but the planned ground-attack role was abandoned in 1975.

Trials of an air-to-ground F-15 began during 1982, when McDonnell Douglas modified the second TF-15A as the 'Strike Eagle', funding the project itself. The aircraft was conceived as an ETF (Enhanced Tactical Fighter) replacement for the F-111 and was chosen in preference to the F-16XL Fighting Falcon. The 'Strike Eagle' demonstrator was joined by an F-15C and F-15D, which conducted trials with a variety of fuel and ordnance loads, usually with conformal fuel tanks (CFTs) fitted. The resulting F-15E was given the go-ahead on 24 February 1984 and the first production aircraft made its maiden flight on 11 December 1986. McDonnell's 'Strike Eagle' name was not officially adopted.

Above: For many years an F-4E user, the 4th Wing at Seymour Johnson, North Carolina became the premier F-15E operator, with four squadrons assigned. These examples are from the 335th FS 'Chiefs'. The squadron undertook strike missions over Iraq during Operation Desert Storm in 1991.

Right: The F-15 is potentially the most capable warrior over the battlefield. However, to use the F-15E and its systems to the full requires not only thorough instruction and practice, but also close co-ordination between the two cockpits.

In Strike Eagle guise, McDonnell Douglas's two-seat F-15B demonstrator, 71-0291, was an awesome aircraft. It is illustrated with a full load of Mk 7 Rockeye CBUs on its wing and fuselage pylons.

In introducing new avionics and equipment for a 'mud-moving' role not assigned to earlier variants, the F-15E is very much a second-generation Eagle. The aircraft introduced redesigned controls, a wide field of vision HUD, and three CRTs providing multi-purpose displays of navigation, weapons delivery and systems operation. The rear-cockpit WSO employs four multi-purpose CRT terminals for radar, weapons selection and the monitoring of enemy tracking systems. The WSO also operates an AN/APG-70 synthetic aperture radar and LANTIRN navigation and targeting pods. The navigation pod incorporates its own terrain-following radar, which can be linked to the aircraft's flight control system to allow automatic coupled terrain-following flight. The targeting pod allows the aircraft to self-designate GBU-10 and GBU-24 LGBs. Basic flight controls are provided for the WSO and the crew sit on ACES II zero-zero ejection seats.

Power for the new variant was initially provided by F100-PW-220 turbofans, as used by the F-15C, with a digital engine control system. However, the powerplant was soon replaced under the Improved Performance Engine programme, whereby GE F110-GE-129 and P&W F100-PW-229 engines were both flown in F-15Es under competitive evaluation; the Pratt & Whitney engine was eventually selected. From August 1991 the new engine was fitted on the production line, with earlier aircraft retrofitted.

South Korea's F-15K is the most potent incarnation of the 'Strike Eagle', with AN/APG-63(V)1 radar and an advanced datalink pod for missile guidance.

In 1988, the 405th Tactical Training Wing at Luke AFB, Arizona, became Tactical Air Command's replacement training unit for the F-15E Eagle, and the first operational examples were subsequently delivered to the 4th TFW, Seymour Johnson AFB, North Carolina.

On 12 August 1990, as the US began Operation Desert Shield, F-15E Eagles from the 336th TFS, 4th TFW, deployed to Al Kharj air base, Saudi Arabia. F-15Es of that wing's 335th TFS followed. During Desert Storm, F-15Es were assigned strike missions against a variety of targets, including five/six-hour sorties in search of 'Scud' missile launch sites. Out of 2,200 sorties totalling 7,700 hours, just two F-15E Eagles were lost in combat.

Long-standing F-15 operator Saudi Arabia, ordered 72 aircraft, designated F-15S, similar to the American F-15E but lacking certain ECM equipment. Of these, 24 are configured for the air-to-air mission. Responding to this potential threat from its near neighbour, Israel followed suit with a total order for 25 F-15Is. Known as the Ra'am (thunder) within IDF/AF service, the aircraft were built almost to the full specification of USAF examples. A further customer emerged in 2002 in the form of South Korea, with the first of 40 General Electric F110-229 powered F-15K aircraft being rolled out at St Louis in March 2005.

F-15E Eagle

This aircraft represents that of the 48th FS wing commander, based at RAF Lakenheath, Suffolk, UK. The wing retired its four squadrons of F-111Fs in favour of two F-15E squadrons in 1992. Today, the aircraft fly alongside one squadron of F-15C/D 'fighter' Eagles.

CFTs
The conformal fuel tanks each hold 723 US gal (2737 litres) of fuel, and have a continuous pylon (with three attachment points) and three stub pylons for the carriage of weapons.

Cockpit
The F-15E has a state-of-the-art cockpit, the pilot having a wide-angle HUD and three MFDs. The WSO has four MFDs. All vital flight and attack inputs are made via an upfront control and stick/throttle controls.

Powerplant
Late production F-15Es, like this one, are fitted with the F100-PW-229 IPE, each offering 29,100 lb (130.9 kN) of thrust with full afterburning.

Radar
At the heart of the F-15E's capability is the AN/APG-70 radar, a vastly improved version of the F-15C's AN/APG-63. As well as having improved air-to-air modes, the AN/APG-70 offers a high-resolution synthetic aperture mapping mode. This allows highly accurate 'patch maps' to be taken of the target area which, in turn, allow the precise designation of the desired aimpoint.

LANTIRN pods
The LANTIRN system consists of the AN/AAQ-13 navigation pod under the starboard intake and the AN/AAQ-14 targeting pod under the port. The AN/AAQ-13 consists of a wide-angle FLIR, which projects an image on the pilot's HUD, and terrain-following radar, which interfaces with the aircraft's autopilot system to provide safe low-level flight in all conditions.

Armament
This F-15E is loaded for a close air support/battlefield air interdiction mission with 14 SUU-30H cluster bombs. AIM-9s are carried for self-defence. Lakenheath F-15Es also carry AIM-120 AMRAAMs on the outer launch rail, with Sidewinders on the inner rail.

USAF/ANG operators

Although the Boeing (formerly McDonnell Douglas) F-15 Eagle has been operational for more than 30 years, it is still one of the world's best fighters, and remains the mainstay of America's air defences.

The Eagle entered service with the 1st Tactical Fighter Wing at Langley AFB in Virginia in January 1976. Over the next decade it replaced F-4 Phantom and F-106 Delta Dart interceptors with Tactical Air Command, and was also deployed to the UK, West Germany, Alaska and the Far East with USAFE (US Air Forces Europe) and PACAF (Pacific Air Forces) respectively.

In Europe, the F-15 was on the Cold War front line with fighters on alert with the 32nd FS at Soesterburg in the Netherlands and with the 36th Fighter Wing at Bitburg. With the easing of tensions after the collapse of Communism, most F-15s were withdrawn from the continent, and now the only remaining Eagle fighters serve alongside F-15E 'Strike Eagles' at RAF Lakenheath in England.

Pacific Eagles are based in Alaska, where during the Cold War they regularly intercepted Soviet reconnaissance bombers, and at Kadena in Okinawa. With the reduction in the US fighter presence in Korea, the Kadena Eagles became an increasingly important element in the US commitment to defend Korea, though the rapprochement between North and South, together with Japanese unease at the presence of US Forces on Okinawa make their future a matter for debate.

As the original single-seat F-15As and F-15Bs were replaced with front-line operators by the improved F-15C and F-15D, their old mounts were handed on to Air National Guard Units. The first ANG F-15 unit was the 122nd FS of the Louisiana ANG, which began to trade in its F-4Cs for F-15As in June 1985. The 173rd FW, Oregon ANG was the first unit to operate F-15Cs and F-15Ds.

Apart from combat and reserve units, Eagles have also been flown by the Air Education and Training Command at Tyndall AFB in Florida, by Air Combat Command's Weapons School at Nellis AFB in Nevada, and by the Air Force Material Command's test and evaluation unit at Edwards AFB in California. Maintenance is carried out at AFMC's logistics centre at Warner-Robins AFB in Georgia.

***Above:** An F-15C of the 390th Fighter Squadron, 336th Wing takes off from its base at Mountain Home. The 366th was one of Air Combat Command's first composite wings – in effect air forces in miniature, with several different aircraft types.*

***Below:** An F-15C from the 12th Fighter Squadron at Elmendorf, Alaska, takes on fuel from a KC-135. The 12th FS 'Dirty Dozen' is a former Phantom operator that switched to the Eagle in 1980, their current aircraft having advanced AN/APG-63(V)2 AESA radar.*

Above: The 57th Fighter Interceptor Squadron flew missions from Iceland for much of the Cold War, exchanging their Phantoms for F-15C Eagles in 1985. The squadron was disbanded in 1995, its mission being taken by detachments from other F-15 units.

Below: The 'WA' tailcodes identify these aircraft as Eagles from the F-15 Division of the USAF Weapons School. The school, part of Air Combat Command, is located at Nellis AFB in Nevada.

Above: The latest USAF Eagle operator, the Nellis-based 65th Aggressor Squadron was reactivated in January 2006.

Below: The 159th Fighter Wing, Louisiana Air National Guard was the first ANG unit to re-equip with the Eagle.

33rd Fighter Wing
Seen in the markings it carried in the early 1990s, this aircraft accounted for four out of the 58th TFS's 16 kills during the Gulf War. Among its victorious pilots were Colonel Rick Parsons, Captain David G. Rose and Captain Anthony R. Murphy.

Nomenclature
When it first flew Eagles, the unit this aircraft belongs to was part of Tactical Air Command, and was known as the 58th Tactical Fighter Squadron, 33rd Tactical Fighter Wing. With the USAF re-organisation of the 1990s it became the 58th Fighter Squadron, 33rd Fighter Wing of Air Combat Command.

F-15C Eagle

The F-15 has been the USAF's premier fighter since the 1970s, and during that time it has seen continuous development. The latest improvements go to front-line squadrons first, but eventually they find their way to the whole Eagle community.

MSIP
The Multi-Stage Improvement Program has seen the F-15C/Ds of Air Combat Command, PACAF and USAFE fitted with improved radar, weapons control, avionics and countermeasures.

Israeli operators

Above: The majority of Israel's F-15As, including this example, are operated by No. 133 'The Twin-Tailed' Squadron at Tel Nof. This aircraft carries Python 3 AAMs underwing. It also carries AIM-7 Sparrows.

The F-15 forms the nucleus of Israel's current fighter and ground-attack force. Israel continues to update its inventory and has recently acquired the F-15I.

Israeli air crews evaluated the TF-15A in 1974. Despite an effort during the Carter years (1977-81) to limit US transfers of advanced warplanes to foreign users, the Jewish state has received Eagle deliveries taking place in instalments.

Four F-15A aircraft arrived in Israel beginning 10 December 1976, apparently for developmental work, in the Peace Fox I programme. These were followed by 19 F-15As and two F-15Bs under Peace Fox II. Thereafter came 18 F-15Cs and eight F-15Ds in Peace Fox III. No. 106 Squadron was formed specifically to operate the F-15C/D.

The F-15C/D was given a different name in IDF/AF service – Akef (buzzard), wheras the F-15A/B is known as Baz (eagle). The F-15Cs for Israel were given additional air-to-ground capability through installation of bomb racks and a datalink pod for guiding GBU-15 glide bombs. IDF/AF F-15C/Ds have an indigenous electronic warfare suite and different radios. All Israeli F-15s can carry FAST pack conformal fuel tanks and these can carry tangential bomb pylons. They can carry the indigenous AL/L-8202 electronics countermeasures pod in addition to US-supplied pods.

Eagle action

The first IDF/AF action with Eagles took place on 27 June 1977, during a mission in which a mixed force of F-15s and Kfirs provided top cover for other IDF/AF aircraft carrying out an attack on terrorist bases in southern Lebanon. A number of Syrian MiG-21s attempted to intercept the attacking force, but Israeli AWACS detected this flight and in the ensuing battle, five MiGs were shot down (one by a Kfir), without loss.

On 24 September 1979, Eagles shot down five Syrian fighters and on 27 June 1980 at least one more. In May 1982, two Syrian MiG-23s were claimed. On 7 June 1981, Eagles equipped with FAST packs flew a 1,000-mile (1610-km) mission to provide top cover for F-16 attacks on Iraq's Osirak nuclear reactor. To date, the most successful deployment of F-15s occurred during Operation Peace for Galilee, the Israeli invasion of Lebanon in June 1982. Israeli aircraft succeeded in destroying no less than 92 Syrian fighters during operations between 5-12 June over the Beka'a Valley, and F-15s were responsible for a large proportion of these victories, including three high-flying MiG-25s.

Following Desert Storm, Israel received a batch of early production block F-15As from the USAF that were not scheduled for the MSIP (Multi-Stage Improvement Program).

On 27 January 1994, the Israeli government announced that they intended to purchase the F-15I. A contract was signed in May 1994 and deliveries began under the

An IDF/AF Boeing KC-707 tanker carries out simulated inflight refuelling on three two-seat F-15I Ra'am long-range strike aircraft during Israeli Independence Day celebrations in April 1998.

Bearing the markings of the 601 Flight Test Centre unit, this F-15I was delivered to Israel on 14 September 1999 after a time with AFFTC at Edwards AFB. It carries the standard three-tone IDF/AF attack scheme.

Above: The F-15I serves with No. 69 'Hammer' Sqn at Hatzerim. Outwardly similar to the late-production F-15E, the F-15I features certain Israeli-built components, including the EW suite.

Below: This Tel Nof-based No. 106 Sqn F-15C Akef wears six Syrian 'MiG kills'. The IDF/AF's F-15 fighter force maintains a high-alert status in order to ensure the nation's air defence.

Peace Sun V/VI programme in January 1998.

Known as Ra'am (thunder) in Israel, the F-15I incorporates new and unique weapons, avionics, electronic warfare, and communications capabilities that make it one of the most advanced Eagle variants.

All aircraft are configured with either the F100-PW-229 or F110-GE-129 engines, NVG compatible cockpits, an Elbit display and sight helmet system, conformal fuel tanks, LANTIRN pods, and the capability to employ a variety of air-to-surface munitions. Israeli ordnance can also be carried by the Ra'am, including Python AAMs. A local SPS-2100 integrated EW self-protection suite is incorporated in place of the F-15E's TEWS.

Israel received a total of 25 F-15I aircraft, the last examples being delivered in 1999. The primary operator is No. 69 Squadron, based at Hatzerim.

F-15C Akef

This F-15C Akef (buzzard) wears the markings of Israel's No. 106 Squadron, based at Tel Nof, and carries four victory markings claimed during Operation Peace for Galilee. The nicknamer *Skyblazer* is carried on the nose in Hebrew. Like the F-15A/B, the F-15C/D models carry locally-produced EW equipment. IDF/AF F-15s are claimed to have achieved a kill tally of at least 57 without loss.

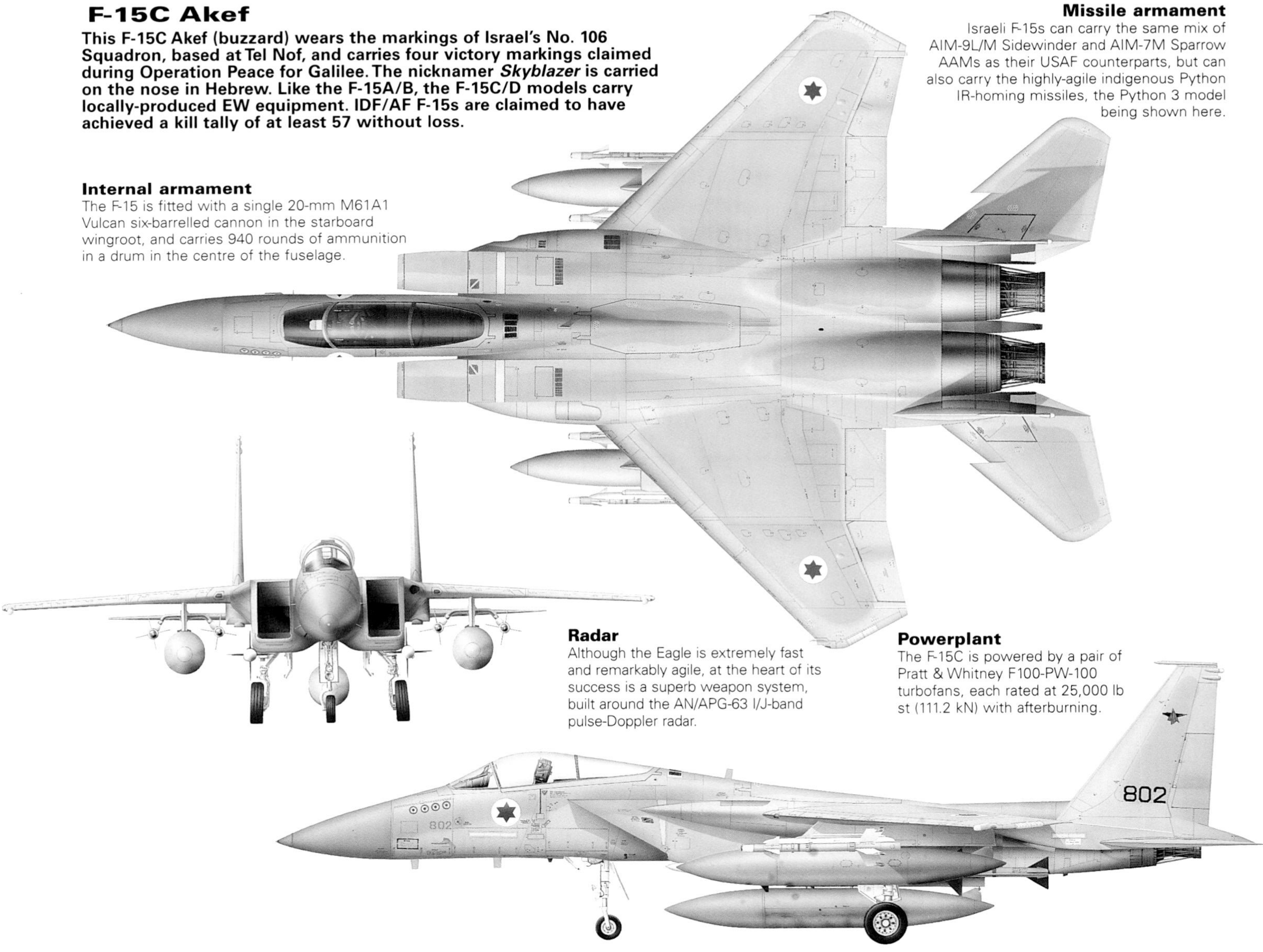

Missile armament
Israeli F-15s can carry the same mix of AIM-9L/M Sidewinder and AIM-7M Sparrow AAMs as their USAF counterparts, but can also carry the highly-agile indigenous Python IR-homing missiles, the Python 3 model being shown here.

Internal armament
The F-15 is fitted with a single 20-mm M61A1 Vulcan six-barrelled cannon in the starboard wingroot, and carries 940 rounds of ammunition in a drum in the centre of the fuselage.

Radar
Although the Eagle is extremely fast and remarkably agile, at the heart of its success is a superb weapon system, built around the AN/APG-63 I/J-band pulse-Doppler radar.

Powerplant
The F-15C is powered by a pair of Pratt & Whitney F100-PW-100 turbofans, each rated at 25,000 lb st (111.2 kN) with afterburning.

In the US at least, the F/A-18 is never more prominent in the public mind than when it is being flown by the US Navy's **Blue Angels** *aerobatic team.*

McDonnell Douglas (Boeing)

F/A-18 Hornet

Regarded as the first of the 'digital' warplanes, the Hornet offers unmatched air-to-air and air-to-ground capabilities in one airframe.

Designed from the start as a multi-role tactical fighter, the F/A-18 was drawn up to meet a challenging requirement. The Hornet had to replace the A-7 Corsair in the light attack role, while also taking over from F-4 Phantoms in both air defence and ground-attack roles. Finally the aircraft had to act as a low-cost complement to the F-14 Tomcat. Moreover, it had to be capable of fulfilling all of these roles with equal facility, while operating from an aircraft carrier or from an austere forward airstrip for the US Marine Corps.

Even more remarkably, the Hornet has proved very popular with a number of entirely land-based air forces, and is generally regarded as the benchmark multi-role fighter of its generation. Extremely capable in all of its roles, reliable and maintainable, the F/A-18 is even regarded as comparatively cheap. The aircraft is, therefore, not only popular with its pilots, but also with those funding new aircraft for its operating arms. In common with the majority of military aircraft programmes however, the F/A-18 has had its critics. To carry bombs over the same range as an A-7 Corsair II or an A-6 Intruder, the F/A-18 must carry large amounts of external fuel, with the effect of limiting the total payload available for the offensive warload.

As it assumes an increasingly important role in the US Navy's carrier air wings, the Hornet has become one of the most common aircraft deployed. With many high-profile foreign sales, the F/A-18 is also commonly seen outside the USN.

Life for carrier aircraft and personnel alike is hectic and demanding during sustained operations. Having introduced the US fleet to a new era of advanced avionics, the F/A-18 has proved highly reliable.

Despite its lack of range, the F/A-18 Hornet has assumed an increasing importance in US Navy carrier air wings. The aircraft is phenomenally reliable and can deliver its weapons with great accuracy. A Hornet can defend itself even when loaded for air-to-ground operations. This was demonstrated in the 1991 Gulf War, when two VFA-81 aircraft heading for a ground target were vectored onto and destroyed two Iraqi Chengdu F-7As. These

***Left:* Perhaps not regarded as a typical F/A-18 weapon load, this aircraft's pair of AGM-84 Harpoons hints at a formidable anti-surface vessel capability. The Hornet has also been cleared to carry the SLAM (Stand-off Land Attack Missile) derivative of the AGM-84.**

factors allow a carrier to drop more bombs actually on target, even if the bombload of an individual F/A-18 Hornet is less than that of earlier dedicated attack aircraft.

Range has, in any case, come to be of less importance. Since the end of the Cold War an increasing emphasis has been placed on operations, closer in to the coastline, and demonstrated in operations over both Afghanistan and Iraq.

Hornet takes over

With the retirement of the A-6E Intruder and F-14 Tomcat, extra F/A-18 units have been embarked on carriers to fly an expanded selection of long-range attack and air defence missions. The US Marine Corps replaced its Intruders with two-seat, night attack F/A-18Ds from May 1990, expanding the role of these units to include FAC (forward air control) duties.

The two-seat F/A-18Ds saw active service in the 1991 Gulf War, and have since been intensively used in support of peacekeeping operations. These have seen the Hornet at its most versatile – self-escorting with close-range and BVR missiles, using radar to check for airspace violation, tracking and identifying helicopters using its FLIR and being available to operate in the CAS (close air support) or FAC roles if called upon.

The arrival of the longer range, more stealthy F/A-18E/F means that the Hornet has become the most important warplane on the US Navy's carrier decks.

***Right:* Known to the Canadian Armed Forces as the CF-188, the F/A-18 was first delivered to Canada on 27 October 1982. All the Canadian machines are air defence dedicated.**

***Below:* For many years the unguided rocket has been a popular target-marking device. USMC F/A-18D crews honed the art of fast FAC and target marking to perfection in operations over Bosnia.**

***Right:* The Royal Malaysian Air Force opted for an eight-aircraft fleet of Harpoon-armed two-seat F/A-18Ds. The aircraft provide an anti-ship capability in a region where shipping operations are vital.**

F/A-18A to D

Early F/A-18s were eagerly received into service and soon managed to chalk up several export orders. A and B models still serve with Australia, Spain and the USMC, among others, despite the arrival of the more potent 'second generation' F/A-18C/D variants.

McDonnell Douglas and Northrop won the US Navy's Navy Air Combat Fighter programme in May 1975, and the first F/A-18 flew in November 1978. It was a new aircraft, sharing only its general layout with its YF-17 predecessor; it was larger and more powerful, with stronger structure and landing gear for carrier operations.

In many respects, the F/A-18 was technologically more advanced than the F-16A. Its 'fly-by-wire' flight control system used digital rather than analogue processors, and it used more composite materials. It had a multi-mode radar and a cockpit which used CRT displays. It was designed to accept pods for electro-optical navigation and targeting aids, and the AIM-7 medium-range AAM – none of these could be carried on the first Fighting Falcons.

Advantages

The F/A-18's new-technology cockpit was also widely acclaimed, and its radar and weapons integration drew no criticism. This was just as well, because other important attributes of the new aircraft were attracting sharp criticism.

The F/A-18 was failing to meet warload and radius specifications. Both of the aircraft which it was supposed to replace (the F-4 and A-7) could carry larger loads over a greater distance. Weight and drag increases also meant that the F/A-18 was limited in its 'bring-back' capability. With normal fuel reserves, the Hornet could not land on a carrier at an acceptable approach speed with more than a minimal ordnance load.

In 1982, US Navy test squadron VX-5 recommended that the F/A-18 programme be suspended until some way of alleviating the range shortfall could be found. The US Navy, however, overrode VX-5's recommendations. The USN's carrier fleet was expanding, and ageing F-4s and A-7s had to be replaced. Cancelling or delaying the F/A-18 would leave the US Navy short of modern aircraft, so the USN decided to put the aircraft straight into production.

Basically identical to the F/A-18A, the two-seat F/A-18B was developed alongside the single-seater. In consequence, two examples of the TF-18A (initial designation, later replaced by F/A-18B) featured in the original contract which covered a batch of 11 prototype aircraft. The provision of a second seat in tandem was accomplished at a modest six per cent penalty in fuel capacity. Otherwise, the F/A-18B was unaltered, possessing identical equipment and near-identical combat capability.

Subsequent procurement of the F/A-18B for service with US Navy and Marine Corps units ended with the 40th production example, and this version has never been employed by front-line forces.

***Above:* US Marine Corps F/A-18D Hornets operated in the skies over Kosovo with a pilot in the front seat and a weapons system operator (WSO) in the back seat. The pilot flew the aircraft, while the WSO operated the radar and the forward-looking infra-red (FLIR) sensor.**

***Right:* F/A-18C/Ds are fitted with an enhanced electronic fuel system that monitors usage and adjusts the aircraft's centre of gravity as fuel is consumed. All fuel tanks are self-sealing, with a foam infill system.**

One of several F/A-18C/D export operators, Switzerland decided to purchase the Hornet over competing aircraft such as the Mirage 2000.

Left: Despite brief front-line careers, F/A-18As and Bs still have a part to play in USN aggressor units. Examples serving with VFC-12 'Omars' are used to represent aircraft such as the MiG-29 or Su-27.

Above: Canada was the first and largest customer for the Hornet. In Canadian service, the CF-188 is a true multi-role fighter, employed on a 50:50 basis for air defence and ground attack.

Pilots were – as always – enthusiastic about the F/A-18A/B when it entered service in 1983. However, historical fact tells a different story. Some 410 of this initial version were built until production switched to the F/A-18C/D in 1987. By 1995, the US Navy had retired most of the A/B models from carrier-based service, the shortest first-line career of any modern fighter.

The fact was that VX-5 had been right. The F/A-18A/B was a somewhat inadequate aircraft, which validated the adage 'jack of all trades, master of none'. It took a series of upgrades to produce a Hornet variant which could be called the master of most of its many missions. This process started with the first F/A-18C/D, delivered from September 1987. Basically designed to accommodate new technologies and weapons, the first F/A-18C/Ds formed the basis for a series of Hornets whose exterior resemblance to the original A/B is entirely deceptive.

The F/A-18C/D airframe is not very different to that of the A/B, and has not changed significantly since it entered production. One significant change, though far from visible, is the addition of 'stealthy' materials to the Hornet. Under the 'Glass Hornet' programme, F/A-18s were given a gold-tinted canopy in order to reflect radar signals away from the transmitter. RAM paint on the engines and inlets also helped to absorb radar signals.

To meet a Swiss requirement, the F404-GE-402 Enhanced Performance Engine (EPE) was developed and this became the standard powerplant on all Hornets from 1992. Delivering 10 per cent more static sea-level thrust than its predecessor, the EPE also offers 18 per cent more excess power at Mach 0.9 and 10,000 ft (3048 m), and increased transonic acceleration.

All of Australia's Hornet squadrons were former Mirage III operators. No. 77 Squadron re-formed on 1 July 1987, receiving its first aircraft shortly afterwards. The unit is primarily responsible for the development of air-to-ground tactics and techniques.

Avionics development

The presence of the multi-sensor integration (MSI) system is another important aspect of the C/D model. With the MSI, the computer receives inputs from different sensors, correlates them and displays them so that each target appears clearly on the pilot's display. This can be used in an air-to-air or air-to-ground role and is particularly useful in the SEAD mission, where the HARM seeker, radar and RWR can be integrated to locate threats and display them to the crew.

By 1994, all later-model F/A-18s were fitted with the new AN/APG-73 radar, as opposed to the AN/APG-65 of earlier variants. The -73 uses the same antenna and transmitter as its predecessor, but the rest of the hardware is new. The receiver/exciter unit is more sophisticated and provides much faster analogue-to-digital conversion, allowing the radar to cut the incoming signal into smaller fragments and therefore achieve better range resolution. What is more, air-to-air detection and tracking ranges are up by 7 to 20 per cent. For air-to-ground mapping and bombing modes, the AN/APG-73 also offers higher resolution than before.

Other systems fitted to the later Hornets include NITE Hawk (Navigation IR Targeting Equipment) FLIR, which can track moving targets on the ground and designate them for LGBs. The Advanced Tactical Air Reconnaissance System (ATARS) fits into the Hornet's nose and incorporates a low- and medium-altitude EO sensor and an infra-red linescan imager.

Representing a massive leap forward in air-to-air capability over the AIM-7 Sparrow is the AIM-120 AMRAAM, operational on the F/A-18C/D since September 1993. A wide range of stand-off weaponry is also available for the Hornet. This includes the land-attack derivative of the Harpoon missile, the SLAM, and its extended-range variant, the SLAM-ER. For shorter-range stand-off attacks, the AGM-154 JSOW is used by C/D-model aircraft. The Hornet is also taking over as the main exponent of SEAD missions and of the AGM-88C HARM.

The second two-seat version of the Hornet is the F/A-18D, broadly similar to the single-seat F/A-18C. Thirty-one aircraft were procured before production switched to the night attack-capable F/A-18D, which has the same avionics improvements as the night attack F/A-18C. This specialist night-attack aircraft replaced the A-6 with the USMC's VMFA(AW) units (All-Weather Attack Squadrons). In November 1989 VMFA(AW)-121 became the first USMC 'D' unit. The VMFA(AW squadrons are tasked with the roles of forward air controller (airborne) – FAC(A) – and tactical air controller (airborne) – TAC(A) – as well as close air support.

An F/A-18E of VFA-143 'Pukin Dogs' lands on USS **Dwight D. Eisenhower** *in the Red Sea in November 2006. As soon as it had entered service, the 'Super Bug; was thrown into action in support of the global war on terrorism.*

F/A-18E/F and EA-18G

Although superficially an enlarged F/A-18C/D, the Super Hornet is very much a new aircraft of considerably more tactical capability. Born out of the cancellation of the Grumman A-12 and rejection of upgraded Intruders and Tomcats, the Super Hornet has invoked both criticism and praise.

When the original F/A-18A made its debut, it was regarded by many as being the world's leading multi-role fighter, and became the benchmark against which all rival fighters were judged. Possessing a formidable BVR capability (endowed by what many described as the world's foremost fighter radar) the F/A-18 was also as agile as the leading lightweight air superiority fighters (and in some respects was more agile), and had a genuine multi-role flexibility, able to 'swing' from air-to-air to air-to-ground operations 'at the flick of a switch'. But the passage of more than 20 years saw the emergence of new fighter prototypes, and while the baseline F/A-18 remains a class leader, new fighters are waiting to supplant it and to steal its crown.

Remarkably, one of these successors is the Super Hornet, known as the F/A-18E in single-seat form, and as the F/A-18F in two-seat guise. The Super Hornet is still very much an F/A-18, an evolutionary development of the earlier aircraft, and which looks superficially the same as its progenitor. But initial appearances are deceptive, and airframe commonality between the F/A-18A and the F/A-18E is put at only 10 per cent, while the new F/A-18E/F is 25 per cent larger, with massive rectangular-section, 'stealthy' raked intakes, bigger LERXes and with larger control surfaces, tailfins and tailplanes. The new variants have a sawtooth wing leading edge and a lengthened fuselage, giving a one third boost in internal fuel capacity. But the imaginative use of advanced materials and manufacturing techniques has allowed this growth to occur without major weight penalty.

The Super Hornet originated from a 1987 requirement for an F/A-18C/D replacement for the US Navy and US Marine Corps for service in the early years of the 21st century. At that time, it was envisaged that the new Hornet derivative would be augmented on US Navy carrier decks by the Naval ATF (replacing the F-14) and the General Dynamics A-12 (replacing the A-6E Intruder). These latter new types were subsequently cancelled, and the

Clutching a mixed LGB/JDAM weapons load, an F/A-18F of VFA-154 'Black Knights' overflies the carrier USS **John C. Stennis** ***in the Arabian Sea in March 2007. The Super Hornet's 'bring-back' capability is a major advance over that of the 'legacy Hornet'.***

As part of the EA-18G test programme, this modified F/A-18E was fitted with a wingtip antenna array and high- and low-band jamming pods. AGM-88 HARMs are also carried underwing, reflecting the Growler's lethal SEAD role.

Super Hornet will fulfil the carrier strike/attack and fighter/intercept roles, effectively replacing the F-14 and A-6, while the smaller, lighter F-35C will replace the first-generation Hornets. This has been made possible by a post-Cold War shift in emphasis from 'blue water' to littoral operations, for which the US Navy's Super Hornet is ideally suited.

The F/A-18E/F retains a high degree of avionics commonality with the original Hornet, resulting in a low unit cost and a smooth and swift transition of production and aircrew from one version to the other. The high commonality figure tends to mask the fact that the F/A-18E/F has a refined FBW flight control system, now without mechanical back-up, as well as a much-improved cockpit.

The aircraft attracted some early controversy (much of it stirred up by those who favoured the development of a longer-range strike aircraft based on the F-14) and there were some early technical difficulties with the aircraft's new F414 engines, even though these were derived from the original Hornet's F404.

While retaining the agility of the original Hornet, the F/A-18E/F is less 'draggy' and enjoys a lower approach speed, despite its higher maximum landing weight.

Super Hornet in service

Following a successful Opeval by VX-9, VF-122 received its first Super Hornets in late 1999, for instructor training. The first front-line unit, VFA-115 at NAS Lemoore, transitioned to the F/A-18E in late 2000. Under 2004 plans, the US Navy is to buy 550 Super Hornets, including 90 EA-18G Growlers. The latter first flew on 16 August 2006 and will replace the EA-6B in the SEAD/ECM role, incorporating an onboard EW suite and retaining multi-mission capability. In March 2007 the Super Hornet enjoyed its first enjoy export success, when Australia announced its intention to acquire 24 F/A-18Fs in order to replace their F-111s.

F/A-18E Super Hornet

Stationed at NAS Lemoore, California, VFA-122 was established in late 1998 and welcomed the Super Hornet to the fleet in January 1999, serving as the initial F/A-18E/F training unit. The first operational unit was VFA-115, which took the Super Hornet on its first cruise, in USS *Abraham Lincoln*, in July 2002, followed by its combat debut over Iraq on 6 November. A total of 22 USN squadrons will re-equip on the type.

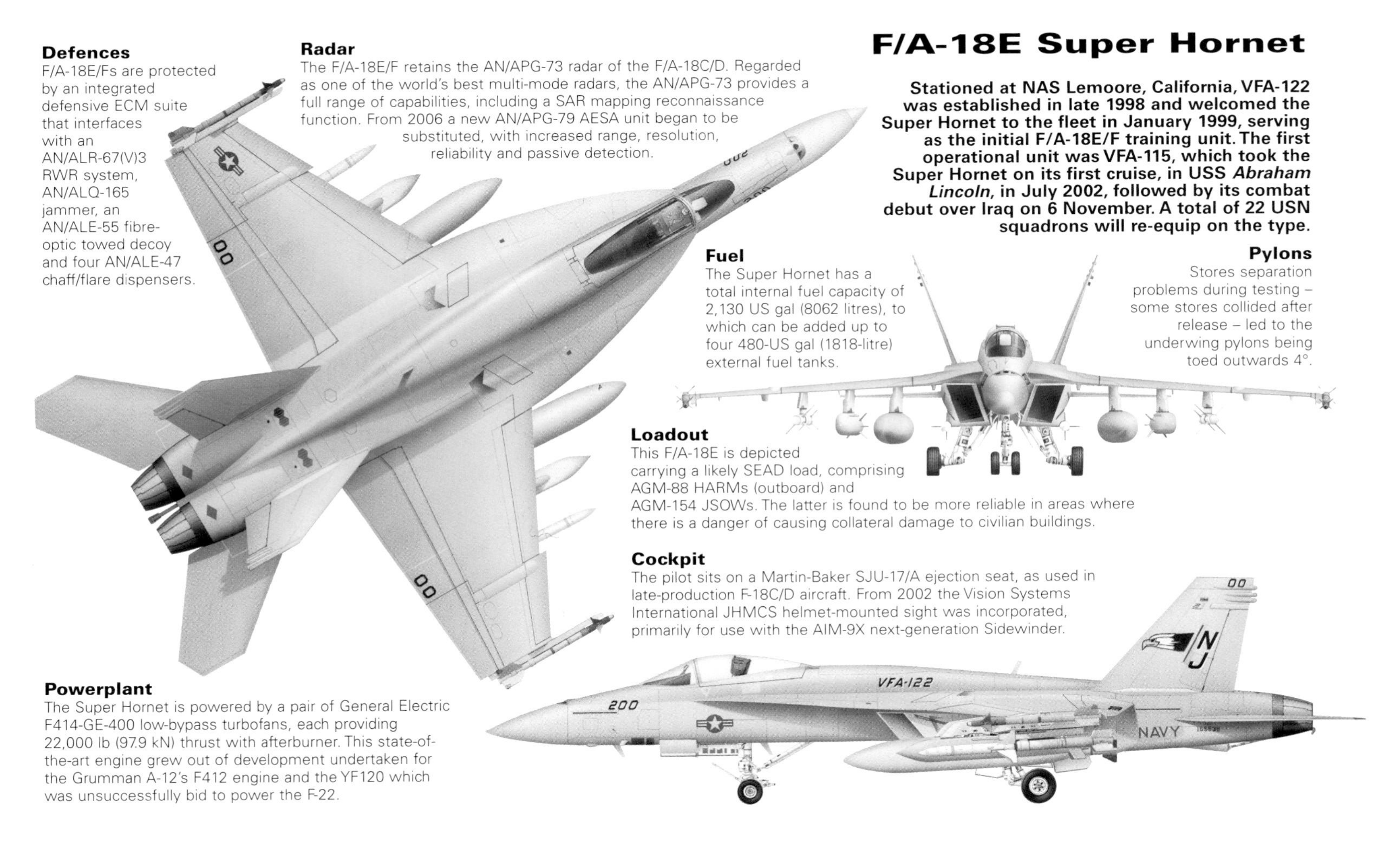

US and Canada

An F/A-18C of the US Navy's VFA-147 'Argonauts' flies over a Kuwaiti oil platform during Operation Southern Watch. The Hornet family will remain the US Navy's most important carrierborne combat aircraft well into the 21st century.

Designed for the US Navy and US Marine Corps, the versatile Hornet is the most important tactical aircraft currently in service with each air arm.

US Navy

The major strike power of the US Navy at sea lies in more than 30 squadrons of F/A-18 Hornets. Ordered in the late 1970s, the first of more than a thousand aircraft destined for USN/USMC units were delivered to the Navy in May 1980. VFA-113 was the first operational Navy unit, forming in October 1983, and along with VFA-25 embarked aboard the USS *Constellation* in February 1985. The original 'A' and 'B' models were followed in production by the improved single-seat F/A-18C and two-seat F/A-18D in 1986. The stretched F/A-18E/F Super Hornet first flew in 1995, and first entered squadron service with VFA-122, the Pacific Fleet's Replacement Unit, in 1999.

US Navy Hornets afloat, Summer 2006

Squadron	*Type*	*Shore base*
CVW-1 (USS *Enterprise*): Tailcode 'AB'		
VFA-211 'Checkmates'	F/A-18F	NAS Oceana, VA
VMFA-251 'Thunderbolts'	F/A-18C	MCAS Beaufort, SC
VFA-136 'Knighthawks'	F/A-18C	NAS Oceana, VA
VFA-86 'Sidewinders'	F/A-18C	MCAS Beaufort, SC
CVW-2 (USS *Abraham Lincoln*): Tailcode 'NE'		
VFA-2 'Bounty Hunters'	F/A-18F	NAS Lemoore, CA
VFA-137 'Kestrels'	F/A-18E	NAS Lemoore, CA
VFA-151 'Vigilantes'	F/A-18C	NAS Lemoore, CA
VFA-34 'Blue Blasters'	F/A-18C	NAS Oceana, VA
CVW-3 (USS *Harry S. Truman*): Tailcode 'AC'		
VFA-32 'Swordsmen'	F/A-18F	NAS Oceana, VA
VFA-37 'Bulls'	F/A-18C	NAS Oceana, VA
VFA-105 'Gunslingers'	F/A-18E	NAS Oceana, VA
VMFA-312 'Checkerboards'	F/A-18A+	MCAS Beaufort, SC
CVW-5 (USS *Kitty Hawk*): Tailcode 'NF'		
VFA-102 'Diamondbacks'	F/A-18F	Atsugi, Japan
VFA-27 'Chargers'	F/A-18E	Atsugi, Japan
VFA-192 'Golden Dragons'	F/A-18C	Atsugi, Japan
VFA-195 'Dambusters'	F/A-18C	Atsugi, Japan
CVW-7 (USS *Dwight D. Eisenhower*): Tail code 'AG'		
VFA-143 'Pukin Dogs'	F/A-18E	NAS Oceana, VA
VFA-103 'Jolly Rogers'	F/A-18F	NAS Oceana, VA
VFA-131 'Wildcats'	F/A-18C	NAS Oceana, VA
VFA-83 'Rampagers'	F/A-18C	NAS Oceana, VA
CVW-8 (USS *Theodore Roosevelt*): Tailcode 'AJ'		
VFA-37 'Bulls'	F/A-18D	NAS Oceana, VA
VFA-15 'Valions'	F/A-18C	NAS Oceana, VA
VFA-87 'Golden Warriors'	F/A-18C	NAS Oceana, VA
CVW-9 (USS *John C. Stennis*): Tail code 'NG'		
VFA-154 'Black Knights'	F/A-18F	NAS Lemoore, CA
VFA-146 'Blue Diamonds'	F/A-18C	NAS Lemoore, CA
VFA-147 'Argonauts'	F/A-18C	NAS Lemoore, CA
VMFA-323 'Death Rattlers'	F/A-18C	MCAS Miramar, CA
CVW-11 (USS *Nimitz*): Tail code 'NH'		
VFA-41 'Black Aces'	F/A-18F	NAS Lemoore, CA
VFA-14 'Tophatters'	F/A-18E	NAS Lemoore, CA
VFA-94 'Mighty Shrikes'	F/A-18C	NAS Lemoore, CA
VMFA-232 'Red Devils'	F/A-18A+	MCAS Miramar, CA

US Navy Hornets afloat, Summer 2006 (cont)

Squadron	*Type*	*Shore base*
CVW-14 (USS *Ronald Reagan*): Tail code 'NK'		
VFA-22 'Fighting Redcocks'	F/A-18E	NAS Lemoore, CA
VFA-25 'Fist of the Fleet'	F/A-18C	NAS Lemoore, CA
VFA-113 'Stingers'	F/A-18C	NAS Lemoore, CA
VFA-115 'Eagles'	F/A-18E	NAS Lemoore, CA
CVW-17 (USS *George Washington*): Tail code 'AA'		
VFA-11 'Red Rippers'	F/A-18F	NAS Oceana, VA
VFA-81 'Sunliners'	F/A-18C	NAS Oceana, VA

Shore-based Navy Hornets, Summer 2001

Squadron	*Type*	*Base*
Strike Fighter Wing Atlantic, NAS Oceana		
Fleet Replenishment Squadron: Tail code 'AD'		
VFA-106 'Gladiators'	F/A-18B/C/D/E/F	NAS Oceana, VA
Strike Fighter Wing Pacific, NAS Lemoore		
Fleet Replenishment Squadrons: Tail code 'NJ'		
VFA-122 'Flying Eagles'	F/A-18E/F	NAS Lemoore, CA
VFA-125 'Rough Raiders'	F/A-18A/B/C/D	NAS Lemoore, CA
Naval Test Wing Atlantic, NAS Patuxent River Tail code 'SD'		
VX-23 'Strike'	F/A-18A/A+/B/C/D/E/F	NAS Patuxent River, MD
USN Test Pilot School	F/A-18B	NAS Patuxent River, MD
Navy Fighter Display Squadron		
Blue Angels	F/A-18A/B	NAS Pensacola, FL
Naval Naval Test Wing Pacific, NAS Point Mugu Tail code 'DD'		
VX-30 'Bloodhounds'	F/A-18A/B	NAS Point Mugu, CA
VX-31 'Dust Devils'	F/A-18A/C/D/E/F	NAWS China Lake, CA
Test and Evaluation Force Tail code 'XE'		
VX-9 'Vampires'	F/A-18C/D/E/F	NAWS China Lake, CA
Naval Strike and Air Warfare Center		
NSAWC 'Strike'	F/A-18A/B/C/D	NAS Fallon, NV

Naval Air Reserve Force, Summer 2001

Squadron	*Type*	*Base*
CVWR-20 Atlanta: Tail code AF		
VFA-201 'Hunters'	F/A-18A+	NAS JRB Fort Worth, TX
VFA-204 'River Rattlers'	F/A-18A+	NAS JRB New Orleans, LA
VFC-12 'Fighting Omars'	F/A-18A/B	NAS Oceana, VA

US Marine Corps

The primary function of US Marine Corps aviation assets is to provide close air support. The two main aircraft used in this mission are the McDonnell Douglas (now part of Boeing) AV-8B Harrier and the F/A-18 Hornet. Marine Corps Hornets are fully carrier capable, and four squadrons are assigned to carrier air wings, serving alongside Navy VFA squadrons. The Marines began using the Hornet even before the Navy, and the first operational F/A-18 unit was VMFA-314 'Black Knights' which converted to the type in 1982. The first Marine Corps carrier deployment came in 1985, when VMFA-314 and VMFA-323 embarked alongside VFA-131 and VFA-132 aboard the USS *Coral Sea*. Marines use the two-seat F/A-18D as an all-weather fighter-bomber and as a 'Fast FAC' forward air control/tactical reconnaissance platform. Marine Corps VMFA(AW) squadrons began to convert to F/A-18Ds in 1990, just in time to take part in the 1991 Gulf War.

Marine Corps Hornet units, Summer 2006

Squadron	Type	Tail code
MAW-1, MAG-12, MCAS Iwakuni,Japan		
VMFA-212 'Lancers'	F/A-18C	'WD'
VMFA-122 'Crusaders'	F/A-18C	'DC'
VMFA-115 'Batmen'	F/A-18A+	'VE'
MAW-2, MAG-31, MCAS Beaufort, SC		
VMFA-115 'Silver Eagles'	F/A-18A+	'VE'
VMFA-122 'Crusaders'	F/A-18C	'DC'
VMFA-251 'Thunderbolts'	F/A-18C	'DW'/'AB'
VMFA-312 'Checkerboards'	F/A-18A+	'DR'/'AC'
VMFA(AW)-224 'Bengals'	F/A-18D/C	'WK'
VMFA(AW)-332 'Moonlighters'	F/A-18D/C	'EA'
VMFA(AW)-533 'Hawks'	F/A-18D	'ED'
MAW-3, MAG-11, MCAS Miramar, CA		
VMFA-232 'Red Devils'	F/A-18A+	'WT'/'NH'
VMFA-314 'Black Knights'	F/A-18C	'VW'
VMFA-323 'Death Rattlers' F/A-18C	'WS'/'NG'	
VMFA(AW)-121 'Green Knights'	F/A-18D	'VK'
VMFA(AW)-225 'Vikings'	F/A-18D	'CE'
VMFA(AW)-242 'Bats'	F/A-18D	'DT'
VMFAT-101 'Sharpshooters'	F/A-18A/B/C/D	'SH'
MAW-4 (Reserve), MAG-41		
VMFA-112 'Cowboys'	F/A-18A+	'MA'
VMFA-142 'Flying Gators'	F/A-18A+	'MB'
VMFA-134 'Smokes'	F/A-18A	'MF'

Marine Corps Reserve Hornet bases, Summer 2006

Squadron	Base
VMFA-112 'Cowboys'	NAS JRB Forth Worth, TX
VMFA-142 'Flying Gators'	NAS Atlanta, GA
VMFA-134 'Smokes'	MCAS Miramar, CA

Canada

By the late 1970s, Canada decided that a single fighter type would be needed to replace its F-101 Voodoos and F-104 Starfighters. The F/A-18 was chosen and was given the designation CF-188. The first export customer for the F/A-18, Canada ordered 138 aircraft, including 24 two-seaters. Canadian Hornets began their service life with 410 OTS in 1982. The CF-188s operate over the great expanses of the Canadian wilderness and were used to defend the nation's airspace, often in conjunction with fighters from the US. Canadian CF-188s were also part of the NATO framework and, as such, were also based in West Germany. During the Gulf War, Canada sent a total of 40 CF-188s to the Persian Gulf, where they performed in the air-to-air, ground-attack and Coalition fleet defence roles. As soon as the CF-188s returned from the Gulf, defence cuts ensured that a decision was made to reduce severely the number of CF-188s in front-line service from 138 to 60. The OTU has a further 23 aircraft, mostly two-seaters. Each of the four operational squadrons has a nominal unit establishment of 15 aircraft. The remainder are stored and cycled back into the active fleet to keep the number of flying hours per aircraft relatively even. In theory, each of the three front-line squadrons (409 and 410 at Cold Lake, 425 at Bagotville) is dual-role but, in practice, each specialises in either air-to-air or air-to-ground. Air-to-ground capabilities received a significant boost with the introduction of PGMs, this leading directly to the deployment of six aircraft to Aviano in 1997, during peacekeeping operations in Bosnia. Canada's CF-188 fleet is currently undergoing an upgrade programme. The two-stage avionics-based upgrade covers 80 aircraft and adds AN/APG-73 radar, jam-resistant radios, new stores management and mission computers, GPS/INS, new datalink, a helmet-mounted sight, new cockpit displays and a new EW suite.

Global operators

While not matching its great rival, the F-16, the Boeing (formerly McDD) Hornet has notched up several high-profile export sales.

Australia

Australia selected the Hornet in October 1981 as its next-generation tactical fighter and Mirage III replacement. The US$2,788 million deal included 57 F/A-18As and 18 F/A-18Bs, all but two of which were assembled by Australia's Government Aircraft Factory. Hornets were delivered to four units between 1985 and 1990 – No. 2 OCU (re-equipped May 1985), No. 3 Sqn (August 1986), No. 77 Sqn (July 1987) and No. 75 Sqn (May 1988). Three of these are based at Williamtown, NSW, which was refurbished to become the main base of RAAF Hornet operations between 1983 and 1985. No. 75 Sqn is based at Tindal, NT. The Aircraft Research and Development Unit (ARDU), based at Edinburgh, SA, routinely has Hornets on strength for weapons and systems trials. Hornet squadrons regularly make mass deployments to other bases and FOLs. As part of a wide-ranging modernisation campaign, Australian Hornets have been upgraded with AN/APG-73 radar in place of the AN/APG-65, and ASRAAM short-range missiles, among other changes.

Finland

After a long and exhaustive evaluation of various fighter types, Finland chose the Hornet to replace its elderly Drakens and MiG-21s in April 1992. An order, placed on 5 June 1992, covered 57 F-18Cs and seven F-18Ds. The two-seaters were all built at St Louis, the first flying there on 21 April 1995. The single-seaters were assembled by Valmet in Finland, the first taking to the air in 1996. All had been delivered by 2000. The Finnish Hornets are fitted with AN/APG-73 radar, AN/ALQ-165 ECM and F404-GE-402 EPE engines, and are armed with AIM-9M Sidewinders and AIM-120B AMRAAMs. They undertake a purely air defence role, and are consequently known as F-18s, although an offensive capability is planned. Three squadrons fly the type: HävLLv 11 at Rovaniemi, HävLLv 21 at Pirkkala and HävLLv 31 at Rissala, covering northern, central and southern sectors, respectively.

Kuwait

The Kuwait air force selected the Hornet to replace its A-4KUs and Mirage F1CKs in 1988, placing a September order for 32 F/A-18Cs and eight F/A-18Ds, plus associated AIM-9L, AIM-7F, AGM-65 Maverick and AGM-84 Harpoon missiles. The 1990 invasion of Kuwait affected Hornet deliveries, but the first three arrived in-country on 25 January 1992, with deliveries completed on 21 August 1993. The aircraft are sometimes designated KAF-18C/D. Initially operating from Kuwait International, the Hornets moved to Ahmed al Jaber AB once it had been rebuilt. The aircraft serve with No. 9 Squadron on air defence tasks and with No. 25 Squadron on attack duties. An option for 38 was cancelled in 1992, and Kuwait has been seen as a potential F/A-18E/F customer.

Malaysia

Faced with replacing a large force of F-5s, Malaysia adopted an unusual two-tier approach, whereby MiG-29s were bought for the air defence role, and two-seat F/A-18s were acquired for the attack role. The 28 October 1993 Hornet order covered eight 'missionised' F/A-18Ds, with AN/APG-73 radar, F404-GE-402 EPE engines, Nite Hawk FLIR, AIM-9S, AIM-7M, CRV-7 rockets, AGM-65 Mavericks and AGM-84 Harpoons. The aircraft are operated in the attack role with an accent on night/precision work, in the same fashion as the US Marine Corps' 'missionised' two-seaters. Four F/A-18Ds arrived at their new base at Butterworth on 27 May 1997, for operation by 18 Skuadron. The initial eight-aircraft order was viewed in Malaysia as a precursor to larger follow-on orders, but the Asian economic crisis intervened. An expected 12-aircraft purchase failed to materialise, although procurement of further Hornets remains a possibility, despite orders for the Su-30MKM.

Switzerland

After one of the most drawn-out and controversial procurement programmes of recent years, Switzerland eventually ordered the Hornet as a Mirage III and (partial) F-5 replacement on 22 June 1993, following a national referendum. The order covered 26 F-18Cs and eight F-18Bs, equipped to a very high standard with AN/APG-73 radar, EPE engines and AN/ALQ-165 jamming system. Initially supplied with AIM-7Ms, the Hornets now also carry AMRAAMs. On 31 October 1996 the first of two St Louis-built aircraft made its first flight: subsequent Swiss aircraft were assembled by SF at Emmen, and all had been delivered by 1999. The Hornets serve with Fliegerstaffel 17 and 18, based (in peacetime) at Payerne, and with Fliegerstaffel 11 at Meiringen.

Spain

Following a five-year evaluation, the Hornet was chosen by Spain to fulfil its FACA (Futuro Avión de Combate y Ataque) requirement in 1983. An initial requirement for 144 aircraft was halved to 72, split between 60 EF-18As and 12 EF-18Bs, known under the Ejército del Aire (EdA) designation system as C.15 and CE.15, respectively. The first was delivered on 10 July 1986.

Between 1992 and 1994 the fleet underwent an upgrade programme, after which the aircraft were known as EF-18A+/B+. The modification improved the central computer, added wiring for carriage of the AIM-120 AMRAAM (ordered in 1990) and AN/AAS-38 Nite Hawk FLIR, and integrated the EW jamming system into the overall defence suite via a new Mil Std 1553 databus. Additional weapons available to the upgraded Hornets included the AGM-84 Harpoon, AGM-88 HARM, Paveway II LGBs and AGM-65 Mavericks.

In December 1995 the EdA began receiving 30 more ex-US Navy Hornets, which were given similar modifications to the existing EF-18A+/B+, while receiving the official designation C.15A.

On 25 May 1995 EdA Hornets dropped bombs in anger for the first time, two EF-18A+s dropping self-designated GBU-16 LGBs on Serb positions at Pale. Subsequent actions were undertaken, leading to full participation in Allied Force over Kosovo.

The current EdA Hornet fleet is allocated to 121 Esc. and 122 Esc. of Ala/Grupo 12 at Torrejón; 151 Esc., 152 Esc. and 153 Esc. of Ala 15 at Zaragoza; 111 Esc. and 112 Esc. of Ala/Grupo 11 (formerly Grupo 21, and now due to convert to the EF2000) at Sevilla-Morón and Ala 46 at Gando. The latter unit consists of a single squadron, 462 Esc., which is charged with the defence of the Canary Islands from its base near Las Palmas. Finally, additional aircraft have been assigned to CLAEX, the EdA's trials unit at Torrejón.

McDD (Boeing)/BAE Systems Harrier II

A new 'jump-jet'

Having reached its operational limit, the early family of Harriers required a dramatic upgrade if it was to remain a potent battlefield support aircraft. The result was the larger and more powerful Harrier II series.

The first-generation Harrier suffered from a number of limitations which severely diminished its usefulness. While the Harrier's unique capabilities were recognised and appreciated by the RAF, it equipped a peak total of only four front-line squadrons, and development of the aircraft was never accorded a very high priority. Britain was to withdraw from what had started as a joint programme for a Harrier replacement, later buying back into the US programme as a sub-contractor instead of as a fully fledged partner.

Although as restricted by the Harrier's poor payload/range capability as the RAF, the USMC never lost sight of the aircraft's potential, and gave powerful support to the programme to produce a second-generation Harrier. When Britain withdrew from the programme, McDonnell Douglas was left to develop the aircraft alone. The AV-8B was based upon a new, larger carbon-fibre composite supercritical wing, together with a series of minor aerodynamic modifications and lift improvement devices.

Revised avionics

The AV-8B was far more sophisticated than the first-generation Harrier, with a modern nav/attack system, HOTAS controls, and a Hornet-type 'glass' cockpit. The new aircraft also has modern defensive systems, and two extra underwing weapons pylons.

Above: The ***GR.Mk 7*** *served with distinction over* ***Bosnia****, where the* ***RAF*** *gained its first combat experience with the type. Attacks were made with* ***CPU-123 Paveway II LGBs****, but the Harrier has since been equipped with more advanced, and accurate, Enhanced Paveways, typifying the versatility of the* ***UK*** *Harrier fleet.*

Below: By comparison with the original Harrier (and the ***RAF's*** *ageing Jaguar), the* ***GR.Mk 7*** *offers massive carrying capacity, with sufficient muscle to bear two 2,000-lb (907-kg)* ***LGBs*** *as well as fuel,* ***AAMs****, a chaff dispenser and even a centreline reconnaissance pod.*

The Harrier II is a superbly equipped air-to-ground aircraft, with genuine precision-attack and night-attack capabilities, and its flexibility, effectiveness and versatility are all being expanded under various upgrade and modification programmes. In-service Harrier IIs and GR.Mk 7s are already a far cry from the first AV-8Bs and GR.Mk 5s, and planned improvements will allow them to remain viable until they are replaced by the F-35 JSF.

The Harrier GR.Mk 7 is the

The Harrier T.Mk 10 is the two-seat trainer version of the RAF's 'second-generation Harrier', and entirely replaced the original T.Mk 4 in RAF service. It is used only for training, despite formidable operational capabilities.

RAF equivalent of the USMC's Night-Attack AV-8B, and uses the same or similar equipment and avionics. It has the same overnose FLIR, and has a fully NVG-compatible 'glass' cockpit. The RAF aircraft lacks the rear fuselage chaff/flare dispensers of the later AV-8Bs, but does feature the Zeus ECM system, consisting of an RWR and a jammer linked to the Missile Approach Warning System.

The Harrier GR.Mk 7 has six underwing pylons, and a centreline station, in addition to two dedicated Sidewinder pylons. The provision of integral BOL chaff dispensers in these pylons frees the aircraft from having to 'lose' a weapon station in order to carry a chaff pod.

The RAF's second-generation Harrier suffered from a series of teething troubles when it entered service. These were soon addressed, however, and by the time the interim GR.Mk 5 gave way to the definitive GR.Mk 7, most of the difficulties had been solved. The exception were the twin ADEN 25-mm cannon, which, despite intensive trials work and innovative engineering, were eventually cancelled. Confusingly, Harrier GR.Mk 7s frequently fly with empty gun pods as an aerodynamic aid.

The first GR.Mk 7s ordered as such were 34 aircraft requested during 1988 (although earlier aircraft were rapidly converted to the later standard). Both pre-series GR.Mk 5s were adapted to accommodate the overnose FLIR and undernose Zeus antennas, serving as GR.Mk 7 prototypes. The first flew in its new guise on 20 November 1989.

The first production GR.Mk 7 was delivered in May 1990, with service deliveries beginning in August 1990 to the Strike Attack OEU at Boscombe Down. Production GR.Mk 7s were also delivered to No. 4 Squadron (replacing first-generation GR.Mk 3s) from September 1990, and began to supplant the GR.Mk 5s of No. 3 Squadron in November 1990.

To ease the planned conversion of GR.Mk 5s to the later-standard aircraft, Nos 42–60 were completed as GR.Mk 5As with provision for GR.Mk 7 avionics (with an empty FLIR hump and Zeus antenna fairings), and were delivered straight to storage to await full conversion. Conversion of these aircraft (and of a damaged GR.Mk 5) began during December 1990.

Nos 3 and 4 Squadrons moved to Laarbruch and came under the control of NATO's Rapid Reaction Force when RAF Gütersloh, Germany, closed in 1993. In 1999 the squadrons finally moved to the UK, taking up station at RAF Cottesmore.

From aircraft No. 77, Harrier GR.Mk 7s were fitted with the larger, so-called 100 per cent, LERX – this further delays the onset of wing rock and improves turn performance. A programme to replace the smaller, compromise, LERX on earlier aircraft was suspended due to the need for commonality, and difficulties in clearing the big LERX for carrier operation.

RAF 'twin-sticker'

A decision to procure the two-seat Harrier T.Mk 10 (an anglicised TAV-8B, with night-attack systems) was taken in February 1990 and an order for 13 aircraft was confirmed early in 1992. This finally gave the Harrier force a trainer that was fully representative of the second-generation Harrier GR.Mk 7 in performance and capability. Powered by the Pegasus Mk 105 engine, the T.Mk 10, which first flew on 7 April 1994, is fully combat-capable, unlike its US Marine Corps counterpart.

The Harrier GR.Mk 7's original, rather limited, armament of bombs and rockets has been augmented by a number of new weapons better suited for medium-level use. These include Paveway II and Paveway III (which the Harrier first dropped 'in anger' during Operation Allied Force over Kosovo) and Enhanced Paveway LGBs.

Out-of-area, medium-level operations also drove the programme to improve the GR.Mk 7's navigation equipment, adding upgraded INS and GPS. From 2000, RAF Harriers and Royal Navy Sea Harriers came under control of Joint Force Harrier, and with the retirement of the Sea Harrier, the RN has become a GR.Mk 7 operator, with 800 and 801 NAS based at RAF Cottesmore.

After introducing the GR.Mk 7A with the uprated Pegasus Mk 107 engine, Joint Force Harrier committed to the upgrade of around 70 Harriers to GR.Mk 9 standard (or GR.Mk 9A with the Pegasus Mk 107), based on the introduction of advanced PGMs (including Brimstone anti-armour missiles), an airframe upgrade, new communications, and other avionics improvements. Two-seat aircraft are being brought up to a similar standard, and are known as T.Mk 12.

Operating the Harrier GR.Mk 7 from September 1990, No. 4 (Army Co-operation) Squadron has established an impressive record with the aircraft. The squadron's Harriers participated in operational sorties during Deliberate Force, the UN's pre-prepared response to Bosnian Serb violations in the former Yugoslavia.

AV-8B in service

Above: Seen unleashing an AGM-65E Maverick semi-active laser-guided missile, this AV-8B flew with VMA-223 'Bulldogs'. The squadron was formerly the last operational East Coast A-4M Skyhawk operator.

The Harrier's ability to operate independently of fixed bases has provided the US Marine Corps with a potent asset with which to fulfil the Corps' vital role in limited and contingency warfare situations.

The US Marine Corps functions as a self-contained and complete force, and has a great tradition of self-sufficiency. It is a matter of pride that the USMC provides its soldiers with their own CAS (close air support), and the AV-8B Harrier II plays a major part in fulfilling that 'debt of honour'. The AV-8B replaced the AV-8A and A-4M in USMC service, and equips a training unit and seven front-line squadrons.

Administratively, the USMC is divided into two Forces, each with a geographical primary 'area of responsibility'. The Marines Force Command includes the 2nd Marine Air Wing at MCAS Cherry Point, North Carolina, which in turn includes the Marine Air Group 14 with VMA-223, VMA-231, VMA-542 and VMAT-203 flying the AV-8B.

The Marine Force Pacific includes the 3rd MAW whose Harrier element comprises MAG-13 at MCAS Yuma, Arizona, with AV-8Bs in VMA-211, VMA-214, VMA-311 and VMA-513. During the Gulf War, MAG-13 (Forward Deployed) was based at King Abdul Aziz AB with VMA-231, VMA-311, VMA-542 and VMA-513 Det B. More Harriers participated in the war in the form of VMA-331, which formed part of MAG-40 aboard USS *Nassau*. Another AV-8B operating unit is MAG 12, which maintains a constant AV-8B presence at MCAS Iwakuni through a rotational deployment of the seven 'gun' squadrons.

Four 500-lb (227-kg) Mk 82 dumb bombs (in this case inert), a pair of Sidewinder rails and the two underfuselage pods associated with the GAU-12/U 25-mm cannon system hint at the impressive capabilities of the AV-8B Harrier II Plus.

MEF deployment

Marine aviation exists to deploy, usually as part of a marine air-ground task force. The largest such force is a Marine Expeditionary Force (MEF), with one division and a full marine air wing, including up to 60 AV-8Bs. The forward echelon of an MEF would be provided by an MEF with an infantry regiment and a MAG, including perhaps as many as 40 AV-8Bs. They would deploy in full squadrons, and would retain their unit identities. MEFs deploy aboard the 'Wasp'-class amphibious assault ships, which can each embark up to 20 Harriers, plus helicopters.

The older 'Tarawa'-class amphibious assault ships are Harrier capable and can operate a mix of six AV-8Bs alongside helicopters, as required.

Next down the scale is the Marine Expeditionary Unit, with a reinforced infantry battalion and a reinforced helicopter squadron, usually incorporating six Harriers, which routinely wear the unit titles of the parent helicopter unit. Two special operations-capable MEUs are permanently deployed, each with a reinforced

Spain ordered eight new-build Harrier II Pluses and a TAV-8B two-seater, and declared that 11 AV-8Bs would be upgraded to II Plus standard. The aircraft deploy aboard the Principe de Asturias.

helicopter squadron and a reinforced infantry battalion. The aviation element usually includes a total of six AV-8Bs.

From the 167th airframe, all USMC AV-8Bs were provided with a night-attack capability with the installation of a FLIR, an improved HUD, an HDD and a colour moving map. The terms 'Night Attack Harrier II' or 'Night Attack AV-8B' are sometimes applied unofficially to these aircraft. The 205th AV-8B off the production line was the first fully equipped AV-8B Harrier II Plus. It made its maiden flight on 22 September 1992. Equipped with the AN/APG-65 radar, the Harrier II Plus has a revised FLIR fairing, but is otherwise externally identical to late AV-8Bs. AN/APG-65 gives compatibility with AIM-7 and AIM-120 AAMs and AGM-84 Harpoon anti-ship missiles. The last 24 USMC aircraft were built as AV-8B II Pluses, while many more were converted.

AV-8B exports

Spain signed a contract for 12 AV-8Bs in March 1983, designating its new aircraft as VA.2 Matador IIs, although the Matador name was even less commonly used than in the AV-8S era. McDonnell Douglas referred to the aircraft as EAV-8Bs. Following initial pilot conversion in the US, the first three aircraft were ferried to Rota in October 1987.

The wooden-decked *Dedalo* (the former cruiser USS *Cabot*) was retired in 1988 and was replaced by the *Principe de Asturias* in July 1989, the new carrier having a 12° ski jump.

EAV-8B ski jump trials were conducted later, by USMC and US Navy test pilots at Patuxent River. The smaller, older *Dedalo* had no ski jump, so such training had not hitherto been necessary. Both Spanish carriers were home-ported at Rota, close to the airfield housing the Armada Harrier squadrons.

9ª Escuadrilla was formed at Rota in September 1987 to operate the Armada's EAV-8Bs, which were delivered between October 1987 and September 1988. The squadron forms part of the Alpha Carrier Air Group together with co-located helicopter squadrons.

Under the Tripartite MoU of 1990, Spain received eight new-build Harrier II Pluses and a TAV-8B two-seater, and announced plans to upgrade the 10 surviving AV-8Bs to the same Harrier II Plus standard.

Italian interest

When Italy's new helicopter-carrier *Giuseppe Garibaldi* was launched in 1983, it was clearly intended to be capable of operating fixed-wing STOVL aircraft as well as helicopters. The vessel was fitted with a 6° 30' ski-jump from the start, long before the Marina Militare Italiana (MMI) procured Harriers.

After gaining government approval to operate fixed-wing aircraft, the MMI ordered two TAV-8B trainers in May 1989. Sixteen Harrier II Pluses were ordered (with options on eight more), and the first three of these aircraft were diverted from the USMC's allocation in April 1994, being delivered to MCAS Cherry Point for training.

The MMI's two TAV-8Bs were delivered in August 1991 to their new base at Grottaglie. The first (US-built) aircraft were delivered in December 1994 with the final deliveries completed in 1998.

VMAT-203, the Marines' training unit, flies both single- and two-seat Harriers. The single-seaters undertake instructor currency training, chase duties and final student mission qualification.

The tail flash on this VMA-542 Harrier II Plus is evidence of the subtle return of squadron markings to the Marines' universally grey Harrier fleet. The 'Flying Tigers' are one of the longest-standing AV-8 units, having swapped their F-4Bs for AV-8As in June 1970.

TAV-8B Harrier II

Italy joined the Harrier club in May 1989 when it ordered two TAV-8Bs for initial pilot training, to be conducted in the United States. A front-line force of 16 Harrier II Plus aircraft followed. The TAV-8Bs were delivered in August 1991, at a reported cost of US$25 million each. This aircraft wears the markings of 1 Gruppo Aereo of the MMI, based at Grottaglie.

TAV-8B changes

This two-seat operational trainer version of the Harrier II, delivered to the USMC and Italian navy, has a forward fuselage stretch of 3 ft 9 in (1.2 m) compared to the AV-8B. Compensating for the resultant change in centre of gravity, the fin has been extended, by 1 ft 5 in (0.43 m). Internal fuel capacity is unchanged, but underwing pylons are reduced to two hardpoints under each wing.

Italian naval aviation

Until new legislation was passed on 29 January 1989, Italy's naval air arm was forbidden from operating fixed-wing aircraft, at the instigation of the air force. As a result, until the arrival of the Harrier, the only aircraft embarked upon Marina Militare vessels were helicopters.

Messerschmitt Me 262

Fighting 'Stormbird'

Young German gunners, huddled around their flak weapons, could be excused for a slight lack of attention to their task at their first sight of the Messerschmitt Me 262s on the snow-covered expanses of Rheine-Hopsten air base in 1944. In every sense the sleek, shark-like fuselage, beset with razor wings from which hung the huge turbojets, was a portent of the future.

The noise, the high-pitched whine and howl of the Jumo 004B-1 turbines, the swirls of snow, the hot paraffin-tainted blast: all were of a different time. This was the present, however, and, beset by Allied air superiority on all sides, black-helmeted pilots, crouched forward in the narrow cockpits of their Messerschmitt Me 262A-2a fighter-bombers, code-named *Sturmvogel* ('stormbird') by the Luftwaffe, anxiously scanned the overcast skies for the first signs of the diving Hawker Tempests, North American P-51s or Supermarine Spitfires, as they coaxed throttles and jabbed brakes prior to take-off.

In the heady days of 1941, when the Messerschmitt Me 262 was born, not one person in the Third Reich could foresee the desperate need for an outstanding aircraft with which to wrest air supremacy from the hands of the

***Above:** Four months after the Me 262A-1a fighter entered service, in April 1944, the Me 262A-2a (also known as the Me 262A-1a/Jabo) fighter-bomber entered the fray against targets in northern France. This example carries the usual pair of 250-kg (551-lb) SC 250 bombs; the A-2a differed from the fighter solely in having bomb pylons and bomb-fusing equipment fitted.*

Among a number of Me 262 variants that failed to see more than experimental service was the Me 262C-1a Heimatschützer I ('Home Protector I'), fitted with a rear-fuselage rocket motor to boost climb rate. The C-1a could reach 38,400 ft (11704 m) in 4½ minutes. In V186 (pictured) Oberstleutnant Heinz Bär, CO of III./EJG 2 and one of the top scorers on the Me 262, scored a kill over a P-47 in early March 1945, shortly before the aircraft was destroyed on the ground by an Allied fighter sweep.

***Top:** Seen at Lager-Lechfeld in the late summer of 1944, this Me 262A-1a was on strength with Erprobungskommando (EKdo) 262, the operational test detachment established in late 1943. Standing on the wing is believed to be Leutnant Fritz Müller, who later achieved ace status on the type, while flying with JG 7.*

An American GI guards the engineless remains of an Me 262, abandoned in a German forest in the last weeks of the war. By the end of April 1945 only JV 44 and III./JG 7 were still operational. JV 44 was finally overrun by US armour on 3 May.

enemy. Heinkel was already involved in the development of a fighter powered by the new reaction-turbine engines when, on 4 January 1939, Messerschmitt received orders from the Reichsluftfahrtministerium (RLM, or German air ministry) to produce specifications for a similar type of aircraft. Neither of the two then-existing turbojet designs was considered to be powerful enough for a single-engined fighter, and as a result Messerschmitt was forced to resort to the design of a twin-engined aircraft.

Heinkel had already turned to twin engines with the development of the promising He 280 series powered by the axial-flow BMW P.3302 engines, and Germany's first definitive jet fighter, the Heinkel He 280 V2 prototype, first flew on 30 March 1941. At Messerschmitt, work had proceeded slowly on the design of what at first bore none of the hallmarks that graced the Heinkel product, or gave any hint of the fineness of line that was a characteristic of the company's piston-engined fighters.

The Me 262 V1 was taken into the air for the first time on 18 April 1941, powered by a piston engine. The jet engines for the Me 262 V1 eventually arrived in mid-November 1941, being BMW 003s each of 5.39 kN (1,213 lb) static thrust. On its first flight with the BMW 003s, the Me 262 suffered a double flame-out shortly after take-off and was forced to land with some damage.

Fortunately, an alternative to the touchy BMWs was available – Junkers' Jumo 004. By August 1941, the Jumo 004 was giving 1,323 lb (5.88 kN) static thrust, and many of the earlier problems had been cured. Jumo 004s were installed on the Me 262 V3, first flown on 18 July 1942. Henceforth the fortunes of the Me 262 were to rise at the expense of its nearest rival, the He 280, which suffered a series of setbacks until its eventual cancellation in March 1943.

Service test pilots showed interest in the Me 262 from its earliest days. The experienced Major Wolfgang Späte had already reported his enthusiastic findings when the General der Jagdflieger, Adolf Galland, flew the Me 262 V4 on 22 May 1943 and became unequivocal in his praise for this revolutionary aircraft. A production order for 100 examples followed at the end of the month.

Production problems

In the meantime, on 17 August 1943 the US 8th Air Force's attack on Regensburg destroyed much of the embryonic Me 262 production lines, forcing Messerschmitt to move its jet development centre to Oberammergau. The delay occasioned by the move was increased by a chronic shortage of skilled labour, and production slipped by many months.

By autumn 1943, Germany was on the defensive in the USSR and Italy, and was being subjected to furious aerial assault by day and by night. Therefore, nobody could have been surprised when many senior commanders, including Hitler, mooted the concept of the Me 262 as a fighter-bomber as opposed to an interceptor, for the idea was tactically sound. The Me-262 could carry up to 2,205 lb (1000 kg) of bombs with uncomplicated conversion work.

So, from that day the Me 262 was destined to play a dual role, that of a fighter-bomber and that of a pure air-superiority fighter. Neither the role nor the aircraft could by then have had any influence on the outcome of the war. It was too late to start a major production scheme, as oil and aviation kerosene, precious alloys, and skilled airframe and engine specialists were all at a premium. The Me 262 had been recognised in its full potential, but too late in the war.

Over the period March 1944 to 20 April 1945, the Luftwaffe took delivery of 1,433 Me 262s, but for the Allies the impact of this fine aircraft was largely psychological. On inspection after the war's end, it was acknowledged that in design of airframe and engine the Me 262 was years ahead of aircraft of other nations, and its secrets permitted the Allied powers to accelerate development of jet fighter and bomber aircraft to the magic of Mach 1.0 and beyond over the ensuing years.

Below: Major Me 262 components were produced in Czechoslovakia during the war, and a considerable stockpile of these led to Avia producing an S.92 prototype (pictured). By the early 1950s eight aircraft were in service with the newly reformed Czech air force.

Above: The Me 262 was at its most vulnerable during take-off and landing; it was during this low-speed regime that Allied pilots claimed most of their kills over the fighter, though they needed to down the jet before it reached the protection of flak batteries protecting its base.

Fortunately for Allied bomber crews, only limited numbers of Me 262 two-seaters saw operational service. They arrived much too late to make any impact on the Luftwaffe's night-fighter operations.

Nocturnal 'Stormbird'

The Luftwaffe's desperate attempts to stem the night-time Allied bomber offensive led to the development of the Me 262 night-fighter. Only small numbers were finished in time to equip the first and only jet night-fighter unit of World War II.

Despite the huge advance in technology represented by the Messerschmitt Me 262, and the fundamental differences in its flight and handling characteristics, single-seater piston-engined pilots were expected to solo on it after only a brief course of ground instruction and some 20 flying hours in a piston-engined twin with its throttles locked in one position to simulate jet handling (the Me 262's Jumo engines were prone to flame-out at any sudden or violent throttle movement).

This syllabus, barely adequate to begin with, suffered further cutbacks as Germany's situation worsened. Belatedly, it was realised that training would be greatly simplified if a suitable two-seat dual-control conversion trainer could be produced.

Above: It is believed that only 15 or so Me 262B-1a tandem two-seat trainers were converted into Me 262B-1a/U1 night-fighters. This example (Werk/nr 110306) was briefly operated in the defence of Berlin by the Kommando Welter. After the end of the war, it was transferred from RAF hands to the USAAF's Air Technical Intelligence unit. Led by Colonel Harold Watson, and known as 'Watson's Whizzers', the team collected intelligence on German aircraft projects.

This resulted in the Me 262B-1a, which differed from the standard single-seater primarily in having a second seat for the instructor in the aft section of the lengthened cockpit. This seat displaced the rear main fuel tank and necessitated the introduction of a pair of auxiliary fuel tanks mounted side-by-side on pylons beneath the forward fuselage. Full dual controls were provided and the machine retained the standard single-seater nose-mounted armament of four 30-mm MK 108 cannon.

Limited numbers

Little more than a dozen Me 262B-1as were built, however, before an even greater need was identified, for an aircraft which could combat the growing number of high-speed RAF Mosquitos which were roaming the night skies of the Reich with virtual impunity. A series of trials carried out at Rechlin in October 1944 using an Me 262A-1a experimentally fitted

Below: This Me 262B-1a/U1 (Werk/nr 111980) was assigned to 10./NGJ 11, known more familiarly as Kommando Welter. 'Red 12' was operated from Burg bei Magdeburg until May 1945. After the end of the war, it was evaluated by an RAE team from Farnborough led by famed test pilot Captain Eric 'Winkle' Brown, RN.

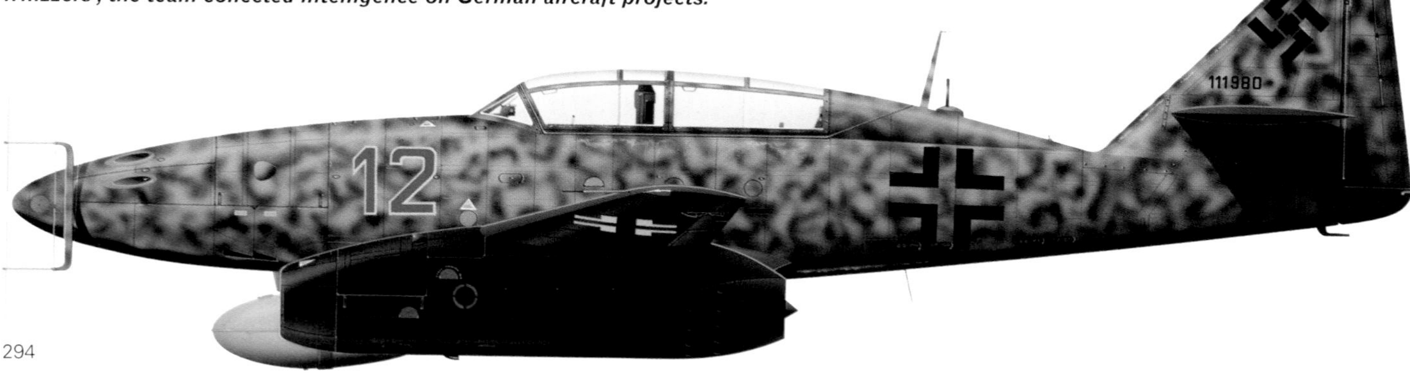

Development of the Me 262B night-fighter went ahead despite a significant reduction in performance caused by the drag of its* Hirschgeweih *(stag's antlers) antenna array. The $^3/_{16}$-in (7-mm) diameter dipoles reduced top speed by around 30 mph (50 km/h).

Me 262 two-seater operational history

The main recipient for the majority of the few Me 262B-1a trainers which were produced was III./Ergänzungsjagdgeschwader 2. This unit, roughly the equivalent of an RAF OTU, was based for much of its brief career at Lager-Lechfeld. It was responsible for the entire output of new Me 262 pilots for the Luftwaffe and, as such, was to have a planned establishment of 122 aircraft. In reality, it rarely mustered more than 30 Me 262s (known as *Schwalbe* or 'swallow' by its pilots) at any one time, only one or two of which would be B-1a two-seaters.

Some of the trainers did not even make it as far as Lager-Lechfeld. There were several crashes during ferry flights, including at least one fatality. Predictably, the combination of inexperienced pilots and unfamiliar – often unreliable – aircraft also produced its share of accidents during the training programme itself.

The only operational unit to fly the Me 262B-1a/U1 night-fighter was the Kommando Welter, which had been activated at Burg near Magdeburg early in November 1944 with just two Me 262A-1a single-seaters. The Kommandoführer, Leutnant Kurt Welter, who had served as a flying instructor until 1943, had since emerged as a leading exponent of *helle Nachtjagd*, a form of visual night-fighting sortie flown in conjunction with ground-based searchlights. He is believed to have scored the world's first nocturnal jet victory by downing a Mosquito on 27 November.

It was not until March 1945 that the Kommando Welter (which had chosen to ignore its official redesignation of 10./NJG 11 the previous month) received its first B-1a/U1 two-seaters; six examples were added to the similar number of A-1as being flown by the unit. While the single-seaters continued to hunt Mosquitos in the skies over Berlin, the two-seaters – being some 37 mph (60 km/h) slower – were now intended to infiltrate and attack the RAF's heavy bomber streams. It was a task in which they were singularly unsuccessful. It is believed that all 48 of the Kommando's kills (predominantly Mosquitos) were scored by the Me 262A-1a pilots. The two-seaters did, however, contribute two of their number to the unit's total of 11 losses: one aircraft suffered engine flame-out during an operational sortie in March, and the other was buried beneath a hangar roof in an Allied bombing raid on Lübeck-Blankensee airfield in northern Germany.

The Kommando had transferred to Lübeck on 12 April 1945 with just four machines after an earlier raid on Burg. This latest attack prompted another move. On 21 April they abandoned traditional bases, decamping to take up residence on the Lübeck-Hamburg autobahn. Hiding their remaining six aircraft (incredibly, they were still receiving replacement machines, even at this late stage in the war!) under the trees alongside the carriageway, they used a long straight stretch of autobahn near the Reinfeld interchange as a makeshift runway. The Kommando was on its last legs, though. On 7 May 1945 Hauptmann Welter led his half a dozen survivors (including two Me 262B-1a/U1 two-seaters) to Schleswig-Jagel for formal surrender to British forces.

with a FuG 220 Lichtenstein SN-2 intercept radar had proved sufficiently successful for the decision to be taken to adapt the Me 262B-1a two-seat trainers then under construction as interim night-fighters.

With a radar operator now occupying the rear seat, the conversion consisted mainly of the installation of a FuG 218 Neptun V search radar (with attendant *Hirschgeweih* array) together with a FuG 350 ZC Naxos passive homing device for detecting the H_2S emissions of RAF bombers. Work was carried out at the Lufthansa facility at Berlin-Staaken, where the resident engineers' expertise proved invaluable in completing the handful of Me 262B-1a/U1 night-fighters thus produced.

Definitive version

Whereas the B-1a/U1 was simply a hurried adaptation of the existing two-seat trainer variant, design work had already begun on the Me 262B-2a, which was to be the definitive night-fighter version ready for service in mid-1945.

The Me 262B-2a aircraft featured a lengthened fuselage, resulting from the insertion of additional sections fore and aft of the tandem cockpits. The latter were fitted with an aerodynamically refined canopy. Increased fuel capacity provided longer patrol endurance, and the nose armament was augmented by two oblique upward-firing 30-mm *Schräge Musik* cannon situated immediately behind the rear cockpit. In addition, in order to increase range, provision was made for the B-2a to deploy a towed fuel tank, which was similar to the *Deichselschlepp* towed-bomb array tested on single-seaters.

The B-2a mock-up was ready for inspection on 7 December 1944 and, with only minor alterations, first flight was planned for 22 March 1945. In the event, this schedule slipped and the Me 262B-2a was not flown before the German surrender. Although a development report prepared for the occupying US forces in June 1945 declared the aircraft 'ready for take-off', no maiden flight ever took place.

In the months leading up to Germany's final collapse, Messerschmitt had proposed more advanced variations on the basic night-fighter. Needless to say, none of them progressed beyond the drawing board.

The Me 262 demonstrated Germany's clear technological superiority over the Allies. Messerschmitt proposed numerous advanced versions of the two-seat Me 262, including a turboprop version, and two- and three-seat swept-wing variants with HeS 011 turbojets.

Mikoyan-Gurevich MiG-15 'Fagot'

Above: *The square-cropped jetpipe, subsequently shortened and faired, identifies this as one of the I-310 prototypes. Production aircraft were surprisingly similar.*

Top: *Poland was a major MiG-15 user, building the type as the Lim-1/2. The first Polish-built aircraft flew on 17 July 1952. After their front-line days were over, many Polish aircraft were rebuilt as two-seaters (SBLim-1/2), some of which were given a limited reconnaissance capability as the SBLim-1A/2A. This quartet consists of standard Lim-2 day fighters.*

Soviet fighter pioneer

Designed and produced in great haste, the MiG-15 came to be built in enormous numbers in four countries, and formed the basis of the Soviet air force's wholesale entry into the jet age.

While the Mikoyan-Gurevich design bureau was struggling in the race to get its MiG-9 'Fargo' first-generation jet fighter into service, design teams were also working flat-out on a successor. In March 1946 the Soviet bureaux had been called to the Kremlin and issued with a requirement for a jet fighter capable of transonic speeds. MiG realised that the required performance could only be met using swept wings. Research into swept wings was well advanced in the Soviet Union before the war but, as in the US, it was the influx of German aerodynamic data and personnel which allowed it to proceed to the point of hardware.

While aerodynamic and structural design work continued apace, alongside other important work such as the provision of a high-speed ejection seat, the development of a powerplant proved troublesome. Soviet engineers had only the BMW 003 and Jumo 004 jets to work from, and neither could be developed sufficiently to provide anything like the power needed by the new fighter. Soviet powerplant engineers were dispatched to the UK to study at first-hand the excellent Rolls-Royce Nene and Derwent jets. Shortly after, in September 1946, 10 Nenes were sold to the Soviet Union, another 15 following in March 1947.

Reverse-engineered, the Nene soon began pouring from the lines of state aircraft factory (GAZ) no. 45, under the designation RD-45.

MiG, meanwhile, had been working on a variety of studies for the new aircraft. These had evaluated a number of configurations, but settled on a simple fuselage with the engine buried in the rear fuselage, aspirated via a bifurcated intake in the extreme nose. This design was known in-house as the I-310, or simply the S.

Initial flight

Production of three prototypes was conducted through 1947, two powered by the Nene 1 and one powered by the Nene 2 (RD-45). On 30 December 1947, the first S took to the air.

With testing only just started, the Kremlin ordered the aircraft, as the MiG-15, into full-scale production in mid-March 1948.

Flight tests of the first three aircraft led to numerous changes being incorporated into the design, the most obvious being the shortening of the jetpipe to offset a loss of thrust. The MiG showed generally good performance and handling, although the rival Lavochkin La-15 also showed promise, and was also ordered into production.

On 30 December 1948, exactly a year after the first prototype, the first production MiG-15 took to the air. Production quickly ramped up, the first aircraft entering service in January 1949 following clearance in October 1948.

On 21 September 1953, this North Korean MiG-15 defected to Kimpo. The aircraft was shipped to Kadena for trials (flown by, among others, Major 'Chuck' Yeager), and then to the United States. It now resides in the USAF Museum at Wright-Patterson AFB.

Development of the basic MiG-15 continued as rapidly as construction. The early RD-45 aircraft was replaced by the RD-45F, with improved reliability. Production line anomalies, which resulted in some asymmetry in flight, were rectified. More importantly, engine designer Vladimir Klimov had refined the RD-45 to produce considerably more thrust. As the VK-1, this engine was fitted to a MiG-15 prototype known as the SD. Flight trials resulted in the SD going into service as the MiG-15bis, which became the most numerous variant.

Armament was also improved: the first MiG-15s featured one NS-37 37-mm cannon and two NS-23 23-mm cannon, mounted on a removable pack under the nose. The SV variant replaced the NS-23s with newer NR-23s, and later replaced the NS-37 with the better N-37. These changes, and others, were introduced gradually on the production lines.

In January 1949 the first MiG-15s reached operational units of the PVO (Troops of Air Defence), and deliveries to the VVS (air force) began shortly after. The more powerful MiG-15bis version reached the front line in early 1950.

During late 1948 the NII confirmed its interest in a two-seat trainer version. MiG was already well advanced with the ST, or I-312T. A prototype flew in January 1949, and the first production MiG-15UTIs were delivered during the spring.

As a simple and inherently good aircraft, the MiG-15UTI enjoyed a long career as an advanced/ conversion trainer, proving admirable for conversion to the MiG-17 and MiG-19.

Single-seat development

For the escort role, long-range versions of both basic fighter variants were developed as the MiG-15S and MiG-15bisS. These had oversized underwing tanks and were employed as escorts for heavy bombers. The SR, or MiG-15bisR, was a tactical reconnaissance version with cameras mounted in an underfuselage fairing.

The MiG-15 also played its part in the nascent fighter radar industry, although the only radar-equipped version to reach (limited) production, was the MiG-15P (SP-5), which sported *Izumrud* radar and two NR-23 cannon.

Other Soviet versions worthy of mention are the MiG-15T/ bisT, which was used for target-towing, the MiG-15bisF with cameras in a faired pod under the forward fuselage, and the MiG-15SB fighter-bomber with wing racks for bombs and rockets.

Although Soviet factories churned out MiG-15s by the hundred, additional sources were sought. WSK-Mielec in Poland built the MiG-15 as the Lim-1, MiG-15UTI as the SBLim-1, and the MiG-15bis as the Lim-2. In Czechoslovakia Letov and, later, Aero built the type as the S.102 (MiG-15), S.103 (MiG-15bis) and CS.102 (MiG-15UTI). Chinese unlicensed production was handled by Shenyang, which built the J-2 (MiG-15bis) and JJ-2 (MiG-15UTI). In total, at least 7,500 MiG-15s were built.

On 1 November 1950 MiG-15s entered the fray in the Korean War, operated by Soviet, Chinese and North Korean forces. In addition, virtually all of the Soviet Union's client states received the type, many taking aircraft from Czech or Polish production.

The MiG-15UTI (NATO/ASCC codename 'Midget') outlived the single-seat versions by a considerable margin. The installation of the second cockpit reduced internal fuel capacity and armament.

Below: In Czechoslovakia the MiG-15 was built in some numbers for local use. Agreement for production was signed in April 1951, leading to a first flight by a Czechoslovak aircraft on 6 November. One hundred and sixty were built at Letnany before production transferred to Aero Vodochody in 1953, which provided another 821 S.102s and 620 S.103s by the time production ended in 1957. Two-seater CS.102 (MiG-15UTI) production reached a staggering 2,013 machines by 1961, many for overseas customers. This aircraft is one of the roughly 1,000 in Czechoslovak service in the type's peak period in 1957, painted in a special scheme as part of a three-ship aerobatic team.

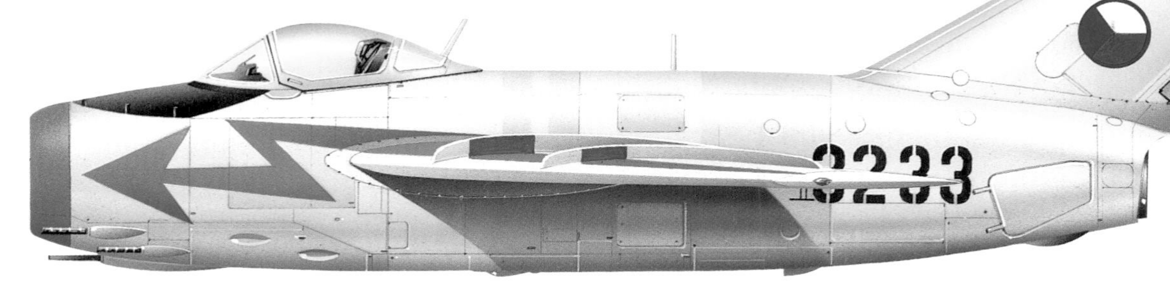

Mikoyan-Gurevich MiG-17 'Fresco'

Above: In excess of 1,700 MiG-17s were exported, the majority of them MiG-17 'Fresco-Cs'. This aircraft, seen with a SAAF Mirage F1, was delivered to Mozambique.

A better MiG-15

The MiG-17 is an unjustly neglected aircraft. Often considered either as a postscript to the story of its immediate predecessor, the MiG-15, or as a transitional aircraft falling between the high-subsonic and transonic ages, the MiG-17 has actually earned a place in jet combat history in its own right.

Following the rapid and highly successful development of the S-1, and its entry into production and service as the MiG-15, Mikoyan-Gurevich embarked on the design of an improved version. Primarily, it was aimed at rectifying faults in the MiG-15 and achieving higher Mach numbers; the MiG-15 became unstable at Mach numbers in excess of 0.92, and was a poor gun platform above Mach 0.88, as so many of its adversaries could elude it in a dive.

Design of the SI started in early 1949, three prototypes being authorised. The first of these (SI-2) flew in December 1949 (SI-1 was a static test airframe). Only two months later, however, it was destroyed in a fatal accident. SI-3 was never flown, but two more prototypes were authorised, the design having been extensively revised. The second of the these machines, SI-02, was the next to fly, in the second half of 1950.

Configuration

In configuration the SI-2 was virtually identical to the MiG-15. The powerplant of the SI-2 was essentially the same as that of the contemporary production version of the MiG-15. The MiG-15 prototype had been powered by an imported Rolls-Royce Nene, and initial production aircraft used the RD-45, a copy of the Nene. Meanwhile, the Klimov design bureau developed a version of the Nene with aerodynamic improvements permitting a 30 per cent increase in airflow within the same overall dimensions. The new engine, the Klimov VK-1, was installed in the improved MiG-15bis and the SI

Above: SI-01 made its first flight after SI-02 and was representative of the first production MiG-17s. Service aircraft were initially limited to a Mach 1.03 top speed; this was raised to Mach 1.15 in 1954.

Below: MiG-17 deliveries began late in 1952, so the new aircraft was not available in time to take part in the Korean War, where the MiG-15bis distinguished itself. In fact, the improvements offered by the original MiG-17 were probably not enough to warrant interrupting production of the MiG-15 in wartime. While the MiG-17 had higher Mach limits than the MiG-15bis, its turning, climb and acceleration performance were little improved over those of the earlier fighter and were probably worse in some areas as a result of its greater weight and shorter wingspan.

prototypes. An improved version, the VK-1A, with a longer TBO (time-between-overhauls), was to power the first MiG-17s.

The new aircraft had a mixed-calibre armament similar to that of the MiG-15. A removable pack aft of the nosewheel bay housed a single N-37 cannon of 37-mm calibre to port and two 23-mm NR-23s to starboard. Early aircraft were usually armed with guns alone, but there were four underwing hardpoints each able to carry a 250-kg (551-lb) bomb, rockets or a 53-Imp gal (240-litre) drop tank.

Despite its similarities to the MiG-15, SI-02 was a new aircraft in detail. The primary change was a new wing, structurally similar to that of the MiG-15 but with greater sweepback (45° compared with 35°), slightly thinner section and fractionally less span. The tail surfaces were larger, and more sharply swept, and the rear fuselage was extended and more gently tapered than that of the MiG-15. Apart from parts of the forward fuselage, including the inlets, canopy and armament installation, the new aircraft had few components in common with its predecessor.

Too late for Korea

Production of the new aircraft, designated MiG-17 in Soviet service and 'Fresco-A' by NATO, was authorised at six factories in September 1951.

The same applied to the near-contemporary MiG-17P 'Fresco-D' (first flown in April 1952), modified to carry the original RP-1 *Izumrud* S-band search and ranging radar. Armament was revised to comprise three NR-23s. With an extended forward fuselage to accommodate the new electronics, the MiG-17P suffered a further degradation in performance and only about 100 were built – the first light, radar-equipped interceptor to see Soviet service.

In 1950/51, however, the Klimov bureau had developed an afterburning version of the VK-1, producing some 30 per cent more thrust than the dry powerplant, more than restoring lost performance. Designated VK-1F, the engine was not compatible with the short-bodied MiG-15, but was destined for the new aircraft and tested in a MiG-17 in 1951. Production of the afterburner-equipped aircraft, the MiG-17F 'Fresco-C', started in early 1953. The only other major change to the design was the introduction of larger airbrakes. Because the MiG-17F carried no more internal fuel than the original MiG-15, and had 50 per cent more thrust and the fuel-thirsty afterburning system, the inboard wing pylons were cleared to carry 132-Imp gal (600-litre) drop tanks.

Derivatives

The great majority of the subsequent production aircraft were MiG-17Fs or essentially similar aircraft; the only other variants to be produced in quantity were limited night/adverse-weather interceptors stemming from the MiG-17P. The first of these versions was the MiG-17PF 'Fresco-D', essentially a MiG-17P with improved radar equipment and the afterburning VK-1F engine of the MiG-17F. First flown in 1952, the variant served in large numbers, 1,000 being delivered to PVO units. From 1956 surviving examples were returned to factories for conversion to MiG-17PFU ('Fresco-E') standard. This was the first missile-armed fighter to enter Soviet service, and among the first to become operational anywhere. The guns were removed, and four examples of the RS-2US AAM (known to NATO as AA-1 'Alkali') were carried on wing pylons.

This view of a MiG-17PF shows the variant's intake-mounted RP-1 radar. Ranging radar was housed in the upper lip of the intake; search radar was housed in an intake bullet.

Launch rails fitted to the MiG-17PFU, seen carrying RS-2US beam-riding AAMs on this example, were also able to carry ARS-160 and -212M unguided air-to-air rockets.

Licensed production

The MiG-17 was built under licence in three other countries. About 900 MiG-17Fs were built in Poland, under the designations Lim-5M (MiG-17F) and Lim-5P (MiG-17PF), by the WSK-Mielec works. From the Lim-5P, WSK-Mielec developed a specialised ground-attack variant, the remarkable Lim-6. This had a much deepened, long-chord, inboard wing section accommodating as much extra fuel as the normal drop tanks in addition to new, dual-wheel rough-field main landing gear units. The Lim-6 remained a prototype, and the Sukhoi Su-7 was supplied to Poland instead. The MiG-17F and -17PF were also built in Czechoslovakia, as the S-103 (left) and S-104, respectively.

The 1950s policy of licensing aircraft manufacture to allied countries extended to China. Chinese-assembled MiG-17Fs began to appear in 1956, and by 1959 the Shenyang aircraft factory was building the MiG-17F and VK-IF engine without outside assistance. The Sino-Soviet rift of 1960 did not interrupt production of the type, which is believed to have continued into the 1970s. The standard MiG-17F is designated J-5 (F-5 when exported); an equivalent to the MiG-17PF, probably reverse-engineered together with its radar equipment from examples supplied by the Soviet Union, was the J-5 Jia (or J-5A).

Additionally, the Chengdu organisation developed a trainer version of the J-5, first flown in 1966, with an instructor's seat behind the pilot, no afterburner and a single cannon. Some of these JJ-5 aircraft (known as FT-5 when exported) had a ranging radar, similar to that of the J-5A, but no search radar.

Among the best-known 'Farmers' are the Shenyang F-6s supplied to the Pakistan air force. Here, a single-seat F-6 peels away from a two-seat FT-6 of Pakistan's No. 25 Squadron, which acted as the OCU.

Mikoyan-Gurevich MiG-19 'Farmer'

Soviet survivor

The MiG-19 was one of the world's first level supersonic fighters to enter service. However, unlike many of its contemporaries, the MiG-19 and its derivatives remain in operational use, albeit with developing nations. Licence-built by the Chinese as the J-6/F-6, the 'Farmer' family has proved to be simple, reliable and effective.

Below: Unusually coded with a yellow number, the SM-9/3T was a weapons testbed for the R-13 missile, which was a reverse-engineered AIM-9B Sidewinder. The R-13 was given the NATO codename AA-2 'Atoll.'

In many ways the 'forgotten' MiG, the MiG-19 bridged the gap between the pugnacious MiG-17, which was built in huge numbers, and the ubiquitous MiG-21. Production was limited by the Soviet standards of the day – reaching around 2,000 examples – and there were only four major operational variants. However, the airframe was also the subject of a great deal of experimentation, resulting in a large number of other variants. Together with the operational variants, these trials machines were instrumental in taking the Soviet air force from the subsonic, gun-armed day-fighter era into the supersonic 1960s world of radar and missiles.

Initial production was of the basic MiG-19, which was hastily produced to provide supersonic capability at minimum notice. The key to the aircraft's enviable performance (easily eclipsing that of the contemporary F-100) was the thin, high-aspect ratio, sharply swept wing. Apart from minor aerodynamic improvements, such as larger fences, the wing remained little changed, and proved to be something of a masterpiece right from the start.

Initial MiG-19 production was quickly superseded by that of the MiG-19S, which addressed many of the handling problems of the first production aircraft. These problems were symptomatic of the abbreviated development programme required to field an operational aircraft hastily, and were soon rectified.

MiG-19s went into service with the PVO as interceptors, and subsequent Soviet development was largely to follow this path, leading to the radar-equipped MiG-19P, and finally the MiG-19PM with radar and missiles. As the USSR's first supersonic-capable fighter, the MiG-19 also became the subject of many test programmes, many of which would lead to features of later production fighters. A myriad of experimental aircraft tested refuelling, new launch and recovery techniques, extreme-altitude potential, new weapons and revised propulsion systems.

In China, the basic MiG-19S day-fighter was built in vast numbers to form the backbone of the People's Liberation Army Air Force. Chinese development accounted for several new variants – most significantly the Nanchang A-5 'Fantan' – while the type was widely exported from both Soviet and Chinese sources.

Although rapidly supplanted in Soviet PVO service by more capable types, the MiG-19 was to enjoy a very long career elsewhere. Appreciated for its 'no-nonsense' sturdiness and impressive performance, the MiG-19/J-6 was involved in much action, including Cold War confrontations, cross-border skirmishes and full-blown wars.

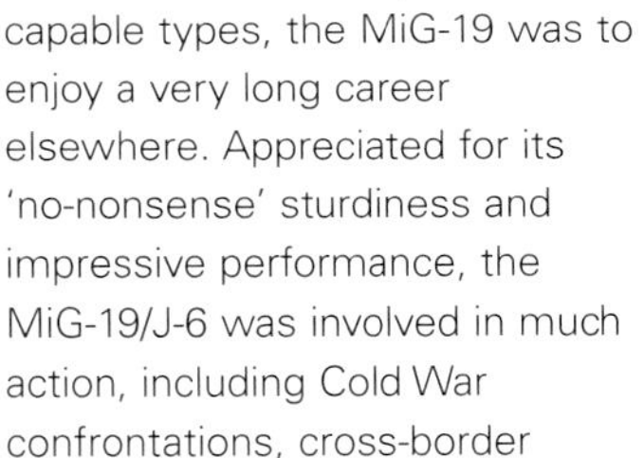

USSR activity

The MiG-19's arch-nemesis was the U-2. The first encounter between the MiG-19 and the U-2 was in the autumn of 1957. In May 1960, MiG-19s were involved in Gary Powers' U-2 shootdown. However, while rising to intercept the U-2, one of the 'Farmers' was hit by a Soviet-fired SAM and the pilot was killed. The other MiG played no real part in the downing

An East German MiG-19S is prepared for a night flight. Although lacking radar, the MiG-19S could still provide a limited nocturnal capability when flown under strict GCI control in good weather.

of the U-2. Other Cold War clashes saw MiG-19s shoot down two USAF RB-47Hs in 1960, another in 1963, a T-39 in 1963 and an RB-66D was forced down in 1964, with the crew later being returned to the West.

Czech airspace often suffered intrusions from Western aircraft, and an Italian F-84F and a USAF F-100 were both forced down. Bulgarian MiG-19s had to deal with Greek and Turkish invaders, scoring several victories. Cuba was an active operator of the type, using it against CIA aircraft and intelligence ships.

In 1968, Warsaw Pact forces helped to suppress 'deviations from the socialist course' in Czechoslovakia. MiG-19s were stationed in the area in case of any NATO involvement.

Shenyang J-6s (licence-built MiG-19Ss) formed the mainstay of the Chinese air force from 1960 and still existed into the 21st century, albeit in varying forms, despite the appearance of modern fighters. Chinese J-6s engaged Taiwanese U-2s and clashed with American aircraft during the Vietnam War and while prowling about Chinese airspace. J-6s also intruded into Soviet airspace during Sino-Soviet border disputes.

North Vietnam purchased F-6s from China and used them to a significant extent during the Vietnam War, where they partnered MiG-21s and scored a credible number of kills.

The Middle East witnessed fierce battles between the forces of the United Arab Republic and Israel. Here, the MiGs fared badly when faced with the skilful and capable Israelis and, according to Israeli claims, over 50 MiG-19s were destroyed without loss.

Iraq also purchased MiG-19s, initially buying the MiG-19S from the Soviet Union, followed by the F-6 from China, although the latter was not airworthy by the time of Desert Storm.

Indo-Pakistan war

The largest conflict in which the F-6 took part was the Indo-Pakistan war which began in December 1971. The F-6 was the backbone of the PAF and was used in the counter-air and ground attack roles. Results were moderately successful, with the PAF's F-6s notching up 10 kills, with four losses. F-6s have also played a minor part in several African wars in Tanzania, Sudan and Somalia.

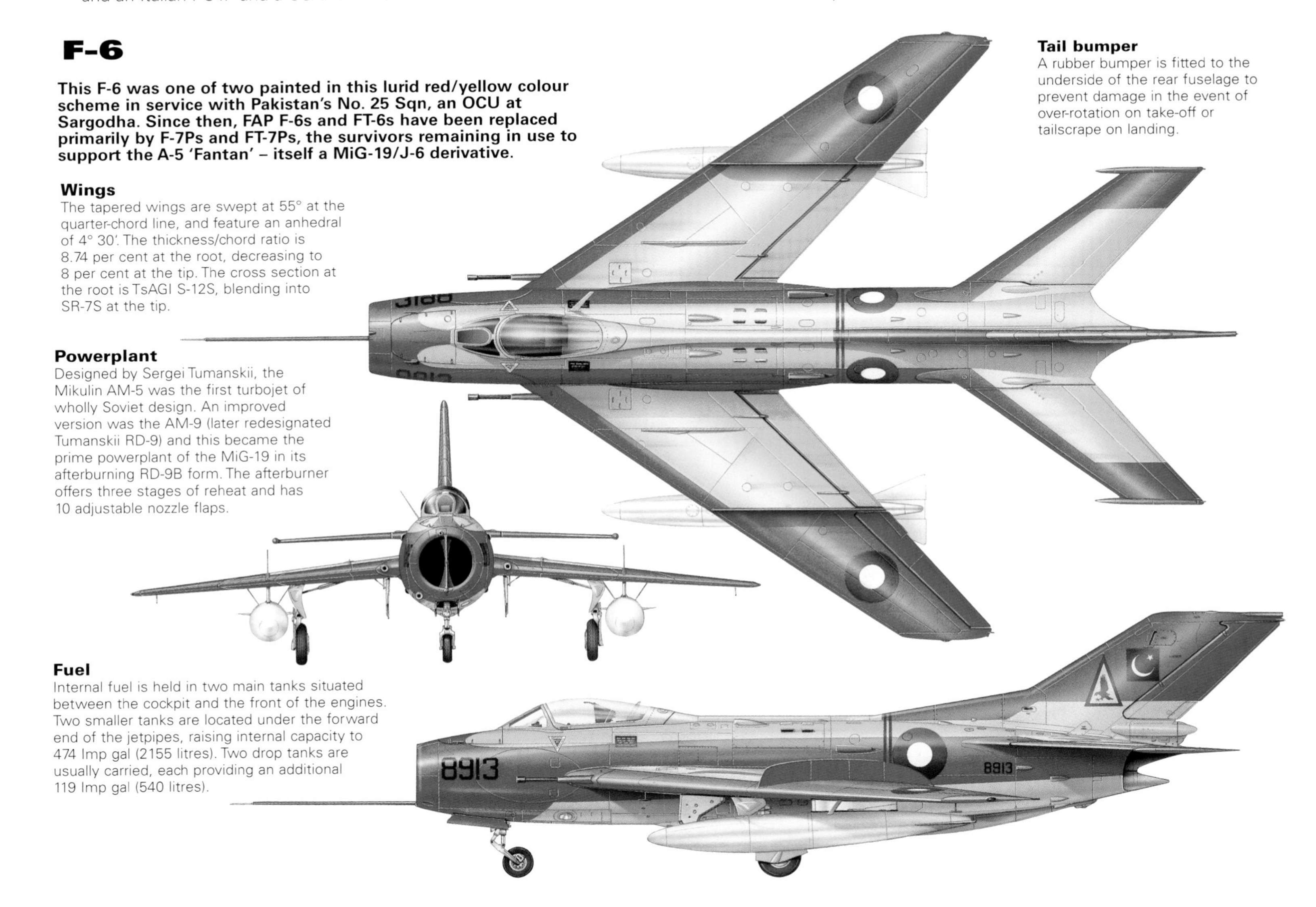

F-6

This F-6 was one of two painted in this lurid red/yellow colour scheme in service with Pakistan's No. 25 Sqn, an OCU at Sargodha. Since then, FAP F-6s and FT-6s have been replaced primarily by F-7Ps and FT-7Ps, the survivors remaining in use to support the A-5 'Fantan' – itself a MiG-19/J-6 derivative.

Wings
The tapered wings are swept at 55° at the quarter-chord line, and feature an anhedral of 4° 30'. The thickness/chord ratio is 8.74 per cent at the root, decreasing to 8 per cent at the tip. The cross section at the root is TsAGI S-12S, blending into SR-7S at the tip.

Powerplant
Designed by Sergei Tumanskii, the Mikulin AM-5 was the first turbojet of wholly Soviet design. An improved version was the AM-9 (later redesignated Tumanskii RD-9) and this became the prime powerplant of the MiG-19 in its afterburning RD-9B form. The afterburner offers three stages of reheat and has 10 adjustable nozzle flaps.

Fuel
Internal fuel is held in two main tanks situated between the cockpit and the front of the engines. Two smaller tanks are located under the forward end of the jetpipes, raising internal capacity to 474 Imp gal (2155 litres). Two drop tanks are usually carried, each providing an additional 119 Imp gal (540 litres).

Tail bumper
A rubber bumper is fitted to the underside of the rear fuselage to prevent damage in the event of over-rotation on take-off or tailscrape on landing.

Despite being introduced in the late 1950s, the MiG-21 continues to serve in some numbers. This example is a MiG-21UM of the Slovakian air force, which had retired the type by January 2003.

Mikoyan-Gurevich MiG-21 'Fishbed'

Best-selling fighter

Produced in immense numbers, the MiG-21's success has helped to make MiG virtually a household name. In service with the Soviet Union and its client states during the Cold War, the aircraft remains on the strength of air forces worldwide.

It would be fair to claim that the MiG-21 is one of the most famous military aircraft in the world. Since the end of World War II, no other fighter has been built in such large numbers (over 10,000 in the Soviet Union and a further 2,000 in China and India), or in so many versions. Moreover, no other fighter has ever served with so many forces or been involved in so many conflicts. What is remarkable is that the MiG-21 has always been a rather small and limited aircraft, possessing equipment of no outstanding ability. Indeed, in modern conflicts, the MiG-21 has found itself outclassed by the bigger, more sophisticated and more powerful Western fighters. Nevertheless, the MiG-21 has proved popular with those who have flown it and the fact that it is easy to maintain, reliable and cheap has meant that today's air forces are still keen to operate it.

In 1953, the NII VVS, the scientific research institute of the Soviet air force, issued a specification for a new fighter and Mikoyan came up with a proposal for a small, supersonic aircraft, powered by a single afterburning turbojet, which would not carry heavy loads of fuel, electronics or weapons. The VVS required this new fighter purely to shoot down Century-series fighters and jet bombers. However, it was soon accepted that it could not do everything that was asked of it and a new requirement was accordingly issued, which called for a fighter to carry out local defence in daylight, operate under close ground control and attack with guns only.

The Mikoyan OKB built two prototypes – the Ye-2 (with swept wings) and the Ye-4 (delta). Both aircraft were to be equipped with the R-11 engine, but they were designed before the engine was completed and so were fitted instead with the less powerful RD-9Ye. The Ye-2 first flew on 14 February 1955 and was well received, if considered to be a little underpowered, with the delta-winged Ye-4 flying a few days later. Over the following two years, a number of modifications were made to both designs and, in a final fly-off in 1957, the delta-winged variant was picked by Mikoyan and the NII VVS.

The next two years saw a number of further changes to the initial design, which resulted in the Ye-6/3. Flown in December 1958, it led straight into a series of 30 production aircraft, designated MiG-21F. While the Soviets used a Ye-6/3 to gain a number of records including the world speed record, Mikoyan was building the first true series version, the MiG-21F-13, which had new armament.

China first manufactured the MiG-21 in 1961, naming its domestic aircraft J-7s, and those for its export customers F-7s. This example is an F-7MG with upgraded weapons capabilities, allowing the carriage of AIM-9 Sidewinders and R.550 Magic AAMs.

The Czech Republic retained a number of MiG-21MF 'Fishbed-Js' for air defence and attack purposes after partition, and these equipped three squadrons of the Czech air force, the last being retired in 2005.

Hundreds of these aircraft were constructed, including aircraft designated S-106 which were made in Czechoslovakia, and unlicensed J-7/F-7 copies in China.

Multivariant MiG

From the outset, the MiG-21 was constantly upgraded and it went through three generational changes which each resulted in an aircraft far removed from the prototype. After the MiG-21F-13 came the -21P, which dispensed with the cannon and was only armed with two missiles. This was followed by the -21PF which had a new radar, the FL for export purposes, and the PFM with a new canopy, avionics, weapons and equipment.

Later-generation models moved away from the original lightweight fighter concept, gradually becoming heavier and more sophisticated. There was the -21R recce aircraft with reconnaissance and IR pods, TV cameras and laser sensors; the -21S fighter variant of the R; the -21SM with increased manoeuvrability; the -21MF with a more powerful engine, radar and weapons fit; and the -21SMT which was capable of carrying a greater fuel load.

The third generation MiG-21bis is by far the most advanced and capable production variant, although a lack of BVR missile capability, limited radar and poor endurance limit its usefulness. It was developed as a multi-role fighter for Soviet Frontal Aviation and has a greater weapons capability than earlier variants. The MiG-21bis model has served with a number of nations and, alongside earlier models, continues in front-line service in a few countries.

The end of the Cold War did not mean the end of the MiG-21, and several companies have made efforts to upgrade the surviving aircraft. IAI has produced the MiG-21-2000, while the Mikoyan OKB itself constructed the MiG-21-93. A host of other companies have offered upgrades, new avionics and weapons fits.

'Fishbed' at war

With its wide range of operators, it was inevitable that the MiG-21 would see combat. The first true conflict in which the aircraft appeared was that between India and Pakistan in 1965, its main opponents being the F-86F and F-104A. However, combat was limited and it was not until the resumption of hostilities in 1971 that the MiG-21 really found itself at war. The first kill was a PAF F-6, although F-104s were soon added to the kill lists.

The next major area of conflict for the MiG-21 was in the Middle East, where Egyptian, Syrian and Iraqi aircraft found themselves attacking Israel. Here, the MiG-21 was less than successful and many fell prey to Israeli Mirage IIICJs. In the Yom Kippur war of 1973, the Arab coalition's air forces again found themselves outclassed by Israeli F-4Es, Mirages and Neshers.

In Africa, Cuban-piloted Angolan MiG-21s were used against the UNITA and FNLA opposition parties, some falling prey to South African Mirage F1s. Iraqi MiG-21s held their own against Iranian F-4s and F-5s while Somalian MiG-21s fared badly against Ethiopian F-5s.

During Vietnam, the agile MiG-21s performed well against the heavier, more sophisticated US aircraft in close combat when under tight ground control, although they suffered when fighting at greater distances. Since then, MiG-21s have been involved in a number of conflicts around Israel and Syria (including one over the Lebanon in 1982 in which over 80 MiG-21/23s were shot down), and in the localised conflicts across Africa.

It is unlikely that any fighter will ever again match the sales success of the MiG-21. In a world of shrinking defence budgets, few nations have the finances to spend great sums on squadrons of aircraft. Instead, the trend now seems to be to equip squadrons with small numbers of powerful, high-tech multi-purpose aircraft – the opposite of the original MiG-21 ideal.

Above: Pictured is an engineering ground demonstrator of IAI's MiG-21-2000. IAI completely refurbished the MiG-21, giving it enhanced capabilities, a totally redesigned cockpit and new radar. The Royal Cambodian air force was to have been the initial recipient of this type, before the deal fell through.

This symbol of the Cold War – a pair of MiG-21s launching for another interception or training mission – was a common occurrence for over 30 years.

Production variants

Early MiG-21s

The original concept of the MiG-21 was for a simple, lightweight fighter, in which sophistication and considerations of endurance and firepower were sacrificed for outright performance. The production MiG-21 was preceded by a series of prototypes. Some had swept wings, while others had the delta-wing planform which was eventually chosen. The 40 pre-production MiG-21F (Ye-6T or Type 72) fighters, which attained limited service in 1959, were allocated the ASCC/NATO reporting name 'Fishbed-B', but the first full production version was the MIG-21F-13 'Fishbed-C', or Type 74. Initial operational capability came in January 1963, with the 28th Regiment based at Odessa, with the first export sales being made to Finland (seen above). The first 114 MiG-21F-13s had a narrow-chord vertical tail, but all had their armament reduced from two to one NR-30 cannon, on the starboard side, with underwing pylons for two AA-2 'Atoll' heat-seeking AAMs or rocket pods. Fuel capacity was increased from 602 US gal (2280 litres) to 674 US gal (2550 litres). China built a copy as the Shenyang J-7 (below, in export F-7 form, with Bangladesh).

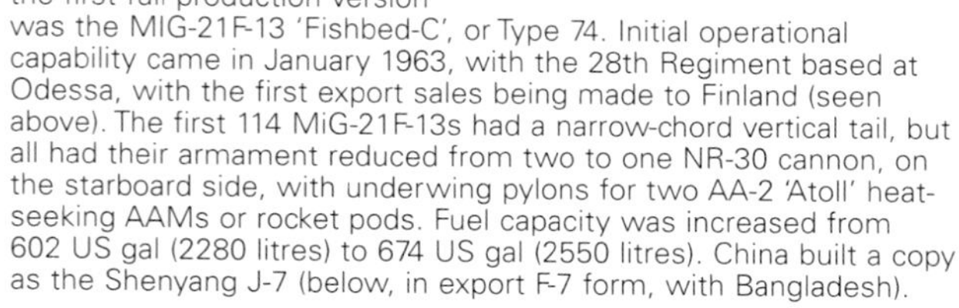

Early radar-equipped MiG-21s

The MiG-21P 'Fishbed-D' dispensed with cannon altogether. The large inlet centrebody housed a TsD-30T R1L 'Spin Scan' radar. The canopy and spine were modified, with a bulge immediately aft of the cockpit. Internal fuel was increased to 726 US gal (2750 litres). The MiG-21P was followed by the R11F2-300-engined MiG-21PF (Type 76), which had the pitot probe relocated to the top of the nose and was equipped with the improved RP-21 Sapfir radar. NATO allocated these aircraft the reporting name 'Fishbed-E'. The MiG-21FL was externally identical to the late MiG-21PF. Intended for export, it had less powerful R-2L radar and the original engine. Approximately 200 were built under licence in India. The Type 94 sub-variants, the MiG-21PFS and the MiG-21PFM 'Fishbed-F' had two-piece canopies with fixed windscreens, blown flaps, a cruciform brake 'chute, R-11F2S-300 engines and RP-21M radar. They could fire semi-active radar-homing RS-2US (AA-1 'Alkali') missiles.

Second-generation MiG-21s

Later MiG-21s gained heavier armament and increasingly sophisticated avionics. All had R-11F2S-300 or R-13-300 engines, blown flaps, pitot probes offset to the right of the centreline, two-piece canopies and broad-chord tailfins. The first of the new generation was the reconnaissance MiG-21R (Type 94R), based on the MiG-21PFM but with an enlarged dorsal fairing. The MiG-21S (Type 95) was the fighter version, with new radar and with a belly gun pod. It was followed by the MiG-21SM (Type 15), which also introduced a high-*g* combat gunsight and a GSh-23L cannon recessed into the belly. The MiG-21M (Type 96) (below and right) was an export version of the SM, also built under licence in India. The MiG-21MF 'Fishbed-J' (Type 96F) was a MiG-21M derivative for VVS use. It introduced AAM capability on all four underwing pylons.

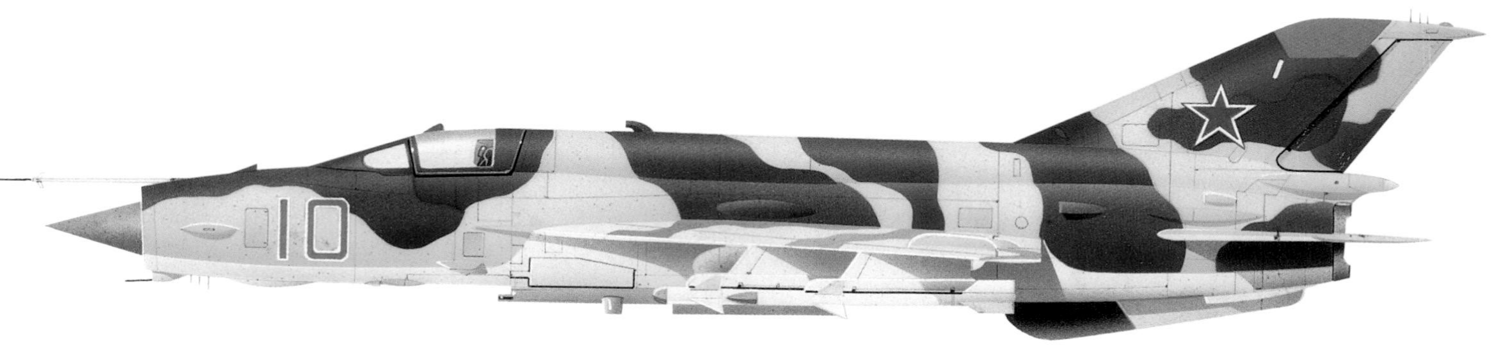

MiG-21bis

The third-generation MiG-21bis was the most advanced and most capable production 'Fishbed' variant, although by modern standards its lack of BVR missile capability, limited radar range, mediocre low-speed handling and poor endurance limit its usefulness. The ASCC/NATO reporting name 'Fishbed-L' was allocated to the first version, which entered service in February 1972. 'Fishbed-N' was applied to later production aircraft which had an undernose 'Swift Rod' ILS antenna and improved avionics. The MiG-21bis was developed as a multi-role fighter for Frontal Aviation, with better close combat capability through improved avionics and the ability to carry the new R-60 (AA-8 'Aphid') AAM. It was optimised for air combat at lower altitudes against more agile opponents, and also had an enhanced ground attack capability. It can carry four UV-16-57 rocket pods, or four 240-mm (9½-in) rockets, or two 500-kg (1,102-lb) and two 250-kg (551-lb) bombs. Equipped with improved Sapfir-21 radar and powered by the 15,653-lb (69.65-kN) Tumanskii R-25-300 engine, the MiG-21bis features a completely redesigned dorsal spine which looks little different from that fitted to most second-generation 'Fishbeds', but which holds twice as much fuel. The 'Fishbed-N' was built under licence in India between 1980 and 1987. Another version of the MiG-21bis was optimised for nuclear strike. The reconnaissance version of the MiG-21bis remained in Soviet and Russian service into the 1990s. Elsewhere, the MiG-21bis still serves in some strength with a number of operators.

MiG-21U and MiG-21US

Proposed two-seat trainer versions of the MiG-17 'Fresco' and MiG-19 'Farmer' were never produced, and it soon became apparent that the subsonic MiG-15UTI would be inadequate for the conversion training of pilots expected to fly the Mach-2 MiG-21. Mikoyan accordingly designed a two-seat trainer based on the MiG-21F-13 'Fishbed-C'. Armament and radar were deleted, although provision was made for a ventral gun pack, and the aircraft also had two underwing pylons. It was fitted with a one-piece airbrake below the forward fuselage and the pitot boom was repositioned above the nose. The instructor's cockpit was added behind the normal cockpit, and both were covered by separate sideways-hingeing canopies. Internal fuel was reduced to 620 US gal (23150 litres).The new trainer first flew, as the Ye-6U, on 17 October 1960, and entered production as the MiG-21U (Type 66). Early production aircraft had the original narrow-chord fin and had a brake 'chute at the rear of the ventral fin. The basic MiG-21U received the NATO reporting name 'Mongol-A' and was built by Znamya Truda between 1964 and 1968. From the start, the more capable MiG-21US 'Mongol-B' (Type 68) had the increased-chord tailfin fitted to later fighter versions of the MiG-21. Built at Tbilisi between 1966 and 1970, it had improved ejection seats, a bigger spine raising internal fuel capacity to 647 US gal (2450 litres), a retractable periscope and blown flaps. The MIG-21UM (Type 69) introduced updated instruments, autopilot and avionics (as fitted to the MiG-21R and subsequent single-seaters), and was fitted with an angle-of-attack sensor on the starboard side of the nose. It was built at Tbilisi from 1971. MiG-21 trainers have served with most operators of single-seat 'Fishbeds', primarily as conversion or continuation trainers. However, in the former USSR and still in India, two-seat MiG-21 trainers were and are used as dedicated advanced trainers, introducing new pilots to the special challenges of supersonic flight.

The Polish air force's 3 PLM flew this MiG-21MF from Poznan-Krzesiny until 2002. The unit also operated MiG-21R reconnaissance aircraft. As well as air force service, the MiG-21MF also equipped two squadrons of the Polish naval air arm, the last being disbanded in 2003.

Soviet & East European users

The USSR and its close allies in the Warsaw Pact received the lion's share of MiG-21 production. During the 1960s and early 1970s it was the Warsaw Pact's main tactical fighter.

Soviet Union/former Soviet republics

Over 10,000 MiG-21s were built, and over half went to the air forces of the USSR (right). Most were assigned to Frontal Aviation fighter units, although some also served with IA-PVO (air defence organisation) squadrons. A handful of pre-production MiG-21Fs were followed by large numbers of MiG-21F-13 day fighters. Successive major versions in use were the MiG-21PF with new radar in a larger intake centrebody, MiG-21PFM with two-piece canopy, blown flaps and upgraded radar, MiG-21M and SM with GSh-23L cannon, MiG-21MF with R-13-300 engine and four-AAM capability, MiG-21SMT with huge dorsal spine, and finally the MiG-21bis with R-25-300 engine and increased multi-role capability. The MiG-21R was a tactical reconnaissance version, while two-seat trainers were the MiG-21U, MiG-21US and MiG-21UM.
By the time the Soviet Union was formally dissolved in December 1991, the MiG-21 was fast approaching the end of its front-line career. Only a few flew on with Russia, the last front-line examples being MiG-21bis aircraft employed in a reconnaissance role. Subsequently, only a tiny handful remained active as test aircraft and for advanced training. A few examples may remain active with former Soviet republics, but this is

unlikely. Belarus, Kazakhstan and Ukraine certainly acquired MiG-21s, but they were not retained for long by their new masters, which quickly disposed of all single-engined fighters. Azerbaijan took over around 18 MiG-21Ms, but their serviceability is questionable, and at least one was lost in clashes with Armenia in the early 1990s. Kyrgyzstan took over a sizeable MiG-21/21UM force, but they are thought to have been stored. Turkmenistan was reported to be operating three in the advanced training role, but their continued use is highly unlikely.

Warsaw Pact/East European operators

The Warsaw Pact nations followed the Soviet Union in acquiring a succession of MiG-21 variants, all beginning with the MiG-21F-13. Bulgaria retains the MiG-21bis and MiG-21UM in a single squadron, 3 IAB at Graf Ignatievo. Czechoslovakia received large numbers of MiG-21s up to the MF. The Aero factory also produced 195 MiG-21F-13s, locally designated S-107 (right). On 1 January 1993 the country split into the Czech Republic, whose air force took 69 MiG-21MFs, 20 MiG-21UMs and 5 MiG-21USs, and Slovakia, which acquired 49 MiG-21MFs, eight MiG-21Rs (retired in 1995), 11 MiG-21UMs and two MiG-21USs. The Czechs replaced their fleet with the Aero L-159 and the Saab Gripen, while Slovakia disposed of its 'Fishbed' fleet without replacement. One of the largest recipients was East Germany, which acquired all major versions from MiG-21F-13 to MiG-21bis. When the two Germanies were reunited, the MiG-21 force was withdrawn and most were scrapped. A few served on test duties. Hungary (below) enjoyed a stream of MiG-21

deliveries throughout the 1960s and 1970s, culminating in MiG-21bis/UM deliveries. These variants latterly served with a single regiment at Pápa, before replacement by the Gripen. Poland also received large numbers – which equipped nine fighter regiments – and was notable for operating the MiG-21R. Many of these remained in use into the 21st century. While other East European operators opted for new Western equipment, Romania adopted a major upgrade to keep its MiG-21s in service for the forseeable future. Aerostar joined forces with the Israeli Elbit company to upgrade 75 MiG-21M/MFs to Lancer A ground-attack standard, 10 MiG-21UMs to Lancer B trainer standard, and 25 MiG-21M/MFs to Lancer C air defence configuration. The upgrade includes new radar, modern cockpit and new weapons. The earlier MiG-21F-13s, MiG-21PFs and MiG-21FLs have since been retired.

Worldwide service

India's MiG-21 total includes 580 built or assembled by HAL. Variants used have included the MiG-21F, MiG-21FL, MiG-21PFMA, MiG-21M, MiG-21MF, MiG-21U/UM and MiG-21bis (illustrated). The latter were the subject of an upgrade programme to produce the Bison, preceded by two MiG-21bis-UPG prototypes.

Available and cheap, the MiG-21 was supplied to a great number of nations around the world. It often formed the basis of Soviet military aid packages to nations emerging from a colonial past.

Middle East

Iraq received about 100 MiG-21s (PFM, MF, U) from the USSR, although many were lost in the war with Iran, or destroyed during Desert Storm. Post-1991 war, around 50 reportedly remained in use. Syria also lost a large number of its 'Fishbeds' (PF, MF, bis, U), most in air fighting with the Israeli air force. A small number may remain operational in 2007. North Yemen acquired 40 MiG-21MFs in 1979/80, along with MiG-21Us, plus around 40 MiG-21bis fighters later. These became the most numerous type in the Republic of Yemen Air Force, when north and south unified in May 1990.

Europe

Outside of eastern Europe, the MiG-21 was most famously operated by Finland, whose air force was tied by the Treaty of Paris to purchase its equipment from both East and West. This resulted in the acquisition of 22 MiG-21F-13s (below) and two MiG-21Us, followed later by 27 MiG-21bis and four MiG-21UMs. The Finnish air force also operated Drakens in the interceptor role. Freed from the aforementioned treaty by the dissolution of the Soviet Union, Finland acquired F-18 Hornets to replace both fighter types: the MiG-21 was retired in March 1998. Not a Warsaw Pact member, Yugoslavia nevertheless enjoyed good relations with Moscow, and acquired around 45 MiG-21F-13s, 35 MiG-21PFMs, 68 MiG-21PFMAs, 35 MiG-21bis, and 40 MiG-21U/UMs. These were assigned local designations from L-12 to L-17. Although several were lost during NATO attacks, a number remain in service with Serbia. During the Croatian war three defected to the breakaway republic of Croatia, one of which was used to build a new force which later acquired 20 MiG-21bis and four MiG-21UMs, probably from the Ukraine. Survivors have been upgraded by Aerostar or Romania.

The Americas/Caribbean

Apart from the aircraft (notably a number of MiG-21F-13s tested from the late 1960s) acquired and evaluated by the United States, the only MiG-21 operator in the Americas is Cuba. The Fuerza Aérea Revolucionaria acquired around 30 MiG-21F-13s, 35 MiG-21PFMs, 20 MiG-21PFMAs, 80 MiG-21bis, at least 10 MiG-21U/UMs and some MiG-21Rs. These originally equipped nine fighter squadrons, and a dwindling number of survivors continue to contribute to the island's air defences. Despite reports to the contrary, the MiG-21s assembled in Cuba for the Sandinista regime in Nicaragua were not delivered.

Central/Southern Asia

Outside the Soviet Union, India was, and is, the most important MiG-21 user, having bought and built 830 aircraft. The MiG-21bis remains the most numerous, with 295 having been delivered. All 70 two-seaters were built in the USSR. Afghanistan operated 45 MiG-21F-13s before the Soviet invasion, and received later models after the withdrawal. Bangladesh operated 12 MiG-21MFs and two MiG-21Us from 1973, subsequently retired, while Mongolia received around 30 MiG-21PFMs, survivors apparently being grounded by 2001.

Far East

Cambodia received 19 MiG-21bis and three MiG-21UM in 1986, of which 12 were planned to be overhauled by IAI. Indonesia briefly operated MiG-21F-13s in the 1960s. North Korea received its first MiG-21F-13 in 1965 and subsequently acquired PFs and PFMs. Around 30 MiG-21s (comprising eight MiG-21Fs, two MiG-21Us and 20 MiG-21PFMs) were supplied to Laos, while neighbour Vietnam received a large number of aircraft in many versions. These were heavily involved in the Vietnam War, and today as many as 120 MiG-21MFs may remain in air force use.

Africa

Around 100 'Fishbeds' (MiG-21F/MF/bis/U) were delivered to Algeria and finally retired in 2003. Angola received eight MiG-21MFs in 1976, and subsequently built a force of up to 75. Burkina Faso received eight MiG-21s and two trainers in 1984, but they have since been grounded, while the Congo Republic received 16 in 1986 (also grounded). Egypt (below) was perhaps the best-known overseas user, acquiring over 400 in many versions (including Chinese-built F-7s) and using them in bloody battles with the Israelis. In 2007, five F-7 and MiG-21MF squadrons remained, these units including two-seat MiG-21UMs and FT-7s. Ethiopia had a large force of around 100 aircraft before the civil war began in 1991. A few continued to serve post-1991, and at least one was lost in clashes with Eritrea. Guinea-Bissau received 10 MiG-21MFs and two MiG-21UMs in the late 1980s, while neighbour Guinea Republic began to operate eight MiG-21PFMs in 1986. Libya acquired around 75 'Fishbeds' for fighter-bomber duties. Madagascar operated eight MiG-21FLs and two MiG-21UMs, and Mali received 12 MiG-21MFs and two MiG-21UMs in 1976. Mozambique acquired 48 MiG-21MFs from 1977 which flew combat against Renamo guerrillas. Around 15 were still active into the 1990s. Nigeria received 25 MiG-21MFs in 1975 with eight MiG-21UMs. More were on order but were not delivered. Seven MiG-21MFs and two MiG-21UMs were delivered to Somalia in July 1974 before being abandoned in the country's civil war. Sudan acquired 16 MiG-21PFMs in 1969, and Uganda received 12 MiG-21MFs. Seven of these were destroyed during the Israeli hostage rescue at Entebbe. Finally, Zambia received 16 MiG-21MFs and four MiG-21US.

MiG-21 upgrades

Cost-effective MiG-21 upgrades, typified by that offered by Romania's Aerostar in collaboration with Israel, provide a solution to the problems of modernising an otherwise aging 'Fishbed' force.

Seen during its maiden flight on 24 May 1995, the MiG-21-2000 conversion, developed by IAI's Lahav division, suffered an uncertain fate after the collapse of a deal with Cambodia.

Israel was an early aircraft upgrader, as arms embargoes forced the nation towards self-sufficiency. Israel's aviation industry developed integrated structural, avionics, weapons, and cockpit upgrade packages for Israeli combat aircraft and marketed upgrades to types already in Israeli service. It soon became clear that the company's F-4 upgrade could form the basis of a MiG-21 modernisation.

IAI's Lavi- and F-4E-2000 based MiG-21-2000 upgrade included a Mil Std 1553B digital databus, a one-piece wrap-round windscreen, a Martin-Baker ejection seat, a wide-angle HUD, and a modernised semi-glass cockpit, with HOTAS controls. IAI also offered to improve the existing Sapfir radar, or to install a new Elta EL/M-2032 multi-mode pulse-Doppler radar.

But IAI's first MiG-21 upgrade contract was for the more modest modernisation of eight Cambodian MiG-21s, restoring the aircraft to airworthiness, without adding many new systems, and hopes that it would gain the lucrative contract to upgrade Romania's MiG-21s were dashed.

When Romania finalised plans for an upgrade of 110 MiG-21s, Elbit was awarded the contract, providing programme management and supplying and integrating the avionics, while Aerostar refurbished the aircraft and installed the new equipment.

Advanced avionics

Upgraded Romanian MiG-21 Lancers feature a Mil Std 1553B avionics system, with full HOTAS controls and multi-function display screens, a new HUD and provision for the DASH (Display and Sight Helmet) as well as modern navigation, RWR and self-defence systems. The 75 close air support aircraft and the 10 trainers have an Elta ranging radar, while the 25 air defence-configured aircraft have an Elta EL/M-2032 multi-mode pulse-Doppler radar. The prototype Lancer flew on 23 August 1995, two months ahead of schedule. Several squadrons are fully operational, using weapons of Western and Soviet origin.

Romania's Lancers were all converted from MiG-21MF and MiG-21UM/US airframes, but it was soon decided that the same upgrade should be available for the MiG-21bis (widely used outside Romania), and Elbit and Aerostar modified a newly acquired bis as the prototype Lancer III, which made a maiden flight in October 1998.

The MiG-21's original manufacturer was a late entrant to the upgrade market. Russian OKBs and factories were unused to refurbishing and modifying old aircraft rather than building new ones, while the major weakness of even the latest Russian fighters lay in their poor cockpit ergonomics, primitive displays, lack of processing speed and capacity, and fire control system software design, the very areas which would have to be upgraded on the MiG-21. This gave Western companies greater credibility as upgrade providers.

When it became clear that foreign companies were earning money from MiG-21 upgrades, MiG OKB teamed with Sokol to offer the MiG-21-93 upgrade. The

Undertaking operational conversion training for the Romanian Lancer fleet, the ten Lancer Bs (ex-MiG-21UM/US aircraft) have a secondary combat role and front-line standard defensive aids.

The 25 Lancer C air defence versions represent the ultimate evolution of the upgraded MiG-21 in Romanian service, and are capable of carrying both Russian R-73 and Israeli Python 3 AAMs.

Sokol GAZ-21 factory had been the source of most of the MiG-21s built, and thus the Russian team had an unrivalled knowledge of the aircraft's structure, aerodynamics and systems as well as tooling.

The MiG-21-93 featured a Kopyo radar, a new one-piece windscreen, a helmet-mounted sighting system, a modernised cockpit, provision for advanced weapons (including fire-and-forget BVR AAMs) and enhanced defensive systems. It soon became clear that there was some customer resistance to Russian avionics equipment, especially in India, and the company began to offer a number of Western avionics system options.

India's upgrade

India is the world's largest remaining MiG-21 operator, having received more than 830 examples (580 of which had been locally assembled or built). Although some early MiG-21s were replaced by new types, large numbers of later MiG-21M, MF and bis (modified) versions remained active. India placed a US$428 million contract with Mikoyan and Sokol on 3 May 1994, covering the upgrade of 100 MiG-21bis fighters to MiG-21-93 standard (now known in India as the Bison). In March 1996 the contract was expanded to cover the upgrade of 125 Indian MiG-21bis airframes, but the first 12 of these aircraft did not become operational until 2002, with 'production' some years behind schedule.

India demanded certain Western systems, including Mil Std 1553 architecture, a Totem 221G ring laser gyro INS, Israeli flare dispensers and indigenous active jammer, radios, radio altimeter, radio compass, and IFF transponder.

The first Indian MiG-21-93 flew on 3 October 1998 and the second followed in February 1999. Deliveries of upgrade kits began after the December 2000 hand-over of the prototypes.

Mikoyan and Sokol have since offered the MiG-21-93 upgrade to Ethiopia, and to meet Vietnam's upgrade requirement, introduced a new upgrade configuration, known as the MiG-21-98, which is applicable to older MiG-21 variants. This configuration includes a modern 'glass' cockpit with colour LCD displays and offers a choice of compact radars.

Rafael Python 3
The Python 3 is based upon the earlier Shafrir missiles and was the baseline AAM in Israeli service during the 1980s and early 1990s. Now replaced by the Python 4, it remains an effective weapon. Python 3 has a 24-lb (11-kg) HE warhead, triggered by a contact or radar proximity fuse. Its all-aspect IR seeker can be slaved to the radar and has an off-boresight launch capability of 30°

MiG-21 Lancer A

Romania's Lancer A force is currently concentrated at three bases: Bacau, Borcea-Festesti and Câmpia Turzii. Aircraft do not wear individual group or squadron markings, but large white titles have been applied to some aircraft, particularly those involved with NATO PfP (Partnership for Peace) exercises. All MiG-21M/MFs considered for upgrade by Aerostar were built post-1975, and so represent the most modern 'new-build' MiG-21s of that version.

Opher IR-guided bomb
Elbit's Opher terminal guidance system is typically fitted to a 500-lb (227-kg) Mk 82 bomb. It resembles a Paveway II LGB, but uses an IR seeker rather than laser guidance. Developed as an anti-armour weapon, it is nevertheless capable of engaging a range of static and mobile targets. The sensitive seeker is able to differentiate between attacked (burning) targets and unattacked ones. Typical employment range is 4.3 miles (7 km). The seeker acquires its target at about 3,280 ft (1000 m). The Mk 82 bomb version has a 192-lb (97-kg) HE warhead.

Mikoyan-Gurevich

MiG-23/27 'Flogger'

Swing-wing fighters

The West's first view of the 'Flogger' came in 1978, when six MiG-23MLs visited Finland and France. As a measure of security, the Soviets had sanitised the aircraft by removing the undernose IRST sensor, gun pods and AAMs.

Serving in huge numbers with the Soviet air forces and with virtually all of its client states, the MiG-23/27 is one of the most widely operated jet fighters ever. The key to its success lay in its basic design configuration, which offered a unique blend of robustness, performance and versatility.

Development of the MiG-23 began in the early 1960s, when the Mikoyan-Gurevich OKB began studies for a replacement for its MiG-21 tactical fighter. Aware of the shortcomings of the MiG-21, the Design Bureau wanted to produce a fighter with greater payload, range and firepower, and with more sensors to give freedom from the constraints of tight ground-controlled interception (GCI). The new aircraft was to be faster, and able to climb more rapidly than the 'Fishbed'. The new fighter would therefore have to be larger and heavier, but this would result in the aircraft having an exceptionally long take-off run. MiG studied many alternative approaches to the problem of producing a STOL fighter.

Variable geometry

The variable-geometry (VG) wing had been recognised by MiG OKB as the best way of overcoming the primary shortcomings of the 'Fishbed', i.e. short range and a small weapons load. Fully spread, the VG wing offered a shorter take-off/landing roll while enabling the aircraft to carry a heavier weapons load. In the fully swept position, the wing allowed for a high top speed and good supersonic handling characteristics. There were disadvantages to the VG wing, however, as the construction of the wing sweep mechanism required a larger fuselage and was relatively heavy. These factors, together with the importance of the position to be held by the new aircraft within the Soviet air force, resulted in MiG developing two parallel designs simultaneously.

Although both designs utilised similar fuselages, the first design, designated 23-01 (and later MiG-23PD), had a fixed delta wing and was powered by a single main engine (a Tumanskii R-27-300), with two lift 'sustainer' engines (actually Koliesov RD-36-35s) located in the centre fuselage for take-off and landing. The aircraft accomplished its first flight on 3 April 1967 and was exhibited at the Domododevo air show in July of that year, where the new design was designated 'Faithless' by Western observers.

Having accomplished only 14 flights, Mikoyan realised that the lift-jet concept was flawed and the programme was terminated. While this design was being developed, a second design team was constructing 23-11, which was intended to be a VG version of the 23-01. However, only the nose section, empennage design and turbojet powerplant (the Tumanskii R-27F-300) were common to the two aircraft. Following the failure of the earlier design, the 23-11 was given the highest priority within the Soviet government, with the result that the aircraft accomplished its first flight on 10 April 1967, a little over two years since the VG design had first been studied. Within weeks of its maiden flight, the new design was displayed to the public at Domododevo, where NATO assigned it the name 'Flogger'. Basic flight trials ended in July 1968, after 98 highly successful flights, resulting in the 'Flogger' being quickly ordered for front-line squadrons.

The first variant to enter operational squadron service was the MiG-23S, which was intended to utilise the advanced *Sapfir* radar (hence the 'S' suffix) and a more powerful variant of the Tumanskii turbojet. However, development of the radar was not completed by the time the aircraft entered service, resulting in early 'Floggers' being equipped with the far less capable 'Jay Bird' radar adopted from the MiG-21S. In a single stroke, the capabilities of the new aircraft were compromised, for the 'Flogger' completely lacked any BVR capability.

Aware of the operating limitations of the MiG-23S, a new model was quickly introduced, as the MiG-23M. Equipped with the intended pulse-Doppler *Sapfir* radar, the 'Flogger' was at last free from the constraints of tight GCI. This meant that, coupled with the newly developed R-23 (AA-7 'Apex') AAM, the 'Flogger' had emerged as a highly competent interceptor.

Rapid technological developments spawned a host of 'Flogger' variants of the MiG-23S, many the result of an uprated powerplant or improvements to the radar. For many client states, the prestige of operating one of the first generations of VG aircraft

Above: Seen flying high over the Gulf, this is one of the less sophisticated variants of the 'Flogger' (MiG-23MS) supplied to non-Warsaw Pact export customers, in this case Libya. The variant lacked any BVR capability and served only in the visual dogfight arena, thus running contrary to US Navy reports on the shooting down of two such 'Floggers' on 4 January 1989 by F-14 Tomcats. The reports claimed that the Libyan aircraft had posed a threat to the carrier battle fleet.

Serving among the many Soviet air force units based in East Germany during the 1980s, this MiG-27K was capable of bad weather blind-bombing with laser-guided air-to-surface missiles.

was too good to miss, but Mikoyan was reluctant to offer the highly sophisticated models to Third World clients. This resulted in sanitised variants which lacked the sophisticated avionics – these models were designated the MiG-23MS or MF.

Ground-attack 'Flogger'

The 'Flogger' design had already provided the Soviet air force and its customers with highly capable variants when the additional role of ground-attack was added. This initially took the form of the MiG-23B family, based on the MiG-23S airframe but with a radarless nose of steeper-sloping profile, providing better forward visibility. These were followed by the definitive MiG-27 family, which dispensed with the variable-geometry intakes and jetpipe, in addition to other changes. Ordered straight off the drawing board by the Soviet air force, the MiG-27 only served to increase the reputation of its elder cousin, the MiG-23. A host of client states adopted the new aircraft, resulting in many operating both 'Flogger' variants at the same time, as well as two-seat versions. Throughout its operational career, the MiG-27 underwent continual upgrading, with no fewer than four basic models, each of which in turn spawned a host of production sub-variants.

Mikoyan continued to improve the 'Flogger' into the 1990s. One potential upgrade is illustrated on this MiG-23MLD, which is equipped with R-77 AAMs

MiG-23MLD 'Flogger-K'

This MiG-23MLD was used by Major Anatoly Stipanjk during his squadron's deployment to Afghanistan in 1986. The aircraft carried mission markings in the form of small white stars below the cockpit. Sometimes, individual stars were initialled by the pilot responsible for each mission.

Missile threat
'Flogger-Gs' in Afghanistan carried chaff/flare launchers mounted on the upper fuselage. These were used to decoy IR-guided, shoulder-launched anti-aircraft missiles, such as the American Stinger, fired by rebel forces.

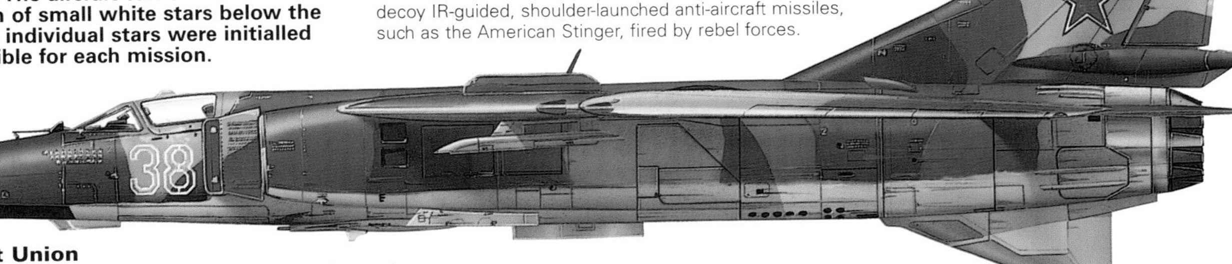

Hero of the Soviet Union
'Flogger' pilot Col Anatolij Levchenko flew 188 missions during the war in Afghanistan, his last being on 27 December 1986. Having attacked traffic on the Salang Pass, his aircraft was hit by AAA. Unable to eject, he dived into the enemy gun position, subsequently destroying it, and enabling the rest of his squadron to escape. Levchenko was posthumously awarded the USSR's highest honour.

Air-to-air combat
With the Mujahideen lacking any air force, most 'Floggers' served as ground-attack aircraft. However, when attacking rebel camps in Pakistan, aerial engagements with PAF F-16s resulted in several kill claims and 'close calls'.

MiG-23/27 Variants

Widely dismissed in the West as an obsolete and ineffective aircraft, the MiG-23/27 family proved to be remarkably versatile and robust, and spawned a number of variants.

MiG-23S/M/MF/MS 'Flogger-A/B/E'

During the 1960s, the need for a MiG-21 replacement was conceived and Mikoyan-Gurevich began design work on the MiG-23. The authorities were determined that the increased size and weight of the new fighter would not impose longer take-off distances. A series of trials confirmed that the variable-geometry Model 23-11 represented the most effective configuration, and this was ordered into production as the MiG-23S with a powerful 22,046-lb st (98.1-kN) R-27F2M-300 engine. Initially, an RP-22 'Jay Bird' radar (like that of the MiG-21S) was installed, giving a very recognisable short radome and removing BVR capability. The aircraft was also fitted with a TP-23 IRST. Fifty were built between mid-1969 and the end of 1970 and were used for operational trials before production switched to the MiG-23M, dubbed 'Flogger-B' by NATO. This featured the pulse-Doppler *Sapfir*-23 ('High Lark') radar and new fire control system and autopilot. The MiG-23M could fire the R-23 (AA-7 'Apex') semi-active radar-homing missile. A new 27,557-lb st (122.63-kN) Soyuz (Tumanskii) R-29-300 (with shorter jetpipe) was fitted, while at the same time the aircraft's horizontal tail surfaces were moved aft, giving a very different appearance. A fourth fuel tank was added in the rear fuselage. A new Type 1 wing, with an extended leading edge, was introduced, having a pronounced dogtooth inboard. Leading-edge slats were deleted (Type 2 wing), then reintroduced in 1973 with the Type 3 wing.

MiG-23Ms were delivered to Frontal Aviation as MiG-21 replacements, operating mainly in the battlefield air superiority role, but with an important secondary ground-attack capability. Others went to the IA-PVO, where they augmented MiG-21s, Su-9s, Su-11s and Su-15s in the air defence role. Two downgraded export versions of the MiG-23M were produced, the second gaining the new reporting name 'Flogger-E'. The MiG-23MS was a substantially downgraded version with MiG-21-type 'Jay Bird' radar in a short radome, with no BVR missile capability. The MiG-23MF was less radically sanitised and retained the 'High Lark' fire control radar, AA-7 'Apex' missile capability and 'Flogger-B' reporting name of the MiG-23M, and was delivered to Russia's Warsaw Pact allies, then later to Syria, Angola, Iraq, India and Libya.

MiG-23ML/P/MLD 'Flogger-G/K'

The MiG-23ML 'Flogger-G' (allocated the OKB designation 23-12) featured improved handling, especially at high angles of attack, enhanced manoeuvrability and higher *g* limits. It featured a lightened airframe, with the fourth fuselage fuel tank removed and the dorsal fin fillet deleted. More power was provided by installing the Soyuz (Tumanskii) R-35-300 engine.

A very similar aircraft, designated MiG-23P (23-14), was used by the PVO and had a new digital computer that allowed the aircraft to be automatically steered onto its target from the ground, cueing the pilot to engage afterburner and launch weapons. The MiG-23ML also served as the basis for the MiG-23MLD (23-18), codenamed 'Flogger-K' by NATO. The new version, reportedly produced by conversion of MiG-23ML airframes, incorporated vortex generators on the pitot probe and notches in its vestigial leading-edge root extensions. Large chaff/flare dispensers could now be fitted above the rear fuselage, linked to the new RWR system. A new IFF system was also fitted, and a missile-firing simulator allowed economic training. Further modifications included swivelling pylons under the outboard wing panels, which moved to remain aligned with the airflow even when the wings were swept.

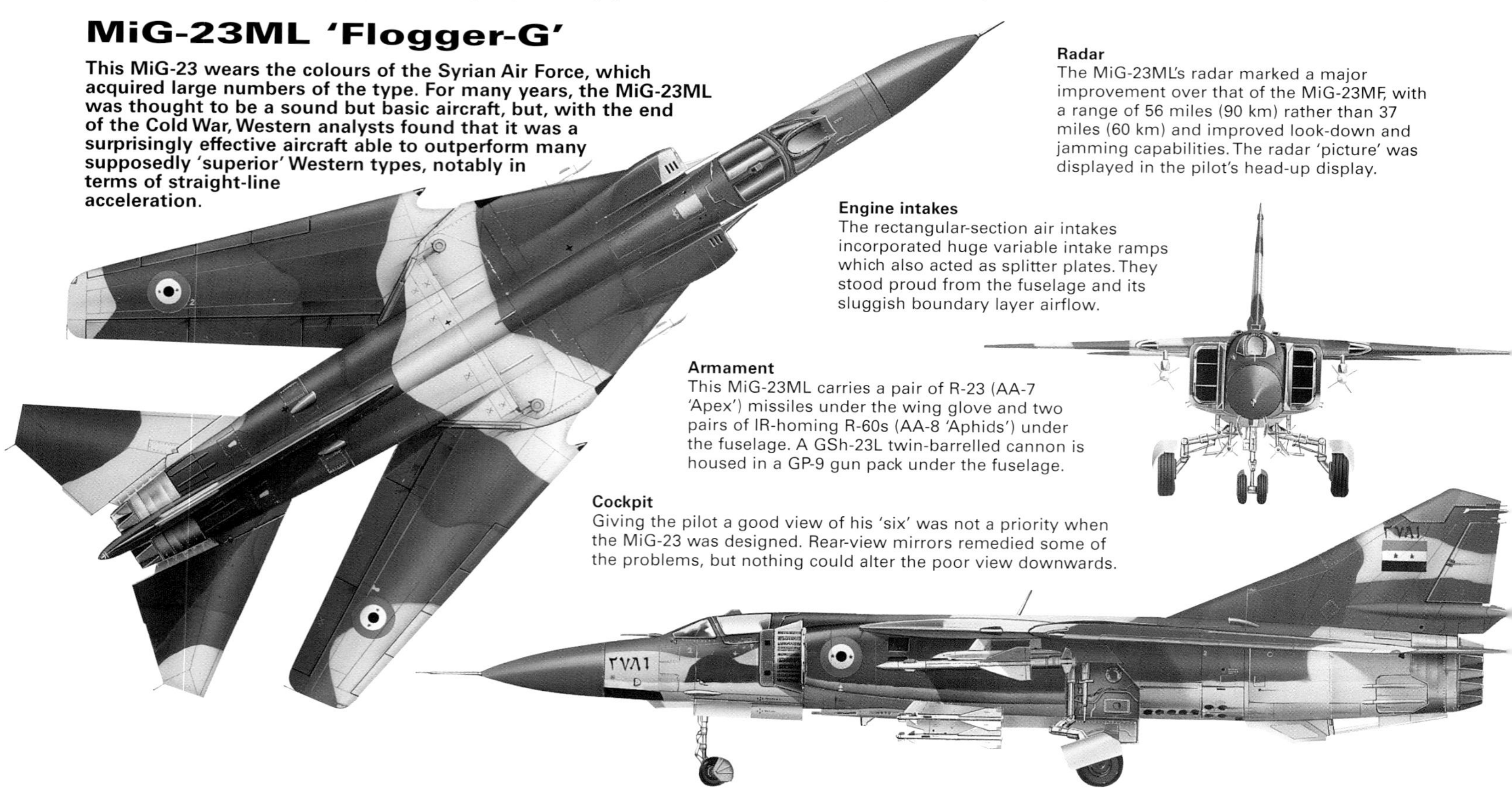

MiG-23ML 'Flogger-G'

This MiG-23 wears the colours of the Syrian Air Force, which acquired large numbers of the type. For many years, the MiG-23ML was thought to be a sound but basic aircraft, but, with the end of the Cold War, Western analysts found that it was a surprisingly effective aircraft able to outperform many supposedly 'superior' Western types, notably in terms of straight-line acceleration.

Radar
The MiG-23ML's radar marked a major improvement over that of the MiG-23MF, with a range of 56 miles (90 km) rather than 37 miles (60 km) and improved look-down and jamming capabilities. The radar 'picture' was displayed in the pilot's head-up display.

Engine intakes
The rectangular-section air intakes incorporated huge variable intake ramps which also acted as splitter plates. They stood proud from the fuselage and its sluggish boundary layer airflow.

Armament
This MiG-23ML carries a pair of R-23 (AA-7 'Apex') missiles under the wing glove and two pairs of IR-homing R-60s (AA-8 'Aphids') under the fuselage. A GSh-23L twin-barrelled cannon is housed in a GP-9 gun pack under the fuselage.

Cockpit
Giving the pilot a good view of his 'six' was not a priority when the MiG-23 was designed. Rear-view mirrors remedied some of the problems, but nothing could alter the poor view downwards.

MiG-23UB 'Flogger-C'

The handling characteristics of the MiG-23 were very different from those of other aircraft in the Soviet inventory, so development of a two-seat trainer version was authorised in May 1968, six months after the the go-ahead had been given for the single-seat aircraft. The MiG-23UB (23-51) prototype, or 'Flogger-C', made its maiden flight in May 1969. The MiG-23UB was always supposed to be used for both pilot conversion and weapons training, and even to have a restricted combat capability. Accordingly, a separate guidance and illuminator pod for the AA-7 'Apex' missile was fitted in a conical fairing on the starboard wingroot. Production aircraft all received the 'clawed' No. 3 wing (compatible with the carriage of outboard underwing fuel tanks on non-swivelling pylons), and the two tandem cockpits were covered by separate upward-hinging canopies. The instructor was provided with a retractable periscope to give a better view forward on approach. MiG-23UBs were fitted with an AoA limiter or an AoA warning system, together with a comprehensive avionics suite that featured a sophisticated system allowing the backseater to simulate emergencies and threats for the student pilot in the front cockpit. Almost all MiG-23 and MiG-27 operators also used the MiG-23UB, and the type, although phased out of production in 1978, continued to serve with Russian MiG-29 and Su-27 units into the 1990s.

MiG-23B/BK/BM/BN 'Flogger-F/H'

In 1969, Mikoyan began studies of a cheap, mass-produced attack aircraft. However, instead of a new aircraft, economic constraints forced Mikoyan to examine the possibility of using a derivative of the MiG-23S, whose supersonic dash capability was felt to be a useful bonus. Mikoyan allocated a new designation (Model 32) but the air force – perhaps feeling that funding for a new aircraft would be harder to obtain – retained the MiG-23 designation.

The original MiG-23 had been developed as a multi-role tactical fighter and, with its rugged airframe, strong undercarriage, powerful engine and variable-geometry wing, it had the ability to operate from primitive, semi-prepared airstrips. It was extremely suitable for conversion or adaptation to the fighter-bomber role. The basic MiG-23B (32-24) was based on the airframe of the MiG-23S, but with a new, more sloping nose that gave the pilot an improved view forward and downward, and with a 112.78-kN (25,353-lb st) Lyul'ka AL-21F-300 powerplant in a shortened rear fuselage. Also like the MiG-23M, the new ground-attack variant featured the No. 2 wing and was later fitted with the No. 3 wing. The new aircraft received a PrNK *Sokol*-23S nav/attack system. Armour was scabbed on to the sides of the forward fuselage to protect the pilot, and the fuel tanks were fitted with an inert gas-injection fire protection system. A missile illuminator and a TV camera were housed in bullet-like fairings on the wingroot gloves. Some 24 MiG-23Bs were built before production switched to an improved variant. The MiG-23BN (32-23) featured an upgraded PrNK *Sokol*-23N nav/attack system and was powered by a slightly derated version of the Soyuz (Tumanskii) R-29B-300 engine. The MiG-23BN was intended to have been the first attack version, but was delayed by equipment and engine problems. It introduced the leading-edge bullet fairings on the fixed wing gloves that are usually associated with the Kh-23 (AS-7 'Kerry') ASM. The MiG-23B and MiG-23BN shared the NATO reporting name 'Flogger-F'.

The MiG-23B and MiG-23BN proved disappointing in service, and many were subsequently upgraded to MiG-23BK (32-26) or MiG-23BM (32-25) standards, or exported. Improved avionics were desperately needed, and two new fighter-bombers were quickly developed, both sharing the name 'Flogger-H'. This was assigned because they had new RWR fairings on the lower 'corners' of the fuselage, just ahead of the nosewheel bay. Cuban attack MiG-23s were 'Flogger-Fs', without the intake-mounted RWR fairings, for example, while German and Czech aircraft had these fairings and were therefore 'Flogger-Hs'. The first of the new variants was the MiG-23BK, which had the same nav/attack system and laser rangefinder as the MiG-27K. The MiG-23BM was similar, but with the same PrNK *Sokol*-23M nav/ attack system as the MiG-27D. Confusingly, the MiG-23BN designation seems to have been adopted as an overall service designation, sometimes being applied to aircraft designated BM or BK by the OKB. Many export 'Flogger-Hs' were usually described as MiG-23BNs, and were perhaps built as such, but were actually to MiG-23BK standards. Such aircraft included East Germany's MiG-23BKs, whose documentation described them as MiG-24BNs. Bulgarian, Czech, Indian and Iraqi 'Flogger-Hs' looked identical, although many of the latter later received fixed inflight-refuelling probes above the nose.

MiG-27D/K/L/M 'Flogger-D/J/J2'

The MiG-27 designation was originally applied to a number of designs drawn up by the Mikoyan OKB for the requirement eventually filled by the Su-25. After Vietnam, the need for subsonic aircraft which could provide conventional close air support/battlefield air interdiction was realised. The original MiG-27 and similar MiG-27K 'Flogger-D' were ordered into production directly off the drawing board, and the prototype made its maiden flight during 1972. Early examples were soon in service with the Group of Soviet Forces in Germany. The 'straight' MiG-27 was very soon replaced by the MiG-27K, equipped with the PrNK-23K nav/attack system and a *Fone* laser rangefinder/target tracker mounted behind a small window in the nose. The MiG-27K was capable of night or bad weather blind bombing with a very high degree of accuracy. RWR and ECM equipment was highly automated, and a new stores management system gave the pilot greater flexibility in selecting and using weapons.

There were several sub-variants of the aircraft known to NATO as 'Flogger-J'. All had wing glove bullet fairings removed and extended wing leading-edge root extensions. The latter were added to serve as a location for the forward hemisphere RWR antennas, but also had the beneficial side effect of improving high-Alpha handling. All 'Flogger-Js' received a new *Klen* laser rangefinder in place of the MiG-27K's *Fone* unit. The 'Swift Rod' ILS antenna was moved from below the nose to the port side of the nose, opposite the pitot.

There is some confusion regarding Soviet designations of some of the aircraft. The first of the 'Flogger-Js' was the new-build MiG-27M, which had an enlarged laser window in the nose. Some externally identical aircraft allegedly bore the Soviet air force designation MiG-27D. This variant incorporated the RSBN-6S navigation system, which was associated with the nuclear strike role. The twin pitot probes which served the nav/attack system were mounted high on the nose, providing the main recognition features between the basic MiG-27D/MiG-27K 'Flogger-J' and the MiG-27K 'Flogger-J2'. The latter variant was produced as a new-build aircraft, and by conversion of MiG-27s, -27Ds and perhaps -27Ms. It had a noticeable fairing below the nose, with a broad rectangular window for a FLIR system, and an upper window for the laser target designator which was a new system and a member of the *Kaira* family. The twin pitots were mounted low on the nose and the 'pimple' radome was enlarged.

The Soviet Union exported its most capable aircraft only to a handful of highly trusted Warsaw Pact allies and a few favoured client states, so the MiG-27 was not made widely available to foreign customers. The most significant exception was India, which built the MiG-27 under licence, operating a version named the MiG-27M, but which Mikoyan refers to as the MiG-27L. The aircraft has the same nose contours as the MiG-27M/D, with only a single window in the undernose fairing, and shares the same 'Flogger-J' reporting name. Soviet MiG-27s first saw combat in Afghanistan where a regiment of MiG-27Ds was deployed to Shindand for offensive operations against Mujahideen guerrilla positions.

Mikoyan MiG-25 'Foxbat'

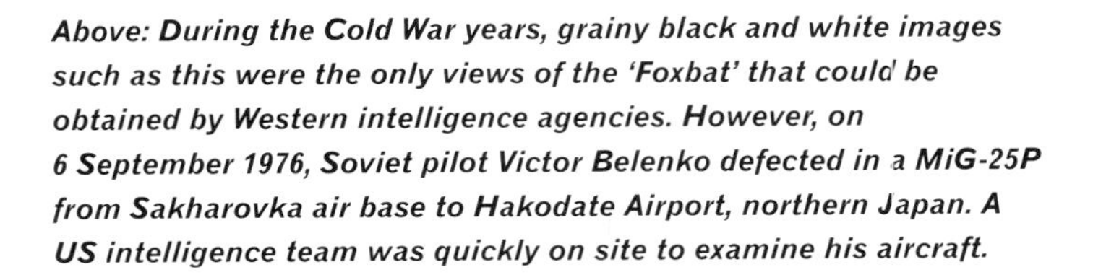

Above: During the Cold War years, grainy black and white images such as this were the only views of the 'Foxbat' that could be obtained by Western intelligence agencies. However, on 6 September 1976, Soviet pilot Victor Belenko defected in a MiG-25P from Sakharovka air base to Hakodate Airport, northern Japan. A US intelligence team was quickly on site to examine his aircraft.

Top: The imposing size and boxy shape of the MiG-25 set it apart from other combat aircraft. The 'Foxbat' was built from a unique mix of steel, aluminium and titanium that gave it the structural strength to survive in its high-speed, high-altitude operational environment – yet the design was robust enough to be maintained on a flight line, even in poor weather conditions.

Cold War heavyweight

The MiG-25 'Foxbat' became a great symbol of the postwar Soviet threat. The large family of variants remained a potent force up until the collapse of the Soviet Union, and the type remains in export use.

The MiG-25 was developed in response to the North American XB-70 Valkyrie strategic bomber, whose Mach 3 performance and high-altitude capability threatened to present Soviet air defences with insoluble problems. When development of the Valkyrie was halted in 1961, work on the MiG-25 was well advanced, and the USSR continued with the project, perhaps knowing that a Mach-3 capable reconnaissance aircraft, the Lockheed A-12 (later SR-71), was about to begin flight tests.

In designing an aircraft for sustained flight at Mach 3, the biggest problem facing the design bureau was the so-called heat barrier. Those parts of the airframe that had to withstand the greatest heat, such as the nose and leading edges, had to be of titanium construction, but many other areas that could theoretically have been made of riveted aluminium – such as the wing skins – had to be of welded steel because no suitable heat-resistant sealant could be found, and because there was a shortage of skilled riveters. Eventually, 80 per cent of the aircraft was of tempered steel, 11 per cent of aluminium alloys and 9 per cent of titanium.

Original interceptor

Development of the Ye-155P (the original MiG-25 designation) interceptor was approved in February 1962, and the prototype made its maiden flight on 9 September 1964. The aircraft was powered by a pair of 22,500-lb (100-kN) Mikulin (later Tumanskii) R-15B-300 turbojets, and was fitted with a *Smerch*-A radar, known to NATO as 'Fox Fire'; the radar had a detection range of 62 miles (100 km). The aircraft carried two R-40 air-to-air missiles, in mixed pairs of R-40R and R-40T semi-active radar- and IR-homing versions.

Performance was up to expectations and, in March 1965 – under the cover designation Ye-266 – an early aircraft was used to establish several performance records. Between 1965 and 1977, the Ye-266 and another variant, the Ye-266M, eventually made 21 FAI-notified record-breaking flights.

Production began in 1969, but the aircraft did not enter full air force service until 1973, having been plagued by engine problems. Even in service the MiG-25 was subject to severe operating limitations, which strictly constrained the amount of time that could be spent at very high speeds, which limited the use of full engine power.

The ultimate MiG-25PD 'Foxbat-

The MiG-25PU 'Foxbat-C' was a highly valued type. Serving as trainers, familiarisation aircraft and weather recce ships, the two-seaters saw more flying hours than any other MiG-25 version.

E' fighter variant entered production in 1978, and featured a new RP-25 look-down/shoot-down radar, an undernose IRST and more powerful engines. Surviving Soviet 'Foxbat-As' were brought up to the same standard from 1979, under the designation MiG-25PDS. Normal armament comprised two R-40 series (AA-6 'Acrid') and four short-range R-60 (AA-8 'Aphid') AAMs.

Pilot trainer

The MiG-25PU 'Foxbat-C' two-seat conversion trainer was rolled out in 1968. It lacked radar and had no combat capability. The type featured a new forward cockpit for the instructor, stepped down in front of the standard single-seat cockpit.

The MiG-25PU and the MiG-25P fighter were exported to Algeria, Iraq, Libya and Syria. An Iraqi MiG-25P was credited with shooting down a single US Navy F/A-18 during the 1991 Gulf War.

Although the MiG-25 was originally designed as an interceptor, it had obvious potential as a reconnaissance platform. The prototype recce aircraft, the Ye-155R-1, made its maiden flight six months before the prototype fighter, on 6 March 1964. As the MiG-25R, the reconnaissance version passed its state acceptance tests in 1969, and series production began in April of that year. The MiG-25R had five camera ports in the nose (one vertical and four oblique), with flush antennas further forward on the nose.

The original MiG-25R was replaced on the production line by the MiG-25RB 'Foxbat-B' in 1970, this type remaining in production until 1982. The MiG-25RB was a dual-role reconnaissance bomber, with a *Peleng* automatic bombing system, as well as having the USSR's first operational inertial navigation system. Camera-equipped MiG-25RBs were exported to Algeria, Bulgaria, India, Iraq, Libya and Syria.

The basic MiG-25RB also formed the basis of a model dedicated to Elint duties, with its optical sensors replaced by a variety of passive receivers and active SLAR systems. This example received the NATO reporting name 'Foxbat-D'. The first 'camera-less' recce 'Foxbat' was the MiG-25RBK, in which the usual flush antennas and cameras were removed and replaced by a large dielectric panel, housing the new *Kub* SLAR, on each side of the cockpit. The MiG-25RBK entered service in 1972 and remained in production until 1980. The final reconnaissance variant was the MiG-25RBF, with expanded jamming capability.

The camera provision of earlier RB variants was omitted from the MiG-25RBF. Instead, the nose was fitted with two pairs of dielectric panels for its Elint system. This particular example wears an 'outstanding unit citation' badge just below the cockpit.

Unusually, the reconnaissance 'Foxbat' has its own dedicated two-seat trainer, designated MiG-25RU – this variant has no operational equipment.

Having closely followed the development of dedicated 'Wild Weasel' aircraft by the US, Mikoyan developed the MiG-25BM. Developed in 1972 and known as the 'Foxbat-F' by NATO, the MiG-25BM was adapted to carry four Kh-58 (AS-11 'Kilter') anti-radiation missiles. The aircraft are believed to be equipped with a sophisticated avionics package including a *Sych-M* radar. Fewer than 100 MiG-25BMs were built between 1982 and 1985 and all were delivered to Frontal Aviation units originally based in East Germany and Poland.

Above: Pictured wearing full-pressure suits (required for high-altitude operations), these two Frontal Aviation pilots are seen in front of a 'Foxbat-F'. Changes to the cockpit were limited to the addition of revised mission equipment panels.

Left: The Indian air force took delivery of six MiG-25RBs and all wore the stylised eagle badge of No. 102 Sqn. One of the IAF's 'Foxbat-Bs' was written off in a crash, but others remained operational up until 2006.

Mikoyan MiG-29 'Fulcrum'

Poland became the second non-Soviet Warsaw Pact operator of the 'Fulcrum' in June 1989. Polish 'Fulcrums' are used for air defence and ground-attack missions and the fleet has been bolstered by former East German examples retired by the Luftwaffe.

MiG's agile performer

Despite controversial statements by various Western intelligence agencies regarding the poor performance of the MiG-29, the 'Fulcrum' proved its critics wrong by becoming a highly capable aircraft. Later 'Fulcrums' provide serious competition to Western designs.

The MiG-29 is indisputably one of the most impressive airshow performers in the world. Its superb high-Alpha capability, and its ability to point its nose away from the direction of flight (off axis) make for spectacular airshow manoeuvres (which cannot be emulated by comparable Western fighters). The MiG-29 pilot enjoys generous *g* and Alpha limits, and can, in any case, override these if the tactical situation demands. In order to defeat a missile or to pull up to avoid terrain, for example, the MiG-29 pilot can deliberately pull through his or her stick-stops and enter that portion of the flight envelope where departure will become increasingly likely. This ability to make brief excursions into the 'tatty area of the envelope' is unknown in the West, where most fighters have FBW control systems which will not allow the pilot to exceed the placard limits, whatever the circumstances. These capabilities also give the aircraft tremendous advantages in a close-in manoeuvring dogfight, allowing the MiG-29 pilot to point the aircraft's nose (and thus the weapons) at the enemy without necessarily having to manoeuvre into a position where he or she is flying towards the target. Moreover, the pilot can designate targets which are 'off-boresight', using the helmet sight or infra-red tracking. Pilots claim to be unbeatable in a close-in dogfight, and, while this may be an exaggeration, it is certainly true that this aircraft is a formidable combat opponent.

The MiG-29 is a popular mount for aerobatic teams, including the Ukrainian Falcons (illustrated) and Russia's Swifts.

Threat to the West

The MiG-29 has been built in substantial numbers and has been exported very widely. It is probably now the most common 'threat' aircraft likely to be faced by a Western fighter pilot. The MiG-29 is exceptionally rugged and dependable, and has followed standard Soviet practice in having been built for war, rather than for peacetime training. The aircraft thus has relatively short overhaul intervals, but is exceptionally quick and easy to service routinely and to 'turnaround' between sorties. The 'Fulcrum' is also capable of operating from primitive, semi-prepared strips, with minimal support infrastructure.

But while the MiG-29 may be 'probably one of the best

dogfighters in the world', it is fundamentally flawed. Mikoyan's MiG-29 is very much a product of its time, and of the uniquely Soviet concept of fighter operations which spawned it. Thus its ability to engage targets at great distances relies very heavily on information from ground installations or orbiting airborne early warning (AEW) platforms, particularly for threat prioritisation purposes. The MiG-29 can operate autonomously, but its radar and tactical displays do not maximise pilot situational awareness (the ability to observe and react within a combat scenario), and thus the pilot's task inflight is made more difficult than it should be.

Missile limitations

Moreover, while the MiG-29's close-in armament is unequalled, the aircraft's primary BVR weapon, the R-27 (AA-10 'Alamo') is no more than adequate.

As if this were not enough, the baseline MiG-29 is further handicapped by its lack of range and endurance. One of Mikoyan's designers once jokingly remarked that the MiG-29 was a fighter to defend its own airfield boundaries. It is certainly true that the aircraft does not have sufficient internal fuel to mount meaningful long-range escort missions, or to carry out CAPs at any great distance from base. Point defence or Quick Reaction Alert (QRA) are the roles to which the aircraft is best suited, although the OKB has worked hard to extend the aircraft's range, radius of action and endurance (with some success), just as it has tried to remedy shortcomings in beyond visual range (BVR) capability.

Since the Cold War, Mikoyan has progressively improved the systems and capabilities of the basic MiG-29, and dramatically transformed the aircraft's multi-role and BVR capabilities. The result is a warplane that remains credible into the 21st century.

Left: Following evaluation by NATO pilots, the 'Fulcrum' was found to be a highly capable aircraft, although its pulse-Doppler radar was regarded as inferior to equivalent Western units. A Luftwaffe single-seat 'Fulcrum-A' is illustrated.

Above: The Polish air force, as with many other former Warsaw Pact air arms, found the MiG-29 provided a quantum leap in capability.

Above: Mikoyan has long been eager to sell the 'Fulcrum' on the lucrative world military fighter market. As a publicity sales drive during the late 1980s, single- and two-seat examples of the 'Fulcrum' were exhibited at both the Farnborough and Paris airshows. While attending these events, the two-seat MiG-29UB was utilised as a demonstration aircraft, offering flights to high-profile aviation personalities and pilots. All were suitably impressed with the aircraft's performance, although the weapon systems and HUD remained firmly switched off during the flights.

Below: Developed from the MiG-29M, the dedicated carrierborne variant of the 'Fulcrum' is known as the MiG-29K. First flying on 23 June 1988, the MiG-29K was intended for Russia's ill-fated aircraft carrier programme but has since been adopted by India.

'Fulcrum-A/B'
The early MiG-29s

Following the commencement of Mikoyan's 1971 *legkiy* (lightweight) fighter project, the resulting MiG-29 was hurried through development and entered Soviet service in the early 1980s.

Compared to the Su-27 'Flanker', the development of the MiG-29 was relatively untroubled; the aircraft began to enter service in 1982, becoming widely operational by 1986. In the same year, East German regiments began to re-equip with the new fighter, Indian Air Force deliveries began, and production had reached a suitably high rate.

The first production single-seat MiG-29s were known to NATO as the 'Fulcrum-A', and to the factory as 9.12. Externally identical to the nine pre-production aircraft, they differed from later MiG-29s by their initial retention of ventral fins, and lack of overwing chaff/flare dispensers.

Following the formation of the first MiG-29 regiment, the 234th 'Proskuroskii' GvIAP at Kubinka, followed by the 'Combat Leader' regiment at Ros in the Ukraine, some 250 early production MiG-29s entered service, going on to form a total of 14 Frontal Aviation regiments. During the early 1990s, when the Soviet airborne presence in Eastern Europe was at its peak, more than 30 early production MiG-29s were in service within East Germany alone.

Remaining early production, ventral-finned MiG-29 'Fulcrum-As' were retrofitted with the extended chord rudders and updated flight control system of later variants. A few others lost their ventral fins and received chaff/flare dispensers, rendering them identical to later 'Fulcrum-A' aircraft.

Afghanistan experience

In addition to lacking the ventral fin, another feature of the principal production 9.12 'Fulcrum-A' was the fitting of the long-chord wingroot strakes containing a chaff and flare dispenser. The dispenser was a direct result of Soviet experience gained in Afghanistan.

In service, the main production 'Fulcrum-A' gained further refinements, including an improved flight control system

Above: The MiG-29 was 'officially' unveiled to Western onlookers when six Kubinka-based examples mounted a goodwill visit to Finland in August 1986. Early models retained ventral fins.

Top: India received 70 baseline single-seat 'Fulcrums' in 1986. Designated MiG-29B by the manufacturer, they lack Soviet model IFF and datalink, and serve with Nos 28, 47 and 233 Squadrons.

(expanding Alpha limits), modified flight control surface actuators, nose-mounted vortex generator strakes and increased-area rudders, the latter also being retrofitted to early production examples. A small number of main production 'Fulcrum-As' were given the capability to carry underwing fuel tanks, and to fire their refined-muzzle cannon when carrying a centreline fuel tank.

Reflecting the tactical role envisaged for the MiG-29 in future European air wars, the 'Fulcrum-A' was given a nuclear capability early in its service life, with the RN-40 free-fall bomb.

The break-up of the USSR left some 486 9.12 'Fulcrum-As' in Russian service, 245 in the Ukraine, 80 in Belarus, 36 in Uzbekistan, 34 in Moldova, and 22 in Kazakhstan.

The air forces of Warsaw Pact nations (except the non-Warsaw Pact Yugoslavia) were supplied with 9.12 'Fulcrum-As', which were of a very similar standard to Soviet service aircraft. Designated MiG-29A or 9.12A,

***Left:* The outstanding manoeuvrability and power-to-weight ratio of the MiG-29 led to it being an obvious mount for the Russian Swifts display team, equipped with the 9.12 and two-seat 9.51.**

***Below:* Wearing an all-over 'stars' display scheme, this MiG-29A (9.12A) 'Fulcrum-A' served with the Hungarian air force's 59 HRE unit. Hungary's fleet of 'Fulcrums' is based at Kecskemét.**

these export aircraft lacked nuclear capability and carried a slightly different IFF system. Reports suggest that German MiG-29As had only three radar modes, compared to the five modes of the Soviet aircraft.

The MiG-29B (9.12B) was an export variant intended for use by less close allies, including Yugoslavia, Cuba, Syria, North Korea, India, Iran and Iraq. The MiG-29B was further downgraded compared to the standard Soviet 'Fulcrum-A', lacking Soviet IFF and datalink, and perhaps fitted with downgraded radar. Following the dissolution of the Warsaw Pact, it seems likely that East European 9.12As were effectively reduced to 9.12B standard.

Although downgraded MiG-29 versions (9.12A and 9.12B) were specifically tailored for export, ex-Frontal Aviation machines have also, more recently, been exported second-hand. Peru, for example, purchased 12 MiG-29s from Belarus. In addition, Moldova provided Yemen with 12 of its 34 MiG-29s, one of which was soon shot down, and seven of which were captured in Yemeni service. More surprisingly, the USAF took at least 21 MiG-29s from Moldova in 1997.

'Fulcrum-B'

The 9.51 MiG-29UB (*Uchebno-Boevoi*, trainer-combat) two-seat trainer was always planned, although the Soviets introduced the aircraft only slowly into front-line units, continuing to rely on the MiG-23UB into the 1990s. A dedicated trainer, the 'Fulcrum-B' lacks radar and BVR missile capability, unlike the Su-27UB. An advanced training system, however, provides synthetic targets for the front cockpit displays.

Maiden flight

The first MiG-29UB/9.51, based on a ventral fin-equipped single-seater airframe, made its maiden flight in April 1981. Entering service in 1986, and built at a separate plant at Gorkii (now Nizhny Novgorod), the production 'Fulcrum-B' lacks the ventral fins of the early 'Fulcrum-A' and the chaff/flare dispensers of later single-seaters.

There is no difference between former Soviet MiG-29UBs and those intended for export, except in the case of the MiG-29N-compatible, English-instrumented two-seaters delivered to Malaysia, which are designated MiG-29NUB.

***Above:* Wearing unconventional 'sharkmouth' nose art, as well as non-standard two-digit and inner tailfin codes, this Russian air force MiG-29UB may be used in a dissimilar or 'aggressor' training role.**

***Left:* Trailing a single brake-chute, this Hungarian 59 HRE MiG-29A (9.12A) taxies in at its Kecskemét base. Export MiG-29As came from the same production line as standard Frontal Aviation 'Fulcrums'.**

Improved MiG-29s

Offering a modest increase in internal fuel, the 'Fulcrum-C' spearheaded Soviet tactical aviation elements in East Germany, and has since been developed into a plethora of upgraded sub-types.

When the MiG-29 'Fulcrum-C' (company designation 9.13) first appeared, Western analysts assumed that the aircraft's swollen spine incorporated a significantly increased internal fuel tankage. In reality, the increase in fuel was minimal, but the redesigned spine did house a *Gardeniya* active jammer: as a result the variant was not exported to overseas operators.

The prototype 9.13 first flew in 1986, preceded by a number of converted 9.12s, which first flew in this form in 1984. The 9.13 received no new Soviet air force designation, but was allocated the 'Fulcrum-C' reporting name by NATO's ASCC. The type began to appear in front-line units in 1986/87, with production based upon the airframe of the main production series 9.12 'Fulcrum-A', with the later cannon muzzle, increased-chord rudders and nose strakes.

Production of the 'Fulcrum-C' reached around 200 aircraft, which were built alongside the standard 9.12 at the MPO factory, and often served alongside the earlier variant in Frontal Aviation regiments.

Upgraded variant

Although associated with later export efforts, the original MiG-29S configuration was the result of a Soviet requirement. The MiG-29S appears to have originated after 1985, when it was discovered that a Phazotron employee had sold secrets to the West, compromising the MiG-29's radar system. A crash programme was thus initiated in order to improve and upgrade compromised equipment.

The original package of MiG-29S modifications included a 'modified sighting system' (presumably a reference to the radar being updated to N-019M *Topaz* standard), improvements to the active jammer, provision to fire the gun when carrying a centreline tank, provision for underwing tanks and expanded *g* and Alpha limits.

As the MiG-29S was initially viewed as an upgrade for Soviet MiG-29s, the initial MiG-29S was based on the 9.13 'Fulcrum-C' airframe, with its humped back housing active jammer and fuel. A prototype flew during 1984. The OKB had a clear view of what the total modification package should contain but, in order to put the aircraft into service quickly, produced the modification as a multi-stage upgrade.

The first MiG-29S aircraft for the Russian air force featured a revised flight control system, with four new computers for stability augmentation allowing

Above: The MiG-29SE development aircraft was first displayed at Russia's Test Centre at Zhukhovskii, outside Moscow.

Top: Most 9.13 'Fulcrum-Cs' were assigned to the 16th Air Army in East Germany. This aircraft is seen in use at the weapons training school at Lipetsk, with white markings for high conspicuity.

Ukraine inherited a large number of 9.13 'Fulcrum-Cs'. Ukrainian MiG-29s are today concentrated with the 14th Fighter Aviation Brigade at Ivano-Frankovsk, the 40th Brigade at Vasil'kiv and the 204th Brigade at Bel'bek.

The improved N-019M* Topaz *radar of the MiG-29S enables it to engage two targets simultaneously, and fire the R-77 (AA-12 'Adder') AAM (dubbed 'AMRAAMski' in the West).

higher *g*- and Alpha-limits, and enabling greater angular deflection of the control surfaces. The aircraft also had provision for two underwing fuel tanks and strengthened pylons for air-to-ground ordnance. Finally, the first phase of the MiG-29S upgrade included a revised sighting system (allowing the simulation of IR and radar targets for training purposes) and improved built-in test equipment.

The second phase of the MiG-29S upgrade included software modifications to the N-019M *Topaz* radar, and greater processing capacity, which allowed better simultaneous target tracking. Subsequent improvements brought with them compatibility with the R-77 (AA-12 'Adder') missile, and even simultaneous dual target engagement capability.

At this stage, it became apparent that the MiG-29S upgrade would be of interest to MiG-29 export customers, and that the new variant's enhanced capabilities might even bring new foreign customers.

Accordingly, the MiG-29S was offered with Western navigation and communications equipment, with a Western-compatible IFF, and with instruments and displays placarded in English. With the aircraft being marketed seriously for export, Mikoyan also added a bolt-on retractable refuelling probe package.

Fulcrums for sale

The standard export MiG-29S was known as the MiG-29SD (or as the MiG-29SE when based on the 9.13 airframe). The Malaysian MiG-29Ns were effectively MiG-29SDs but, during the 800-hour overhaul, the aircraft were given new IFF, English instruments and other avionics changes, R-77 capability, and an inflight refuelling probe.

With the MiG-29SM came compatibility with TV- and laser-guided air-to-surface weapons, a radar mapping mode and simultaneous dual target engagement capability.

The 9.17 or MiG-29SMT was intended to substitute the MiG-29M as a MiG-29 replacement in the Frontal fighter role, and like the MiG-29M also gives capabilities once offered by dedicated fighter-bombers.

The SMT addresses the original aircraft's range/endurance deficiency, introduces a modern 'glass' cockpit and a true multi-role capability. Using the basic 'Fulcrum' airframe as the basis for a radical upgrade, the SMT carries new avionics, massive new internal fuel tanks and other refinements. Reflecting the type's links to the MiG-29SM, the new aircraft's designation signifies *Toplivo*, or fuel.

The first MiG-29SMT demonstrator first flew on 29 November 1997, and flew with a new 9.17 spine in April 1998. The first full-standard SMT was first flown on 14 July 1998.

Two-seat derivative

The two-seat 9.51T MiG-29UBT incorporates the same 'glass' cockpit, enhanced avionics and increased fuel capacity of the single-seat SMT. As well as offering the expanded capabilities of a twin-seat multi-role fighter, the MiG-29UBT can also operate as a useful trainer, with expanded training modes and new capabilities for the airborne simulation of using different weapons.

Right: The second MiG-29UBT at Zhukovskii. Seen as a possible replacement for the Su-24, the type provides a rival to Sukhoi's Su-30M family.

The first production MiG-29SMT, fitted with bolt-on inflight refuelling probe, and carrying Kh-31P passive radar homing ASMs and R-73 AAMs.

MiG-29M/K
The 'new generation'

In order to improve the baseline MiG-29 'Fulcrum-A', Mikoyan set out to produce a MiG-29 derivative. With greater range and better radar than the original MiG-29, the MiG-29M had the potential to become a world-beating fighter, but did not enter production.

The shortcomings of the original, baseline MiG-29 were apparent from an early stage. The aircraft was handicapped by its relatively poor range/endurance characteristics, and by a lack of multi-role versatility. It was arguably the best short-range point defence interceptor of its era, but had only the most rudimentary air-to-ground capability.

One of the least obvious changes to the MiG-29M was its reprofiled canopy. As well as having an ARK radio compass antenna embedded in the rear section, the whole canopy was both lengthened and raised, allowing a higher seating position, and thereby giving the pilot a better all-round view, particularly over the nose.

Developed to replace the MiG-29, the MiG-29M married the former's highly successful aerodynamic configuration with more powerful engines, a new multi-role avionics and weapons system, genuine all-weather autonomous precision attack capability, a structurally redesigned airframe of reduced weight, and a massive increase in internal fuel capacity.

A finer 'Fulcrum'

Six prototypes were built, as well as two prototypes of a similar navalised variant, the MiG-29K. With the first prototype flying on 25 April 1986, these improved variants quickly demonstrated that the MiG-29's fundamental shortcomings had been convincingly addressed, and the way seemed clear for development to be completed, and production to begin. But then the Cold War ended, and development of the MiG-29M and MiG-29K was halted.

When the post-Cold War spending cuts bit deep, development of the MiG-29M had reached a more advanced stage than that of the rival Su-27M, but it was the MiG fighter that was halted, while Su-27M development continued. The smaller, lighter and cheaper MiG-29M was a better post-Cold War aircraft than the Su-27M, and promised to be a superior performer on the export market. Existing MiG-29 customers could be expected to purchase the new MiG-29 variant, which enjoyed some commonality with the original aircraft, and used much of the same support equipment. As far as Russia was concerned, the MiG-29M also formed the basis of the carrier-based MiG-29K, which was more versatile and useful than its Sukhoi competitor, the Su-27K.

Instead, the Su-27M and

***Above:** Later 'Fulcrums' are able to carry an impressive warload. The medium-range Vympel R-77 air-to-air missile was intended to be one of the MiG-29M's primary weapons, although integration of this missile with the aircraft's systems proved troublesome.*

***Top:** Although outwardly the MiG-29M closely resembles the basic 'Fulcrum', it has far more versatility and range.*

Before its cancellation, the MiG-29M was exhibited at both the Farnborough and Paris airshows. Although cheaper than the American F-16 Fighting Falcon and F/A-18 Hornet, no foreign orders for the new 'Fulcrum' were forthcoming.

While the first MiG-29K was finished in a standard light-grey scheme, the second aircraft sported this slate-grey paint. Additional markings were MiG and MAPO (Moscow Aircraft Production Organisation) badges, and the Russian navy's St Andrew's Cross.

Su-27K continued while the advanced MiG-29 developments were suspended.

The origins of the MiG-29K remain shrouded in some mystery. Most sources suggest that the project was launched to provide a multi-role strike fighter to complement the single-role Su-27K interceptor. A handful of analysts maintain that the MiG-29K was only ever planned as a fall-back, in case the Su-27K proved too heavy to operate from the new carriers.

Trials with the hooked MiG-29KVP proved that the MiG-29 could be operated safely from a ski-jump, and that arrested landings were possible at operationally useful weights. Although the MiG-29KVP could have formed the basis of a practical carrierborne fighter, it was decided that the ideal carrierborne MiG-29 would require both additional wing area and additional thrust. Further, improved high-lift devices might produce a useful reduction in approach speed, without unacceptably raising the angle of attack on touch-down.

Since a new variant of the MiG-29 would be required, Mikoyan took the courageous decision to adapt it from the new multi-role MiG-29M, with its lightweight airframe, multi-mode/multi-role radar and PGM capability. Detail design began in 1985, one year before the MiG-29M made its maiden flight.

Uprated engines

There was a degree of cross-fertilisation between the MiG-29M and the MiG-29K, with the uprated RD-33K engines developed for the carrier aircraft eventually being adopted for the MiG-29M, too. The new engine had an 'exceptional regime' giving 20,725 lb st (92.17 kN) thrust for a limited period, useful on launch and in the event of a missed approach or go-around. It also has FADEC (full-authority digital engine control), advanced materials and single-crystal turbine blades. These allow the engine to operate at higher temperatures, and the basic maximum thrust figure is increased from 18,298 lb st (81.42 kN) to 19,400 lb st (86.33 kN).

The quintessence of the MiG-29K lay in its new wing, designed with power-folding at roughly one-third span. The wing was fitted with broader-chord double-slotted trailing-edge flaps, and featured the extended-span ailerons of the MiG-29M, though they were modified to droop (as flaperons) at low speed. In addition to the new wing, the MiG-29K introduced a new, strengthened long-stroke undercarriage, and had a tailhook. The MiG-29K prototypes introduced a neat, fully retractable inflight-refuelling probe below the forward edge of the port side of the windscreen.

When the time came to select the aircraft for Russia's one remaining carrier, the choice was made in favour of the Su-27K. However, the two MiG-29K prototypes remained active and MiG's persistence was ultimately rewarded by an order from India, to equip the former Russian navy carrier *Admiral Gorshkov* in Indian navy service. An initial contract was signed in January 2004, covering delivery of 12 single-seat MiG-29Ks and four of the newly developed two-seat MiG-29KUB variant. India has also taken out options for a further 30 aircraft up to 2015.

The first MiG-29K is seen during trials aboard the carrier* Tbilisi. *These included landing aboard with R-73 and R-77 missiles, the main air-to-air weapons of the type. The extended and bulged wingtips of the MiG-29K house electronic warfare equipment.

MiG-29M

All six MiG-29M prototypes were newly built, and wore standard camouflage. False overwing intake louvres (later removed) were painted on several of the prototypes in order to fool US spy satellites into thinking that they were ordinary MiG-29s.

Spine
The MiG-29M had an increased-volume fuselage spine containing extra fuel and avionics, displaced by other internal changes. This was of a less obvious profile than the big spine fitted to the 'Fulcrum-C', although it was of greater volume.

Radome
The new flat plate antenna of the N-010 multi-mode pulse-Doppler radar allowed the radome shape to be refined, omitting the prominent bulge which was necessary on the MiG-29 to accommodate the bulky front element of the N-019's twist cassegrain antenna.

Operators

While the MiG-29 served almost exclusively with Warsaw Pact nations during the Cold War, today, due to Russia's financial woes, it is being offered in all major fighter procurement competitions.

Below: Russia has naturally been the largest operator of the MiG-29, with approximately 650 examples serving with the V-VS. Of these, the 500 single-seaters are predominantly 9-12 'Fulcrum-As', 9-13 'Fulcrum-Cs' and 9-13S MiG-29S 'Fulcrum-Cs' (approximately 40 of the latter are said to be in service). The remaining 150 aircraft are two-seat UB trainers. While the advanced M and naval K models failed to enter Russian service, the Russian air force, funds providing, is set to receive the multi-role MiG-29SMT, though only a handful have so far entered service. When completed, the SMT upgrade is likely to cover 150 aircraft.

Above: With the collapse of the Soviet Union, the Ukraine inherited 225 MiG-29 'Fulcrum-A/Cs', a number of which remain in front-line service with three brigades. The fleet has suffered from low serviceability and much-reduced pilot flying hours. These MiG-29s (one UB and three single-seaters) are part of the Ukrainian Falcons national aerobatic team.

Above: Belarus was another recipient of post-Soviet Union 'Fulcrums', with 80 examples of the 'Fulcrum-C' being taken on in 1991. However, budgetary constraints have meant a dwindling force and 18 surplus examples were sold to Peru in 1996.

Ex-Soviet nations

With the gaining of independence in 1991, Kazakhstan nevertheless remained friendly with Russia and, in turn for allowing the Russians to operate the Baikonur Cosmodrome, received 21 MiG-29s, which form a single squadron at Lugovoya. The Uzbekistan air force operates around 30 MiG-29s as multi-role fighters and six trainer MiG-29UBs; all are based at Kakaydy as part of 61 IAP. Turkmenistan's 24 MiG-29s are based at Mary-2 as part of 67 ShAP and are tasked with air defence and attack.

Above: Bulgaria operates a single squadron of 'Fulcrum-As', based at Graf Ignatievo. Tasked with interceptor duties, Bulgaria has opted to upgrade its MiG-29s in order to extend their service life. The upgrade relies on Russian assistance, although a series of delays to the programme saw the fleet briefly grounded.

Above: Formerly the cornerstone of Romanian air defence, Romania's air force acquired 17 MiG-29 'Fulcrum-As' and three MiG-29UBs for the two squadrons of 57 FBAB at Constanta.

Above: For many years the most potent aircraft in the Polish inventory, 10 'Fulcrum-As' and two 'Fulcrum-Bs' were acquired as new from MiG in 1989; they have since been supplemented by 10 aircraft obtained from the Czech Republic and 23 from Germany. Due to Poland's integration into the NATO structure, the MiG-29s have undergone a series of programmes to 'Westernise' them and the Polish 'Fulcrums' are now regular visitors to NATO exercises.

Left: With the retirement of the Su-22M, MiG-23 and MiG-21MF, the two squadrons of MiG-29s equipping the 59th Tactical Fighter Regiment represented the cutting edge of the Hungarian air force prior to the arrival of the Saab Gripen. The MiG-29 and JAS 39C/D Gripen now operate together from Kecskemét and the 'Fulcrum' fleet is likely to remain in service until around 2010.

Above: With the partition of* Czechoslovakia*, the* Slovak Republic *received half of the assets of the former republic's air force, which included nine 'Fulcrum-As'. Due to their age, it was decided in 1994 that further examples would be needed. Six additional 'Fulcrums', including a* UB *(illustrated and wearing low-visibility tiger markings), were therefore purchased. An additional eight were added shortly afterwards.

Middle East

In 1990, Iran set about acquiring fighters from Russia, the first examples being 14 'Fulcrum-As'. With the Gulf War, the air force was boosted with the defection of 14 further 'Fulcrums' from Iraq. Six MiG-29UBs are also on strength for training. Solid details about Syria's air force are fairly sketchy, although as many as 45 MiG-29 'Fulcrum-A' fighters and six MiG-29UB trainers are said to be operated. After the decimation caused by the Allies during Desert Storm in 1991, Iraq's once proud air force was left with an estimated 15 MiG-29s. Other Middle Eastern 'Fulcrum' operators include Algeria, which received as many as 75 examples.

Above: Spearheading the air defence network of* Malaysia *are two squadrons of* MiG-29N *fighters, of which 16 were delivered from 1995. They were initially distributed between* Nos 17 *and* 19 Skuadrons*, both based at* Kuantan*, although* No. 17 Skuadron *has since been disbanded and will reform with the* Su-30MKM*.

Other nations

In November 1999, North Korea was said to have purchased 10 'Fulcrum-As' from Russia. It is not known how the debt-ridden nation can afford the machines, but it is believed to have had a requirement for 30 aircraft – 25 MiG-29 'Fulcrum-As' and five MiG-29UBs. By December 1999, Bangladesh accepted four of eight MiG-29s from Russia with the remaining aircraft due during 2000. Eritrea purchased 10 MiG-29s from Moldova in 1998 and these have operated in the clashes with Ethiopia. Peru obtained 18 'Fulcrum-As' from Belarus in 1998, one of which was lost in an accident shortly afterwards. A further three brand-new MiG-29s were purchased from the manufacturer in 1999. During 1999, two Japanese pilots spent six months evaluating MiG-29s in Russia. The nature of this test was principally to evaluate the aircraft due to its operation by Japan's belligerent neighbour, North Korea. Due to the short 'legs' of the 'Fulcrum', it cannot be regarded as a significant threat to Japan, which makes the long 'hands-on' evaluation intriguing. In addition, the MiG-29 has been acquired by Myanmar (formerly Burma) and Sudan, which are reported to have received 10 and 24, respectively.

Above: Prior to the* Kosovo *conflict, the* Yugoslav *air force was believed to have operated 14* MiG-29Bs *(local designation L.18), serving with the 204th* Lovacki Avijacijski Puk *at* Batajnica*. However, the majority was destroyed during the* NATO Allied Force *campaign. The five survivors are in storage in* Serbia*.

Above:* Moldova *inherited 34* MiG-29s *from the* Soviet *navy's 86 IAP that had been based in the country. However, financial difficulties meant that the aircraft were surplus to requirements. Some of the aircraft were loaned to* Yemen*, most being subsequently returned. In 1997, 21 examples were sold to the* US*, officially as part of the* US *policy of stopping aircraft falling into the hands of 'rogue' states, but also for evaluation. Approximately 10 more examples were sold to* Eritrea *in late 1998.

Above:* Cuba*'s close links with the* Soviet Union *and the resulting aid it received meant that it was natural that* MiG-29s*, the most potent aircraft on offer, would be purchased. While the exact number of aircraft purchased is open to debate, it is estimated that between 16 and 36 aircraft entered service.

Above:* India *has a diverse mix of* Western *and* Eastern *bloc aircraft and was one of the first non-*Warsaw Pact *nations to buy the 'Fulcrum'. In 1986, 42 single- and eight two-seaters were purchased and these were supplemented by 20 further single-seaters in 1989, and 10* MiG-29SDs *in 1995. In November 1999,* India *and* Russia *signed an agreement that will supply* India *with 60* MiG-29Ks*; this was later cancelled and a new order placed for 16 navalised 'Fulcrums' was announced in 2004. These will operate from the carrier* Admiral Goshkov *(which* India *will put into service as* INS Vikramaditya*) and from shore bases.

Left: With the reunification of* Germany*, the* Luftwaffe *inherited 24* MiG-29s *from the* Luftstreitkäfte und Luftverteidigung (LSK/LV)*. These 'Fulcrums' were the sole combat aircraft of the* LSK/LV *to remain in* Luftwaffe *service and were tasked with the air defence of eastern* Germany*. As well as this role, the* MiG-29s *also found themselves regularly involved in dissimilar air combat training with the aircraft of other nations. While they underwent upgrades to integrate them with other* NATO *air arms, they were replaced by the* EF2000 *and the survivors donated to* Poland*.

Large and equipped with extremely powerful engines, the MiG-31 'Foxhound' is typical of Cold War Soviet design philosophy.

Mikoyan MiG-31 'Foxhound'

Soviet interceptor

Dismissed in the West as a crude, brutish adaptation of the MiG-25, the MiG-31 'Foxhound' is in fact one of the world's most sophisticated interceptors.

By the 1970s, Soviet air defences were in a pitiful state. Russia's Tu-114 'Moss' AWACS platform was available only in very small numbers, and was of limited capability, while the vast network of SAMs had progressed little since the U-2 of Francis Gary Powers had been blasted from the sky over Sverdlovsk on 1 May 1960. The huge IA-PVO interceptor force was equipped with a variety of aircraft, from ageing Sukhoi Su-11 'Fishpots' and MiG-21 'Fishbeds' to newer MiG-25 'Foxbats'. None of the types in service was capable of meeting the threat posed by low-level NATO strike aircraft, by new long-range stand-off missiles or by the new generation of agile Western fighters. Many of the types in use, particularly the lumbering Tupolev Tu-128 'Fiddlers' and Yak-28 'Firebars', were showing their age.

Work on overhauling Soviet air defences was accorded a high priority, and development began on two new AWACS platforms (including the A-50 'Mainstay'), an array of new SAMs, and various new fighters. The most ambitious of these were the MiG-29 (intended as a tactical fighter for Frontal Aviation) and the Su-27 (a long-range agile interceptor and escort fighter for the PVO and Frontal Aviation). Both of these aircraft were single-seaters, and neither promised to be in service before 1985, so a number of interim fighter projects were instituted. New lookdown/shootdown radar was fitted to the existing Su-15 to produce the Su-15 'Flagon-F', while a similar process produced the MiG-25 'Foxbat-E'. The PVO also took delivery of large numbers of MiG-23s with a limited lookdown/shootdown capability.

New design

Although often assumed to have originated as an interim aircraft, or at best as an insurance policy in case of the failure of the Su-27, the MiG-31 actually represented an attempt to produce a long-range interceptor capable of operating independently of ground control, and whose two crew members would also enhance mission performance in a hostile electronic warfare environment.

The MiG-31 airframe seems to have originated from that of the Ye-155M, a research derivative of the MiG-25 intended to explore ways of increasing the speed and range of the MiG-25 family. It had been intended to undertake a two-stage programme, first fitting new 29,761-lb (132-kN) R-15BF-2-300 engines (with 7,253 lb/32 kN more thrust than the R-15B-300 of the standard MiG-

Aware of the limitations of the single-seat MiG-25 'Foxbat', Mikoyan developed a two-seat variant. Though constructed in complete secrecy, the cover of the 'Foxhound' was blown when defecting 'Foxbat' pilot Lt Victor Belenko landed in Japan. He revealed that the Soviet air force was about to receive a two-seat model with a much improved radar and new missiles.

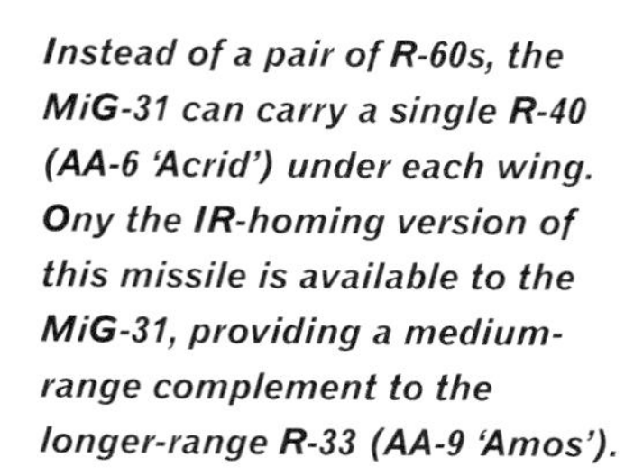

Instead of a pair of R-60s, the MiG-31 can carry a single R-40 (AA-6 'Acrid') under each wing. Ony the IR-homing version of this missile is available to the MiG-31, providing a medium-range complement to the longer-range R-33 (AA-9 'Amos').

25) and then revising the aircraft structure to raise the limiting Mach number (which was then thermally limited to Mach 2.83). With the new engines, service ceiling was raised to 79,396 ft (24200 m), and range increased to 1,193 miles (1920 km) or 1,559 miles (2510 km) with an external fuel tank. Unfortunately, engine development took longer than anticipated, and the second stage of the programme, covering structural and material changes, was shelved. The two Ye-155M prototypes still had a role to play, however. They were converted to serve as testbeds for the new 34,170-lb (152-kN) Soloviev D-30F6 turbojets being developed for the MiG-31, after a competition between Soloviev and Tumanskii.

Under the 'cover' designation Ye-266M the re-engined Ye-155M broke a number of world records in the time-to-height and altitude categories within its class.

A 'Super MiG-25'

The MiG-31 was so closely based on the experimental Ye-155M that it was originally designated Ye-155MP, and was expected to gain the service designation MiG-25MP. The first prototype first flew on 16 September 1975.

In the West, the first indication that a 'Super MiG-25' was under development came in September 1976, when Lt Victor Belenko defected to Japan in an early-model MiG-25. He described a MiG-25 with a stronger airframe for supersonic flight at low altitude (the MiG-25 was limited to 575 mph/925 km/h at sea level), with uprated engines, new avionics and new fuselage pylons for six examples of a new long-range missile. He also revealed that the new aircraft would have an internal gun, advanced lookdown/shootdown radar and an anti-cruise missile capability.

The West began to refer to the new aircraft as the MiG-31 in 1977, and began to sit up and take notice when a MiG-31 prototype was observed by a satellite destroying a target at below 200 ft (61 m), at some 12 miles (20 km) range, while itself at 20,000 ft (6096 m). In a later test a MiG-31 at 55,000 ft (16765 m) destroyed a target flying at 70,000 ft (21336 m). The reporting name 'Foxhound' was announced in mid-1982, and examples of the new type started to be intercepted by Norwegian fighters from 1985.

Production of the MiG-31 commenced at Gorkii (now Nizhny Novgorod) in 1979, after intensive trials. These were not without incident, and numerous modifications were incorporated into the production aircraft. One of the major improvements was the repositioning of the airbrakes underneath the intake duct, rather than on the 'shoulders' of the intake ducts.

By comparison with the MiG-25, the MiG-31 has larger and more complex engine intakes, and these have been tailored to reduce airflow problems and reduce fuel consumption during missions.

Initial trials revealed the need for inflight refuelling, and a crude semi-retractable probe was added to the port forward fuselage. This was not fitted to early production aircraft, but is now standard equipment. At the time inflight refuelling was fairly uncommon in the Soviet Union, at least outside of the long-range bomber force.

Once mastered, the capabilities of the MiG-31 soon became apparent. Flights of more than five hours were now possible coupled with a highly sophisticated radar. Capabilities such as these saw that the early MiG-31 'Foxhounds' were quickly deployed to Russia's front-line interceptor bases.

At least one MiG-31 (the seventh) was fitted with streamlined cylindrical ESM pods. These were later replaced by anti-flutter weights. The large 'winglets' are thought to be related to some form of MiG-31 aerodynamic development.

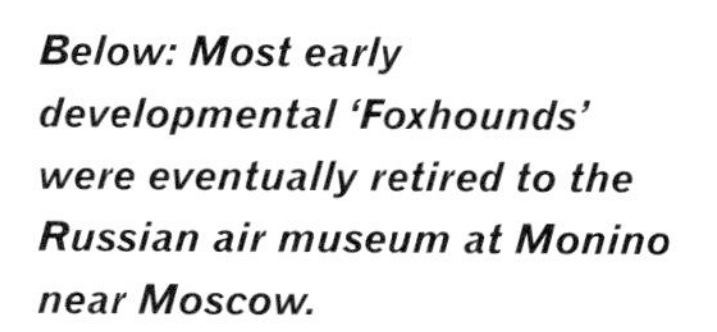

Below: Most early developmental 'Foxhounds' were eventually retired to the Russian air museum at Monino near Moscow.

Mitsubishi F-1

Ship-killing Samurai

A derivative of the T-2 trainer, the Mitsubishi F-1 was Japan's first major postwar combat aircraft and has performed a vital anti-shipping role for the JASDF since the late 1970s.

By the 1970s the Japanese Air Self-Defense Force was keen to acquire a dedicated support fighter – a type it had never operated – and had an outstanding need for a supersonic trainer to better prepare pilots for its Starfighters. Thus it was decided to combine the SF-X and T-X requirements in a single type.

Initially Japan looked abroad, the Northrop F-5 and SEPECAT Jaguar being obvious candidates. In fact, the latter was intensively evaluated and licence production was discussed, but negotiations foundered. However, Japan's enthusiasm for the Jaguar should not be underestimated, and it had a major influence on the configuration and detail design of the eventual F-1/T-2 design.

Indigenous solution

In the event, a decision to proceed with an entirely indigenous trainer was taken in November 1966, after intensive lobbying by Japanese aircraft manufacturers, and in September 1967 Mitsubishi was awarded a development contract for the T-2 trainer, with a basic design contract following in March 1968.

The JASDF shares its Misawa Air Base with the F-16s of the 35th Fighter Wing (formerly the 432nd FW) of the USAF's Pacific Air Forces. The 35th Wing eventually adopted the 'WW' tailcode.

Above: From most angles the similarities between the F-1 and the Anglo-French Jaguar are obvious. Note also the F-1's pronounced 'humped back', a legacy of its origins in the T-2 two-seater.

Top: A Mitsubishi F-1 of 3 Hikotai roars into the air from its base at Misawa AB. By the time it is retired, the type will have seen more than 30 years of service with the JASDF.

The T-2 (T-X) prototype made its first flight on 20 July 1971. The new trainer was developed from the start with a view to providing the basis for a fighter-bomber, and Mitsubishi continued feasibility studies of a fighter-bomber version of the aircraft.

For a while the future of the SF-X derivative looked in doubt, the Ministry of Finance favouring the purchase of a batch of F-5A fighter-bombers. Eventually, in 1972, the government decided to fund the development of an indigenous fighter-bomber based on the T-2. A prototype development contract was placed by the Defense Agency in 1973. Mitsubishi was commissioned to take the sixth and seventh T-2s from the production line, and to rebuild them as single-seat fighter-bombers. These two aircraft were initially known as Special Spec T-2s, and then as T-2(FS)s, before taking the designation FS-T2 Kai.

Changes from the T-2 were kept to an absolute minimum, in order to minimise cost and delay. The fuselage shape and cross section was maintained. The rear cockpit was adapted as an avionics bay, and was covered by a simple access hatch, which followed the shape of the old rear canopy. Because virtually all of the changes were internal, FS-T2 Kai

Above: Despite encroaching obsolescence, the F-1 remains extremely popular with its pilots, who are proud to fly what was for many years Japan's only indigenous front-line fighter.

Above right: The inner pair of underwing pylons and the centreline station are each plumbed to carry a 220-US gal (821-litre) drop tank.

flight tests could be limited mainly to exploring the effect of carrying external stores, and to proving the new avionics and systems.

The seventh T-2 was the first of the two aircraft to fly in single-seat form on 3 June 1975. At the conclusion of the test programme the JASDF placed its first order for 18 of the new aircraft. The JASDF had wanted to place an initial order for 50 aircraft in Fiscal Year 1976, but the deteriorating financial situation saw the order 'drip-fed' over several fiscal years. A large single order would have allowed more rapid re-equipment of the three-squadron fighter-bomber force, whereas limiting the original order to only 18 aircraft delayed formation of the second and third units by one and two years, respectively.

Initial prototype

The first true F-1 prototype made its maiden flight on 16 June 1977. After brief flight trials, it was handed over to the JASDF on 16 September 1977.

The first JASDF unit to convert to the Mitsubishi F-1 was 3 Hikotai at Misawa, which began re-equipment in September 1977, transferring to the control of the 3 Kokudan on 1 March 1978 when conversion was complete. 3 Kokudan's second squadron, the 8 Hikotai, began conversion to the F-1 in June 1979, and when this was complete the 6 Hikotai began transitioning to the new type, in March 1980. This was the sole F-1 unit assigned to the 8 Kokudan at Tsuiki. Squadrons originally formed with 18 aircraft each (plus attrition replacements), but this was felt to be too small a number, and the JASDF pushed for squadrons with 25 aircraft each. This prompted a move by the Japanese defence ministry to cut the number of squadrons to two, and the JASDF rapidly decided that three 18-aircraft squadrons were ideal, or at least better than two 25-aircraft units.

The search for a replacement fighter support aircraft began in 1982 and culminated in the FS-X programme which spawned the Mitsubishi F-2. This much-modified F-16 derivative was first delivered for operational trials in 2000, initially at Misawa. It has since replaced the F-1 with both 3 Hikotai and 8 Hikotai.

Mitsubishi F-1

This aircraft, 70-8203, was the 3rd of 77 production F-1s delivered to the JASDF. It carries the black panther badge of 8 Hikotai (8th Sqn), 3 Kokudan (3rd Air Wing) based at Misawa AB on the island of Honshu.

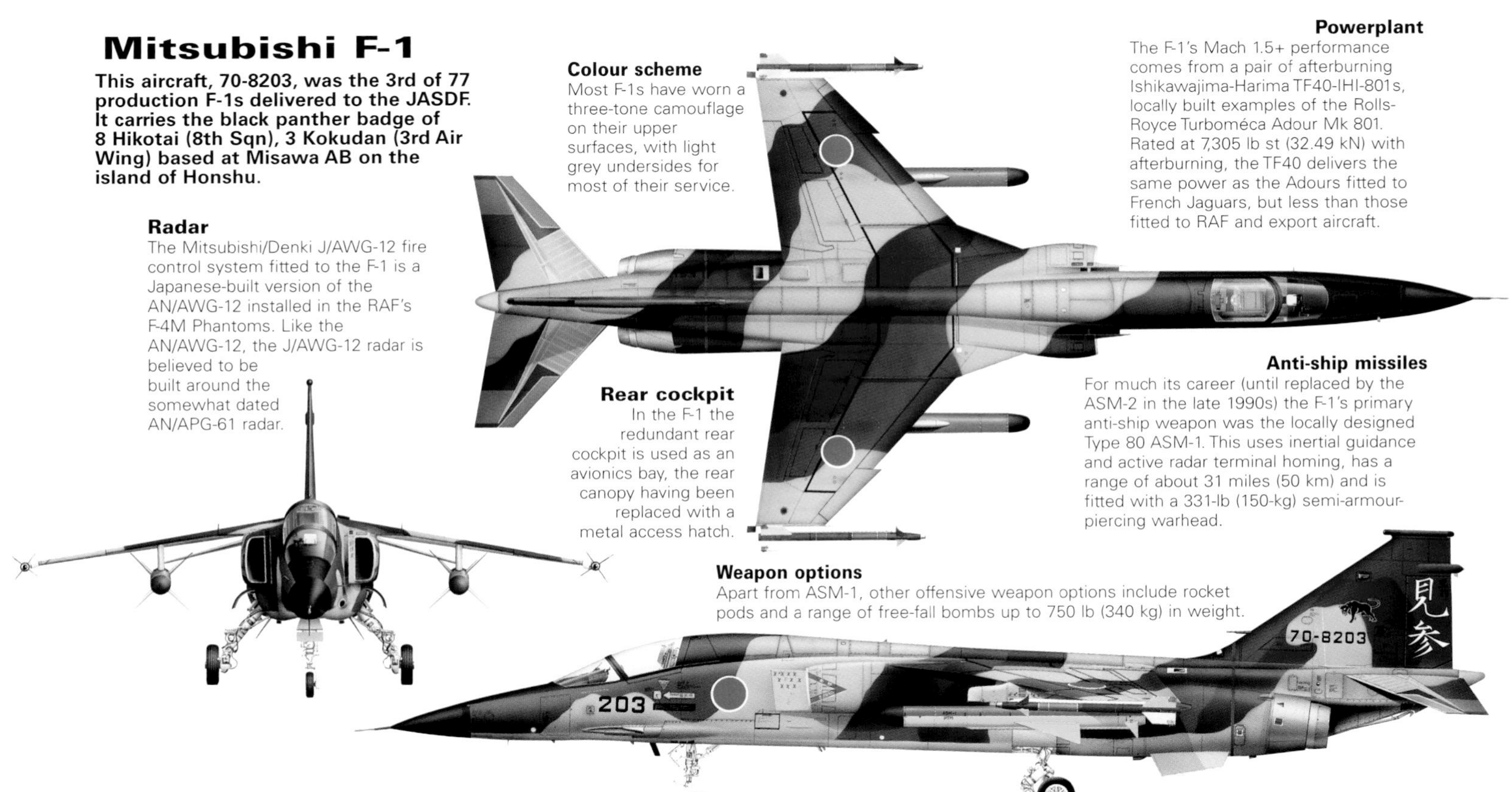

Radar
The Mitsubishi/Denki J/AWG-12 fire control system fitted to the F-1 is a Japanese-built version of the AN/AWG-12 installed in the RAF's F-4M Phantoms. Like the AN/AWG-12, the J/AWG-12 radar is believed to be built around the somewhat dated AN/APG-61 radar.

Colour scheme
Most F-1s have worn a three-tone camouflage on their upper surfaces, with light grey undersides for most of their service.

Rear cockpit
In the F-1 the redundant rear cockpit is used as an avionics bay, the rear canopy having been replaced with a metal access hatch.

Powerplant
The F-1's Mach 1.5+ performance comes from a pair of afterburning Ishikawajima-Harima TF40-IHI-801s, locally built examples of the Rolls-Royce Turboméca Adour Mk 801. Rated at 7,305 lb st (32.49 kN) with afterburning, the TF40 delivers the same power as the Adours fitted to French Jaguars, but less than those fitted to RAF and export aircraft.

Anti-ship missiles
For much its career (until replaced by the ASM-2 in the late 1990s) the F-1's primary anti-ship weapon was the locally designed Type 80 ASM-1. This uses inertial guidance and active radar terminal homing, has a range of about 31 miles (50 km) and is fitted with a 331-lb (150-kg) semi-armour-piercing warhead.

Weapon options
Apart from ASM-1, other offensive weapon options include rocket pods and a range of free-fall bombs up to 750 lb (340 kg) in weight.

Standing before the well-known neon signs that advertised North American's first and most famous jet products, the first Vigilante prototype is seen shortly after roll-out in ***May 1958. It*** *took to the air for the first time on the last day of* ***August,*** *in the hands of chief company test pilot* ***Dick Wenzel.***

North American (Rockwell) A3J/A-5 Vigilante

High-tech A-bomber

North American's A3J-1 was sold to the US Navy as a nuclear bomber with a top speed of Mach 2 and with a weapons delivery capability years ahead of its time. However, plagued by problems with its weapons delivery system, cost overruns and a general complexity that caused maintenance nightmares, the Vigilante bomber's career was to be a brief one.

USS **Saratoga** ***steams into wind and her crew look on as one of the pre-production A3J-1s is prepared for another test flight. The Vigilante was one of the largest aircraft to serve from an aircraft-carrier anywhere – only certain versions of the Douglas A3D Skywarrior were heavier.***

By the mid-1950s, a new tactic supplemented the US Navy's traditional concept of high-altitude delivery of an atomic bomb using heavy attack aircraft. The advent of smaller-sized nuclear weapons enabled smaller carrier-based aircraft to carry them to the target. In this scenario, propeller-driven A-1 Skyraiders and A-4 Skyhawks, the latter a jet designed specifically as a nuclear-capable light attack aircraft, would proceed to the target at low altitude, avoiding enemy radar. Reaching the target area, the pilots would pull back on the stick into a climb and release the weapon, which would arc away from the aircraft and follow a downward-arced trajectory toward the target, allowing time for the pilot, completing an Immelman manoeuvre, to get away from the blast. Though appearing effective on paper, this toss bombing technique, referred to by the US Navy acronym LABS (Low-Altitude Bombing System), presented some problems. 'We are fooling no one but ourselves if we believe that the AD [Skyraider] can perform a low-altitude, low-visibility attack under wartime conditions,' wrote one flag officer. 'It cannot be used in all-weather conditions, there is no certainty that an accurate IP [Initial Point] can be located...and the over-the-shoulder method, if the target is located, will subject our bombers to heavy losses.'

Offered to the USN as an unsolicited proposal in 1954, the North American General Purpose Attack Weapon (NAGPAW) sought to address these problems. Suitably impressed, the US Navy added two further stipulations in January 1955: that the aircraft have a zero-wind launch capability and that it be optimised for supersonic high-altitude penetration rather than the LABS delivery method

A-5A Vigilante

The A3J-1 became the A-5A in 1962. BuNo. 149283 was one of the last A-5As built and is depicted as it appeared during the first cruise by Heavy Attack Squadron 7 (VAH-7), aboard USS *Enterprise* (CVAN-65), to the Mediterranean in 1962. Standard Gull Gray/Insignia White colours and markings for the period were used, with the exception of the stylised '7' on the fin in Insignia Blue, behind 12 white stars.

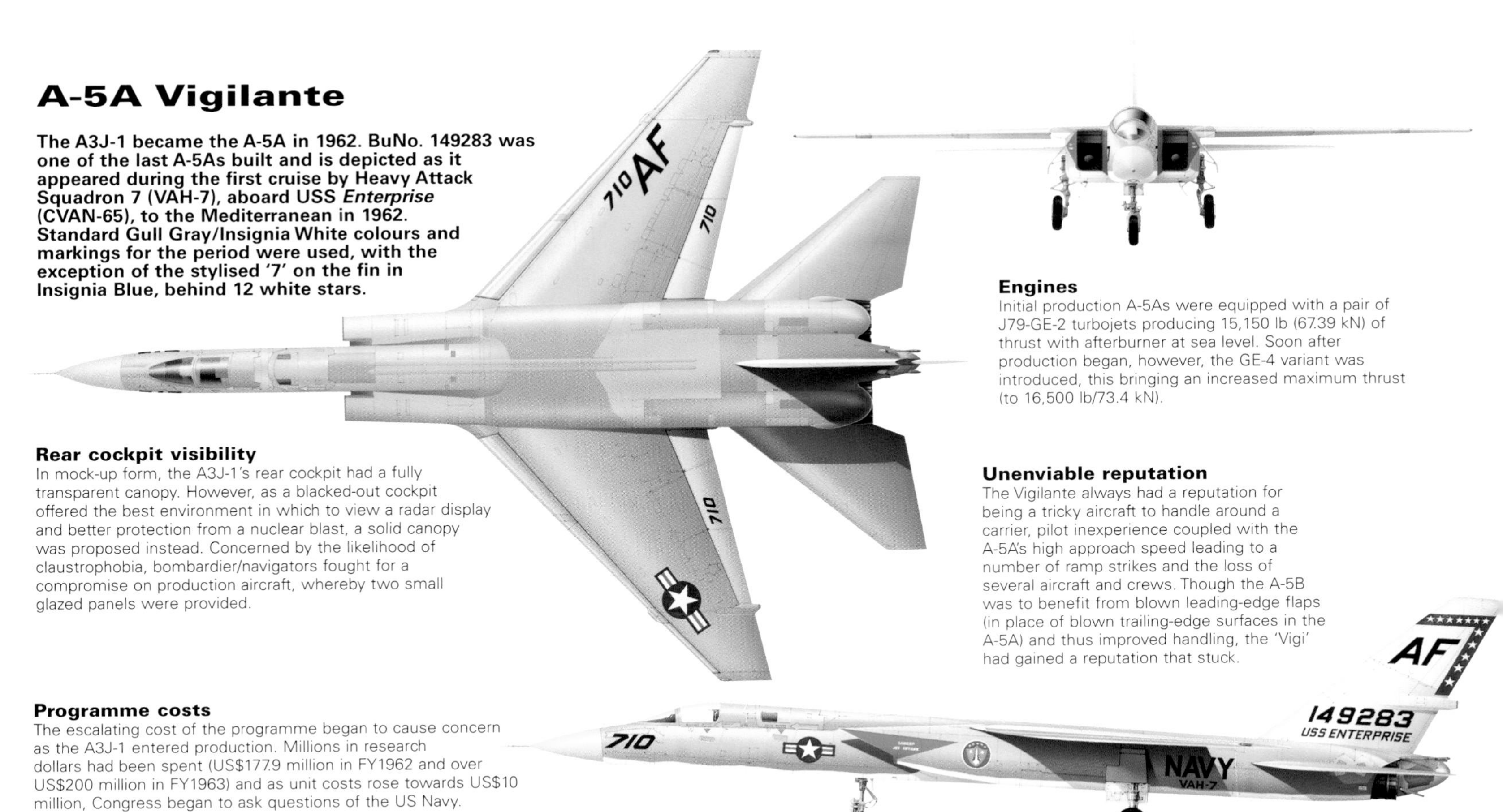

Engines
Initial production A-5As were equipped with a pair of J79-GE-2 turbojets producing 15,150 lb (67.39 kN) of thrust with afterburner at sea level. Soon after production began, however, the GE-4 variant was introduced, this bringing an increased maximum thrust (to 16,500 lb/73.4 kN).

Rear cockpit visibility
In mock-up form, the A3J-1's rear cockpit had a fully transparent canopy. However, as a blacked-out cockpit offered the best environment in which to view a radar display and better protection from a nuclear blast, a solid canopy was proposed instead. Concerned by the likelihood of claustrophobia, bombardier/navigators fought for a compromise on production aircraft, whereby two small glazed panels were provided.

Unenviable reputation
The Vigilante always had a reputation for being a tricky aircraft to handle around a carrier, pilot inexperience coupled with the A-5A's high approach speed leading to a number of ramp strikes and the loss of several aircraft and crews. Though the A-5B was to benefit from blown leading-edge flaps (in place of blown trailing-edge surfaces in the A-5A) and thus improved handling, the 'Vigi' had gained a reputation that stuck.

Programme costs
The escalating cost of the programme began to cause concern as the A3J-1 entered production. Millions in research dollars had been spent (US$177.9 million in FY1962 and over US$200 million in FY1963) and as unit costs rose towards US$10 million, Congress began to ask questions of the US Navy.

originally envisaged. By then named Vigilante and soon to be designated A3J, North American's NA-233 proposal became the subject of an US$86 million contract for two prototypes, awarded on 29 August 1956. The first of these made its maiden flight on 31 August 1958.

By anybody's standards in the 1950s, and compared to the types in service with the USN at the time, the Vigilante was an exciting and futuristic aircraft. The huge, box-like rear fuselage was a new departure and a feature mimicked in a number of later designs. Also much-copied was the Vigilante's variable-intake ramp system, which allowed the aircraft's engines to breathe subsonic air at supersonic speeds. The large one-piece tail surfaces and innovative mainplane, with its system of spoilers and deflectors (in place of conventional ailerons) and blown flaps – all made necessary by the zero-wind launch requirement – represented something of an aerodynamic *tour de force*. The early fly-by-wire system used to control them was also a novelty.

Tests and failures

An exhaustive flight and systems test programme followed the first flight. Though it possessed an impressive performance, the Vigilante proved to have some tricky handling characteristics, especially at the low speeds encountered on approach to a carrier deck. It was also found that its innovative linear weapons bay would not function satisfactorily and, in the event, it was deleted from production A3J-1s.

The Vigilante's operational debut came in August 1962 when VAH-7 took 12 A3J-1s to join USS *Enterprise* for a short cruise with the Sixth Fleet in the Mediterranean. A Readiness Air Group (VAH-3) and one other operational Heavy Attack Squadron (VAH-1) were also equipped, but the first-generation Vigilante, which had proved to be complex and maintenance-intensive in service (even without a functioning weapons delivery system), was not an unqualified success. Finally, the Joint Chiefs of Staff came to the decision that the US Navy's future contribution to the American strategic nuclear deterrent should be confined to ballistic missile-equipped submarines. The carrierborne heavy nuclear bomber was dead.

So it was that the A-5A left the front-line USN inventory in 1964. However, in the meantime, NAA had developed the much improved A-5B which, although it was too late to serve as a bomber, was the basis for the more successful RA-5C.

VAH-7's 'boss bird', 'AE/700', leads a trio of VAH-7 aircraft over NAS Sanford. Only two operational units were equipped with Vigilante bombers, the other being US Navy 'Heavy One' (VAH-1).

RA-5C Vigilante

Naval PR master

Above: This pair of RA-5C Vigilantes of RVAH-3 (the Vigilante RAG) was among the 43 A-5A bombers converted to RA-5C standard for a new role as carrierborne reconnaissance platforms. Another 18 A-5Bs were converted to the same standard, bringing total RA-5 production to 140 aircraft, including 79 new-build machines.

The development, by NAA, of the improved A-5B unfortunately coincided with the withdrawal of the strategic nuclear strike role from USN carrier aviation. However, the USN's requirement for a carrierborne reconnaissance platform provided a new tasking for this highly capable airframe.

Briefly known as the A3J-3 (though never officially as the, perhaps more logical, A3J-3P), the RA-5C grew out of the USN's lack of fleet reconnaissance capability, a situation that gave Secretary of Defense Robert McNamara the reason he needed to keep the Vigilante programme alive after the impending withdrawal of the A-5A and cancellation of its A-5B (A3J-2) successor.

Approved by the tri-service Darrow committee (which considered all reconnaissance systems with a view to integrating the services' various systems platforms and eliminating overlap), the A3J-3 was to be equipped not only with cameras, but also with a SLAR and passive ECM (Elint) equipment. These were operated, for the most part, by a Radar Navigator (RAN), who had replaced the A-5A's Bombardier/Navigator in the rear seat of the aircraft.

Before cancellation, A3J-2 production got under way, the first prototype flying in April 1962. Eighteen were completed; of the first six examples, two were delivered to the USN and the remainder converted as YA-5C prototypes, while the other 12 were eventually converted to RA-5C standard. The first purpose-built RA-5C got airborne on 30 June and was followed by another 42 production articles. These were augmented by aircraft converted from redundant A-5As/Bs – 61 in all. As attrition and combat losses took their toll, an unprecedented reopening of the Vigilante production line was authorised, another 36 aircraft being produced during 1969/70.

RA-5C prototypes

By mid-1964, A-3 Skywarrior-equipped VAH-5 had begun converting to the Vigilante in preparation for taking the aircraft to sea as RVAH-5 – the first operational RA-5C unit. At the same time, the last of the A-5As was returned to the North American plant at Columbus, Ohio, for conversion to photo-reconnaissance duties. Finally, the VAH designation became a thing of the past for Vigilante squadrons, which from spring 1964 were redesignated Reconnaissance Heavy Attack Squadrons (RVAH). In short order, Heavy Attack Wing One, the command that for so many years had carried the nuclear torch for naval aviation, was renamed Reconnaissance Attack Wing One. Including the RAG (RVAH-3), 10 RVAH squadrons (seven redesignated VAH and VC units and three formed from scratch) were equipped with the RA-5C between 1964 and 1979.

This view of a late-production RA-5C, at a typically high pitch angle as it touches down on a carrier, shows the salient features of the aircraft's sensor package. All were installed in the long ventral 'canoe', which meant that little internal modification of the A-5B airframe was required in designing the RA-5C.

The number of Vigilantes assigned to each squadron was largely determined by the scarcity of the aircraft throughout its career. The nine operational squadrons were initially assigned six aircraft each, this allocation

The first production RA-5C and the first example of the reconnaissance Vigilante constructed from scratch (the prototypes having been converted from A-5Bs), BuNo. 150823 cruises with 'everything down' for the camera. The aircraft is equipped with four underwing 400-US gal (1514-litre) drop tanks. These were rarely used in service, as the Vigilante was able to carry a prodigious amount of internal fuel. Note also the deployed leading-edge slats, intended to improve low-speed handling.

Left: This well known view was one of a number of BuNo. 156608, photographed during RVAH-7's last cruise. This RA-5C made the last catapulted carrier launch by a Vigilante, from USS Ranger for NAS Key West on 21 September 1979. The same aircraft was to make the last field arrested landing, at Key West on 14 November, and the last Vigilante flight of all on the 20th, when it departed Key West for Davis-Monthan AFB and went into storage.

remaining fixed until around 1971, when attrition began to take its toll on those aircraft held in reserve and production was restarted. From then on, unit establishment stabilised at four or five machines, but by 1973 it had dropped to just three – a figure that remained fairly constant until the type's retirement. Had the number of RA-5 units not been reduced from 1974, this figure may have dropped further.

The success or failure of the Vigilante in its new role depended on the pilots and RANs who launched from carrier decks and the ground echelons which kept them flying. In the case of the RA-5C, the learning curve was steep, for the aircraft's maiden cruise was not in tranquil waters, but in the Tonkin Gulf off the coast of Vietnam, to which RVAH-5 deployed in USS *Ranger* in 1965.

One of the first tasks entrusted to the Vigilantes, given the inaccuracy of American maps of the region, was the provision of imagery of the entire country – a task that took some two weeks to accomplish. The Vigilante's career in the region spanned nine years.

Primarily assigned the hazardous pre- and post-strike reconnaissance task, the RA-5C suffered the highest loss rate of a USN type involved in the conflict. Initially, the sensitivity of the RA-5C's equipment and the USN's inexperience with the type restricted it to South Vietnamese targets. However, it was not long before the usefulness of its sensors would outweigh any security worries and, before long, 'Vigis' were being sent 'up north'.

Final withdrawal

During the Vietnam War, eight RA-5C squadrons logged a total of 32 deployments to the Tonkin Gulf. Though no longer flying in hostile skies after 1973, the Vigilante remained an integral part of carrier air wings in the Mediterranean and western Pacific for the remainder of the 1970s. RA-5Cs also logged traps onboard the USN's second nuclear-powered carrier, USS *Nimitz*, on Mediterranean cruises during the period 1976 to 1978. The end finally came in 1979 when RVAH-7, ironically the first squadron to deploy the Vigilante, was finally disestablished.

Vigilante derivatives

To fill a requirement for a replacement for its ageing English Electric Canberras, the Royal Australian Air Force evaluated the McDonnell Douglas F-4 Phantom, BAC TSR.2, Dassault Mirage IV and the North American A-5 (right) before, in October 1963, placing an order for 18 General Dynamics F-111As and six RF-111As (later amended to comprise 24 F-111Cs). NAA's Columbus Division made numerous representations to the USAF, attempting to interest the service in Vigilante derivatives. In 1960 the most likely operator appeared to be Air Defense Command (ADC) and most NAA proposals were intended to meet the ADC's requirements. 'Retaliator' was the most promising of these, incorporating a single liquid-fuel rocket, intended to improve speed and altitude performance. Though it was shelved, the concept was revived 10 years later as the NR-349 (left). This sported a third GE J79 powerplant, positioned above and between the existing turbojets and was to be armed with radar-guided AAMs. Neither design was built.

A factory-fresh F-86F flies over the Pacific during a test flight after completion at North American's Inglewood plant. The key to the Sabre's success was its wing swept back at 35°, which allowed the aircraft to enter the transonic regime without encountering the compressibility effects suffered by earlier, straight-wing designs.

North American F-86 Sabre

Korean War 'ace'

By any criteria, the Sabre was one of the greatest aircraft of all time. Built in huge numbers and operated by a large number of air forces, the F-86 also achieved one of the greatest and most emphatic victories in the history of air combat.

First flying on 1 October 1947, the XP-86 was the prototype for a series of fighters that would change the face of aerial warfare and become the standard combat aircraft of the free world throughout the 1950s. North American had taken a big gamble by waiting to incorporate captured German swept-wing technology into their first jet fighter design for USAF, but the result was an aircraft which could, at last, overcome the steep drag rise encountered at speeds above 500 mph (805 km/h).

First supersonic?

The XP-86 prototype almost certainly beat the Bell X-1 through the sound barrier, although figures which confirmed its supersonic capability (in a dive) were not taken until five days after Yeager's rocket-powered flight.

As the F-86A, the Sabre entered service in February 1949 as a day-fighter. In November 1950 the first aircraft reached Korea to counter the deployment by the North Koreans of the swept-wing MiG-15. For the next 31 months, the two types were locked in monumental air battles over the Korean peninsula. Despite enjoying a slight performance margin over the Sabre, the MiG-15 fell in huge numbers, the discrepancy being largely due to the superior training and tactics employed by the US (and allied) pilots flying the F-86, and by continual improvements made to the aircraft during the course of the war. These included the F-86E with a more powerful engine and an all-flying tail which arrived in July 1951, the F-86F with yet more

Built by Mitsubishi, Japan's Sabres were F-86F-40s, this sub-variant reintroducing leading-edge slats (added to the '6-3' wing) and with lengthened wings. Many other aircraft were retrofitted with these modifications.

***Left:* Hastily developed to provide an interim all-weather interceptor to cover for delays in the F-89 Scorpion programme, the F-86D had nose-mounted radar. Instead of the six-gun armament of the day-fighter, the 'Dog' had a retractable tray for 24 Mighty Mouse unguided rockets.**

***Below:* From about 1955, the USAF began transferring F-86Fs to South Korea. As with many other air arms, the Sabre had a career with the RoKAF which lasted into the 1980s.**

power from September 1952, and the '6-3' unslatted wing which provided better control at the outer edge of the envelope. In the final tally, Sabre pilots racked up a kill/loss tally of roughly 10:1 against the MiGs.

As more Sabres became available in Korea, so the tasks were widened. RF-86A/F reconnaissance aircraft were converted with cameras, while in the last year of the war F-86F-30s arrived (with added hardpoints) to undertake the fighter-bomber mission. The factory-built RF-86F was too late to see combat, but became the standard tactical recce type for several air arms. In Europe, F-86F-35s were assigned a tactical nuclear mission.

Back in the US, the threat of a Soviet bomber attack was perceived as very real. Interceptors were required in large numbers and short order. Accordingly, the Sabre was reworked as the F-86D (universally known as the 'Sabre Dog') with all-weather radar in a nose radome, afterburning engine and rocket armament. This interim interceptor served in the defence of the US, and many were modified as the F-86L with automatic ground control equipment. A version with a downgraded fire control system and cannon armament was built for NATO as the F-86K.

'Sabre Hog'

The final major US variant was the F-86H, which introduced a new engine in the shape of the J73. This required a redesign of the fuselage, which became much deeper. The H was mainly a ground-attack aircraft with full nuclear capability. Its front-line service was cut short by the introduction of NAA's F-100.

In addition to North American production, large numbers were built by Canadair, which supplied many to NATO air arms, enabling the Sabre to become the standard day-fighter in Europe during the 1950s. Others were licence-built in Japan by Mitsubishi, while Fiat built F-86Ks in Italy. Sabres built in Australia had yet another engine, the Rolls-Royce Avon, and these were the best performing of all the versions.

Sabres of all variants enjoyed a long life with many air arms, seeing action in several skirmishes around the world, notably with Pakistan against India and with Taiwan against mainland China. In the latter conflict, Sabres became the first aircraft to launch AAMs in combat. F-86s remained in front-line service into the 1980s, some aircraft flying with their third military operator, while others performed second-line duties.

***Above:* Pilots of Taiwan's No. 28 Squadron practise a scramble. Many of the Taiwanese aircraft were Korean War veteran F-86Fs which were to see action again during the 1958 Taiwan Straits clash with Communist China.**

***Left:* Even the early Sabres had an element of ground attack capability in the form of bombs or, as here, 5-in (12.7-cm) HVAR rockets. The carriage of HVARs precluded the use of any other stores, including drop tanks.**

Above: Bearing the Air Training Command badge, these F-86A-5s were with the 3596th Fighter Squadron (nicknamed 'The Cadillac Flight'), a training unit based at Nellis AFB, Nevada.

F-86 variants

Series production of the F-86 Sabre day-fighter began with the manufacturer's NA-151, or USAF F-86A-1, powered by the 5,200-lb (23.1-kN) thrust General Electric J47-GE-13 turbojet.

The F-86A-1 made its first flight on 20 May 1948. The early production aircraft was heavier than the XP-86 prototype and had a more powerful engine, allowing it to claim the world air speed record in September 1948.

Also in late 1948, North American began to turn out the F-86A-5 version, with slightly more powerful J47-GE-7 and GE-13 engines. The armament of six 0.5-in (12.7-mm) machine-guns was to be standard on nearly all USAF F-86 day-fighters.

The F-86A-5 model introduced a V-shaped bulletproof windscreen and heated gun compartments. It could also carry drop tanks, rockets, and bombs.

In early Sabres, the A-1CM gunsight was coupled with an AN/APG-30 radar in the upper lip of the nose intake. F-86A-5 aircraft retrofitted with the A-1CM sight were redesignated F-86A-6 when they retained AN/APG-5C radar, and F-86A-7 when retrofitted with the AN/APG-30.

Recce conversions

After the 554th and last F-86A model was delivered in December 1950, a number of F-86A Sabres were converted to RF-86A reconnaissance aircraft.

The first flight of the F-86E-1 Sabre was made on 23 September 1950. The 'all-flying tail' and the irreversible hydraulic systems introduced in the F-86E were one of the most important advances of the era. However, the early version of the 'all-flying tail' gave sluggish manoeuvrability and artificial 'feel'. North American and the Air Force worked together on changing and improving the F-86E's key features until the problems were resolved and the F-86E became a world-beater.

Sixty F-86E-1 models were followed by 111 E-5s which differed only in minor details. The designation F-86E-6 went to a batch of 60 Canadair-built CL-13 Sabre Mk 2 fighters built in Canada for the USAF. The designation F-86E-10 went to the first 132 examples of the company NA-172, which were powered by the J47-GE-13, as the planned -27 models were not yet available – in short, the aircraft

The last front-line Sabre variant to enter USAF service was the F-86L, which added computerised datalink system to low-time F-86D airframes. The aircraft were fitted with the latest J47-GE-33 engine.

L'il Stinker was among the 'Hog' Sabres that equipped the 104th FIS (later TFS), Maryland ANG between December 1957 and August 1970. The 104th was called to active service during the 1968 Pueblo Crisis.

Above: The hydraulically operated 'all-flying tail' was the main distinguishing feature of the F-86E. First flown in September 1950, the E-model was sent to Korea in mid-1951.

was an F-86F with an F-86E engine. The total F-86E build totalled 396 aircraft (or 456 including Canadian-built Sabres).

This total included 93 aircraft which were to have been delivered as F-86F-15s. These reverted to the -27 engine because of further powerplant delays and were given the out-of-order designation F-86E-15.

The '6-3 wing' appeared on several Sabre versions, but is associated with the definitive F-86F Sabre, along with the -27 engine. The F-86F was first flown on 19 March 1952 (although early F-86Fs lacked the wing). The combination of 'all-flying tail' and '6-3 wing' were to be vital to the outcome in the Korean War.

F-86F manufacture reached a total of 1,539 examples.

The F-86H 'Sabre Hog' was supposed to be the ultimate Sabre design, with a bigger engine, heavier firepower, nuclear capabilities and longer range.

The H was powered by a new J73-GE-3 engine rated at almost 9,250-lb (41.14-kN) static thrust. The J73 was larger than the J47, and required more air. This meant that a bigger fuselage was needed. The fuselage was split longitudinally, splicing an additional 6 in (15 cm) into the depth of the fuselage. Additionally, the fuselage was lengthened and widened. Other changes included a clamshell opening canopy and increased internal fuel capacity.

'Hog' features

The vertical tail assembly was taller and wider through the chord, but had a smaller rudder. The horizontal control surfaces were changed from the 'all-flying tail' design with a split stabiliser and elevator, to a single-piece slab. The first 14 aircraft off the assembly line were completed with the old-style slatted wing, without the '6-3' extension. The '6-3 hard wing' was added later.

Since the H was developed as a fighter-bomber with a nuclear strike capability, an M-1 toss-bombing computer was installed.

The prototype F-86H made its first flight on 9 May.

The first production F-86H left the factory in September 1953, the initial batch covering 113 F-86H-1s. Next off the line would be the H-5, with the J73-GE-3A engine and four 20-mm cannon. North American built 60 F-86H-5s. The H-10 was nearly identical to the H-5, having only some minor internal changes and the GE-3E engine. Three hundred F-86H-10s were built before production of all types ended on 16 March 1956.

Although the first 14 H-1s were completed with the standard F-86F dual-store wing with leading-edge slats, the rest of the H-1 production, all of the H-5s, and the first 290 H-10s were built with the '6-3' solid leading-edge wing. The final 10 aircraft were completed using the so-called 'F-40' wing, which had the '6-3' chord increase, an extension on each tip, and the leading-edge slats reinstalled for low-speed control. Eventually, all remaining Hs in both USAF and ANG inventories were retrofitted with the 'F-40' wing.

Left: Neither the F-86B nor the F-86C (illustrated) reached production. The latter, a 'penetration interceptor' later redesignated YF-93, was derived from the Sabre but in fact had little, other than its wing, in common with the F-86. Only two prototypes were built.

ROKAF
55 006

Sabre schemes

RoKAF F-86s originally wore standard USAF colours (natural metal, with ID sashes) with colourful local embellishments. The aircraft which survived into the 1970s were painted in a green/brown camouflage.

F-86F Sabre

The Republic of Korea Air Force, supplied with F-86Fs in 1955, was among a number of air arms to fly ex-USAF Sabres of this variant. RoKAF F-86Fs were modified to carry AIM-9 Sidewinder AAMs.

Foreign production

While North American concentrated on producing F-86s for the USAF, Canadair and CAC developed versions of the Sabre that were superior in terms of performance to their American cousins.

In the aftermath of World War II, Canada was in the market for a new jet fighter. The F-86 Sabre was the obvious choice and a deal was signed in 1949 whereby the aircraft would be built in Canada, albeit with US-supplied J47 engines. The first aircraft, an F-86A-5, was shipped in parts from the US and was re-assembled by Canadair as the sole CL-13 Sabre Mk 1. It first flew on 8 August 1950.

The contract with North American covered the F-86E with all-flying tail, so production CL-13 aircraft were of the E-1 version, designated Sabre Mk 2 locally. Production totalled 350. Operations by the RCAF began in April 1951, 410 'Cougar' Squadron being the first unit to equip with the type.

Meanwhile, the Avro Canada company had developed the Orenda turbojet. One NAA-built aircraft was experimentally fitted with the engine, showing such an improvement in performance that Canadair produced a similar

Above: The ultimate Canadair Sabre was the Mk 6 which, with the Orenda 14 engine, easily outperformed US-built aircraft.

Below: Wearing the sharkmouth markings first applied to Curtiss P-40s in the desert, these Sabre Mk 4s served with No. 112 Sqn, one of 10 RAF Germany units which re-equipped with Sabres.

CL-13 Sabre Mk 2

The J47-engined Mk 2 was the first Sabre variant in RCAF service. As well as equipping Air Defence Command units at home, the Sabres were dispatched to Europe to equip four fighter wings at Marville and Gros Tenquin in France, and Baden-Söllingen and Zweibrücken in West Germany. This aircraft served with No. 434 'Bluenose' Squadron, part of No. 3 Wing at Zweibrücken.

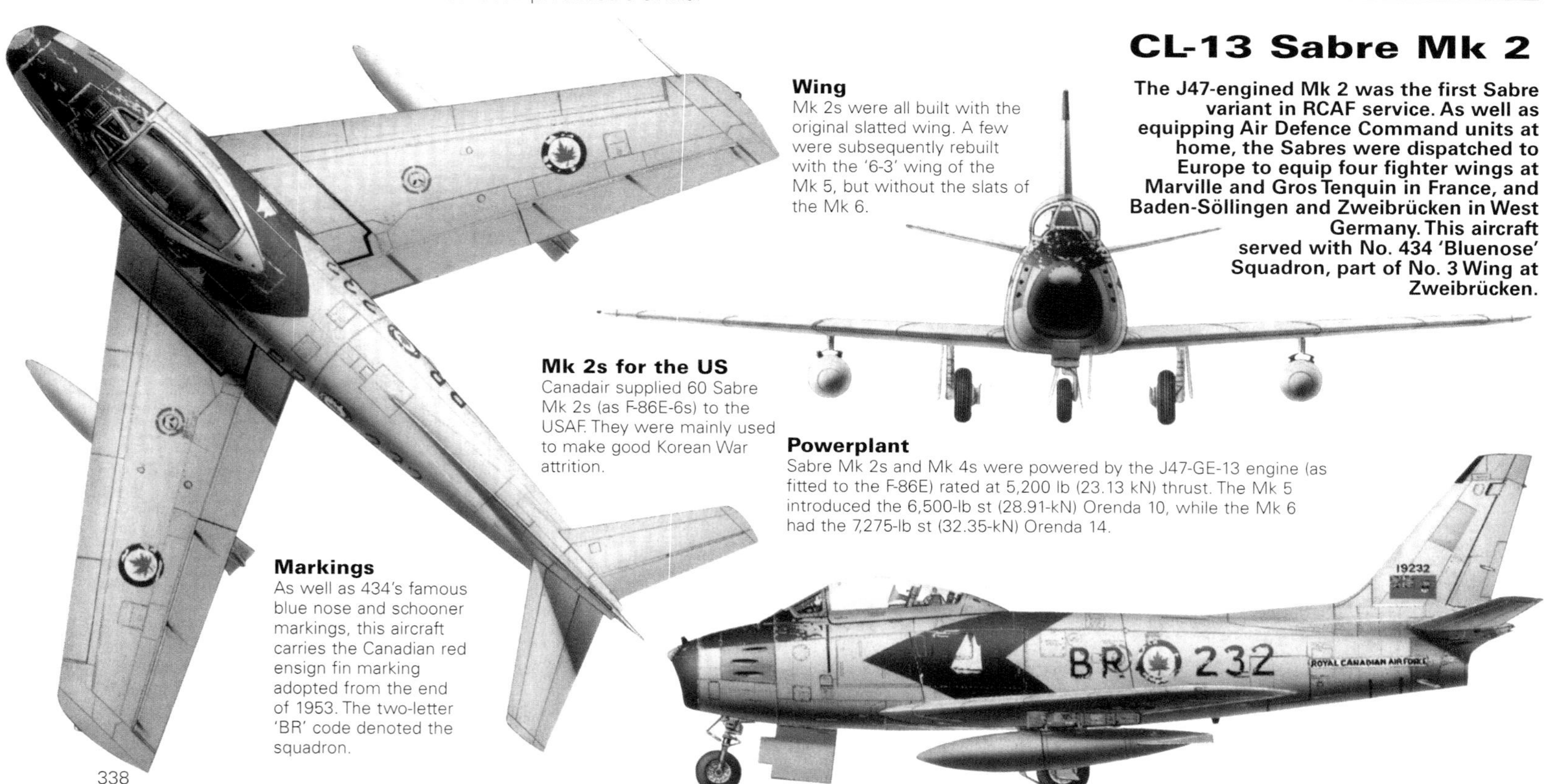

Wing
Mk 2s were all built with the original slatted wing. A few were subsequently rebuilt with the '6-3' wing of the Mk 5, but without the slats of the Mk 6.

Mk 2s for the US
Canadair supplied 60 Sabre Mk 2s (as F-86E-6s) to the USAF. They were mainly used to make good Korean War attrition.

Powerplant
Sabre Mk 2s and Mk 4s were powered by the J47-GE-13 engine (as fitted to the F-86E) rated at 5,200 lb (23.13 kN) thrust. The Mk 5 introduced the 6,500-lb st (28.91-kN) Orenda 10, while the Mk 6 had the 7,275-lb st (32.35-kN) Orenda 14.

Markings
As well as 434's famous blue nose and schooner markings, this aircraft carries the Canadian red ensign fin marking adopted from the end of 1953. The two-letter 'BR' code denoted the squadron.

Above: A94-101 was the CA-26 Avon Sabre prototype. It was trucked to Avalon for its first flight on 3 August 1953, flown by Flight Lieutenant W. Scott. Note the single gun trough for the ADEN cannon, and the slightly revised intake and nose profile.

Left: Sabre Mk 32s of Nos 3 (foreground) and 77 Squadrons are seen at RAAF Butterworth in Malaya. Australian Sabres, operating with No. 78 Wing, undertook a few combat missions at the tail end of the Malayan Emergency, the first in August 1959.

conversion of a Sabre Mk 2. The resulting Sabre Mk 3 first flew on 29 September 1952.

While production of the Orenda was gearing up, Canadair built 438 Sabre Mk 4s with J47 engines, of which the RAF took the bulk to hastily re-equip its fighter squadrons – notably in RAF Germany. These aircraft had a relatively brief service life, although many went on to serve with other air arms, notably in Italy and Yugoslavia.

With the Orenda ready for production, Canadair started building the CL-13A Sabre Mk 5, which had an Orenda 10 engine and a '6-3' wing. It first flew on 30 July 1953. Most of the 370 built went to the RCAF, but 75 began the rebuilding of the post-war Luftwaffe's fighter force. On 19 October 1954 Canadair first flew the Sabre Mk 6, which had a slatted '6-3' wing and a more powerful Orenda 14 engine. Production of this model reached 655, of which the RCAF took 390 and the Luftwaffe 225. The remainder went to South Africa (34) and Colombia (six).

Canadair production came to an end in October 1958, by which time 1,815 Sabres had been built. The type was the backbone of NATO's day fighter force in Europe, and in its Orenda-powered versions serving with the RCAF and Luftwaffe, was the best fighter of its day. Following the end of their initial front-line careers, Canadair Sabres went on to serve with the air forces of Bangladesh, Burma, Greece, Honduras, Iran, Italy, Pakistan, Portugal, Turkey and Yugoslavia.

Avon Sabre

Meanwhile, in the opposite corner of the Commonwealth, Australia chose the Sabre to be its new fighter in late 1950. A production line was established by Commonwealth Aircraft Corporation. Early Korean experience had highlighted two areas – thrust and armament 'punch' – which needed improvement, and so the Australian Sabres were remodelled with new guns and a new engine, requiring virtually a new fuselage structure.

Rolls-Royce's excellent RA.7 Avon was the chosen powerplant, offering more thrust than the J47 for less weight. It did, however, require around 25 per cent more air, necessitating a redesign of the forward fuselage to accommodate a larger intake and duct. The reduced engine weight required it to be moved back in the fuselage for centre of gravity purposes, entailing a major redesign. Instead of six machine-guns, the Avon Sabre had two ADEN 30-mm cannon. Under the company designation CA-26, CAC flew the first Avon Sabre on 3 August 1953.

Production aircraft were designated CA-27, and the first 22 were completed as Sabre Mk 30s with standard slatted wings. Twenty Mk 31s followed with unslatted '6-3' wings, and 69 Mk 32s with slatted '6-3' wings. Earlier survivors were upgraded to this configuration. Including the CA-26, 112 Sabres were built by CAC, the last being delivered in December 1961. Avon Sabres entered RAAF service in August 1954. The Sabre was retired from RAAF service in 1971 and Mk 32s were donated to Malaysia (18 in 1969) and Indonesia (18 in 1973, and five ex-Malaysian in 1976).

Japanese production and the F-86K

Mitsubishi in Japan assembled 300 F-86F-40 Sabres (right) from NAA-supplied parts to equip JASDF squadrons. This version had extended wingtips for better air combat turning performance, and was a multi-role fighter/attacker. They joined around 135 ex-USAF F-86Fs and 122 F-86Ds in JASDF service. The F-40s had a very long career, serving on subsequently in secondary roles.

Eighty-eight F-86Ks were procured for two wings of the Luftwaffe's all-weather fighter force. This aircraft wears the 'JD' codes of JG 74.

Meanwhile, to answer NATO calls for an all-weather fighter, but restricted by security concerns surrounding the F-86D's fire control system, North American produced the F-86K. This was a downgraded version of the F-86D with MG-4 fire control system in place of the Dog's E-4, and four 20-mm cannon in place of the rocket armament. Assembly of NAA-built parts was entrusted to Fiat, but demand outstripped Fiat's capacity, and NAA built 50. Fiat eventually produced 221 F-86Ks, which served with France, Italy, the Netherlands, Norway and West Germany. When these aircraft were replaced by F-104s in the 1960s, the redundant Sabres were passed on to Honduras, Turkey and Venezuela.

North American F-100 Super Sabre

The 'Hun'

The F-100 and the MiG-19 were the world's first operational supersonic aircraft. Although the F-100 never came close to its predecessor, the F-86, in terms of its array of variants or numbers built, it enjoyed a very long active life, with a widespread distribution throughout USAF forces and in the hands of four overseas users.

Perhaps the ultimate expression of the 'Hun' was the F-100D fighter-bomber variant which served with distinction in Vietnam, pulverising Viet Cong positions with rockets, bombs and napalm.

The mid-1950s witnessed the frightening spectre of an atomic nightmare descending on air bases, destroying aircraft before they could get into the air. As VTOL technology was still in its infancy, the Zero-Length Launch (ZELL) system was devised. This incorporated a solid-propellant rocket that produced 130,000 lb (585 kN) of thrust for four seconds, enough to accelerate an F-100 from zero to 275 kt (316 mph; 509 km/h). While the system proved to be safe, it was never adopted for regular service use.

'Huns' fought a successful war in Vietnam, with two-seat F-100Fs performing FAC and Wild Weasel duties in support of their single-seat cousins.

Below: The sun glints off the first YF-100A as it soars above the Air Force Flight Test Center. The aircraft was flown initially by test pilot George Welch, who successfully bet (winning two beers) that the aircraft would go supersonic on its first flight.

After a series of experimental programmes aimed at finding a successor to the F-86 Sabre, North American decided upon an aircraft which would have a wing sweep of 45°, slab tailplanes, a sharp-lipped nose inlet and which would be powered by the J48 afterburning turbojet. Armament would comprise four 20-mm cannon and the wing would eventually carry 6,000 lb (2722 kg) of stores. With NACA help, the design team made rapid progress and after a mock-up review in January 1951, the USAF gave the go-ahead for the aircraft as the F-100, in the day-fighter role.

The first USAF contract was received on 1 November 1951 and, over the following year, a number of refinements to the YF-100 resulted in the new designation of YF-100A; in early 1953 the new fighter was named Super Sabre. The first example flew on 24 April 1953, reaching Mach 1, and on 14 October, the second example flew. By October, the first production machine had flown and the world speed record had been broken. The following month the 479th Fighter Day Wing began to convert and deliveries continued at pace. However, all was not well with the new fighter and by October 1954, after a series of accidents in which F-100s had inexplicably broken up in mid-air, all the aircraft were grounded. The cause was traced to roll-coupling, which had turned a hard-dive pull-out into an uncontrollable swerve to the right, at the highest possible air speed. The cure was to enlarge the fin and to extend the wings by 26 in (0.60 m).

Deliveries resume

Deliveries of new F-100As resumed in the spring of 1955 and 203 of this model were delivered. The F-100A served as a day fighter, with some subsequently being passed on to Taiwan, but it was quickly replaced in USAF service by later models. The abortive YF-100B was eventually built as the YF-107A and was basically a more advanced derivative with a larger engine, while the F-100C made full use of the potential attack capability by having the wing strengthened, six pylons installed and the powerful J57-21 engine fitted. On 20 August 1955, an F-100C set the first world absolute speed record under new high-altitude rules, and also the first over Mach 1. The F-100C was the first model to be flown overseas, to Bitburg, West Germany, in March 1956. Before the end of the year the 8th Fighter Bomber Group was at readiness in Japan.

The definitive single-seat version, the F-100D took development even more strongly in the direction of ground-attack. Advanced avionics, new autopilot and the LABS (low-altitude bombing system) for automatic toss delivery ensured a highly competent attack aircraft. Buddy refuelling, using a hose reel in an external pod, was also possible.

A total of 1,274 F-100Ds were built, with the first example flying on 12 June 1956. Some 85 were supplied new to France and 48 to Denmark, where they had an extremely long, active career. In addition, Turkey received up to 310 F-100C/D/F aircraft.

The F-100E, an improved F-100D, was not built and the final model was the two-seat F-100F, with the first, a converted F-100C, flying on 6 August 1956.

From 1957, the 'Hun' equipped 16 USAF wings, and in Vietnam, various models flew with such intensity that, by 1969, four wings alone had exceeded the number of missions flown by the 15,000-plus Mustangs in World War II. The 'Hun' proved equally proficient at top cover and low attack, and after progressive updating with missile armament, ECM, IFF, ILS and secure voice communications, it did a tremendous job. This included many two-seaters used for 'fast-mover FAC' duties and others converted for the Wild Weasel role.

By 1970 'Huns' were being replaced by F-4s and F-111s, with the last regular units not converting until 1972. Even then, 'Huns' soldiered on with ANG units until 1980. In foreign service, French 'Huns' served into 1978 and Danish aircraft remained in service until 1982, while Turkish aircraft were still serving up until 1989.

The fuselage on the F-100F was extended by 36 in (0.91 m) to accommodate the tandem dual-control cockpit, with a one-piece clamshell canopy – a total of 339 were built.

'Huns' over Vietnam

Above: A 481st TFS F-100D rolls in with divebrake deployed. The centreline pod contained a strike camera which was used for post-strike battle damage assessment (BDA).

While F-4s and F-105s stole the glory battling the Communists 'up North', the F-100 became the stalwart of the dirty war against the Viet Cong in South Vietnam. Serving in-theatre in large numbers, it flew far more combat missions than any other type.

The F-100 was introduced to combat by the USAF, not in Vietnam but in Laos. There, the US flirted briefly from 1962 to 1964 with a conflict that was soon to become all-too familiar next door in Vietnam.

The 1964 Gulf of Tonkin incident – when the US bombed North Vietnam for the first time – was followed by the sustained campaign against the North beginning in early 1965 and dubbed Operation Rolling Thunder. At the same time, the massive build-up of forces in Vietnam was under way. By then in Vietnam in larger numbers, but still there temporarily, Super Sabres began escorting bombing missions that went north.

The F-100 was soon to settle into its niche as an air-to-ground tactical bomber. When the first raids into North Vietnam were launched in 1965 – airfields at Da Nang and Tan Son Nhut being the temporary location of the Super Sabre – the 'Hun' even enjoyed a brief final gasp in the air-to-air realm, flying MiGCAP (fighter escort) missions.

MiG kill

On 4 April 1965, Captain Don Kilgus of the 416th Tactical Fighter Squadron poured burst after burst of 20-mm cannon fire into a fleeing MiG-17, inflicting mortal damage, and causing the MiG to fall from the sky. The captain was credited only with a 'probable' kill. No US F-100 pilot ever toted up an aerial victory. Once the F-4 Phantom arrived, the Super Sabre reverted to its mud-moving mandate. Da Nang went back to being used for other purposes and was not one of the four principal bases at which the 'Hun' settled for the long slog from 1965 to 1973.

Munition specialists load 1,000-lb (454-kg) bombs onto an F-100D; while most forms of ordnance were expended by the F-100 while in southeast Asia, it was to be the 750-lb (340-kg) general-purpose bomb that was used in the greatest numbers.

The US went from 15,000 troops in Vietnam in 1964 to 535,000 in 1969. When the US began its massive build-up of forces, there was not enough infrastructure to support the number of tactical fighters needed. Air bases in South Vietnam were rapidly expanded for this build-up while other bases were constructed from scratch on open terrain. It was impossible for this tiny country to contain all the wings of tactical aircraft that were felt to be needed, so a programme was devised that

Vortices stream from a hard-turning Super Sabre as it pulls out of yet another strike on Viet Cong positions. This example wears the pre-1965 silver scheme and it was partly as a result of the F-100's inherently dangerous low-level role that a more appropriate camouflage was adopted from 1965.

A weapon which gave good area coverage against soft targets was the 2.75-in (70-mm) unguided rocket, usually fired from a 19-round launcher. However, the weapon needed to be fired from close range to achieve good results, putting the F-100 into the groundfire danger area. Graphically shown to the left is the dispersion of the unguided projectiles after launch while, below, the image from a ventral strike camera shows two pods being fired from close range at a suspected Viet Cong position.

would send a squadron at a time from tactical wings to air bases in Vietnam for 90 to 120 days before being replaced by companion units, usually drawn from the same parent wing.

Four bases in South Vietnam became home to the F-100. Bien Hoa, Phan Rang, Phu Cat and Tuy Hoa were the fields from which the Super Sabre flew air-to-ground missions, not against North Vietnam but in support of friendly troops in South Vietnam. F-100Ds and F-100Fs were operated by active-duty USAF personnel, while F-100Cs and F-100Fs were flown by activated Air National Guardsmen. Later in the conflict, the two-seat F-100F evolved into new roles as a forward air control (Misty FAC) spotter and as a pioneer air defence radar site (Wild Weasel) nemesis.

The first flush of F-100 action against the Pathet Lao in 1964 was a false start, if anyone expected it to define the war that followed. The F-100 Super Sabre flew the bulk of its combat missions in South Vietnam in support of friendly troops. Around 1968, Super Sabres returned to Laos for a sustained serial campaign, with a purpose different from the original actions in that country – not to strike Laotian insurgents, but to attack North Vietnamese forces.

The 'in-country war' was the combat in South Vietnam in which Super Sabre pilots supported Allied troops, employing rockets, CBUs, napalm and HE (high-explosive) bombs against enemy forces pinpointed by an FAC aircraft. The 'out-country war' was a campaign of aerial interdiction of troops and supplies in North Vietnam and along the tributaries of the Ho Chi Minh Trail which snaked their way through Laos (two sectors of Laos were known in US jargon as Barrel Roll and Steel Tiger).

In 1969, when a high-ranking official of the Nixon administration asserted that no American had been killed in Laos, in fact hundreds had, F-100 pilots among them. In 1970, a secret bombing campaign in Cambodia added another country to the roster of F-100 targets. Another astonishing fact is that at least one two-aircraft night strike was flown by F-100s against a target in China, apparently with the purpose of killing a political figure whose identity is unknown.

The 'Hun' described

The F-100D of the Vietnam era was a mature combat aircraft with a solid record of performance. A decade earlier, the F-100 had overcome the teething troubles which often beset a new aircraft, but since then the F-100 had become the USAF's standard fighter.

Twelve F-86 air aces from the Korean War flew the F-100 operationally and most commanded squadrons. The USAF was rapidly skipping ahead to its next-generation fighter, the F-4 Phantom, but the new fighter had yet to prove itself.

By the time of Vietnam, all F-100s had been modified at USAF depots with a tail hook identical to that used on US Navy carrier-based warplanes. The hook enabled a pilot to use a cable arresting system when making an emergency landing.

The F-100 was never the easiest aircraft to maintain and service, especially in the primitive conditions at southeast Asian airfields. But once they were settled into a regular cycle of operations, F-100s performed remarkably well. The F-100 had the highest sortie-generation rate of any US warplane in southeast Asia. The F-100 also flew by far the largest number of combat sorties of any US aircraft in southeast Asia. At the height of Super Sabre operations, 490 aircraft were committed to battle in four augmented fighter wings.

The last combat F-100 departed Vietnam in 1971, after nearly eight years of fighting. According to official figures, Super Sabres flew a total of 360,283 combat sorties. The USAF lost 186 F-100s to anti-aircraft fire, none to MiGs, seven during Viet Cong assaults on its air bases, and 45 to operational incidents.

Three F-100Ds from the 614th TFS 'Lucky Devils' taxi at Phan Rang, ready to launch for another mission. Serving from 18 September 1966 to 1931 July 1971, the unit lost a total of 13 aircraft during its tour.

Three F-5As from the USAF's 4441st CCTS at Williams AFB fly a neat formation for the camera. The Williams-based F-5s briefly wore unit markings in the shape of a yellow lightning flash, but the markings were short-lived due to the high aircraft turnover.

Northrop F-5 family

Long-lived lightweight

The F-5 was developed as a lightweight fighter for use by nations too poor to afford the latest hardware. Its combination of performance and economy proved powerful, however, and the aircraft was refined and improved, and widely exported.

At the height of the Cold War, military spending was exorbitant and, while major powers such as the US were able to re-equip with increasingly expensive and sophisticated fighters, other nations needed a reasonably priced combat aircraft that could be deployed in large numbers, could operate from less well-equipped airfields and would require less extravagant logistics.

Fang to Freedom Fighter

Northrop took up the challenge and commissioned a study to examine what kind of fighter was needed by the Free World. It discovered that reducing operating costs was the best way of producing an affordable fighter. It also deduced that operating costs were directly proportional to size, weight and complexity, and set about designing a lightweight fighter, the N-102. Reliance on powerplants such as the General Electric J79, Pratt & Whitney J57 and Wright J65 ensured that the N-102 (later named 'Fang') would never be a true lightweight; weight and cost had spiralled upwards and it was cancelled in favour of a lighter aircraft.

The design of such a fighter began in 1955, as the N-156. The availability of GE's miniature J85 made possible the development of a smaller, lighter aircraft. The final design chosen for wind-tunnel testing was tested in two related forms – the single-seat N-156F and two-seat N-156T.

The J85 engines were installed side-by-side in the rear fuselage. They could be accessed and removed by taking off the lower part of the rear fuselage, using manpower alone. The aircraft was designed for a maximum speed of Mach 1.5. The wingtips incorporated launch rails originally intended for AAMs. Internally, there were few surprises. All fuel was carried in fuselage tanks, the wing remaining dry. The cockpit

Liberally applied with Dayglo and with its nose painted black to resemble an enormous radome, the Sidewinder-equipped N-156F takes to the sky during early flight-testing.

Below: Shortly after being shipped to Edwards AFB, the first N-156F is seen in company with the first two YT-38 Talons. Northrop's J. D. Wells and Hank Chouteau are seen with Captains Swart Nelson and Norvin Evans, respective USAF pilots of the T-38 and N-156F.

***Above:* The F-5B prototype made its maiden flight on 24 February 1964. The first production model was accepted by the USAF within a month and the type entered service on 30 April 1964.**

***Right:* Three Norwegian F-5A(G)s (in the foreground) and a single F-5B(G) are seen on a pre-delivery test-flight. Due to Norway's adverse weather conditions, Norwegian F-5s had provision for RATO bottles, arrester hooks and windscreen de-icing.**

was large and well appointed, with a remarkably good all-round view through a massive canopy.

In November 1955 Northrop was told to concentrate on the two-seater as this seemed to have the greatest chance of finding a customer. The N-156T was therefore quickly developed to fulfil a USAF 1955 requirement for a supersonic basic trainer. The aircraft was selected for purchase in June 1956, and the USAF authorised construction of three YT-38 prototypes.

Development of the N-156F fighter was not abandoned, and was resumed at full speed once the T-38 Talon was underway. The work carried out was invaluable for the N-156F team, who soon had access to wind-tunnel data and flight-test results.

The N-156F retained maximum commonality with the T-38, and the T-38 mock-up was rapidly rebuilt to serve as the fighter mock-up. The aircraft, quickly dubbed 'Freedom Fighter', was still a private venture, so it was important to limit changes as far as was possible.

The N-156F was rolled out on 31 May 1959 and shipped to Edwards AFB, where it made its maiden flight on 30 July 1959, four months after the first flight of the YT-38. The company quickly completed and flew the second prototype, but suspended work on the third when the USAF decided that planned testing could be achieved with just two aircraft.

With the two flying aircraft turning in unprecedented levels of reliability and availability, Northrop completed far more testing than expected. However, despite tests and studies demonstrating the effectiveness of the N-156F, the USAF decided in August 1960 that there was no immediate requirement for the aircraft and the programme was cancelled. The Northrop N-156F was dead. Or so it seemed.

Freedom Fighter reborn

The USAF always remained sceptical about the N-156, however, the US Army took a closer interest in the aircraft, evaluating a prototype in its fixed-wing close support aircraft trials. The US Army evaluated the Fiat G.91, A4D-2N Skyhawk and N-156F in a series of comparative trials. However, the USAF did not want the army to operate its own close-support aircraft and pressed for the competition to be cancelled.

The army went on to use helicopters in the fire support role, but USAF interest in the N-156F had been reawakened and the type was re-examined. USAF selection of the N-156F to meet the FX requirement was formally approved in April 1962, and resulted in immediate interest, much of which translated into orders. The designation F-5 was allocated on 9 August. A contract was signed in October 1962, initiating production. This called for a mix of single-seat F-5As and two-seat F-5B operational trainers, in a ratio of 9:1. The third N-156F was completed to the production configuration under the designation YF-5A, powered by a pair of J85-GE-13 engines. It had a strengthened wing to allow the fitting of an extra pair of hardpoints (bringing the total to seven), and also had strengthened undercarriage. With the flight-test programme well under way, a second contract followed in August 1963, bringing the total number of aircraft to 170.

Norway announced its order for 64 F-5As in February 1964. The first USAF F-5A was accepted in January 1964, but it lacked nose guns and the type did not enter service until August 1964, with the 4441st Combat Crew Training Squadron at Williams AFB.

The first 'twin-sticker'

The two-seat F-5B combined the tandem two-seat cockpit of the T-38 with the airframe of the F-5A, retaining the single-seater's underwing hardpoints, wing and bigger engine intakes. Only the two 20-mm cannon were missing. On the day on which the F-5B entered service – 30 April 1964 – the TAC's F-5 training programme was initiated with the 4441st CCTS, which was soon equipped with seven F-5As and five F-5Bs.

The first operational F-5 squadron was an Iranian unit based at Mehrabad. This was declared combat-ready in June 1965. Greek F-5As were declared operational with 341 Mira in July 1965, while the first Norwegian aircraft were declared operational the same month.

This F-5A from the 4441st CCTS wears a TAC badge on its tail, superimposed over the yellow lightning flash. The type entered service with the 4441st in August 1964.

The Netherlands ordered 75 NF-5As and 30 NF-5Bs in 1967 to meet its requirement for an F-84F Thunderstreak replacement, and deliveries finished in 1972. Dutch F-5s had a long and successful career, with the last NF-5 unit transitioning to the F-16 in 1991.

Foreign 'Fives'

Although not built in quite the numbers enjoyed by the F-4 and F-104, the F-5 proved to be one of the most successful products of the US aircraft industry in the post-war era. Reliable, effective and easy to maintain, the early variants of the Freedom Fighter remain in service to this day.

As early as 1959, Northrop announced that it was discussing licence-production of the N-156F with a consortium of European countries plus Australia and the UK. Ultimately, the F-104G won the licence contract in Europe, and, while several nations operated both the F-5 and the F-104, it was to be Canada that was unique in manufacturing both aircraft.

In Canada, licence production was undertaken by Canadair for the CF-5A/D versions of the F-5A/B (Canadian Armed Forces designation CF-116) and for versions designated NF-5A/B for the Netherlands. The CF-5A differed in some respects from contemporary F-5s, most notably with the inclusion of the J85-CAN-15 engine, rather than the J85-GE-13. During the 1960s and 1970s, the cut-price CF-5 represented a major saving. Nevertheless, the inauguration of a new government in 1968 saw CF-5 production reduced from 118 to 54 aircraft.

Some CF-5As could be fitted with a camera nose and were then designated CF-5A(R). The CF-5As could also be fitted with refuelling probes, but neither these nor the reconnaissance nose could be carried by the two-seat CF-5Ds. The Freedom Fighters enjoyed an active service life with the Canadian Armed Forces, even when squadron strength was reduced to two units. With the purchase of the CF-188, Canada's F-5s were reduced in role to that of a lead-in fighter trainer, a mission they enjoyed until retirement in the mid-1990s.

In order to help finance the purchase of new-build CF-5Ds, 20 CF-5As and CF-5Ds were sold to Venezuela in 1972, these being locally known as VF-5As and VF-5Bs.

Despite opposition from Northrop, Canadair set about licence-production of the CF-5 for resale to other nations. Holland's first NF-5A flew on 24 March 1969 and the type equipped three operational units, with the last examples retired in 1991.

Northrop had a stake in the Spanish company CASA and this led to a licence-building agreement after Spain selected the F-5A in 1966. The remaining two squadrons of SF-5Bs have been upgraded and continue to provide advanced flying training.

As part of a US-led re-equipment programme, a large force of F-5s was supplied to Greece by the US between

Right: CASA-assembled SF-5Bs continue to be used in the lead-in fighter training role by the Spanish air force. Of the 34 two-seaters built, upgraded SF-5B+ and F-5Ms survive in service with Ala 23, at Talavera.

Below: Turkey is still a major operator of the F-5A/B. Operated in the attack, reconnaissance and lead-in fighter trainer roles, they are a useful complement for the Turkish F-16 force.

1960 and 1965. A decade later, 12 F-5As and Bs, acquired from Iranian surplus stock, were supplied, and in 1983 Jordan supplied 13 F-5As and six F-5Bs. Over the next decade, Norway, Jordan and the Netherlands all supplied further aircraft.

Iran was the first true export operator of the F-5A and pilots of the Imperial Iranian Air Force were trained at Williams AFB in the US. The first Iranian F-5 unit became operational in 1965 and ultimately 104 F-5As and F-5Bs were supplied from the US. However, from 1974, the F-5As were gradually replaced by F-5Es, though a number of F-5Bs were retained for training.

With Iran's retirement of the earlier models, a number of aircraft were passed on to Jordan, which also subsequently retired its early Freedom Fighters in exchange for F-5Es.

South Korea was another early recipient of the F-5A/B and the initial batch of 20 was delivered to the 105th Fighter Squadron in 1965. By 1971, 87 F-5As, eight RF-5As and 35 F-5Bs had been delivered to the RoKAF.

Vietnamese service

However, the following year, 36 F-5As and all the RF-5As were transferred to South Vietnam. The US supplied 18 F-5As to Morocco in 1966 and these were later supplemented by further F-5As, RF-5As and F-5Bs. The type was replaced by the F-5E and Mirage F1C/E.

Norway was another F-16 operator which relied on its F-5s as lead-in fighter trainers. A total of 78 F-5As, 16 RF-5As and 14 F-5Bs were received, but as in so many countries the appearance of the F-16 spelt the end for the Freedom Fighters.

As a result of its considerable oil-derived wealth, Venezuela has long operated a highly competent air force. In 1972, a total of 27 Canadair VF-5A/Bs was purchased from Canada.

With the retirement of the F-8, the F-5 became the Philippines' sole jet combat aircraft, though the few that did remain had a questionable service record.

During the late 1960s, some 92 F-5As and 23 F-5Bs were acquired by Taiwan, the majority with US financial assistance. During the 1970s, most of these aircraft were transferred to South Vietnam, though two squadrons of F-5As were retained for training purposes.

Thailand received its first F-5s in 1967 as part of an agreement that would see Thai soldiers fight with the South Vietnamese during the Vietnam War. The initial aircraft were all ground-attack variants and it was only with the purchase of F-5E Tiger IIs that an air defence capability was achieved.

F-5A Freedom Fighter

This Kongelige Norske Luförsvaret/Royal Norwegian Air Force F-5A was not actually a Tiger-PAWS aircraft, but despite this, it carried the banner for 336 Skv and its NATO Tiger credentials since it made its public debut outside Norway at the 1994 Battle of Britain air show, at RAF Leuchars.

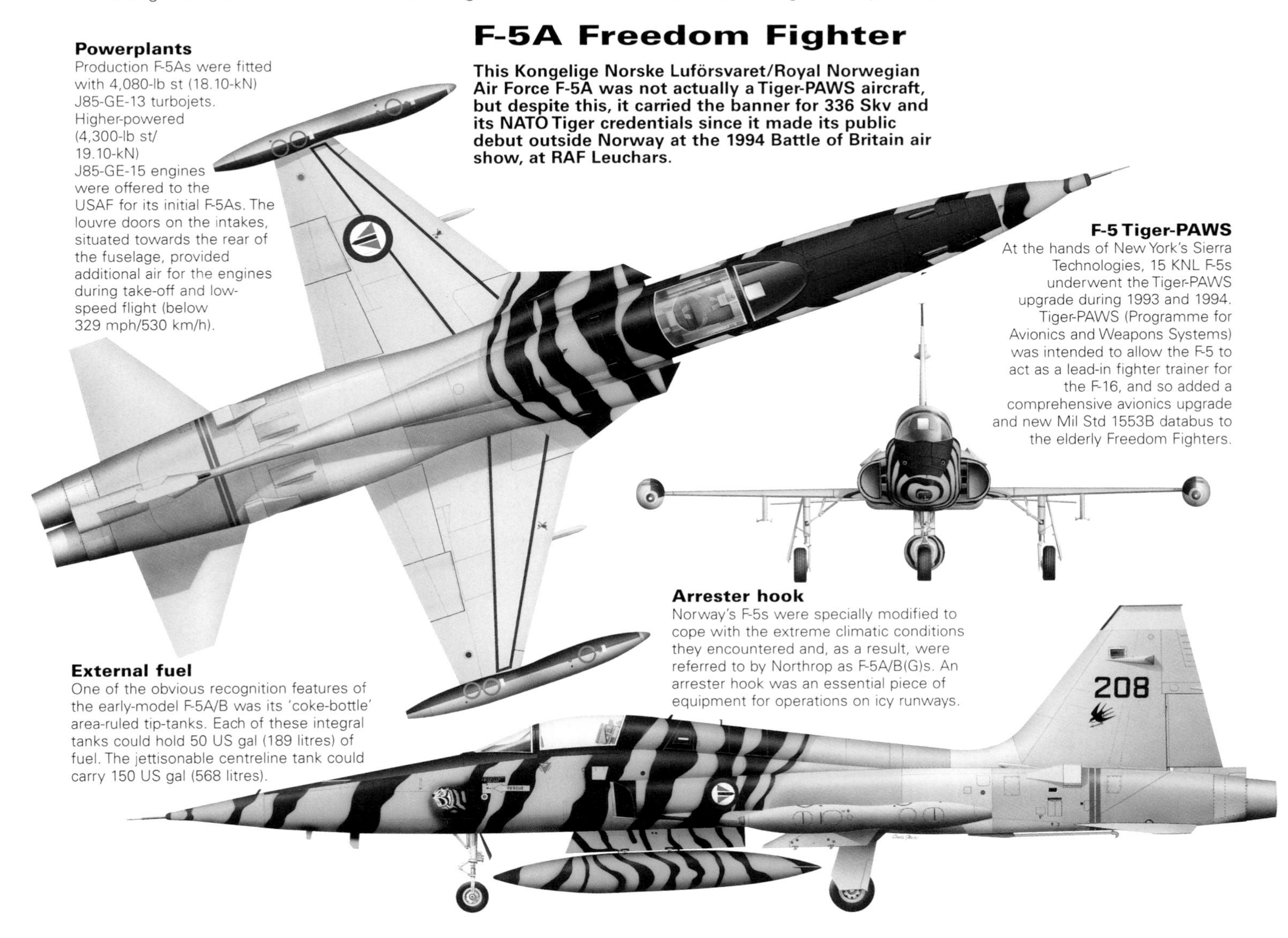

Powerplants
Production F-5As were fitted with 4,080-lb st (18.10-kN) J85-GE-13 turbojets. Higher-powered (4,300-lb st/ 19.10-kN) J85-GE-15 engines were offered to the USAF for its initial F-5As. The louvre doors on the intakes, situated towards the rear of the fuselage, provided additional air for the engines during take-off and low-speed flight (below 329 mph/530 km/h).

F-5 Tiger-PAWS
At the hands of New York's Sierra Technologies, 15 KNL F-5s underwent the Tiger-PAWS upgrade during 1993 and 1994. Tiger-PAWS (Programme for Avionics and Weapons Systems) was intended to allow the F-5 to act as a lead-in fighter trainer for the F-16, and so added a comprehensive avionics upgrade and new Mil Std 1553B databus to the elderly Freedom Fighters.

Arrester hook
Norway's F-5s were specially modified to cope with the extreme climatic conditions they encountered and, as a result, were referred to by Northrop as F-5A/B(G)s. An arrester hook was an essential piece of equipment for operations on icy runways.

External fuel
One of the obvious recognition features of the early-model F-5A/B was its 'coke-bottle' area-ruled tip-tanks. Each of these integral tanks could hold 50 US gal (189 litres) of fuel. The jettisonable centreline tank could carry 150 US gal (568 litres).

F-5E/F Tiger II

F-5s for the world

While the F-5A was agile and quick, it lacked even the most basic tools for air-to-air combat, with no radar and no lead-computing gunsight. Northrop hoped to demonstrate a second-generation F-5, with a larger wing and more powerful engines to increase performance and agility, and with radar and avionics improvements to enhance operational capability.

General Electric had launched a J85 growth programme in 1962, and had tested a larger compressor in 1963. However, neither the Secretary of Defense nor the USAF were prepared to endorse Northrop's unsolicited proposal for a more powerful F-5 without demonstration of the advantages of a re-engined F-5.

Accordingly, the sixth F-5B served as an engine development testbed. The aircraft was fitted with enlarged intakes and intake ducts, modified engine bays, extra wingroot sections and extended wingspan and area. The aircraft was soon fitted with a pair of experimental YJ85-GE-21 engines, and in this form was known as the YF-5B-21. The new engine conferred a useful increase in thrust and, so equipped, the YF-5B-21 flew for the first time on 28 March 1969.

Congress required that the follow-on to the Freedom Fighter should be selected competitively, and on 26 February 1970 the USAF asked for proposals. The competition took six months, at the end of which production of the Northrop design was approved. The USAF selected the Northrop aircraft to meet its International Fighter Aircraft requirement, and its decision was announced in November 1970. An initial contract was signed in December, for 325 aircraft. The single-seat F-5A-21 was formally designated F-5E in the same month.

The first F-5E made its maiden flight on 11 August 1972. Development did not proceed without a hitch. In order to reduce weight, Northrop redesigned the aft fuselage and was forced to use titanium in the new engine/exhaust shroud. This increased costs and imposed delays. Aggressive marketing of the new aircraft led to higher than expected orders, which helped reduce the losses, much to the surprise of the USAF.

***Above:** This Sidewinder-armed F-5E is one of a large number that was delivered to South Korea, 68 of which were assembled locally. Note the flattened nose radome, the oval cross-section of which eliminated directional stability problems, especially at high angles of attack. This was fitted, in the main, to late production F-5E/Fs.*

***Top:** F-5E/Fs and locally converted RF-5Es have served the Republic of Singapore Air Force for more than 25 years. These examples bear the kite badge of No. 144 Sqn. Initially used for air defence, the type took on a tactical fighter role in the wake of F-16 deliveries.*

Unfortunately, the J85-GE-21 engine proved less reliable than had been hoped, and malfunctions were experienced during August 1972, leading to a suspension of flight trials. Even though flight testing resumed, the engine was not formally re-approved until April 1973.

Of the 13 F-5Es accepted by the USAF during FY 1973, six were used for testing and seven went to equip TAC's training unit, which was intended to work up to an initial establishment of 20 F-5Es, in addition to its two-seat F-5Bs. The first F-5E entered service with the 425th TFTS on 4 April 1973. The 425th TFTS fulfilled the same role as the

RF-5E TigerEye – Tiger II camera ships

Northrop originally intended to provide a limited reconnaissance capability for the F-5E by installing an RF-5A-type nose containing four KS-121A cameras in six different configurations. Such a nose was fitted to a handful of Saudi F-5Es, which were used in the tactical reconnaissance role pending the availability of the dedicated RF-5E TigerEye. By the mid-1970s this original nose offered inadequate volume for a modern reconnaissance suite. The F-5E was too small to carry a high-drag recce pod, and had only limited ground clearance with its short-stroke undercarriage. The answer was to redesign the nose to provide integral bays which would provide increased volume. Northrop went back to the drawing board and designed an entirely new nose section (8 in/20 cm longer than that of the basic fighter) with 26 cu ft (0.74 m^3) of capacity, nine times the space available in the RF-5A. The dedicated RF-5E TigerEye offered virtually the same level of capability as the RF-4E but in a smaller, cheaper airframe which was compatible with existing F-5E fighter fleets. A variety of camera fits were available, Northrop claiming 90 per cent of the capability of the RF-4E at about 60 per cent of the lifecycle cost. The aircraft was optimised to appeal to existing F-5E operators who could not justify procuring a separate dedicated type for the reconnaissance mission. The launch customer was Malaysia, who took two aircraft (one pictured above), while Saudi Arabia took 10 more. Singapore also converted six of its own F-5E fighters to RF-5E configuration.

4441st CCTS had done, of providing crew training for F-5 customer nations.

F-5F – the Twin Tiger

Production tooling for the F-5E was 75 per cent common with F-5A tooling, while the aircraft parts inventory was 40 per cent the same. Despite its higher performance and different avionics fit, Northrop had not initially anticipated any requirement for a two-seat version of the Tiger II. However, initial operational experience soon showed that a two-seater based on the F-5E would be a worthwhile development, since the performance differential between the F-5B and the F-5E was a wide one. In May 1973, the USAF gained approval to examine a Northrop proposal to develop a two-seat Tiger II.

Instead of simply building a trainer aircraft with the nose of the F-5B, Northrop chose to produce an entirely new two-seat forward fuselage. This was stretched to accommodate the second cockpit, instead of locating the front cockpit further forward in the nose avionics and cannon bays, as had been done in the T-38 and F-5B. This allowed the F-5F to retain one of the F-5E's 20-mm cannon. The rear seat was raised above the front seat (as in the T-38 and F-5B) to give the instructor an adequate forward view. The rear cockpit contained a radar display, in addition to full dual controls.

The F-5F flew for the first time on 25 September 1974. The first two F-5Fs joined the F-5E/F Joint Test Force at Edwards, where development was swift and trouble free. The F-5F was slightly heavier than the F-5E, with slightly inferior take-off performance as a result.

F-5E Tiger II

Once a renowned Hawker Hunter display team, *La Patrouille Suisse* swapped its elderly, but much-loved Hunters for the F-5E in 1994. Concurrently, a radically new colour scheme was introduced, incorporating the Swiss flag.

Airframe changes
To accommodate the new engines the fuselage was lengthened by 15 in (38 cm) and widened by 16 in (40 cm). This allowed the internal fuel tanks to be enlarged, giving an extra 570 lb (258 kg) of fuel. The increase in width also increased overall wingspan and wing area. The wingroot leading-edge extensions were refined and enlarged until they represented 4.4 per cent of the total wing area.

Tiger II operators
As well as about 100 F-5E/Fs operated in the aggressor role by the USAF, US Navy and USMC, the Tiger II was exported widely and has served with the air arms of Bahrain, Brazil, Chile, Honduras, Indonesia, Iran, Jordan, Kenya, Malaysia, Mexico, Morocco, Saudi Arabia, Singapore, South Korea, Sudan, Switzerland, Taiwan, Thailand, Tunisia and Yemen.

Armament
MAP and FMS F-5Es were sold with a delivery package which included five non-jettisonable external pylons, two wingtip missile launch rails, one centreline 265-US gal (1003-litre) tank and a baggage pod. Other fuel tanks (including the wingtip tanks) were optional items, as was the inflight-refuelling probe. The Tiger's secondary ground-attack role was not ignored. Indeed, two of the earliest FMS customers for the F-5E – Iran and Saudi Arabia – both acquired the aircraft primarily to fulfil an air-to-ground role.

Improved performance
With the addition of the 5,000-lb (22.24-kN) thrust GE J85-GE-21 engines and other improvements, including the increased wing area and new equipment, maximum speed crept up from Mach 1.4 to Mach 1.6 (Mach 1.5 with wingtip AIM-9s fitted). More significantly, maximum cruise went up from Mach 1.2 to Mach 1.45. The new engines allowed even a heavily-laden aircraft to attain more economic cruising altitudes, thereby increasing radius of action and endurance.

Radar
The radar chosen for the F-5E was the Emerson AN/APQ-159(V). It provided limited air-to-air search and tracking capabilities, in-range envelope computation for the Sidewinders and ranging for the guns.

Fuel system
Unlike the F-5A, which had tip tanks, the F-5E's wing was completely dry. Two internal fuel cells in the fuselage have a capacity of 671 US gal (2540 litres).

*Since its teething troubles have been solved, the **B-2** is proving its huge potential in regular **USAF** squadron service.*

Northrop Grumman B-2 Spirit 'Stealth bomber'

An aircraft like no other, the B-2 was designed to penetrate Soviet airspace and destroy the ballistic forces of the Soviet Strategic Rocket Forces.

Developed in great secrecy, the Northrop Grumman B-2 flying wing was designed as a 'stealthy', or radar-evading bomber for the Cold War mission of attacking Soviet strategic targets with nuclear bombs and stand-off weapons. The B-2 began as a 'black' programme, known in its infancy as Project Senior C. J. and later as the ATB (Advanced Technology Bomber). In its early days, USAF leaders believed that the service's top priority was the B-1B bomber, and only a handful even knew of the B-2 project. To the latter group, the B-1B was an 'interim' weapon awaiting the B-2; at the height of the Cold War, the USAF expected to procure no fewer than 132 examples of the B-2.

Drawing heavily on its previous flying wing designs, Northrop was aided extensively by Boeing, Vought and General Electric, using

*Seen here alongside airframe **AV-6** at **Edwards** is one of the original **Northrop N-9MB**, part of a series of **Northrop**-designed flying wings. It was restored to airworthy condition in **November 1994** for the **50th** anniversary of its first flight.*

***Left:** One of a series of early **ATB** models from **Northrop** gives some idea of the configuration changes undergone by the **B-2** during its design phase. Although the 'notched' flying wing shape was quickly decided upon, further refinements took more time. This model has inward canted vertical fins at the extreme rear of the centrebody, which was longer than that of the ultimate configuration.*

a three-dimensional computer-aided design and manufacturing system to create the B-2's unique 'blended wing/double-W' shape. More than 100,000 radar cross-section images of B-2 models and components were analysed to assess their 'stealth' properties, followed by a total of 550,000 hours of wind tunnel tests. Nine hundred new manufacturing processes had to be developed for the programme as well as the use of rugged, high-temperature composite materials, ultrasonic cutting machinery, automated tooling via the 3D database and laser sheraography inspection. Northrop built the forward and mid-fuselage sections, aluminium, titanium and composite parts and cockpit, while Boeing built the aft centre and outboard sections.

Graphite/epoxy composites are extensively used on the B-2 to provide a radar-absorbent honeycomb structure. To reduce infra-red signature, the four General Electric F118-GE-110 turbofan engines exhaust through V-shaped outlets set back and above the trailing edges to hide these heat sources from the ground-based defences.

Avionics

The B-2 Spirit's swept (33°) leading edge and sawtooth trailing edge configuration trap radar energy. Further low-observable (LO) measures include 'S'-curved engine intakes and stealthy dielectric panels covering the AN/APQ-181 J-band radar that hide its antenna from reflecting hostile radar waves while allowing it to function normally. The cockpit is equipped for two, with upward-firing ACES II ejection seats, and there is room for a third crew member. The pilot has charge of the mission computer, which handles target tasking (or retasking in flight). Navigation and weapons delivery is the responsibility of the WSO, in the right-hand seat. The two primary positions have four colour MFDs. The aircraft has a quadruply-redundant digital fly-by-wire system, actuating movable surfaces on the wing trailing edges, the latter combining aileron, elevator and flap functions and occupying 15 per cent of the wing area. A beaver tail acts as a pitch-axis trimming surface and, along with the elevons, helps in gust alleviation.

To verify targets at the last moment, the B-2 briefly turns on its AN/APQ-181, spotlighting only a small area, and then attacks. The B-2 is equipped with an electronic warfare system, comprising the AN/APR-50 RWR and the secretive ZSR-62 defensive aids system.

The B-2 Spirit was originally envisaged as a high-level penetrator but, by the time its design was frozen in 1983, a low-level role had been assumed. Modifications needed to adapt the original ATB design to this new role included moving the cockpit and engine inlets, adding inboard elevons (resulting in the distinctive 'double-W' planform), modifying the leading edge and making substantial internal changes, including new bulkheads.

The B-2 has taken the USAF into a new era of warfare. An enormous undertaking, its value has been the source of constant debate in the House and the Senate, but it has since been combat proven.

Right: Seen coming in to land at Vandenberg AFB is aircraft AV-4 which is wearing white markers on its leading edges for icing tests. The drag rudders are also noticeable as they are opened to 45° to help slow down the aircraft on the approach.

Left: **Spirit of Missouri** ***was the first operational B-2 'stealth bomber' and can be seen here returning to Whiteman AFB. Development of the B-2 was fraught with problems, not least of which was the fact that every worker had to undergo a security vetting process. This increased the cost of the programme by an estimated 10 to 15 per cent.***

Inset: When viewed from the rear, the B-2's shape becomes dramatically altered. The thin structure further enhances the B-2's survivability by making it harder to see visually as well as electronically.

Left: Ahead of each engine inlet is a small auxiliary inlet which removes the turbulent boundary layer that might otherwise impede engine performance. It also provides cool air to mix with the exhaust efflux to reduce the bomber's IR signature.

Spirit in the sky

Despite a host of detractors, the B-2 finally made it into service, though in somewhat limited numbers. While secrecy is still tight, the aircraft has undertaken combat missions from Afghanistan to Yugoslavia.

Six B-2 prototypes (five for the USAF) were funded in 1982, the first being rolled out at Palmdale on 22 November 1988. The B-2's first flight took place on 17 July 1990, when the first aircraft (also referred to as AV-1/Air Vehicle One) was delivered to the USAF at Edwards AFB to begin the test programme. This had been preceded by a series of high-speed taxi runs on 13 July.

A test schedule of 3,600 hours was set out, commencing with 16 flights (67 hours) of airworthiness and handling trials. Completed June 1991, these flights also included the first air-to-air refuelling in November 1989. Block 2 testing had begun in October 1990, investigating the LO characteristics of the 'real thing'. These flights revealed the first signs that all was not as advertised with the 'stealthy' B-2, and subsequent flights were halted while modifications were carried out. 'Stealth' testing continued into 1993, together with further performance and load trials. The third aircraft made its maiden flight on 18 June 1991 and was the first to carry the full avionics mission fit, with the AN/APQ-181 LPI (low-probability of intercept) radar. The first weapons drop by a B-2 was made by the fourth aircraft, which initially took to the air on 17 April 1992. A single inert Mk 84 2,000-lb (908-kg) bomb was dropped by this aircraft on 4 September 1992.

Earmarked for further weapons, LO and climatic testing, the fifth B-2 made its first flight on 5 October 1992. By the end of 1993, the programme had achieved 1,500 flying hours.

Early problems

In July 1991, deficiencies were revealed in the B-2's 'stealth' profile. It has been admitted that the aircraft could be detected by some high-powered, land-based, early warning radars. However, comment has not been passed on Russian claims that the bomber is vulnerable to its new-generation SAM systems. The USAF implemented a 'set of treatments' to the leading edges and flying surfaces to reduce the aircraft's signature across a range of frequencies.

Problems with the B-2's performance did not help in the battle for funding. The original target was for a fleet of 133

The US's enemies face the problem of having to cope with the B-2A as well as the F-117A. The former first went to war striking Serbian targets during Operation Allied Force in 1999.

Tanking trials for the B-2 were not restricted to specialist refuelling units although, for the sake of convenience, locally based units (such as the 22nd Air Refueling Wing at March AFB) were used to support missions from Edwards AFB. The enormous span of the B-2A can be fully appreciated when compared to this KC-135E.

airframes, including prototypes but, by 1991, this had been cut back to 76 aircraft. After the original six aircraft were ordered in 1982, three more were funded while the B-2 was still a 'black' project. In 1989, money was allocated for a further three, followed by two in 1990 and two in 1991. Congress then froze acquisition at 16 (15 for the USAF). The USAF claimed that it could not provide effective operational capability with fewer than 20 aircraft, and five more were subsequently approved by 1993. This approval came with the caveat that the type's LO problems should be rectified before any production occurred. In May 1995 US$500 million was added to the FY96 defence budget to build two more B-2s. However, in recent years, the USAF has opposed the purchasing of more aircraft on the grounds that they are costly to maintain and operate.

The first aircraft for the USAF was delivered to the 509th BW at Whiteman AFB, Missouri, on 17 December 1993. This was the eighth B-2, the first aircraft to production standard. At present, the USAF operates 21 B-2As.

Spirit shortcomings

In August 1997, a highly publicised report by the General Accounting Office highlighted a number of shortcomings in the B-2. Most notable of these was the fact that the B-2's 'stealthy' qualities were degraded by excessive moisture, and thus the aircraft required extensive field maintenance. In short, the B-2 could not operate in the rain as it should do. The maintenance time for each flight hour has also risen from the projected 50 hours to 124 hours. However, in addition to flying operational missions from Whiteman AFB, generally on a non-stop basis, and supported by tankers (as was the case during the B-2's Allied Force combat debut in 1999), the B-2A has also conducted more recent combat missions over Afghanistan and Iraq flying from Diego Garcia in the Indian Ocean.

B-2 artwork

One question facing the B-2 has been the matter of where to place artwork. Bright badges would be impossible on a 'stealth' warplane and so the decision was made to place artwork on the nosewheel door. Test aircraft received artwork that symbolised the virtues of the B-2; *The Ghost* badge (above) relates to the 'stealthy' abilities of the aircraft, while *Christine* displays the links with Stephen King's supernatural car. The badge *Fire & Ice* (left) relates to the all-weather testing phase of the B-2. In-service aircraft, such as *Spirit of California* or *Spirit of Texas*, have been named after US states, while the thirteenth production aircraft was named *Spirit of Kitty Hawk* in honour of the first sustained powered flight.

Below: The uniqueness of the B-2 has given rise to a host of rumours about its capabilities. It has also been claimed by Ben E. Rich, Skunk Works chief of the F-117 project, that the B-2 project was named Aurora during competition for funding and that the near-mystical Aurora hypersonic spyplane does not, in fact, exist.

Panavia Tornado

Multi-Role Combat Aircraft

Once derided by critics as being a jack of all trades but a master of none, the Tornado is, today, the king of low-level, all-weather strike aircraft.

A Tornado GR.Mk 1B from No. 617 'Dambusters' Squadron carries a brace of Sea Eagle anti-ship missiles beneath its fuselage. Having supplanted the Buccaneer in the anti-shipping role, the Tornado GR.Mk 1B variant was itself withdrawn without replacement.

The Panavia Tornado was a triumph of international industrial and military collaboration, an aircraft built by three nations to meet a common requirement agreed by no less than four air arms (including Germany's air force and navy). Although some elements of the programme were undoubtedly unnecessarily duplicated (three assembly lines, three flight test centres), there was a great deal of rationalisation in the production of components and sub-assemblies, and the programme thereby enjoyed economies of scale and a large home market. Even with only one major export order, Tornado production reached just short of the 1,000 aircraft mark – an impressive achievement.

The Tornado itself is often profoundly misunderstood, and has been the subject of a great deal of usually ill-informed and often baseless criticism. During the 1991 Gulf War, for example, the popular press intimated that losses during the low-level anti-airfield campaign had been so heavy that the aircraft had been forced to switch to medium-level attacks. In fact, the loss rate was lower than expected, and only four were downed during the low-level campaign, with two destroyed during medium-level operations later in the war. There is no doubt that the Tornado took on one of the most dangerous tasks of the 1991 war, and performed it with conspicuous success, minimising losses through the use of well-conceived and practised tactics. Moreover, the Tornado's switch to medium-level operations took place only after the low-level anti-airfield campaign was over, its objectives having been achieved.

The Tornado was conceived to meet a Cold War requirement for a long-range, all-weather strike/attack and interdictor aircraft, operating at ultra low level to 'slip in' under the enemy's radar, and to avoid the enemy air threat. In order to conduct such operations,

Above: The first British prototype MRCA (as the Tornado was previously known) is pictured with another product of a joint European venture, the Anglo-French SEPECAT Jaguar. The Jaguar entered service in 1973, some seven years before the Tornado.

Left: Chosen to be the first squadron to receive the fighter/interceptor Tornado F.Mk 3, No. 29 Squadron became operational on 1 November 1987. The squadron was responsible for maritime defence, as well as performing regular intercept missions.

***Left:* The German navy's MFG 2 wing mounted regular 'Eastern Express' reconnaissance flights to plot shipping movements in the Baltic Sea.**

***Below:* Emphasising the adaptability of the basic design, the ADV has a stretched fuselage and different radar and avionics. Its role is long-range air defence for the UK and (as illustrated) Saudi Arabia.**

the aircraft was designed around a highly accurate and sophisticated navigation, attack and weapons system. This included an attack radar to help acquire targets, navigational features and waypoints, and a terrain-following radar which could automatically fly the aircraft over undulating terrain or down narrow valleys, in the dark or in bad weather. A variable geometry wing was designed to give the best possible compromise between short take-off and landing capability, manoeuvrability, and high-speed, low-level performance. Newly designed high-technology afterburning turbofans gave the Tornado superb performance characteristics 'on the deck', yet were also surprisingly fuel efficient.

Tornado developments

In service, the Tornado has fathered a series of sub-variants and these have embraced a range of new roles, from reconnaissance and anti-shipping attack to defence suppression. Britain even developed a dedicated Tornado beyond-visual-range fighter-interceptor, the Tornado Air Defence Variant (ADV), which replaced the F-4 Phantoms operated as part of Britain's air defence network.

The Tornado remains arguably unequalled in its primary low-level, all-weather strike/attack role, while recent and ongoing upgrade programmes have dramatically increased the aircraft's flexibility and versatility. The upgraded RAF GR.Mk 4 aircraft continue to be capable of low-level penetration, but have enhanced night attack capability and more accurate emission-free navigation equipment (freeing the Tornado from reliance on radar, except in bad weather). A range of new weapons give greater stand-off range and improved precision attack capability, while simultaneously allowing the aircraft to operate successfully at medium level, when necessary.

Since the end of the Cold War, all of the nations operating Tornados have used the aircraft to fly operational missions, whether it be during Desert Storm or over Bosnia. Numerically speaking, Tornados remain the backbone of the RAF, Luftwaffe and AMI. Despite post-Cold War defence cuts and the gradual introduction of the Eurofighter Typhoon, the Tornado remains perhaps the most important single aircraft type in each of the air arms in which it is operated, and its future looks to be assured for many years to come.

P.12 was the second of the six pre-production aircraft, making its first flight on 14 March 1977. Flying from Boscombe Down, it participated in British trials that were designed to take the Tornado into squadron service.

GR.Mk 1 and 4

Since entering service in 1982, the Tornado has served as the RAF's premier strike/attack platform. In later years it adopted additional roles such as defence suppression, reconnaissance and anti-ship attack.

Above: Clutching a pair of Sea Eagle missiles, a No. 617 Squadron GR.Mk 1B flies over the Orkneys from its Lossiemouth base.

Below: The Marham Reconnaissance Wing consisted of two Tornado GR.Mk 1A squadrons (Nos 2 and 13) and a single Canberra unit. Despite their recce tasking, the Marham Tornados were the last in the RAF to have a nuclear role with the WE177 bomb.

Production of GR.Mk 1 aircraft for the RAF totalled 229 aircraft. They were built in different batches, which had small but important differences. Batch 1 aircraft numbered 23 and were not fitted with the undernose LRMTS (laser rangefinder/marked target seeker). These aircraft were used for basic conversion training.

Batch 2 production contained 55 aircraft for the RAF, again without LRMTS. These were the first operational aircraft, being assigned to No. 9 Squadron and the Tornado Weapons Conversion Unit. Batch 3 included 68 RAF aircraft and represented a considerable increase in capability over the earliest machines. LRMTS was fitted from the beginning, the engines were the more powerful RB.199 Mk 103, with a rating in afterburner of 16,900-lb (75.26-kN) thrust. Most of this batch began the re-equipment of RAF Germany.

RAF GR.Mk 1s accounted for 53 aircraft in Batch 4 and these equipped the second wing in Germany, at RAF Brüggen. These may have been the first RAF aircraft to be fitted with nuclear weapon delivery systems, for use with the WE177B tactical laydown weapon. The final RAF GR.Mk 1 block (not including those built as GR.Mk 1As) was Batch 7, including 27 RAF aircraft.

Into service

No. 9 Squadron was chosen as the first RAF Tornado squadron and it began trading in its Vulcans in spring 1982. Two more UK-based squadrons, Nos 27 and 617, began transitioning soon after. At a time when the Cold War was still 'hot', it was imperative that RAF Germany should receive the new type, beginning with Nos 15, 16 and 20 Squadrons at RAF Laarbruch. The Brüggen wing (Nos 14, 17 and 31 Squadrons) followed soon after and were joined by No. IX from the UK. RAF Germany Tornados took over the important nuclear alert mission from Jaguars, although they retained a potent overland attack role, with conventional weapons.

This immaculate four-ship is from No. 31 Squadron, formerly a Brüggen-based unit. During the Cold War era, the Brüggen Wing had an important nuclear strike mission.

A total of 142 aircraft was converted to GR.Mk 4 standard, including the reconnaissance aircraft (which became GR.Mk 4As). The GR.Mk 4 has a much expanded weapons repertoire, including the Brimstone anti-armour weapon and Storm Shadow missile.

From the outset of Tornado development, it was always intended that the aircraft should fulfil a number of roles. Having established the aircraft in the overland strike/attack role, further developments in weapon systems and changes in international politics (notably the end of the Cold War) saw the RAF's Tornado force restructured into 'mini-fleets'. Two of the 'mini-fleets' flew the GR.Mk 1A (reconnaissance fitted with a panoramic infra-red linescan and two side-looking infra-red systems) and GR.Mk 1B (anti-surface unit warfare), while two retained the GR.Mk 1. Nos 9 and 31 Squadrons fly Tornados modified to carry the Alarm anti-radiation missile on lethal SEAD missions. Nos 14 and 17 Squadrons were TIALD specialists, using the targeting pod for delivery of LGBs. The remainder of the RAF's GR.Mk 1 fleet remained in the training role, with the Trinational Tornado Training Establishment and No. 15 (Reserve) Squadron, the latter absorbing the RAF portion of the TTTE when it closed. By late 2003, no front-line Tornado GR.Mk 1s remained operational.

Mid-life update

While the Cold War was still raging, the RAF drew up plans to enhance the survivability and effectiveness of its Tornado fleet, resulting in the GR.Mk 4 programme. The Tornado GR.Mk 4 has a fixed FLIR mounted under the port side of the nose, wide-angle HUD, new cockpit displays and night-vision goggles, Mil Std 1553 databus, and Mil Std 1760 weapons architecture, the latter allowing it to easily carry all weapons designed to this common NATO standard. A fully embedded GPS is provided. A total of 142 aircraft was covered by the GR.Mk 4 programme, of which several emerged as GR.Mk 4A reconnaissance platforms. These latter aircraft are able to carry the new Raptor long-range oblique infra-red/visible light sensor for high-altitude reconnaissance at long stand-off ranges. The first GR.Mk 4 conversion flew on 29 May 1993, with first squadron deliveries made in 1998.

Laser-bomber
Previously reliant on Buccaneers to provide laser designation, the Tornado desperately required an autonomous designation capability. This came courtesy of the GEC-Marconi TIALD (Thermal Imaging Airborne Laser Designator) pod, of which two prototypes made a high-profile combat debut in the Gulf War. The TIALD consists of a TV, thermal imager and laser designator, mounted in a swivelling turret, itself mounted on an articulated head to provide complete freedom of movement. TIALD was initially brought into service by a No. 617 Squadron detachment, but subsequently became a speciality of No. 14 and (the now Typhoon-equipped) 17 Squadron.

In 1998 RAF Tornados deployed to Kuwait as part of Operation Bolton, in response to the Iraqi refusal to allow UN inspection teams access to suspected weapons-producing sites. This aircraft is from No. 14 Squadron, seen carrying a TIALD pod.

Defence suppression
To provide the Tornado with a hard-kill capability against radars, the BAe Alarm was developed. The missile has a programmable search function which allows it to prioritise targets and to be launched in various modes. The most common is 'loiter' mode, whereby the weapon climbs under the power of its Nuthatch motor to anything up to 70,000 ft (21336 m) before deploying a parachute. As it hangs under the 'chute, it searches for a target. When one is found, it 'slips the leash', starts its motor and homes straight on to the radar. Two or three ALARMs is a standard load and the weapon is chiefly employed by Nos 9 and 31 Squadrons.

No. 20 Squadron was initially responsible for flying SEAD missions with the Alarm missile; its crews undertook the weapon's first firings during the Gulf War. Most GR.Mk 1s could carry F.Mk 3-style 495-Imp gal (2250-litre) 'Big Jug' fuel tanks.

Germany and Italy

With a requirement to replace its huge fleet of Starfighters, the Luftwaffe became the largest operator of the Tornado IDS. It has developed the type for service in a number of roles, and belatedly introduced the type to operations over Bosnia.

Originally intended as a one-for-one replacement of the F-104 Starfighter, the Tornado finally equipped four front-line Luftwaffe squadrons (and one training wing) for a total of 247 new-build aircraft. Subsequently, the Luftwaffe acquired 40 ex-Marineflieger aircraft in order to establish a tactical reconnaissance wing.

The first Luftwaffe aircraft to enter service were assigned to the TTTE at RAF Cottesmore, England which handled type conversion. Germany-based JBG 38, the operational training unit at Jever, acquired its first aircraft in November 1981. JBG 31 at Nörvenich began conversion in July 1983 to become the first front-line unit, followed by JBG 32 at Lechfeld (July 1984), JBG 33 at Büchel (August 1985) and JBG 34 at Memmingen (October 1987).

Upon the closure of the TTTE in 1999, the initial type conversion training effort was transferred to Holloman AFB, New Mexico.

German improvements

The Luftwaffe Tornado fleet has been gradually updated, beginning with the modification of early aircraft to Batch 5 standards with Mil Std 1553 databus and limited HARM missile capability. Thirty-five new-build aircraft were completed to ECR (Electronic Combat and Reconnaissance) standard, fitted with an infra-red linescan system, forward-looking infra-red and an emitter location system. In the event, the linescan system proved troublesome and was removed, although the underfuselage fairing is retained. The ECR aircraft, which all fly with JBG 32, are now used almost exclusively in the Wild Weasel defence suppression role.

For reconnaissance, the Luftwaffe replaced its RF-4Es with ex-navy Tornados now assigned to the re-formed AG 51 at Schleswig-Jagel.

Both ECRs and reconnaissance aircraft were active over the former Yugoslavia with Einsatzgeschwader 1, a composite unit based at Piacenza in Italy. In early 2007 AG 51 deployed a number of its aircraft to Afghanistan.

The Marineflieger acquired the Tornado to replace Starfighters operating in the strike, attack, anti-shipping and reconnaissance roles. Some 112 examples of the Tornado were eventually ordered, including 12 twin-stickers. This allowed each wing to have a nominal strength of 48 aircraft, plus reserves. MFG 1 became a Tornado unit before the first Luftwaffe wing converted to the type, and recommissioned on 2 July 1982. MFG 1 was declared operational on 1 January 1984. The end of the Cold War forced the navy to sacrifice one of its units and MFG 1 deactivated on 1 January 1994. MFG 2 was the fifth and penultimate front-line German Tornado wing, receiving its first Tornado on 11 September 1986. However, the decision to retire the navy's fast-jet fleet saw MFG 2 complete its Tornado operations in summer 2005, with its aircraft, AS.34 Kormoran and AGM-88 HARM weaponry and its maritime tasking handed over to the Luftwaffe's AG 51.

The AMI received 100 Tornado IDS aircraft, of which one was a refurbished pre-production aircraft, 15 were from Batch 2 production, 28 from Batch 3, 27 from Batch 4

***Above:** The development of the ECR version resulted in the Luftwaffe possessing arguably the best defence suppression platform in Europe.*

***Top:** Italy sent eight Tornados to participate in Desert Storm. These aircraft were assigned low-level missions against Iraqi airfields; one was lost on the first night of the war.*

Some surprise was expressed that MFG 1's identity was not preserved by redesignating the surviving MFG 2 (illustrated), but in fact both units had formed in 1958 and had very similar histories.

A yellow lightning flash on the tail identifies that this Tornado is from 36° Stormo at Gioia del Colle in southern Italy. The aircraft is armed with two Kormoran anti-ship missiles.

and 29 from Batch 5. Of the total, 12 were twin-stickers.

Service deliveries began on 17 May 1982 when the first aircraft arrived at the central maintenance unit. Later that year 154° Gruppo/6° Stormo stood up at Ghedi to become the first operational unit. Italian Tornado crews converted to the type at the TTTE, before progressing to Ghedi for operational conversion with 154° Gruppo.

Two further operational units formed in 1984/85: 156° Gruppo/36° Stormo at Gioia del Colle and 155° Gruppo/6° Stormo at Ghedi, to form a front-line force of 54 aircraft plus 12 trainers. The remaining 34 aircraft were later used to form a fourth squadron in the shape of 102° Gruppo, which stood up at Ghedi in 1993 as part of 6° Stormo. Ghedi had earlier (in 1990) lost 155° Gruppo to 50° Stormo at Piacenza.

With its key position in the Mediterranean, Italy placed a heavy emphasis on anti-ship operations, and from an early date the Tornado force was equipped with AS.34 Kormoran 1 missiles. The principal maritime attack unit is 156° Gruppo at Gioia del Colle, which also has a secondary overland role.

Another role undertaken by the AMI Tornado fleet is that of reconnaissance, using a multi-sensor reconnaissance pod. Initially these were allocated to all of the operational units, although some specialisation among units has since crept in, with 102° Gruppo becoming the main reconnaissance squadron. 155° Gruppo became the principal SEAD unit, acquiring HARM missiles in 1994 after the missile had been deployed on an interim basis to other units in 1991/92.

Gulf War and after

Italian Tornados first saw action during Operation Locusta, the codename for the AMI participation in Desert Storm. A dozen aircraft were deployed to Al Dhafra in Abu Dhabi, from where they conducted 226 sorties in 32 missions, dropping 565 Mk 83 bombs. Subsequently the AMI has employed its aircraft over Bosnia and Albania, 6° Stormo Tornados flying their first mission on 2 September 1995 from Gioia del Colle. Five days later bombs were dropped in anger for the first time, Mk 83s being released against Serbian targets. Reconnaissance and tanking missions have also been flown over Bosnia.

The Italian Tornado fleet has benefited from two upgrade programmes. The first was ITECR (Italian Electronic Combat and Reconnaissance), under which 16 IDS aircraft were converted to a similar standard to the German ECR defence suppression aircraft. The prototype conversion first flew in July 1992, and thereafter production aircraft entered service with 155° Gruppo.

For the remaining IDS fleet an AMI mid-life update programme has enhanced the central computer, added a microwave landing system and active ECM, and provides PGM capability. The first step was the modification of six aircraft to carry the CLDP laser designator pod for use in conjunction with GBU-16 Paveway II LGBs. The CLDP/GBU-16 combination was carried operationally over Bosnia.

This Luftwaffe Tornado ECR is shown carrying four AGM-88 HARM missiles, the type's principal weapon for anti-radar operations. ECRs flew operational missions over Bosnia until November 1996, when they withdrew to leave only reconnaissance aircraft based in Italy.

Tornado IDS

This Tornado wears the badge of Jagdbombergeschwader 33, which consists of a Tornado plan-view superimposed on a stylised diving eagle. Based at Büchel, JBG 33 adopted an overland role which included the use of B61 nuclear weapons. Most of its aircraft came from Batch 5 production. This aircraft is depicted carrying the MW-1 dispenser which could be used against a variety of area targets.

Radar
The AEG-Telefunken radome covers the Texas Instruments radar set. This, in effect, is two radars: one for ground mapping functions to feed the nav/attack system and one for terrain-following. The latter has a small antenna mounted below the main attack radar antenna.

Fuel
German Tornados do not have the fin tank specified for RAF machines. Total internal capacity is 1,285 Imp gal (5842 litres), usually augmented by two 330-Imp gal (1500-litre) drop tanks on the inner wing pylons. A further pair of tanks can be carried under the fuselage.

Tornado ADV
Stand-off interceptor

Designed to defend Britain from unescorted Soviet bombers such as the Tu-22M, the Tornado ADV has acquitted itself well. However, with the end of the Cold War and the advent of long-range bomber-escorts, this Tornado variant now finds itself to be overspecialised for its changing role.

Above: Aircraft from the Coningsby Wing pose for the camera. In the foreground is an aircraft from the OEU trials unit, while behind is a Tornado from the OCU, No. 56(R) Squadron. The final front-line F.Mk 3 resident at Coningsby was No. 5 Squadron (background).

Saudi Tornado crews trained alongside those of the RAF at Coningsby. Included in the Saudi buy were six twin-stick aircraft. These retain full combat capability but have rudimentary flying controls in the rear cockpit.

Although an interception capability was one of the requirements put forward for the MRCA, only the UK elected to proceed with the development of an Air Defence Variant (ADV) optimised for air-to-air combat. The main danger to Britain was seen as coming from long-range bombers attacking UK targets with cruise missiles and so an all-weather interceptor, able to track and engage multiple targets, was needed. The use of beyond visual range air-to-air missiles was deemed to be the most appropriate way of downing Soviet aircraft.

It was vitally important that the UK operated a fighter capable of stopping the Soviets far away from British shores as it was estimated that, in the event of war, 40 per cent of NATO's air power would congregate in the UK. RAF Strike Command decided upon a policy of all-round, far-reaching air defence with long-legged interceptors, tankers to further increase range, AEW aircraft to cover the Iceland-Faroes-UK gap and ground radars on the western coast. Central to all these factors would be the Tornado ADV.

Airframe modifications

During 1976 it was announced that 165 of the 385 Tornados required by the RAF would be of the ADV version, having 80 per cent commonality with the IDS. One of the main changes was a 4-ft 5½-in (1.36-m) longer fuselage, partly resulting from a more pointed radome, but mainly due to an extra bay added forward of the wings. With its new length, the aircraft could accommodate four BAe Skyflash radar-guided AAMs under the fuselage (the front pair semi-recessed). Two (and later four) AIM-9L Sidewinders were to be attached to the sides of the inboard wing pylons.

Three prototype Tornado ADVs were added to the first batch of Tornado IDSs and the first flew on 27 October 1979. The aircraft was fitted with dummy Skyflash missiles from the outset and managed to reach Mach 1 on its first flight. Supersonic acceleration was found to be better than in the IDS due to the improved shape of the fuselage, but the more forward centre of gravity demanded extra elevator angle at lift-off.

A second ADV joined the programme in July 1980, introducing a main computer and associated cockpit TV displays.

Early in 1982, the development aircraft flew a simulated CAP sortie involving a 2-hour 20-minute loiter at a distance of 375 miles (604 km) from base. This feat was achieved with an extra pair of 330-Imp gal (1500-litre) tanks as used on the IDS, and not the 495-Imp gal (2250-litre) drop tanks as fitted to the definitive interceptor Tornado. RAF IDS and ADV Tornados have an extra fuel tank inside the fin, holding 121 Imp gal (551 litres), and the additional fuselage length of the ADV enables it to

The North Yorkshire base of Leeming was the second to receive Tornado F.Mk 3s, beginning with No. 11 Squadron (pictured, officially formed on 1 July 1988). In 2007, No. 11 Squadron was reformed as the RAF's lead multi-role Typhoon operator.

Completing the Coningsby line-up was No. 5 Squadron, which formally stood up in its new guise on 1 January 1988. Budget cuts demanded that Coningsby's No. 29 Squadron be disbanded in 1999, while No. 5 Squadron gave up its Tornados in 2003.

be fitted with an extra internal tank holding 165 Imp gal (750 litres). The standard internal fuel capacity of German and Italian IDS aircraft is 1,340 Imp gal (6092 litres).

The Tornado's turbofan engines are fuel-efficient at low level, but the trade-off is that, at medium and high levels, thrust is reduced in comparison with a turbojet. Similarly, if forced into close combat, a mission for which it was not designed, the ADV finds itself somewhat outclassed by aircraft which have been designed for the task.

Fighter Tornados have the same wing sweep range as their bomber compatriots (25-67°), except that later production aircraft introduced automatic sweep selection to suit flight conditions. This facility was retrofitted to the software of earlier machines.

Because of the fact that the centre of gravity was further forward, the 'nibs' (inboard, non-moving leading edges) of the wings have their sweep increased from 60 to 67°. Additionally, they include the forward antennas for a radar warning receiver, the rear component of which is mounted on the tailfin trailing edge. In contrast to the 'clip-on' refuelling probe on the starboard side of the IDS's forward fuselage, the ADV has a fully retractable unit on the port side.

Into service

The first of the ADVs reached the RAF in 1984 when 16 F.Mk 2s, as they were now designated, served with No. 229 OCU. These aircraft only flew an average of 250 hours each and were initially delivered without radar, with ballast instead making up the weight. They were eventually placed in storage and cannibalised for spares.

First flying on 20 November 1985, the F.Mk 3 replaced the F.Mk 2 on the production line and introduced a host of improvements, most notably the incorporation of the new RB.199 Mk 104 engine. This had a 14-in (36 cm) extension to the afterburner section and incorporated a digital engine control. This was the world's first example of a full-authority digital engine control (FADEC) unit and gave precise computer controls to the engines, while also offering improved fault diagnosis and engine monitoring. These modifications gave a 10 per cent increase in combat thrust and reduced afterburning fuel consumption by 4 per cent.

Several avionics upgrades including those to the inertial navigation system, and new systems such as the Automatic Manoeuvre Device System (AMDS) were also added, as was provision for two more Sidewinders. The F.Mk 3 became operational in 1989 and, since then, has undergone a series of further upgrades, including the addition of AIM-120 AMRAAM and AIM-132 ASRAAM weapons to replace the Skyflash and AIM-9L respectively, and night-vision goggles for the crew. The RAF's F.Mk 3s were also briefly adapted for the SEAD role, with a pair of Alarm missiles in place of the Skyflash or AMRAAM.

Below: This Tornado F.Mk 3 demonstrates the extended jetpipe associated with the more powerful Mk 104 engine and the filled-in finroot fairing, both of which distinguish it from the Tornado F.Mk 2.

This classic view of one of the RAF's initial Tornado F.Mk 2s was taken from the rear ramp of an RAF Hercules. The semi-recessed positioning of the forward BAe Skyflash missiles is well demonstrated.

Republic F-84

Farmingdale's jets

Under the F-84 designation Republic developed a large family of jet fighters of various configurations, from straight- and swept-wing fighters and fighter-bombers to camera-equipped reconnaissance aircraft.

Republic's successor to the P-47 Thunderbolt, the F-84 Thunderjet gained a reputation for lacking power – its protracted take-off resulted in it being nicknamed 'Ground Hog'. In fact, many hundreds of pilots never made it, running clean out of runway before the unwilling combination of thrust and lift managed to overcome the inbuilt mass of metal.

So how can the Thunderjet and its derivatives, none of which had electrifying performance, be described as some of the world's greatest aircraft? A critic could say that the F-84 simply happened to be made in large numbers and therefore inevitably filled an important niche in the order of battle of the NATO air forces. A fairer assessment would be that the F-84, in all its many quite different versions, has a secure place in history because, over a long and crisis-ridden period, it was ready for battle as a known and trusted (even if, in some ways, marginal) quantity.

These P-84Bs (designated F-84B from June 1948) were among the first Thunderjets delivered to the USAF. The first examples went to the 14th Fighter Group in the summer of 1947.

Left: Known initially as the YF-96A, the YF-84F entered production as the F-84F Thunderstreak. Able to carry 6,000 lb (2722 kg) of ordnance, including an atomic weapon (not shown here), the F-84F entered service in 1954.

The first XP-84 was completed at the Farmingdale, Long Island, plant in December 1945. The XP-84 was a fine-looking machine, much sleeker than the P-47 derivatives but still with an unswept wing of so-called laminar profile. Its General Electric TG-180 turbojet, mass-produced by Allison as the J35, at a rating of 4,000 lb st (39.20 kN), was attached behind the rear spar of the wing and fed by ducts passing on each side of the pressurised cockpit from the plain nose inlet.

Ingenious design

The legs of the XP-84's tricycle gear were exceptionally long to give the correct ground angle and prevent the tail scraping on take-off and landing (a steel bumper skid was still needed). The nose gear retracted to the rear and the main gears, with great cunning, were made to shorten as they folded inwards so that there was just room for the wheels between the spars of the thin wing. The landing gear and split flaps were hydraulically actuated, and there was adjustable hydraulic boost on the ailerons, but not on the rudder

Here, the major differences between the straight-winged Thunderjet and swept-wing Thunderstreak are evident. The YF-84F utilised 60 per cent of the F-84E's airframe, though in production form the F-84F had a new British J65 powerplant.

After 10 years of USAF service, F-84Fs were passed on to the Air National Guard, which finally disposed of its last examples in 1971.

Above: Thunderstreaks and RF-84F Thunderflashes served with NATO air forces in large numbers. This Greek example of the latter was among the last to be retired.

(usually ignored) or elevators on the tailplane, which was mounted well up the fin.

Three prototypes had been ordered, but only the first two were completed, the first making its maiden flight on 28 February 1946. Remarkably, this was also the first flight of the J35 engine. The second XP-84 flew in August, and in September set a national speed record. By this time Republic was well advanced with 15 YP-84As, with the planned armament of six 0.5-in (12.7-mm) guns, four in the upper part of the nose and the other pair in the roots of the wings. Some of the YP-84s had only four guns, while others had improved wheel brakes and provision for 230-US gal (871-litre) tip-tanks. The latter were greatly needed, because there was very limited internal fuel, almost all of it in the wings.

In 1946 Republic had received a remarkably large order for 500 production aircraft, later styled F-84B ('F' for fighter instead of 'P' for pursuit). These had the 4,000-lb st (39.20-kN) J35-15C engine, tip-tanks, six guns, ejection seat and, from the 85th aircraft, retractable zero-length launchers for 32 rockets.

Production did not go on to 500, because at no. 226 it switched to the F-84C with a Dash-13C engine. After the 190th F-84C, production switched to the F-84D. This was a major improvement, with the Dash-17D engine rated at 5,000-lb st (22.50-kN) thrust.

Yet again production was cut short by a further improvement, in this case the F-84E, which took over after 154 of the F-84D model had been built. The F-84E had a 12-in (30.5-cm) longer fuselage, giving more fuel capacity, pylons under the wings for two 1,000-lb (454-kg) bombs, 230-US gal (871-litre) tanks (same as wingtip) or other loads, and numerous other changes. Provision was also made for two 1,000-lb (454-kg) RATO units to assist take-off, because the incidence of write-offs as a result of aircraft failing to become airborne had reached serious proportions.

The F-84E was the first real quantity-production type, 843 being delivered to the USAF and most of the growing NATO air forces. The F-84E also served in large numbers in Korea.

The last straight-wing model far outnumbered all the others. No fewer than 3,025 F-84Gs, developed because of long delays with the swept-wing F-84F, were built. Powered by the Dash-29 engine, rated at 5,600-lb (25.2-kN) thrust, the F-84G was distinguished by its multi-framed canopy, the Boeing Flying Boom receptacle in the left wing and an autopilot. With RATO bottles, up to 4,000 lb (1814 kg) of bombs could be carried by the F-84G.

At least 1,900 F-84Gs were assigned to NATO nations, and many others were exported after USAF service.

What the original F-84 wanted was sweepback, plus an engine of much greater power. A single XF-84F prototype, originally known as the YF-96A – basically an F-84E with new canopy and wing – flew on 3 June 1950. Underpowered, it was followed by a new F-84F, fitted with a J65 engine, the British Sapphire made under licence by Wright.

F-84F Thunderstreak

The first F-84F Thunderstreak flew on 14 February 1951, but engine problems meant that the F-84F did not reach TAC until 1954. Without an afterburner, the new all-swept model was no more lively than its predecessors and the 2,713 that were built served basically in the attack role. These tough machines served with 12 air forces, remaining in the inventory of Greece and Turkey until 1976.

The second F-84F had wingroot inlets, and the RF-84F Thunderflash recce aircraft, whose nose was occupied by six cameras, was based on this reconfigured machine. No fewer than 715 were built, of which 386 were supplied to nine friendly air forces.

The supersonic XF-91 Thunderceptor was powered by a J47 turbojet and an XLR11 rocket motor. Its inverse-taper wings were a distinctive feature.

The third F-105B is seen on a test-flight from Edwards AFB; the area-rule design of the fuselage is clearly illustrated. The first few aircraft were built with small rear-view windows aft of the main canopy – these were deleted on later aircraft.

Republic F-105 Thunderchief

The 'Thud'

Designed as a nuclear bomber to attack the Soviet Union, Republic's mighty 'Thud' found fame in Vietnam, hauling loads of iron bombs over the jungles of southeast Asia. The type earned respect during this conflict as an extremely tough warplane with a 'get-you-home' capability unmatched by the more glamorous Phantom. As well as dropping bombs, it took on SAM radars and shot down MiGs.

Republic test pilot Russell M. 'Rusty' Roth lifts off from Edwards AFB, California, for the 45-minute maiden flight of the first YF-105A, on 22 October 1955. The air intakes and tail shape differed from those of subsequent production F-105Bs.

Known originally in company parlance as Advanced Project 63, the F-105 was first conceived as a private venture in 1951 to fulfil the tactical nuclear strike role then being largely undertaken by another Republic product, namely the F-84. Overall responsibility for the design rested with Alexander Kartveli, the mastermind behind several Republic success stories, the most notable of which was the wartime P-47 Thunderbolt.

Like most of Kartveli's designs, the projected fighter was a large aircraft, and the initial proposal, based on the use of a single Allison J71 engine, was formally submitted to the US Department of Defense in March 1952. It met with a favourable response, culminating that autumn in the award of a contract for tooling and engineering. This was quickly followed by a DoD request that the chosen powerplant be changed to Pratt & Whitney's J57-P-25, rated at 15,000 lb st (68 kN), as an interim measure since it was felt that the J71 might not attain the required thrust. In the event, this proved to be the end of the J71 as far as the

Republic's production line is headed by FH-793, an early model F-105B. Constant revision of the numbers of aircraft required by the USAF during the Thunderchief's testing phase was a source of constant frustration for Republic.

The RF-105 was cancelled, and the planned prototypes were given the unusual designations of JF-1, -2 and -3 by the company. 54-0105 was the first of this trio of test aircraft.

F-105 was concerned, the two prototypes using the J57, while subsequent production machines were powered by the even more powerful Pratt & Whitney J75. Republic's enterprise was further rewarded during March 1953 with a contract covering the manufacture of no fewer than 37 examples of the XF-105A plus nine reconnaissance RF-105s, although these figures were to be constantly adjusted before flight-testing began.

Complications brought about by the USAF's inspection team led to the decision to install the J75 engine in all four of the test aircraft, known as F-105Bs.

Further delays meant that the first flight of the YF-105A did not occur until 22 October 1955, an event marked by the fact that the aircraft exceeded Mach 1.0 – the two YF-105As were never seen, however, as a true representation of the definitive Thunderchief design. The second YF-105A flew in January 1956, the initial flight of the first F-105B following a few months later, in May; on the completion of this flight, however, the aircraft suffered damage on landing. Uncertainty continued to surround the Thunderchief, but a major step forward occurred in March 1956 when funding was released to cover the procurement of 65 production examples of the J75-engined F-105B plus 17 RF-105s, although the recce variant was soon abandoned. A third variant, the two-seat F-105C combat proficiency trainer, was added to the programme in June 1956, but was cancelled during 1957.

Production models of the F-105B eventually began to roll off the Farmingdale line in 1958, with the USAF accepting its first aircraft on 27 May of that year.

While the F-105B was entering squadron service within the USAF, the development of what eventually became the definitive Thunderchief variant, the F-105D, proceeded apace. A shift from nuclear to conventional attack duties then led to the F-105B being phased out, and the definitive all-weather 'D' model came into production. In appearance, it was similar to the earlier F-105B, the most significant external difference relating to the larger nose radome which contained a NASARR (North American Search And Ranging Radar) R-14A all-purpose monopulse radar. This, in conjunction with the AN/ASG-19 Thunderstick fire control system and a toss-bombing computer, permitted the F-105D to perform visual or blind attacks with a variety of ordnance.

One further variant of the F-105D Thunderchief was also developed, the so-called F-105D T-Stick II. Fitted with superior all-weather avionics in a prominent dorsal fairing, a total of 30 aircraft was converted during the late 1960s and early 1970s.

Two-seat variant

Although the original F-105C two-seater proposal had been cancelled, the USAF was anxious to acquire a model of the Thunderchief for training duties. This resulted in the F-105E which did, at least, attain production status before being abandoned in March 1959. The handful of aircraft then under construction eventually emerged as single-seat F-105Ds and it was not until the early 1960s that a two-seater eventually appeared, this being the F-105F model. This retained many of the features of the F-105D, although a slightly taller vertical tail was adopted. Performance was only slightly inferior to the single-seat variant, a factor that proved valuable in later years when the two-seat derivative undertook SAM suppression tasks in Vietnam.

Above: Thirty F-105Ds were modified with the T-Stick II system to improve bombing accuracy. These examples served with the 457th TFS, AFRes at Carswell AFB.

Right: Carrying a blue practice Shrike missile under its left wing, this F-105G is seen on a training mission in January 1979. After Vietnam, F-105Ds and Gs remained operational with second-line elements of the ANG and AFRES until 1984.

The 36th TFW at Bitburg AB, Germany, re-equipped with F-105Ds on 12 May 1961, followed by the 49th TFW at Spangdahlem. Here, with 60-0464 in the foreground, Bitburg 'Thuds' fly in formation in European skies. The tail stripes are red, blue and yellow.

F-105 in service

Despite the outstanding capabilities offered by the Thunderchief in terms of range, speed and weapon load, USAF units underwent a frustrating period of proving the aircraft in operational service. Delays encountered in the delivery of the aircraft tried the patience of Republic officials and USAF generals.

In August 1958, the first production F-105B was delivered to the 355th Tactical Fighter Squadron for test purposes and the transition to operational status began. It took another year until the 4th TFW was fully equipped. Ready or not – and it was not, then – the F-105 had been declared officially operational by the Air Force in January 1959.

The first non-testing operational unit to receive the B models was the 334th TFS, 4th TFW. The initial allotment of four arrived on 16 June 1959.

Like its predecessor, the F-105B, the D model went into testing with the 335th TFS at Eglin AFB. The first two F-105Ds went to Bitburg AB, West Germany, on 12 May 1961, assigned to the 36th TFW. In mid-October 1961, the 49th TFW moved to a second West German field, Spangdahlem AB, with its three squadrons of F-105s.

USAFE maintained a Weapons Center at Wheelus AB, Libya, which was the training ground for the majority of the Command's tactical fighter-bombers and interceptors. Here, crews trained for nuclear weapons delivery.

However, it was by delivering conventional weapons that the Thunderchief would go to war – in the hostile skies over Vietnam.

By the time the Vietnam War began, the original F-105 had changed considerably. The F-105D, considered the ultimate in Thunderchief design, had the R-14A radar and Thunderstick nav/attack system. In the Vietnam War it was modified to carry a maximum amount of non-nuclear ordnance on five hardpoints, one on the centreline and two under each half of the wing. Moreover, each Thunderchief entering North Vietnamese airspace was required to carry items like ECM pods and AIM-9 Sidewinder AAMs for defensive purposes.

First assignments

The first F-105 aircraft to enter the conflict were those assigned to the 36th TFS, which deployed from Yokota AB in Japan to Korat AB in Thailand on 9 August 1964. Their mission was ResCAP (Rescue Combat Air Patrol). Specifically, they were tasked to fly ResCAP for pilots downed in Laos. At least that was their 'official' mission, but in reality the F-105s were at Korat to supply air support for CIA operations in Laos. Several other units deployed to southeast Asia in response to the Gulf of Tonkin Crisis of August 1964, including the 80th, 357th, 67th, and 44th TFSs, and many of these squadrons would figure prominently in F-105 operations well into 1970. All the squadrons that deployed to SEA were on a TDY (temporary duty) status, until activation of the two permanent wings at Korat (388th TFW) and Takhli (355th TFW) in Thailand. From these two air bases, the 'Thuds' operated on a daily basis, flying deep into North Vietnam for the next six years.

During the bombing halt of 1965/66, North Vietnamese defences were considerably

Thunderchiefs arrived in southeast Asia in 1964, finished in an aluminised lacquer. This F-105D is carrying the heaviest load carried by Thunderchiefs in-theatre – 16 750-lb (340-kg) M117 low-drag general-purpose bombs.

F-105B

The original production variant of the Thunderchief was the F-105B, seen here in the markings of the 355th TFS which formed part of the 4th TFW at Seymour Johnson AFB, North Carolina in August 1958, this being the only operational wing to operate this model. Due to the complex nature of the Thunderchief, the 355th had to wait almost 10 months to receive its full complement of 18 aircraft. The most notable recognition feature of the F-105B was the smaller nose radome.

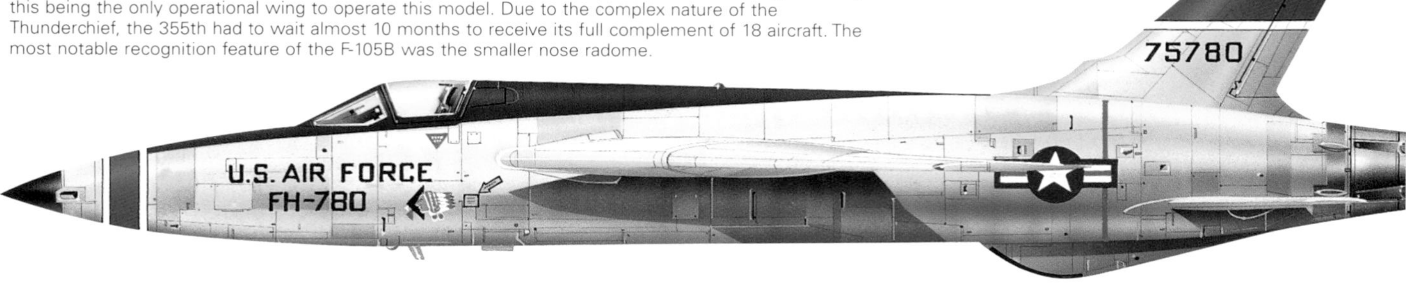

strengthened by the arrival of SA-2 surface-to-air missiles. The situation with regard to F-105 losses to AAA and SAMs became so critical in 1966 that the 7th Air Force issued orders that no F-105 aircraft were permitted to enter North Vietnamese airspace without at least one ECM jamming pod.

Enter the F-105F

Although the F-100F Wild Weasel programme was successful, the F-100F simply did not have the performance needed to stay with F-105 strike packages. As a result F-105 strike aircraft had to slow to the speed of the F-100F, making the entire strike force even more vulnerable. Thus the F-105F was the next logical step in the development of the Wild Weasel concept. On 15 January 1966, the first Wild Weasel III F-105F (unofficially 'EF-105F') made its first flight. On 28 May 1966, the first five such aircraft arrived at Korat AB. The EF-105F scored its first 'kill' on 7 June 1966.

The AGM-45 Shrike anti-radar missile was available beginning in the spring of 1966, and the CBU-24 cluster munition was the standard weapon for use against the SAM launchers. At times, the EF-105Fs flew with Shrike-armed F-105D Thunderchiefs to create 'hunter-killer' teams. On every mission, at least one of the invaluable Wild Weasel aircraft was always 'first in and last out!'

A little favoured weapon, the AGM-12C Bullpup offered rocket-assisted pinpoint accuracy, but lacked the punch to destroy the type of targets against which the weapon was deployed.

The EF-105Fs were soon officially designated F-105G and upgraded with improved ECM and RHAW equipment and AGM-78 Standard ARMs.

The single-seat F-105Ds left the region in 1970, replaced by F-4E Phantoms. The unique Weasel aircraft, on the other hand, remained in southeast Asia for the duration of the war with North Vietnam and beyond. F-105Gs continued to escort RF-4C reconnaissance flights and Arc Light B-72 raids on Loas and Cambodia until August; the last Weasel aircraft left Korat in October 1974.

The combat era of the F-105 Thunderchief had ended. The war in SEA had cost a total of 385 F-105s in the form of 296 F-105D and 38 F-105F/G machines to enemy action, including 22 to MiGs, 32 to SAMs, and 280 to anti-aircraft fire. An additional 51 aircraft had been lost to operational problems. F-105 air crews shot down 27½ MiGs, 24½ of them with the 20-mm Vulcan cannon, two with AIM-9 Sidewinder missiles, and one using a combination of both.

Above: With live bombs on the centreline, outboard and inboard wing pylons, FH-173 is seen on its record-breaking flight. This was achieved when the aircraft lifted some six tons of bombs into the air, the most ever for a single-engined aircraft at the time.

Right: The requirement for a 'Thud' trainer was met by the F, which was a stretched D. The vertical tail had increased height and chord, to compensate for the added area ahead of the centre of gravity.

Rockwell B-1

The early 'Bones'

One of the most controversial modern warplanes, the B-1A was set to give the USAF an unprecedented strike capability. Despite its prowess, political wranglings ensured its untimely cancellation.

***Above:** 74-0158 touches down at Edwards AFB at the end of its inaugural flight. It was to be exactly one month before the aircraft flew again, on 23 January 1975. The first aircraft was the general aerodynamic and performance test vehicle.*

***Top:** The four B-1As continued to fly on the Bomber Penetration Evaluation programme until April 1981. The No. 3 aircraft, shown here, retired from flying on 15 April, having logged more than 829 hours in 138 sorties, the greatest number of all the four prototypes.*

The B-52 was developed in a great hurry in the early 1950s for service with what was then SAC. The aircraft was expected to be progressively withdrawn from service from 1961 to 1962. The replacement was planned to be either the WS (Weapon System)-110 CPB or the WS-125 NPB. The CPB was to be a Chemically-Powered Bomber, so-called because it was to burn high-energy 'zip fuel' in order to cruise at Mach 3 at very high altitudes. The NPB was to be a Nuclear-Powered Bomber, slow but with essentially unlimited range and thus able to attack any target from any direction.

In the event, the NPB was never built, the high-energy fuel was abandoned, and all that was left on the drawing board were two giant 2,000-mph (3220-km/h) prototype XB-70 Valkyries, the first of which flew in 1964.

Undeniably impressive, these aircraft were no longer viable when it was recognised that ICBMs could hit fixed targets with greater speed and reliability. Aircraft deemed as suitable successors included modified B-52s, the B-58 and the FB-111, but all failed to make the grade. Some 50-plus projects were proposed by 14 US aerospace firms from 1960 to fill the need for a new long-range bomber. By 1964, the requirement had been formalised as the Advanced Manned Strategic Aircraft (AMSA).

B-1 genesis

Despite arguments over the need, and fights over the budget, in April 1969 AMSA crystallised into a USAF programme as the B-1. RFPs (Requests for Proposals) were issued seven months later, and in June 1970, the USAF announced that the B-1 would be built by North American Rockwell. The engine award went to General Electric, with its F101-100 augmented turbofan.

The original programme comprised one ground- and three flight-test aircraft. A fourth prototype was ordered in the FY 1976 budget, built virtually to production standard. Some 240 production aircraft were planned, with initial operational capability with SAC scheduled for 1979.

The programme slipped slightly. First flight had been due in April 1974, but in fact the first B-1 was rolled out in October of that year. It made its first flight on 23 December. The No. 3 aircraft (the avionics testbed) flew in March 1976. The second B-1 was initially used for static structural testing, and did not fly until June 1976. The considerably modified No. 4 aircraft first flew in February 1979.

The ruling material throughout the B-1's structure was aluminium, just as in Concorde. Originally, it had been hoped that Mach 1.2 could be sustained during low-level penetration, but this target was lowered to about 650 mph (1046 km/h), or Mach

*SAC's bomber trio formates off the boom of a **KC-135** tanker. The **B-1A** featured the speed and terrain-following ability of the **FB-111**, while exhibiting load-carrying capability and range performance similar to those of the **B-52**.*

Left: The fourth aircraft differed from the first three in being fitted with ejection seats in place of the escape module, a fact denoted by the lack of 'elephant ears'. Inflight refuelling formed an important part of the trials programme.

Below left: The B-1A's only appearance outside the US was in September 1982 when the No. 4 aircraft attended the air show at Farnborough, UK.

0.85, in order to give the crew more time to identify targets. This greatly eased the problem of turbulence, and also enabled the proportion of aluminium alloys to be increased.

About 150,000 lb (68 tonnes) of fuel could be housed in eight integral tanks, one in each outer wing and the rest in the fuselage. Weapons were to be carried in three fuselage bays; each could house about 25,000 lb (11340 kg) of nuclear or conventional weapons, or eight SRAMs.

Numerous modifications and additional equipment were introduced, and throughout the flight test programme the avionics integration contractor, Boeing, made concerted efforts to resolve problems in what was probably the most complex avionics installation ever to fly at that time.

One of the B-1's major hurdles, an IOT&E (Initial Operational Test & Evaluation) that simulated SAC combat missions, was successfully passed in September 1976. The Phase I flight test programme was completed in September 1976, with all test objectives met. In December 1976 the DoD and USAF announced that the B-1 would go into production. Contracts were placed for the first three aircraft and for eight Block 2 aircraft.

Apart from the largely unresolved question of the avionics, the only cloud on the horizon appeared to be that of cost escalation. In 1970 the unit price was US$40 million, but, by 1975, the unit figure had risen to just over US$70 million.

These figures clearly worried the new president, Jimmy Carter, who took office in January 1977. On 30 June 1977, the last day of FY77, in his regular press conference, he announced the cancellation of the B-1. He expressed the view that ICBMs, SLBMs (Submarine-Launched Ballistic Missiles) and modernised B-52s armed with ALCMs would provide adequate defence capability.

Resurrection

Despite the cancellation of the production programme, the Carter administration permitted flight-testing to continue, together with many related development efforts. The greatest effort continued to be focused on the avionics, particularly the defensive system, but GE never ceased to develop the F101 engine, and USAF facilities continued to give direct B-1 support.

The need to reduce RCS (radar cross-section) became increasingly important, achieved by paying the most careful attention to achieving a smooth unbroken external surface, and by covering the exterior skin with RAM (radar-absorbent material). What became known as 'stealth' design grew rapidly in importance, and in 1978, formal work began on a 'black' programme, loosely called the ATB (Advanced Technology Bomber). This programme eventually resulted in the B-2.

Cancellation of the production B-1 did not terminate flying of the prototypes. Less than a month after the decision was taken, in July 1977, the No. 3 aircraft became the first to launch a SRAM. This prototype was later modified with an advanced ECM system and with DBS (Doppler-Beam Sharpening) added to the forward-looking radar. The second aircraft, which only began flying in June 1976, continued with No. 1 to push up the Mach scale. The first aircraft had reached Mach 2 in April 1976. The No. 2 prototype continued with air-loads testing and engine/inlet evaluation, and in October 1978 reached Mach 2.22, the highest speed attained by any B-1. The No. 4 aircraft flew for the first time long after the cancellation of the B-1, and carried out many valuable tests on both offensive and defensive avionics before closing the prototype flight programme in April 1981.

Seen at Edwards AFB in 1976 are the first three B-1A prototypes during Phase 1 of flight-testing. This included evaluation of flying qualities, structural loading and ECM equipment.

B-1B Lancer

In recent years the B-1B has moved to the forefront of conventional warfare. Its ability to carry unrivalled internal ordnance gives an added flexibility to combat operations never before seen.

Following the end of the Cold War, military planners began to appreciate that there was a need for platforms capable of responding to smaller, and perhaps multiple, regional conflicts, as opposed to a major European war. Furthermore, it was apparent that the conventional bomber force was ill-prepared to meet all the current contingencies.

To better suit the B-1B Lancer to the conventional role, the USAF initiated the Conventional Munitions Upgrade Program (CMUP), in 1993, designed to expand the B-1's lethality, survivability and maintainability as a conventional bomber.

Over the past few years, conventional B-1Bs have played a major role in quick-response deployments to Korea, Guam and the Persian Gulf, not to mention the NATO operations over Yugoslavian and US attacks on Afghanistan and Iraq.

While seeing its combat debut in Operation Desert Fox in December 1998, the B-1B's true value as a conventional bomber was demonstrated in Operation Allied Force, during which B-1Bs flew over 100 combat sorties and dropped more than 5,000 Mk 82 500-lb (227-kg) bombs against a variety of targets.

In the meantime, USAF B-1Bs were undergoing the Block D upgrade, which brings to the platform improved communications, a Joint Direct Attack Munition (JDAM) capability and improved self-defence measures.

Conventional munitions

All B-1Bs existing prior to the CMUP were designated as Block A models. Fielded in 1995, Block B added an improved synthetic aperture radar and minor modifications to the defensive countermeasures system.

The next modification came in the Block C, upgrading the B-1B to deliver cluster bombs such as the CBU-87B/B Combined Effects Munitions, the CBU-89 area denial munition and the CBU-97 Sensor Fuzed Weapons. Conversion of the first Block C began in October 1996 and full operational capability (FOC) followed in September 1997.

The Block D upgrade, which began development in 1995, integrates a near-precision conventional munitions delivery capability for guided weapons such as the JDAM. The first operational Block D versions reached Ellsworth AFB in November 1998. Key to this Block upgrade was the addition of the Mil Std 1760 electrical interconnect system (a standard 'smart weapons' interface), a communications upgrade to enhance security, and a Global Positioning System (GPS) for both aircraft and weapons navigation. Another enhancement of the Block D upgrade is the addition of the AN/ALE-50 Towed Decoy System. This provides protection against RF threats by 'seducing'

Above: At the heart of the re-roling of the B-1B is the Conventional Munitions Upgrade Program (CMUP). This B-1B from the 28th Air Expeditionary Wing is heading out on a combat mission against Al Qaeda and Taliban forces in Afghanistan, in support of Operation Enduring Freedom during December 2001.

A 184th Bomb Wing B-1B refuels over France. During Allied Force all B-1B missions involved tanking. The decision to forward-deploy the B-1B to RAF Fairford, England, was welcomed by crews who still undertook seven-hour missions, most of which were at night.

***Left:* B-1Bs continue to employ weapons and defensive systems in new and innovative ways, while also learning to operate in two-ship formations and with other Air Force and Navy assets.**

***Below:* The B-1B stood down from its nuclear role on 27 July 1991. What little remains of the USAF nuclear mission is now solely performed by the B-52H Stratofortress and the B-2A Spirit.**

RF-guided missiles away from the host aircraft. Block D initial operational capability (IOC) was achieved in December 1998, but not in time for Block D B-1Bs to participate in Desert Fox. All B-1Bs were modified to the Block D standard by early 2001.

Block E Upgrades

The Block E upgrade modifies the existing Avionics Control Units for controls and displays, guidance and navigation, weapons delivery, critical resources and terrain-following. A primary objective allows the B-1B to employ up to three different weapons systems (one per bay) on a single sortie. Two weapons modifications included in the Block E configuration further enhance the B-1B's conventional lethality. Wind Corrected Munitions Dispensers (WCMDs) improve high-altitude accuracy of cluster bomb units by using GPS position updates to provide inertial guidance corrections for ballistic and wind errors after release. The B-1B has also added a stand-off precision weapons capability through the deployment of the AGM-154 Joint Standoff Weapon (JSOW) and the stealthy AGM-158A Joint Air-to-Surface Strike Missile (JASSM). These long-range precision strike capabilities are significant because they add a 'built-in' self-defence capability since the B-1Bs are launching from well outside the enemy threat envelope. IOC for Block E B-1B capability was attained in 2003.

Block F was to represent the defensive systems upgrade, but was cancelled in late 2002.

'Bone' at war

Operation Desert Fox saw the B-1B make its combat debut on 17 December 1998, when two of the six deployed Block C B-1Bs attacked Iraqi targets with Mk 82 bombs from approximately 20,000 ft (6100 m). Flying six-hour missions, each B-1B carried a total of 63 bombs. B-1Bs flying in Desert Fox flew a total of six missions and dropped some 126,000 lb (57154 kg) of Mk 82s.

Operation Allied Force began on 24 March 1999, with B-1Bs flying their first missions out of RAF Fairford, beginning 1 April, just 14 hours after the first bombers arrived in theatre. In total, B-1Bs launched over 100 combat sorties and amassed over 700 flight hours in Allied Force, with all missions seeing the bomber drop Mk 82 bombs.

During the initial phase of Operation Enduring Freedom, unleashed upon Afghanistan on the night of 7 October 2001, Diego Garcia-based B-1Bs and B-52Hs accounted for the greatest amount of tonnage dropped, and the B-1B was back in action over Iraq in 2003.

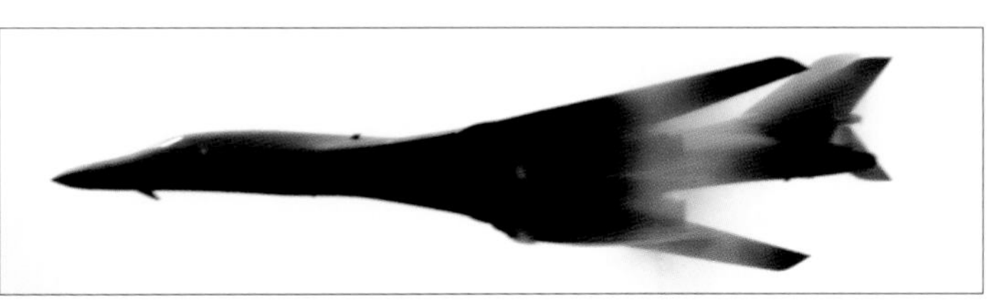

***Above:* A Lancer flies at low-level during Operation Enduring Freedom, October 2001. Fitted with the Conventional Weapons Module (CWM) in each bay, a total of 84 Mk 82s can be carried.**

***Right:* A 28th Air Expeditionary Wing B-1B formates on a KC-10A tanker on its way to Afghanistan. The 'Bone' spearheaded attacks against Afghan air defences and command and control centres.**

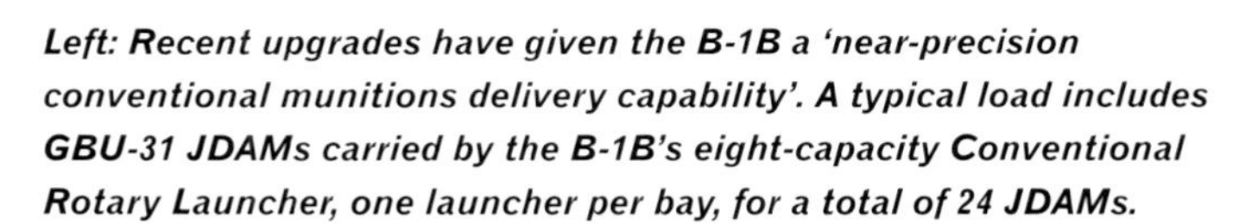

***Left:* Recent upgrades have given the B-1B a 'near-precision conventional munitions delivery capability'. A typical load includes GBU-31 JDAMs carried by the B-1B's eight-capacity Conventional Rotary Launcher, one launcher per bay, for a total of 24 JDAMs.**

Saab 35 Draken

Nordic dragon

Sweden's double-delta Draken was a revolutionary concept, and typical of Saab's bold and independent approach to fighter design. First flown in the mid-1950s, the aircraft remained in front-line service with Austria and Finland more than 40 years later.

The story of the Draken (dragon) dates back to 1949, when the Flygvapen (Swedish air force) issued a requirement for an interceptor to succeed the Saab J 29 and provide air defence against bombers flying at near-sonic speeds. It was felt at that stage that it would be sufficient if the new fighter had a level flight speed of Mach 1.4-1.5, although this requirement was later increased to Mach 1.7-1.8. The J 29 – Europe's first swept-wing fighter – had flown only in the previous year and there was no swept-wing fighter in full operational service anywhere in the world. The F-86 Sabre and MiG-15 were just beginning to be delivered and here was the Swedish air force demanding a speed increase of 50 per cent over these types.

Supersonic pioneer

In addition to genuine supersonic performance (far in advance of that possessed by the F-100 Super Sabre, which did not fly until May 1953), the new fighter was required to have a very high climb rate, and to be operable from straight stretches of highway. Such operations demanded moderate take-off and touchdown speeds, and excellent ground handling.

Faced with the basic problem of achieving a major advance in speed, the Saab project team combined a single afterburning Rolls-Royce Avon with an airframe of very low drag. Minimising drag meant reducing the maximum cross-section, and the use of aerofoil surfaces that were as thin as possible. The minimising of the cross-section area was achieved in effect by 'hiding' one object behind another. Thus, the engine was placed behind the pilot, while the fuel and main landing-gear units were behind the air intakes.

The development of the two-seat trainer, the Sk 35C, was undertaken at an early stage. Space for the second cockpit was made available by reducing the size of the forward fuel cell.

Above: A pair of J 35Ds of F13 wing, Swedish air force, presents the characteristic side-view and wing planform of the Draken. The J 35D introduced the more powerful licence-built RM6C (Avon 300 series), with a Flygmotor afterburner.

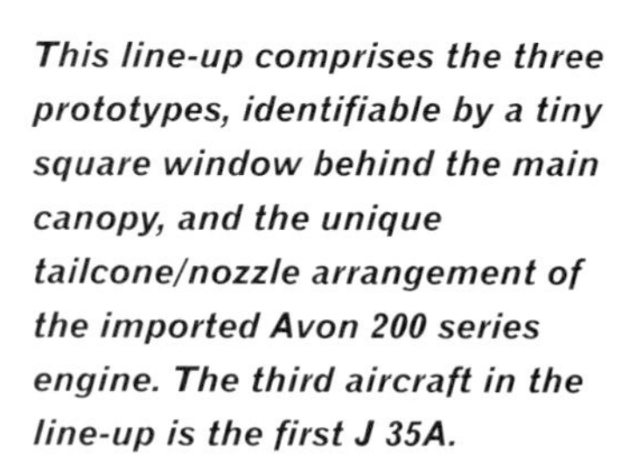

This line-up comprises the three prototypes, identifiable by a tiny square window behind the main canopy, and the unique tailcone/nozzle arrangement of the imported Avon 200 series engine. The third aircraft in the line-up is the first J 35A.

At the end of this preliminary stage, the team had a plain delta wing that was fixed in area by ceiling and fuel capacity. However, a check on landing performance showed that this area was larger than necessary from a stall speed viewpoint. The obvious solution was to reduce the wing chord. This could not be done at the root, where volume was required, so it was done farther outboard by cranking the leading edge. In this way, the distinctive double-delta or cranked delta was produced.

***Above:* The first export order for the Draken occurred in 1968, when Denmark ordered 20 single-seat A 35XDs (fundamentally similar to the J 35F) and three two-seat TF 35s.**

Delivery of the dedicated photo-reconnaissance S 35E began in mid-August 1965. Three squadrons from F11 and F21 wings operated this variant before it was withdrawn in June 1979.

Since there was very little data available on the handling characteristics of delta-wing aircraft, and none whatever on the double-delta, Saab tested the planform with a 0.7-scale manned aircraft, the Saab 210 Lilldraken (little dragon). Powered by an Armstrong Siddeley Adder turbojet, the Lilldraken had a wing planform similar to the full-scale Draken, which at that time had its intakes forward toward the nose.

As confidence in the new concept grew, the Swedish authorities first ordered a mock-up of the proposed J 35 fighter in March 1952. Then, in August 1953, a contract was signed for three prototypes and three pre-series aircraft. The first prototype of the Saab 35 made its maiden flight on 25 October 1955. The three prototypes were powered by imported Avons, the second and third aircraft joining the flight test programme during January and March 1956, respectively. Subsequent Drakens were built with Avons made under licence in Sweden, with a local afterburner that produced far more thrust than the British design. Aside from its wing planform, the Draken was relatively conventional, with fully powered flying controls.

The prototypes proved the soundness of the basic design, and demonstrated speeds of around Mach 1.4. The first pre-series aircraft flew on 15 February 1958, differing mainly in having the locally manufactured RM6B engine with Model 65 afterburner. Although the J 35A was only an interim version, 65 were ordered in a contract signed in August 1956, this number including the three pre-series aircraft.

Deliveries of the J 35A got under way in March 1960, before refinement of the fire control system resulted in the appearance of the J 35B (many of the original J 35As being modified to this standard), deliveries of which took place from 1961. The next single-seat variant was the J 35D which was essentially similar to the J 35B apart from incorporating a rather more powerful version of the licence-built Avon engine. This was in turn followed by the S 35E for reconnaissance duties.

Definitive interceptor

The most capable variant of the Draken, and also the most numerous, was the J 35F. This version entered service during 1965/66, and relied on licence-built radar and semi-active radar homing Rb 27 and infra-red homing Rb 28 Falcon AAMs, as well as Rb 24 Sidewinders. By August 1991, 66 Swedish J 35Fs had been upgraded to J 35J standard, with new avionics and two additional underwing stores pylons. In addition to the single-seaters, the two-seat Sk 35C was built in quantity for operational training.

It was not until shortly before production was due to cease that the Draken succeeded in securing overseas orders, Denmark purchasing fighter-bomber (F-35), reconnaissance (RF-35) and combat trainer (TF-35) versions of the Model 35X export variant. These were delivered from 1970, and the last were retired in 1994. Finland also opted to buy the Draken, acquiring 12 Saab 35S interceptors in 1970, which it operated alongside a number of former Swedish air force J 35Bs (known locally as the 35BS), J 35F (35FS) and Sk 35C (35CS) aircraft, until the final examples were withdrawn in August 2000. Austria, the last Draken operator, took 24 ex-Flygvapen J 35Ds from 1987 to 1989. Designated J 35Ö, Austria's Drakens were delivered without AAM capability, but border violations by Yugoslav aircraft in 1991 saw the fleet receive AIM-9P Sidewinders. They were retired in 2005.

The J 35F could carry two licence-built derivatives of the Hughes Falcon air-to-air missile as well as the AIM-9 Sidewinder.

***Left:* Austria received 24 ex-Swedish air force J 35Ds in the late 1980s. The aircraft were redesignated J 35Ö and were modified to incorporate J 35F-type bulged canopies.**

Above: By comparison with the earlier Draken, the Viggen marked a massive improvement in capability, and proved to have more docile handling characteristics.

Saab 37 Viggen

Thor's hammer

A unique shape in European skies, Sweden's Saab 37 Viggen was a product of its country's fervent desire to remain neutral in a world dominated by the East-West conflicts of the Cold War.

The design of a successor to the revolutionary Saab Draken first commenced in 1952 when a number of attack designs were studied. The Flygvapnet initially wanted an aircraft to replace the Saab Lansen for attack duties and, at a later date, the Draken in the interception role.

The new aircraft was designated Fpl 37, and the powerplant was the first feature that was decided upon. After a number of options were studied, the Pratt & Whitney JT8D-22 was chosen and Svenska Flygmotor soon obtained a license to build the engine. However, the JT8D-22 was not designed to be used with an afterburner and so a number of modifications had to be made.

Working on a scaled-up earlier design, the double-delta Spey-powered 1504B, Saab submitted their resultant model 1534 for approval in February 1962, and was rewarded in September by its formal acceptance as the next combat aircraft for the Flygvapnet.

The Fpl 37 was first made public in December 1962 when its novel wing configuration generated huge interest. As the first canard-equipped military aircraft to enter production, the Fpl 37 was clearly an innovation. The flaps on the canards' trailing edges, acting in unison with, or in opposition to, flaps and elevons at the rear of the wing, allowed the Viggen to avoid the

The Viggen prototype seen in flight. The aircraft wore a Viggen (thunderbolt) badge on the air intake and was fitted with a long test instrument boom on the nose.

The Saab test fleet, minus Aircraft No. 5, is pictured together at the FMV test centre, at Malmen. The unpainted Viggen prototype No. 4 crashed a month later on 7 May 1969.

high landing and take-off speeds which characterised contemporary deltas such as the Dassault Mirage III.

This ability to be able to operate from 1,640 ft (500 m) runways was one of the chief specifications laid down by the Swedish government to the designers and this performance was virtually unrivalled by any contemporary attack jets.

The hefty outward appearance of the Viggen belied the fact that the aircraft was commendably light for one stressed to +12*g*, thanks to an imaginative use of honeycomb panels and metal bonding in the airframe. Care was also taken to ensure that the Viggen was easy to service between flights, so that a high sortie rate could be maintained.

It was soon realised that the Fpl 37 aircraft would need to perform a number of duties and so a number of different variants was planned. The AJ 37 would be an attack aircraft, the SF 37 would replace the Draken in the reconnaissance role, the SH 37 would perform maritime reconnaissance and the SK 37 would be used for training.

Prototypes

An AJ 37 Viggen mock-up was revealed in April 1965 and the first prototype was rolled out in November 1966 and first flew on 8 February 1967.

A second prototype first took to the air in September 1967 with another two aircraft flying over the next year. The second and third prototypes were used for weapon carrying tests, the third being the first aircraft fitted with radar and the complete avionics suite. To improve longitudinal stability when carrying external stores, the fourth Viggen had a saw-tooth in the wing. Aircraft No. 5, which was first flown on 15 April 1969, was used for military trials, and No. 6 conducted tests on a series of systems and weapons. The latter was also the first Viggen to fly at an airshow – Paris in 1969. The final prototype to fly was the SK 37 two-seat trainer which first took to the air on 2 July 1970. Deliveries of the AJ 37 Viggen first began in 1971, with four Swedish air force attack squadrons becoming operational by 1975.

The second and third Viggen prototypes pose during trials. Aircraft No. 2 is unarmed, while No. 3 carries ECM pods inboard and chaff and flare dispensers.

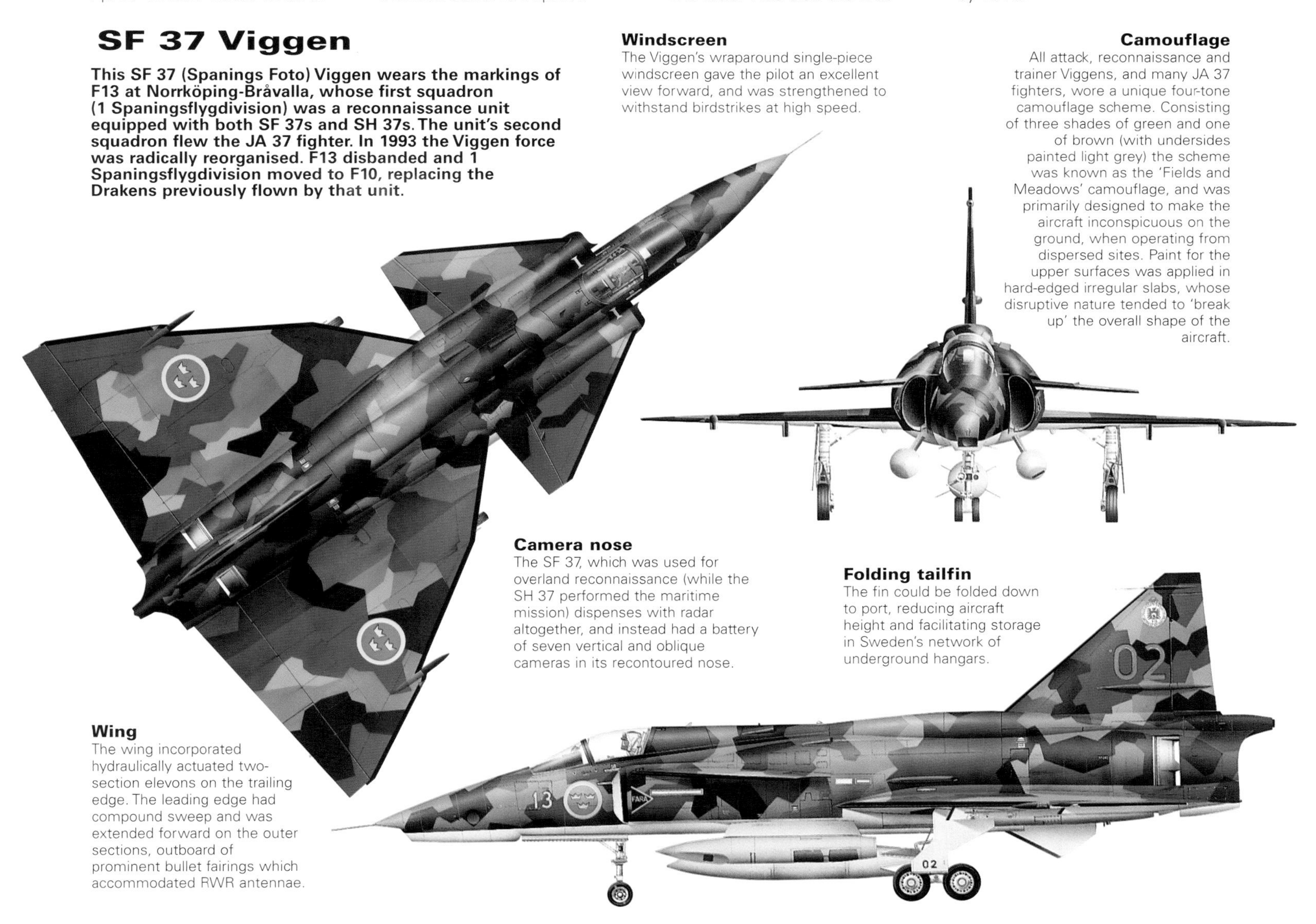

SF 37 Viggen

This SF 37 (Spanings Foto) Viggen wears the markings of F13 at Norrköping-Bråvalla, whose first squadron (1 Spaningsflygdivision) was a reconnaissance unit equipped with both SF 37s and SH 37s. The unit's second squadron flew the JA 37 fighter. In 1993 the Viggen force was radically reorganised. F13 disbanded and 1 Spaningsflygdivision moved to F10, replacing the Drakens previously flown by that unit.

Windscreen
The Viggen's wraparound single-piece windscreen gave the pilot an excellent view forward, and was strengthened to withstand birdstrikes at high speed.

Camouflage
All attack, reconnaissance and trainer Viggens, and many JA 37 fighters, wore a unique four-tone camouflage scheme. Consisting of three shades of green and one of brown (with undersides painted light grey) the scheme was known as the 'Fields and Meadows' camouflage, and was primarily designed to make the aircraft inconspicuous on the ground, when operating from dispersed sites. Paint for the upper surfaces was applied in hard-edged irregular slabs, whose disruptive nature tended to 'break up' the overall shape of the aircraft.

Camera nose
The SF 37, which was used for overland reconnaissance (while the SH 37 performed the maritime mission) dispenses with radar altogether, and instead had a battery of seven vertical and oblique cameras in its recontoured nose.

Folding tailfin
The fin could be folded down to port, reducing aircraft height and facilitating storage in Sweden's network of underground hangars.

Wing
The wing incorporated hydraulically actuated two-section elevons on the trailing edge. The leading edge had compound sweep and was extended forward on the outer sections, outboard of prominent bullet fairings which accommodated RWR antennae.

Viggen variants and operators

Saab AJ 37 Viggen

In the early 1960s, Saab studied a low-cost, single-seat, single-engined fighter capable of supersonic flight at low altitude and Mach 2 at height, but able to take off and land in 1,640 ft (500 m) to replace the multi-role J 32. This demanding specification was necessary if the new aircraft was to operate in Sweden's Stril 60 integrated air defence system and Bas 90 concept dispersed airstrips. For good short-field performance, Saab pioneered the use of flap-equipped canard foreplanes with a delta-wing configuration, in conjunction with an integral thrust-reverser for the RM8 turbofan.

For reliability, the powerplant was based on the 14,771-lb st (65.7-kN) commercial Pratt & Whitney JT8D-22 turbofan, developed and built by Svenska Flygmotor for supersonic flight, and with a Swedish afterburner providing a thrust increase of more than 70 per cent to around 26,014 lb (115.7 kN) for take-off. An autoland technique for minimum landing distance involved automatic approach speed control and selection of reverse thrust in a no-flare touchdown with a 16.4 ft (5 m) per second compression of the main undercarriage oleos. The initial AJ 37 attack aircraft, soon named Viggen (thunderbolt), incorporated many other features novel for its time, including a CK-37 miniaturised digital air data and nav/attack computer, SRA head-up display for primary flight data, and a Cutler-Hammer AIL microwave beam landing-guidance system. A rocket-boosted Saab ejection seat provided zero-zero escape capabilities.

On 5 April 1968, the Swedish government authorised the air force to order 175 AJ/SF/SH 37s for delivery from 1971, and by April 1969 all six single-seat prototypes were flying, the last fully representative of the initial production attack variants. The first of these became airborne on 23 February 1971, deliveries starting soon afterwards, in June, to F7 at Såtenäs to replace A 32A Lansens; four attack wings became operational with AJ 37s by mid-1975. First-generation AJ 37s were either replaced by the upgraded AJS 37 variant or by the new JAS 39 Gripen.

JA 37 Viggen

For the dedicated interception role, with a secondary ground-attack capability, Saab developed the JA 37 Viggen. Although externally similar to the attack variant, the interceptor introduced fundamental changes under the skin, with avionics, armament, engine and structural modifications. The JA 37's primary sensor was the Ericsson PS-46/A medium-PRF multi-mode X-band pulse-Doppler look-down/shoot-down radar, which had four air-to-air modes and a look-down range in excess of 30 miles (48 km). New avionics included an upgraded and higher-capacity Singer-Kearfott SKC-2037 central digital computer and KT-70L INS, Decca Doppler Type 72 nav radar, Garrett AiResearch LD-5 digital air data computer, Saab-Honeywell SA07 digital AFCS, Svenska Radio integrated electronic display system, and an SRA HUD. The RM8B turbofan was uprated by Volvo to develop 16,600 lb (73.84 kN) maximum dry thrust and 28,109 lb (125 kN) with afterburning. This extra power allowed the JA 37 to fly at Mach 1.2 at low altitude, and to exceed Mach 2 at higher altitudes. Airframe changes included a wing restressed for a higher load factor, a fuselage stretch of 4 in (10 cm) ahead of the wing to accommodate the modified powerplant, a 4-in (10-cm) fin extension similar to that of the Sk 37 trainer, and four instead of three elevator actuators under each wing. Four AJ 37 prototypes were modified to JA 37 standard for the development programme, the first making its initial flight on 27 September 1974, a few days after SAF orders for the first 30 production Viggen interceptors. In March 1980, the Swedish government authorised a third batch of 59 JA 37s, increasing overall production of this variant to 149 and the Viggen total to its final figure of 330. JA 37s were planned to replace Flygvapnet J 35 Drakens between 1978 and 1985 and to arm at least eight of the 10 Draken air defence squadrons active at that time. By the 1990s the JA 37 was the most numerous Viggen subtype in service, operational in eight squadrons, but it has since been replaced by the Gripen.

Sk 37 Viggen

With the Viggen fulfilling its role as the Flygvapnet's primary combat aircraft system, there was a pressing need for a trainer version. The Sk 37 Viggen (Skol, or School) tandem two-seat trainer was developed simultaneously with the AJ 37. This variant was somewhat unusual in having two separate cockpits for pilot and instructor. The stepped rear (instructor's) cockpit, fitted with a bulged canopy and twin lateral periscopes, replaced some electronics and a forward fuel tank. Fuel capacity was partially restored by a permanently mounted ventral fuel tank. Other changes included a 4-in (10-cm) taller fin to restore stability following modification of the aircraft to produce the deeper forward fuselage. Because of its height, even the standard AJ 37 fin could be folded on the ground to allow clearance for the SAF's cavern-based hangars. Despite its radome, the Sk 37 had no radar and, therefore, no radar navigation capability, having to rely on Doppler and DME.

SF 37/SH 37 Viggen

Designed as an S 35E Draken replacement, the SF 37 (right) adaptation of the AJ 37 was equipped for all-weather day and night overland reconnaissance, with low- and high-altitude film cameras giving complete horizon-to-horizon lateral coverage, plus a VKA 702 infra-red camera recording thermal images in place of the nose radar. Twin ventral pods also housed night cameras and illumination equipment, the photoflash system operating with light just outside the visible wavelengths. A Red Baron IR line-scan system, with the standard active and passive underwing ECM pods, could also be carried, but the SF 37 had no attack capability and armament was normally confined to defensive Rb 74 (AIM-9L) AAMs. All nine cameras had automatic exposure control and image motion compensation controlled by the aircraft's central computer.

The SH 37 (below right) was modified from the AJ 37 as a successor to the Saab S 32C Lansen for all-weather sea surveillance and patrol, with secondary maritime strike capability, and was fitted with modified radar, plus ventral night reconnaissance and SKA 24D 600-mm lens long-range camera pods. Underwing ECM pods were also normally carried, as well as AAMs on the outboard wing stations. Both the SF and SH 37s normally operated with a ventral fuselage drop tank. F13 at Norköping formed the first SH 37 squadron in late 1976, and the 27 Viggens of this type built between 1977 and 1979 served alongside the SF 37s to equip the three mixed reconnaissance squadrons in F13, F17 and F21. Subsequently, operations of all AJ/SF/SH 'first-generation' Viggens were concentrated in just two squadrons. These aircraft were modified through the AJS 37 upgrade programme prior to retirement in 2005.

AJS 37 Viggen

Between 1993 and 1997, some of the first-generation Viggens were given new life through the AJS programme, comprising the installation of a new mission computer and digital databus to provide integrated attack, fighter and reconnaissance capabilities. Originally, the programme was very ambitious and intended to modify 115 AJ/SF/SH 37 Viggens into AJS 37 multi-role standard. However, financial limitations reduced this number to 98 and the idea of a virtually identical standard was dropped. Thus, the programme eventually resulted in the conversion of 48 AJS 37s (former AJ 37 with additional radar surveillance capability), 25 AJSH 37s (former SH 37 with additional ground-attack capability) and 25 AJSF 37s (former SF 37 with additional fighter capability). The final front-line operators of the AJS/AJSF/AJSH 37 Viggen were 1 Divisionen F10 (Johan Röd) and 1 Divisionen F21 (Urban Röd), and, prior to complete retirement, many high-houred airframes were withdrawn from use and stored, scrapped or given to museums.

The AJS 37 family of Viggens could carry a large and varied weaponload, with air-to-surface armament including Swedish-developed Rb 04E and Rb 15F radar-homing anti-ship missiles, Rb 05A radar-command-guided and Rb 75 (AGM-65 Maverick) TV-guided missiles.

Later service

From a peak of 17 Divisioner (squadrons) in the early 1990s, the Viggen was later reduced to only 10 units (with F6, F13 and F15 all being disbanded). Those Viggens then left in service underwent upgrades, ensuring that they remained in active use until 2005.

F21 Norrbottens Flygflottilj, Luleå

Based at the northernmost permanent Viggen airfield, F21 operated two squadrons of JA 37s (illustrated) plus a unit of AJS 37s, giving it a true multi-role capability. Its maritime surveillance AJSF 37s monitored activities in the Gulf of Bothnia and the Baltic Sea.

F4 Jämtlands Flygflottilj, Östersund

Like most of the later Viggen wings, F4 operated two Jaktflygdivision of JA 37 'Jakt Viggens' (fighter Viggens) – illustrated below – for air defence against hostile invaders. Also at F4 were the Flygvapnet's two-seat Sk 37s. These aircraft were always a precious commodity and were among the highest-timed Viggens.

F17 Blekinge Flygflottilj, Ronneby

Most of Sweden's airfields are in the south of the country. In the event of actual combat during the Cold War, this region would have been criss-crossed by NATO or Soviet fighters, and units such as F17 at Ronneby would have been tasked with defending Sweden's borders from hostile incursions. Pictured below are JA 37s, two divisions of which were operated by F17.

F16 Upplands Flygflottilj, Uppsala

Two Jaktflygdivision of JA 37s were based at Uppsala, tasked with interception. F16 was the fifth and last wing to receive the Jaktviggen.

F10 Skånska Flygflottilj, Ängelholm

One of only two operators of the upgraded AJS 37, the F10 wing located at this southerly base had an attack/fighter/recce) capability, supported by J35J Drakens.

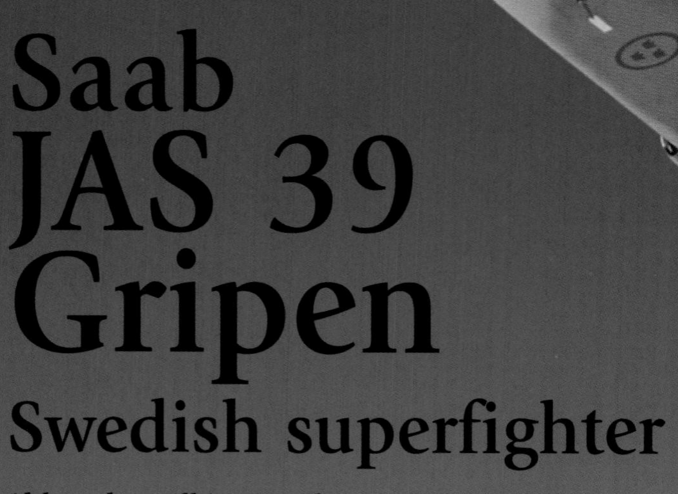

Saab JAS 39 Gripen

Swedish superfighter

Although small in size, the Gripen is a giant in capability. Despite a number of setbacks, Swedish ingenuity has produced an affordable, maintainable and credible fighter which meets and, in some cases, exceeds the Swedish air force's stringent requirements. With the sale of the aircraft to South Africa and the lease of Gripens to Hungary and the Czech Republic, Saab and its partners are looking forward to considerable international success.

Lightweight flexibility is the key to Gripen's success. By cleverly utilising state-of-the-art technology, the Gripen's designers have created a small aircraft which can fulfil the roles previously undertaken by five distinct versions of the much larger Viggen. Here a Sidewinder-armed two-seat JAS 39B and an AMRAAM-armed single-seat JAS 39A break for the camera.

At the start of the 1980s Sweden began development of a new lightweight fighter which would eventually replace the Draken and Viggen in Flygvapnet service. What became the Gripen was designed to meet Cold War threats, however, the inherent flexibility of this state-of-the-art weapon system has allowed it to remain highly relevant in the 21st-century security environment.

By 1981, the requirement had crystallised into the JAS (Jakt, Attack, Spaning – fighter, attack, reconnaissance) programme. The aim was to produce a single fighter that could undertake all the missions assigned to the five Viggen variants.

With Saab was the principal contractor and integrator, the JAS group submitted its Saab 2110 design in 1981, leading to a development contract being issued in June 1982, covering five prototypes and 30 single-seat Batch 1 production aircraft.

Harnessing the latest technological advances, notably in computing power and avionics, the JAS team was able to create an aircraft which could perform all the missions required of it, but in a much smaller, lighter (and therefore cheaper) airframe. The Gripen (griffon), as the JAS 39 was named in September 1982, was a true fourth-generation fighter, with 'glass' cockpit, aerodynamic instability (with fly-by-wire controls), multi-mode radar, modern weapons and carefree-handling turbofan. Furthermore, the aircraft could easily meet the Flygvapnet's demands to be operable from highway strips, and to be easily maintainable by conscript technicians. JAS settled on the F404 to power the Gripen.

The initial Gripen two-seater was designated JAS 39B. A total of 29 were built, including this prototype aircraft which replaced one of the production single-seaters in Batch 1. The final 14 were built as full combat aircraft, and could be used in a command and control function or even as 'UCAV leaders'.

Volvo-Aero and General Electric shared the development of the Gripen version, including a new afterburner. In the Gripen the engine is designated the RM12. Ericsson's PS-05/A radar offers astounding multi-mode performance, from sea search to BVR air-to-air.

Software troubles

What became the most troublesome part of the Gripen programme was the flight control system, a simplified version of which flew from September 1982 in a modified Viggen. Continuing software problems with the FCS kept Gripen firmly on the ground long after its April 1987 roll-out, and it was not to be until 9 December 1988 that the first aircraft took to the air.

On the sixth flight, in February 1989, the aircraft was lost in a landing accident caused by FCS failure. An intense period of FCS work ensued. Gripen no. 2 first flew on 4 May 1990, by which time the programme had slipped three years. By the end of 1991, the remaining three prototypes had flown. Whereas nos 1 and 2 had been flight envelope expansion aircraft, with simplified systems and no 'glass' cockpit, the final three were equipped to a roughly production standard. No. 3 was used primarily for radar, avionics and ECM trials, no. 4 handled avionics and weapons, while no. 5 had a full production system test role.

The first production aircraft flew on 10 September 1992, but it was retained by the test team as a replacement for the lost first prototype. Therefore, the second aircraft became the first aircraft to be handed over to the Flygvapnet, an event occurring on 8 June 1993. Another FCS-induced accident occurred very visibly on 18 August 1993, when the second production machine crashed during an airshow over Stockholm. Further work was rapidly undertaken to rectify this latest FCS problem.

Production of the 30 Batch 1 aircraft continued although one of the aircraft was completed as the prototype two-seat JAS 39B. Adding a second cockpit required removal of the port-side 27-mm cannon, an increase in fuselage length and reduction in fuel capacity. The Flygvapnet subsequently ordered 28 two-seaters in Batches 2 and 3.

Deliveries of single-seat Batch 1 JAS 39As were initially made to the Flygvapnet's F7 Wing at Såtenäs. The first squadron to be declared operational was 2 Div. Gustaf Blå, which achieved this capability on 1 November 1997. 1 Div. Gustaf Röd followed on 30 December 1988, completing the conversion of F7.

Above: The black-painted second prototype handled the high-alpha departure and spin tests, fitted with an anti-spin chute. Production aircraft (rear) were initially built with black radomes.

Left: The key air-to-air weapon for the Gripen is the AIM-120B AMRAAM, known locally as the Rb 99. AMRAAM was cleared operationally in mid-1999, finally allowing the Gripen to justify the 'J' in its JAS 39 designation.

In service

The dominant aircraft in Flygvapnet service, Saab's Gripen is being actively marketed around the world. The sales team has achieved success in South Africa and in eastern Europe.

Sweden's first operational Gripen wing was F7 at Såtenäs, in southwestern Sweden. F7 established a tradition as a 'lead unit' and its first Gripen squadron was Gustaf Blå (blue, 2nd Squadron), which was declared fully operational in November 1997; it was followed by Gustaf Röd (red, 1st squadron) in December 1998.

On 30 September 1999 the first two Gripens arrived at F10 Wing, Ängelholm, to inaugurate the third of Sweden's planned Gripen squadrons. However, a shadow was already looming over the entire Swedish defence forces as a new Defence Decision was being finalised. In March 2000 the government passed a new Defence Bill and confirmed that the Flygvapnet would now have just eight Gripen squadrons, distributed over four wings. F10's home at Ängelholm, which had just completed an expensive modernisation programme to prepare it for Gripen operations, was closed down and the unit subsequently disbanded.

Change of plan

The 2000 decision brought other changes to the introduction of the Gripen system at the different wings. The previous plan called for F16 Wing, at Uppsala, to become the third Gripen wing. Indeed, by late 1999, the initial conversion training process had already begun. Instead, F21 Wing, at Luleå in northern Sweden, became the next unit to transition to the Gripen in January 2003.

This was followed by re-equipment of first of the two squadrons of F4 Wing, based at Östersund, during 2002. That year also saw the F10 Gripens relocating to F17 Wing at Ronneby, which means that all four Flygvapnet wings had partially re-equipped by 2004.

Each of the eight squadrons has approximately 25 Gripens, but F7 Wing maintains two oversized squadrons. The new structure came into effect on

Above: In the air defence role Gripens typically carry a standard load of six missiles, a total which is adequate but hardly ideal. Future plans for the Saab aircraft incorporate the addition of multiple launchers to boost combat persistence.

These Batch Two Gripens line the apron at F10 Wing, Ängelholm. However, with defence cutbacks, the two Gripen squadrons under operational conversion there had ceased operations by 31 December 2002 and transferred to F17 Wing at Ronneby.

The Gripen was aggressively marketed in eastern Europe, with Hungary emerging as the first European export customer. Substantial investment by Sweden was made in Hungarian industry and this attention eventually paid off in the form of a 14-aircraft, 10-year lease deal. As an interim measure, however, Hungary also purchased MiG-29 'Fulcrums'.

Early Gripens were armed only for the air defence role, and then restricted to carrying only Sidewinders. Rapid development expanded this capability. These aircraft display two of the dominant air-to-ground weapons in Sweden's inventory, the Rb 75 Maverick and the DWS 39 glide bomb.

1 July 2000 and was fully implemented during 2003/04.

The success of modern fighters is more often than not gauged by their performance on the export market and this has not traditionally been Saab's strongest field. Sweden's politically neutral stance, coupled with the unique Swedish requirements, have hindered sales. The Gripen suffers from from some of these problems coupled with the fact that some of its systems and equipment are American built and the US vetoes sales to politically undesirable countries, some of which might have been potential Gripen customers. Furthermore, the modern fighter-market is a cut-throat business and despite the fact that it was the first fourth-generation fighter in service, the Gripen has to contend with numerous rivals.

However, the Gripen chalked up a major success in December 1999, when the South African Air Force announced that Saab-BAE would supply 28 Gripens and 24 Hawk 100s to be delivered between 2005 and 2012. Local companies were selected to provide a new fully digital radio system, power unit, communication control and display unit and multi-function weapon pylons.

European exports

In Europe, the Gripen found its first customer in Hungary. In 2001 an agreement was made for the lease of 14 Gripens to the Hungarian air force (12 of the NATO-compatible JAS 39C version, which also introduces a retractable refuelling probe, reinforced wings and undercarriage, colour cockpit displays and updated software, and two of the similar two-seat JAS 39D versions) from Swedish stocks. A lease and purchase contract was agreed in 2003 and the final examples of the Hungarian Gripen will be received by the end of 2007. Hungarian pilots have also trained on the Gripen in Sweden, with the first five aircrew starting their conversion to the new aircraft in 2005.

A similar agreement for the same number of aircraft was made with the Czech Republic in 2004, in order to equip a single NATO-declared squadron under a 10-year lease. Czech pilots began training on the Gripen in 2004 and the final aircraft were received in 2005.

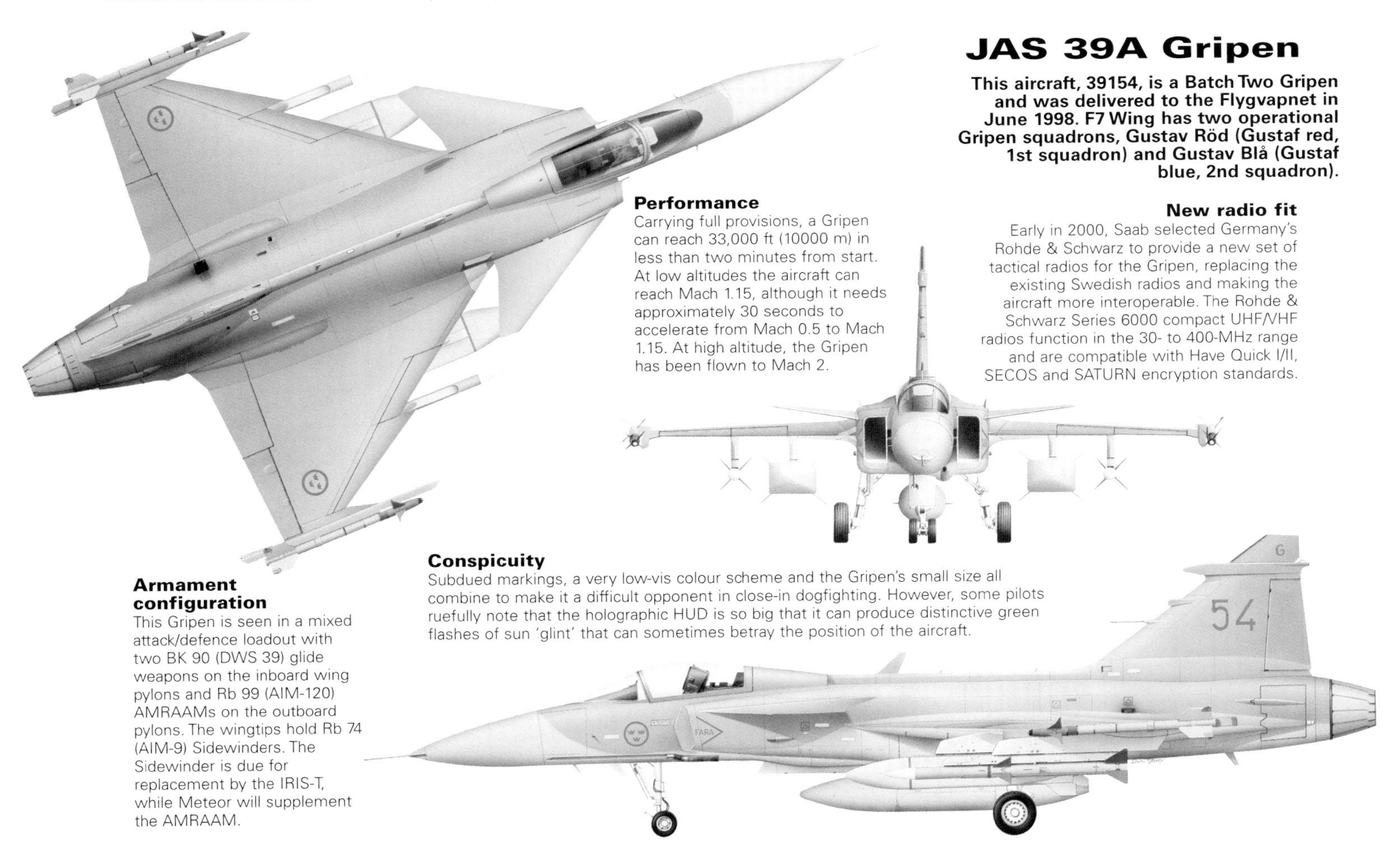

JAS 39A Gripen

This aircraft, 39154, is a Batch Two Gripen and was delivered to the Flygvapnet in June 1998. F7 Wing has two operational Gripen squadrons, Gustav Röd (Gustaf red, 1st squadron) and Gustav Blå (Gustaf blue, 2nd squadron).

Performance
Carrying full provisions, a Gripen can reach 33,000 ft (10000 m) in less than two minutes from start. At low altitudes the aircraft can reach Mach 1.15, although it needs approximately 30 seconds to accelerate from Mach 0.5 to Mach 1.15. At high altitude, the Gripen has been flown to Mach 2.

New radio fit
Early in 2000, Saab selected Germany's Rohde & Schwarz to provide a new set of tactical radios for the Gripen, replacing the existing Swedish radios and making the aircraft more interoperable. The Rohde & Schwarz Series 6000 compact UHF/VHF radios function in the 30- to 400-MHz range and are compatible with Have Quick I/II, SECOS and SATURN encryption standards.

Conspicuity
Subdued markings, a very low-vis colour scheme and the Gripen's small size all combine to make it a difficult opponent in close-in dogfighting. However, some pilots ruefully note that the holographic HUD is so big that it can produce distinctive green flashes of sun 'glint' that can sometimes betray the position of the aircraft.

Armament configuration
This Gripen is seen in a mixed attack/defence loadout with two BK 90 (DWS 39) glide weapons on the inboard wing pylons and Rb 99 (AIM-120) AMRAAMs on the outboard pylons. The wingtips hold Rb 74 (AIM-9) Sidewinders. The Sidewinder is due for replacement by the IRIS-T, while Meteor will supplement the AMRAAM.

SEPECAT Jaguar

Anglo-French success story

It was only after the SEPECAT Jaguar gave up its original strike and interdiction role in Europe that it found its true forte, as a rapid-reaction, out-of-area-bomber, able to operate in the most primitive conditions and hit its target with unerring accuracy.

Based at RAF Coltishall, No. 54 Squadron began operating Jaguar GR.Mk 1s in 1974. With the RAF introducing the multi-role Eurofighter Typhoon in recent years, the Jaguar's days are numbered; the last examples will be retired in 2007.

Rugged and reliable but relatively simple and able to operate from even the most austere airstrips, the Jaguar is an ideal aircraft for out-of-area operations. Thus, whenever the RAF needed to show a presence in a trouble spot, Jaguars were likely to be deployed first. This was the case following the Iraqi invasion of Kuwait on 2 August 1990, when the RAF's Jaguars arrived first and went on to build an impressive war record that equalled, and in some cases bettered, more modern aircraft designs. This was a remarkable feat, considering that the Jaguar had been in front-line squadron service since the mid-1970s.

In many ways the Gulf War represented the Jaguar's finest hour, and certainly silenced doubts about the aircraft's capability. RAF Jaguars flew 618 sorties during the war, performing both reconnaissance and interdiction missions.

Developed jointly by BAC in Britain and Breguet in France under the company name of SEPECAT, the original design stemmed from a common RAF/ Armée de l'Air (French air force) requirement of 1965 for a light tactical attack and training aircraft capable of supersonic performance. So successful was the resulting design that the tandem dual-control trainers which were also produced were made fully combat capable, although in British service they were not equipped with the full range of avionics and weapons fitted to their single-seat cousins.

Under a pre-arranged 50:50 work-share agreement, Breguet was made responsible for designing and building the Jaguar's nose, centre fuselage and undercarriage, with BAC taking the wings, air intakes, rear fuselage and tail unit.

Eight Jaguar prototypes were built, five of them being produced at Breguet's factory at Villacoublay, on the western side of Paris. However, the first two-seat prototype was taken by road to Istres, near Marseilles, for its maiden flight on 8 September 1968. The initial flight of the first single-seat variant followed in March 1969.

Service entry

The Armée de l'Air was first to put the Jaguar into operational service, when the initial batch of trainer variants went into use in May 1972. Known as Jaguar E in French service, they were soon followed by single-seat Jaguar As, which had identical armament and avionics.

British Jaguars were much more sophisticated, equipped with a fully comprehensive

inertial nav/attack system, HUD, projected map display, laser rangefinder (in a 'chisel' nose) and a more comprehensive ECM suite. Known as the Jaguar S by SEPECAT, in RAF circles the aircraft was designated GR.Mk 1A, while the two-seat trainer was the T.Mk 2A. The RAF received 165 of the two versions in all.

The Jaguars soon established themselves an enviable reputation in squadron service, to the extent that the RAF allocated the role of tactical nuclear strike to Jaguar units based in Germany. However, their mission was later changed to interdiction and tactical reconnaissance following the introduction of the Tornado GR.Mk 1 by the RAF during the early 1980s.

French service

France operated its front-line Jaguars in four distinct roles: pre-strategic nuclear strike, conventional tactical air support, electronic warfare and defence suppression. In addition to these combat roles the two-seat variants fulfilled part of the large training requirement for future fast jet pilots. Despite the introduction of the Dassault Mirage 2000, which also reduced the Jaguar's role, the aircraft proved themselves highly versatile in out-of-area operations. France's political links with several African countries resulted in its Jaguars seeing combat action in Chad, Gabon and Senegal, before the aircraft was retired from service in 2005.

Having devised the original requirement in partnership with the RAF, it was only natural that the Armée de l'Air would purchase the aircraft in large quantities. At their operational peak no less than nine squadrons were equipped with Jaguars.

Potential lost

Four customers selected the Jaguar for attack duties; first was Ecuador in 1977, quickly followed by Oman, India and Nigeria. Lack of further export success was allegedly an unexpected consequence of the Anglo-French partnership. The Jaguar was in direct competition with the Mirage III series, also a Dassault-Breguet product, and needless to say the French government was not keen to share Jaguar profits with BAC when it could sell all-French Mirages instead.

Despite these problems, RAF and Armée de l'Air Jaguars achieved outstanding combat records in the 1991 Gulf War. RAF Jaguars flew interdiction missions throughout the war against the Iraqi Republican Guard and later returned to the area to patrol the NATO-enforced no-fly zones.

Subsequent upgrades to the RAF Jaguar fleet – including uprated Adour Mk 106 engines, the TIALD laser designation pod, night-vision goggles and a helmet-mounted sight to produce the GR.Mk 3 and T.Mk 4 variants – ensured that the aircraft remained in service with Britain's last front-line Jaguar squadron until 2007.

Left: Early in its operational career RAF Germany's Jaguar force formed a major element of Britain's tactical nuclear striking power. Maintained at a high state of readiness, they were seldom seen outside their hardened aircraft shelters, except when flying.

The Cross of Jerusalem in a blue pennant on the tail of this Jaguar A identifies it as belonging to 2e Escadrille, Escadron de Chasse 1/7 'Provence', which was based at St Dizier. EC 1/7 was mainly tasked with anti-radar missions, using the AS.37 Martel missile.

At the height of Jaguar deployment, RAF Germany boasted no fewer than five squadrons flying the type. Four formed a nuclear-capable strike wing at Brüggen, while one was at Laarbruch (alongside strike Buccaneers) in the tactical reconnaissance role.

RAF and AdA

In all but one case, the Jaguar replaced the Phantom in the strike/attack/recce role, equipping squadrons at home and in Germany. Three UK-based units continued to provide valuable service until 2005.

No. II (Army Co-operation) Squadron

Tasked with tactical reconnaissance in RAF Germany, No. II Sqn was resident at Laarbruch with Phantoms when it received its first Jaguar on 26 February 1976 (both types are illustrated below). The last Phantom left in July and the squadron was declared operational on the new type in October. For most sorties the Jaguars carried the BAe centreline reconnaissance pod. The Jaguar era ended in late 1988 as No. II converted to Tornado GR.Mk 1As, the final Jaguar mission being flown on 16 December.

No. 14 Squadron

No. 14, a previous Phantom operator, became the first RAF Germany Jaguar squadron on 7 April 1975, although full conversion was not achieved until December. Based at Brüggen, the squadron was also the last Jaguar unit in Germany, flying its final mission on 14 October 1985, by which time Tornado GR.Mk 1s had been taken on strength.

No. 6 Squadron

No. 6 converted from Phantoms on 2 October 1974 and, for its first month, was based at Lossiemouth, before moving to Coltishall. The unit's aircraft carry the Royal Artillery 'gunner's stripe' on the fin and their unofficial 'Flying Can-openers' badge on the intake sides. During the Cold War, No. 6 would have expected to deploy to Tirstrup in Denmark in the event of hostilities. The squadron was one of the last three Coltishall-based Jaguar units, and converted to the updated GR.Mk 3/T.Mk 4. Like the other remaining Jaguar squadrons, it contributed aircraft and crew during Operation Granby (1991 Gulf War) and shared the burden of manning peacekeeping detachments in Italy and over Iraq. In 2007, it was the last RAF Jaguar unit, at Coningsby.

No. 17 Squadron

The black/white zig-zag markings and gauntlet badge (commemorating the squadron's use of the Gloster Gauntlet) of No. 17 Squadron first appeared on the Jaguar in June 1975. The first of the new aircraft began replacement of the Phantom FGR.Mk 2, a process completed by February 1976. Part of the Brüggen wing, the Jaguars were employed on a variety of strike/attack duties, including tactical nuclear strike. On 16 August 1984 the squadron received its first Tornado GR.Mk 1, completing the transition on 1 March 1985 when the Jaguar element was disbanded. Shown below is a squadron aircraft cavorting with a West German F-104G.

No. 20 Squadron

No. 20 Squadron was unique in converting to the Jaguar from the Harrier, rather than from the Phantom. Jaguars began arriving at Brüggen in January 1977 while the squadron continued to operate Harriers from Wildenrath. Conversion to the new type and new base was completed on 1 March and the unit joined the rest of the Brüggen wing on strike/attack duties. The squadron had a relatively brief Jaguar career, being disbanded on 24 June 1984. It stood up the next day as a ready-made Tornado GR.Mk 1 unit. In acquiring the Tornado, it became the only squadron to fly all three of these attack types.

The RAF Germany Jaguar force operated from hardened aircraft shelters, unlike those based in the UK.

No. 31 Squadron

The third of the Brüggen squadrons to form, No. 31 began receiving Jaguars in January 1976 although it was not until 1 July that the final Phantom bowed out. Between 13 June and 1 November 1984, the squadron made the transition from the Jaguar to the Tornado GR.Mk 1.

No. 41 Squadron

No. 41 was the UK-based reconnaissance unit, based at Coltishall but with a war base at Tromsö in Norway. The first aircraft arrived to replace the Phantom on 27 April 1976 and the squadron was declared operational on 1 April 1977. Generally carrying centreline multi-sensor pods (illustrated below), the squadron continued in service until 2006, having supplied aircraft and crews for both Gulf Wars (1991 and 2003).

No. 54 Squadron

The RAF's first front-line Jaguar unit, No. 54 officially stood up with the type at Lossiemouth on 1 July 1974, although squadron members had been training on it since March. On 8 August 1974 the squadron moved to the operational Jaguar base at Coltishall. Like No. 6 Sqn, No. 54 was a NATO-designated Regional Reinforcement Squadron with a wartime base at Tirstrup. The squadron survived at Coltishall on the GR.Mk 3/T.Mk 4, until both base and unit closed down in 2005.

JCT/226 OCU/No. 16 (Reserve) Squadron

Jaguar pilot training commenced at Lossiemouth in September 1973, initially under the auspices of the Jaguar Conversion Team. With No. 54 Squadron's pilots converted to type, the training effort was formalised as 226 Operational Conversion Unit on 1 October 1974. While Jaguar training was at its height, the OCU was split into Nos 1 and 2 Squadrons, beginning on 11 November 1974. No. 1 Squadron was disbanded shortly after. For a short while, the aircraft of No. 2 Squadron wore a leaping jaguar badge on the side of the nose. Aircraft subsequently acquired a tartan fin-band (from 1981) in addition to 226 OCU's torch and quiver markings which had first appeared on Jaguar intakes in 1977. A two-digit code was applied throughout (left). On 1 November 1991 the OCU was assigned the 'shadow' squadron number of No. 16 Sqn and that unit's 'Saint' markings began to appear. Later, the unit was formalised as No. 16 (Reserve) Squadron (below) and all vestiges of 226 OCU markings disappeared. Throughout its history, the training effort remained at Lossiemouth, operating from a hangar/apron complex on the west side of the base until March 2005.

France

The French Jaguar was cruder than the RAF aircraft even when it entered service, lacking the RAF aircraft's HUD, projected moving map and NAVWASS navigation and weapons system. Since then, the RAF modified its Jaguars many times, while the French Jaguar cockpit remained much as it always had been. Furthermore, the French Jaguar retained the original Adour Mk 102 engine. But despite this 'simplicity' and lack of power, the Jaguar was much prized for its maintainability, versatility and ability to deploy at minimal notice and with remarkably little support. It was this deployability that resulted in the aircraft being used in anger against the Polisario in Mauretania in 1977, against Libyan forces in Chad in 1978 and 1986, and during Operation Desert Storm in 1991. Subsequently, French Jaguars flew combat missions over Bosnia, Serbia and Kosovo.

When it became operational in 1974, Jaguars fulfilled the nuclear strike role, using the indigenous AN.52 bomb, and this task was retained until August 1991. EC 7 had three front-line escadrons (EC 1/7 'Provence', EC 3/7 'Languedoc' and EC 4/7 'Limousin' – the latter existing only between April 1980 and July 1989) and another which functioned as the Jaguar OCU (EC 2/7 'Argonne'). It was augmented by a single element of EC 3 (EC 3/3 'Ardennes' at Nancy-Ochey) between April 1977 and June 1987, and by Escadre de Chasse 11. The Toul-based EC 11, with its four escadrons (EC 1/11 'Roussillon', EC 2/11 'Vosges', EC 3/11 'Corse' and EC 4/11 'Jura'), tended to fulfil the out-of-area role. EC 11 disbanded, escadron by escadron, and passed its commitments (and many of its aircraft) to EC 7. EC 3/11 'Corse' finally disbanded in July 1997, while the final French Jaguar unit, EC 1/7, followed in June 2005.

Jaguar International
Operators

Above: *Traditionally an operator of British-built aircraft, Oman ordered a squadron of 12 Jaguar Internationals in 1974 and in the mid-1980s ordered a further squadron. Two trainer aircraft were also obtained in 1982.*

From its earliest days, several nations saw the SEPECAT Jaguar as an answer to a number of their needs. However, because of Dassault's subversive sales techniques, sales were lost to Mirage aircraft.

Serious marketing of the Jaguar began in 1974 when BAC revealed details of export orders from undisclosed customers (in fact Ecuador and Oman). Several days later an RAF aircraft was displayed with Jaguar International titles and a mock radar nose, surrounded by weaponry appropriate to an export variant. This Jaguar was subsequently fitted with Adour Mk 104 engines with 27 per cent higher thrust over the original Mk 102, and became the prototype Jaguar International.

The first production Jaguar International was a two-seat aircraft for Ecuador and was officially designated Jaguar EB. The single seat Ecuador variant went by the name Jaguar ES.

All of the eventual Jaguar export orders were completed by British sales teams and what is more, they did so in the face of adversity from their supposed colleagues at SEPECAT, who rubbished the Jaguar to sell more Mirage aircraft.

Ecuador was the first export customer for the Jaguar, placing an order, for 10 single-seat Jaguar International ESs and two twin-stick EBs, which was announced in 1974. Deliveries began in January 1977, allowing the re-equipment of Escuadrón de Combate 2111 at Taura. Six surviving single-seaters were upgraded with over-wing missile launch rails from 1994, while all eight surviving aircraft had their original NAVWASS replaced by the FIN 1064 INAS.

Ecuador was the first export customer of the Jaguar, ordering 12 – 10 single-seaters and two two-seaters – in 1974. These equipped one squadron of Grupo 211.

Omani Jaguars

Oman's first Jaguar order was one of the two announced anonymously by BAC in August 1974. It was soon revealed that the customer for 10 Jaguar International OS single-seaters and two OB two-seaters was Oman. Delivered from March 1977, the first batch entered service with No. 8 Squadron at Masirah. A second order for another 12 aircraft (again including two trainers) was placed in mid-1980, and the air force subsequently received an ex-Indian loan RAF Jaguar T.Mk 2 and an ex-RAF GR.Mk 1. The second batch of aircraft, fitted with the more powerful Mk 811 engine and upgraded avionics, re-equipped No. 20 Squadron at Masirah from 1983. The Omani Jaguars were subsequently brought up to GR.Mk 1A/T.Mk 2A standards (apart from their more powerful export-standard engines), and a contract was later signed for a further upgrade.

Nigeria ordered 18 Jaguar Internationals (including five two-seat Jaguar BNs) in 1983. The first of these was delivered in May 1984 but was used initially for aircrew training at Warton. The first two aircraft were passed on

Nigeria ordered its 18 Jaguars in 1983, with the option to buy a further 18. The first aircraft arrived the following year and were delivered to a squadron based at Makurdid.

The Indian Air Force's No. 6 Squadron uses the Jaguar IM in the maritime attack role. These aircraft are fitted with the Agave radar and can carry the Sea Eagle anti-ship missile.

to Makurdi on 30 October 1984. The type was withdrawn from use as an economy measure in 1991, when 10 single-seat SNs and four BNs remained in service.

The first Indian expressions of interest in the Jaguar emerged even before the aircraft flew, in 1966, although it was to be 1978 before India placed a firm order for the aircraft. Even before the 1978 announcement, steps had been taken to prepare for the Jaguar, and the first four Indian pilots were posted to the RAF's No. 226 OCU in February 1976. Eight more pilots followed them. These 12 pilots formed the nucleus of the first Indian Jaguar squadron, No. 14, which re-equipped with 18 loaned RAF Jaguars in July 1979. The squadron was declared operational at Ambala in September 1980.

Two of the loaned aircraft were lost in service, and two were retained for trials work, but the rest returned to the UK between 1982 and 1984, as 40 new-build Jaguar Internationals (including five twin-stickers) were delivered. These aircraft were basically similar to the RAF GR.Mk 1, with NAVWASS, but were powered by Adour Mk 804 engines, the export equivalent to the later Adour Mk 104. The aircraft was designated Jaguar IS or Jaguar IT (two-seaters). These early aircraft re-equipped No. 14 Squadron, and also allowed the formation of a second unit, No. 5 Squadron, which became operational in August 1981. Thus, Nos 5 and 14 Squadrons, operating the British-built, NAVWASS-equipped Jaguar International aircraft, made up the wing at Ambala.

The second batch of 45 new-build aircraft was assembled in India from BAe-supplied components and sub-assemblies. The aircraft incorporated a number of improvements, and were powered by more powerful Adour Mk 811 engines. The aircraft featured a new locally integrated DARIN (Display Attack and Ranging Inertial Navigation) nav-attack system. No. 27 Squadron formed with the new DARIN Jaguars at Bangalore in June 1985, moving back to Gorakhpur after conversion and work-up.

Fourth IAF squadron

No. 16 Squadron was the next unit to form, converting to the Indian-assembled DARIN aircraft at Gorakhpur in October 1986. The second batch included eight Jaguar IMs, dedicated maritime aircraft with nose-mounted Agave radar and provision to fire the Sea Eagle missile. The maritime IMs equip No. 6 Squadron at Pune.

A total of 45 Jaguars, assembled by HAL, were to have been followed by the production of 56 more Jaguars, but instead India procured a further 31 aircraft (all single-seaters) which were again assembled largely from BAe-supplied kits. An order for 15 extra strike aircraft was cancelled in 1989 and then resurrected in 1993. A further order was subsequently placed for 37 new-build Jaguars from HAL production, and these will be delivered up to 2009/10.

Left: A trio of No. 14 Squadron Jaguars formates for the camera. Known as the 'Fighting Fourteenth', the squadron was declared operational on the Jaguar in September 1980, after its pilots had completed their training in the UK.

Below: Part of Western Air Command, No. 14 Squadron operates the Jaguar IS in the deep strike role. The aircraft use overwing rails to carry R.550 Magic air-to-air missiles for self-defence.

Sud-Ouest Vautour

Gallic multi-role twin

Above: The three Vautour prototypes each represented the three basic variants: '001' was a two-seat night-fighter, '002' a single-seat attack variant and '003' a two-seat bomber.

Left: Though much smaller, the Vautour had several features in common with the Boeing B-47, including its wing, which had the same sweep angle of 35°, and its tandem landing-gear.

Out of a multitude of warplane prototypes built after World War II, the manufacturer Sud-Ouest produced this versatile machine in bomber, intruder and fighter variants, all of which went on to follow useful careers, including combat in Israeli hands. Big and bulky, the Vautour nevertheless had good range, respectable performance and, above all, good internal capacity.

In the years immediately after World War II, the French aircraft industry exhibited models and mock-ups of more than 70 projected combat aircraft, and more than 30 types were actually flown. One of the greatest of these families was the Vautour (vulture). It was the only product of SNCASO to go into major front-line service after World War II. SNCASO (Société Nationale de Constructions Aéronautiques de Sud-Ouest) was formed by the nationalisation of the French aircraft industry in 1936.

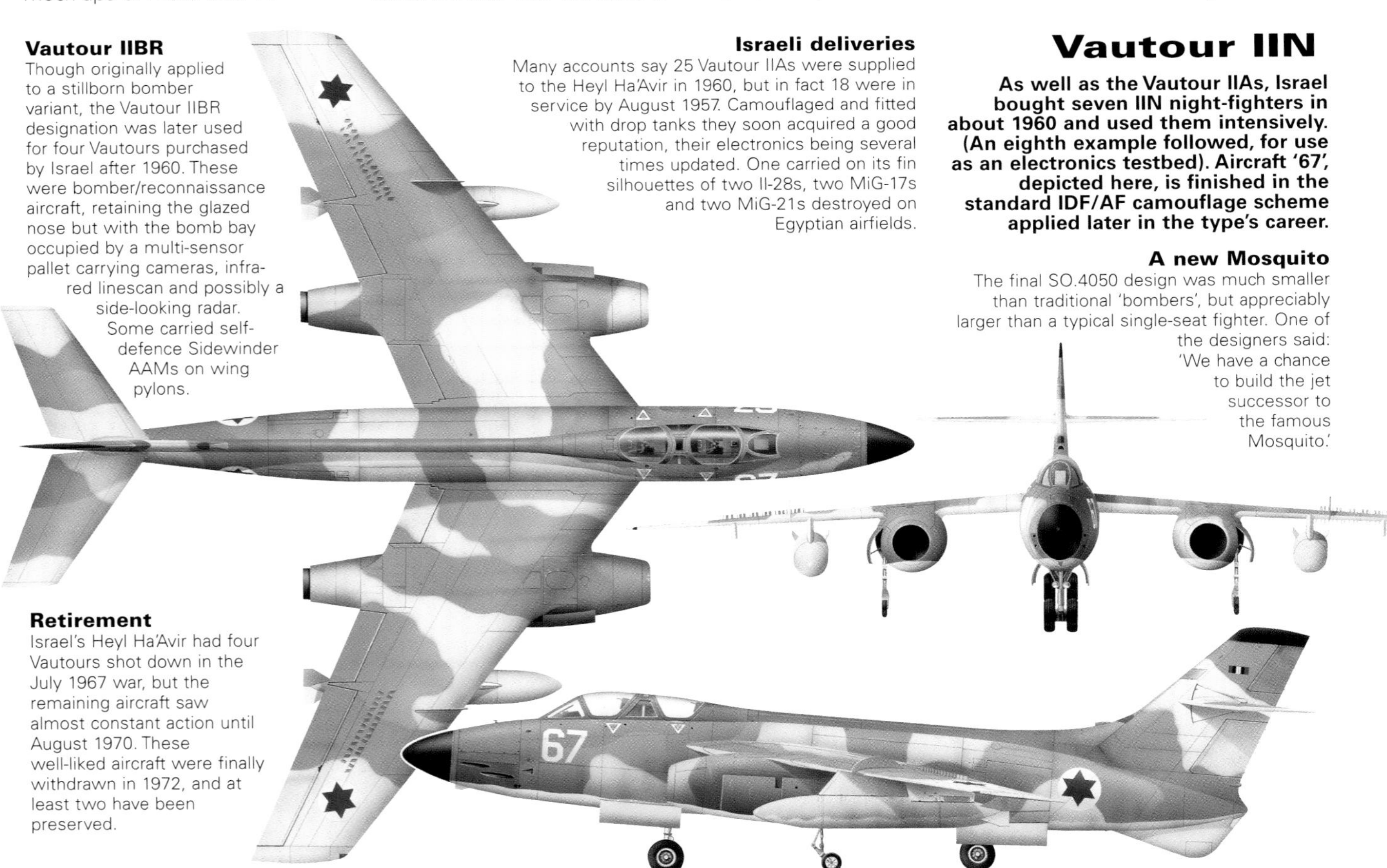

Vautour IIBR
Though originally applied to a stillborn bomber variant, the Vautour IIBR designation was later used for four Vautours purchased by Israel after 1960. These were bomber/reconnaissance aircraft, retaining the glazed nose but with the bomb bay occupied by a multi-sensor pallet carrying cameras, infra-red linescan and possibly a side-looking radar. Some carried self-defence Sidewinder AAMs on wing pylons.

Israeli deliveries
Many accounts say 25 Vautour IIAs were supplied to the Heyl Ha'Avir in 1960, but in fact 18 were in service by August 1957. Camouflaged and fitted with drop tanks they soon acquired a good reputation, their electronics being several times updated. One carried on its fin silhouettes of two Il-28s, two MiG-17s and two MiG-21s destroyed on Egyptian airfields.

Vautour IIN

As well as the Vautour IIAs, Israel bought seven IIN night-fighters in about 1960 and used them intensively. (An eighth example followed, for use as an electronics testbed). Aircraft '67', depicted here, is finished in the standard IDF/AF camouflage scheme applied later in the type's career.

A new Mosquito
The final SO.4050 design was much smaller than traditional 'bombers', but appreciably larger than a typical single-seat fighter. One of the designers said: 'We have a chance to build the jet successor to the famous Mosquito.'

Retirement
Israel's Heyl Ha'Avir had four Vautours shot down in the July 1967 war, but the remaining aircraft saw almost constant action until August 1970. These well-liked aircraft were finally withdrawn in 1972, and at least two have been preserved.

Left: Because they were the simplest, the first to come off the line were Vautour IIA single-seaters, the first flying on 30 April 1956. These were armed with four 30-mm cannon, each with 100 rounds, three 1,000-lb (454-kg) bombs carried in an internal bay plus four bombs of up to 1,000-lb (454-kg) each on wing pylons. Ouest built 30 of this model, but they never served with the Armée de l'Air and were used for testing.

Below: BB 92 operated the Vautour IIB bomber variant from July 1958 until September 1978, during which time it fielded two squadrons, EB 1/92 'Bourgogne' and EB 2/92 'Aquitaine'. Based at Bordeaux, the unit also performed tactical strike and reconnaissance roles. In 1958 Sud-Aviation flew a version designated IIBR, basically a IIB bomber but with the glazed nose replaced by a radar and inflight refuelling probe; it failed to enter production.

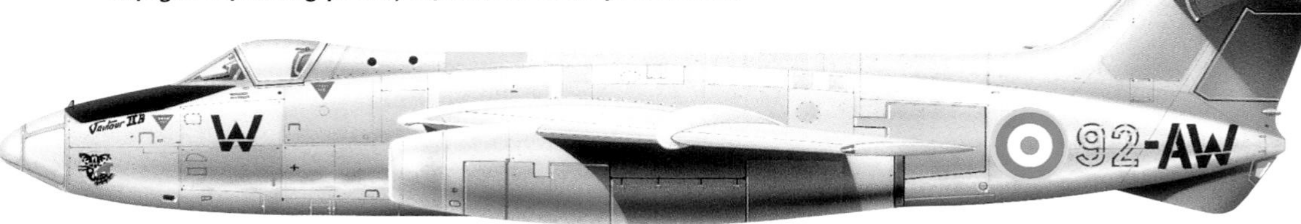

Among its many post-war prototypes was the SO.4000 jet bomber, first flown in March 1951. Though impressive it was, in many ways, clumsy and outdated. The decision was taken to abandon the programme after the first flight, and develop a totally fresh basic design of more modern conception. The new aircraft would be the first twin-engined machine to use the all-French Atar engine. Not least, by starting again the SNCASO designers could incorporate sweepback in the wings and tail, and thereby the aircraft could reach significantly higher speeds.

The French air staff had already prepared a wide-ranging requirement for a new aircraft to meet no fewer than four major combat missions: light level bomber, all-weather interceptor, close tactical support and reconnaissance.

Production go-ahead

SNCASO received an immediate order for three prototypes, and detail design began in June 1951. In 1953 an order was placed for six pre-production Vautours, and this was followed by an order for 140 production aircraft. It was expected that 360 would be ordered in all, but this was finally cut back to only 140.

SNCASO planned three basic versions: Vautour A – a single-seat tactical fighter and close-support aircraft; Vautour B – a two-seat bomber, with a glazed nose for visual bomb-aiming; Vautour C – this was to be a night and all-weather fighter, with radar in the nose managed by a back-seat operator.

SNCASO was told to build the SO.4050-01 in the 'C' configuration. It was completed remarkably quickly and made its first flight on 16 October 1952. The initial test flying was performed with quite low-powered SNECMA Atar 101B engines, but as the engines were uprated, the performance became progressively better. In 1953 the -01 aircraft was re-engined with Atar 101C engines of 6,170 lb (27.45 kN) rating. It was also given a spine linking the canopies and fin, and the interception radar (supplied by the US) was installed in the nose, together with four 30-mm DEFA cannon aimed by the pilot.

SO.4050-02 was completed as a Vautour A single-seater. It had a pointed nose and initially flew with 101C engines on 16 December 1953. In 1954 Atar 101Ds were fitted, rated at 6,611 lb (29.41 kN). Aircraft -03 was the first bomber, with a bombsight in a glazed nose, and it was unique in having Armstrong Siddeley Sapphire engines. It first flew on 5 December 1954.

This completed the prototypes, and the six pre-production Vautours followed. Normally all had Atar 101D engines, but aircraft -04 at one time had engines with afterburners; it was a bomber. Nos -05 and -07 were single-seat Vautour As, -06 and -08 were Vautour N fighters and -09 was another N, unique in having Rolls-Royce Avon engines.

The standard engine for the production aircraft was the 7,716-lb (34.31-kN) Atar 101E-3.

The order for 140 Vautour IIN night and all-weather fighters was cut in half, the 70 aircraft being delivered between 1957 and 1959. They were armed with four 30-mm guns and an internal bay under the radar operator's cockpit housing two retractable launchers each containing 116 rockets. Most of this version served with the 30e Escadre Tout-Temps (all-weather wing), and by late 1958 their armament was enhanced by adding four wing pylons for Matra R.511 AAMs. In the early 1960s the 53 aircraft in service were modified with one-piece 'slab' tailplanes, becoming Vautour II.1N aircraft.

Ouest built 40 of the Vautour IIB bomber version, the first flying on 31 July 1957. All these went to the Armée de l'Air, equipping the Commandement des Forces Aériennes Stratégique until the arrival of the Mirage IVA in 1964-65. As noted, the IIB seated a bombardier in the glazed nose, and it carried the same bombloads as the IIA. In 1960, 35 were in front-line service when slab tailplanes resulted in their redesignation as Vautour II.1Bs.

Equipped with Matra R.511 semi-active radar homing air-to-air missiles, this ECN 1/30 'Loire de Creil' Vautour IIN also carries a pair of SNEB 68-mm (2.68-in) rocket packs in its weapons bay.

Sukhoi Su-7 'Fitter'

In Indian Air Force service, the Su-7 gained a reputation as a formidable combat asset during the confrontation with Pakistan in 1971. Approximately 150 Su-7BMs were operational during the war, equipping seven units, five of which were based on the Western Front. 221 Sqn was particularly active: raiding the sole PAF airbase at Tezgaon, outside Dacca and the airfield at Jessore. Some 32 'Fitter-As' were lost.

The Su-7 story

As a pioneer of supersonic operations in the Soviet Union, the Su-7 found its niche as a ground-attack aircraft and spawned the great 'Fitter' family.

Sukhoi's 'Fitter' family originated in the S-1 prototype swept-wing tactical fighter, the preliminary design of which was first submitted in November 1953. Development was in response to the USSR's urgent need for a new generation of supersonic fighters to supplant the MiG-15s and MiG-17s then in service. The Sukhoi design bureau, which was re-established in April 1953 following Stalin's death, studied both swept-wing and delta-wing configurations for both tactical and interceptor fighters, both to be powered by AL-7F turbojets.

Full-scale development of the resulting S-1 tactical fighter was completed in 1954, and the first prototype was flown on 7 September 1955.

Mach 2 warplane

As the S-1 represented the USSR's first practical Mach 2-capable jet fighter, several problems were encountered during the developmental stages. Air intake control difficulties at high speed resulted in a variety of different nose cone shapes being trialled. Despite setbacks, the S-1 achieved a speed of 1,348 mph (2170 km/h) during a test flight in April 1956, thus exceeding the programme's performance requirements.

In 1955 the requirements for the S-1 were updated by the air force to include a more powerful AL-7F-1 engine, and the second prototype (S-2) was built accordingly, and first flew in September 1956, thereafter joining the S-1 for state tests. While the S-2 was used for aerodynamic trials, the S-1 was designated for testing and developing aircraft systems and operational evaluation.

Left: A relatively simple aircraft, the Sukhoi S-1 prototype had to undergo a great deal of development before a combat-capable aircraft could be produced.

Below: An 11⅘-in (300-mm) fuselage stretch was required to accommodate the extra cockpit tandem two-seat cockpit canopy of the Su-7UM trainer.

With the Su-7BMK – shown here in prototype form – came a range of refinements which were also added to some earlier aircraft by retrofit.

The former was lost in a crash in November 1957, but the S-1 continued testing until December 1958, by which time it had been joined by the first two pre-production examples. Assembly of these first Su-7 aircraft, structurally identical to the S-2, had begun in 1957. A small number of Su-7s was completed and the first operational-standard aircraft were delivered to Soviet air force units in 1958. However, the appearance of the F-100C/D and the F-105 had resulted in the Soviet air force insisting in 1955 on creating a similar fighter-bomber type, based on the Su-7 tactical fighter. Carrying the factory designation S-22, the resulting Su-7B, capable of lifting a 4,409 lb (2000 kg) combat load in order to attack ground targets, first flew on 24 April 1959. The Su-7B was equipped with an uprated AL-7F-1-100 turbojet and improved KS-2 ejection seat.

Enhanced capabilities

The Su-7BM (S-22-2 in prototype form) was a longer-range version with wing fuel tank capacity increased, and provision for the carriage of underwing drop tanks. Series production began in 1962. Results of tests of the fourth S-22 with wheel and ski landing gear, brake 'chute container and SPRD-110 RATO gear provision resulted in the similarly equipped Su-7BKL (factory designation S-22KL), which replaced the Su-7BM on the production line from 1965. This variant also introduced a new AL-7F-1-250 engine with longer service life, and increased fuel capacity. Two additional underfuselage hardpoints were added to production aircraft from 1969. Meanwhile, the Su-7BMK (S-22MK) was produced in parallel with the Su-7BKL as a moderately downgraded version intended for export.

Several prototype Su-7 'Fitter' variants were not selected for production. The S-41 prototype fighter testbed incorporated experimental aerodynamic and structural improvements. As a result of S-41 experience, a lengthened nose and anti-surge doors were added to the production Su-7. Tested between 1959 and 1960, the S-23 carried experimental ski and combined wheel/ski landing gear for rough-field operations. Similar studies were continued by the RATO-equipped S-22-4 (informing development of the Su-7BKL), and the S-26 with pure ski landing gear.

The creation of a combat trainer version of the Su-7 was authorised in January 1961. However, it was not until the Su-7B and Su-7BM were in Soviet service that Sukhoi began development in earnest. The prototype U-22 first flew in October 1965, and after a second prototype had been flown the type was recommended for production.

Although based on the Su-7BM, the Su-7UM 'Moujik' incorporated the powerplant, brake 'chute and RATO capability of the Su-7BKL. Series production of the two-seat Su-7UM together with the Su-7UMK (U-22MK) export variant began in 1968.

Left: This Indian Su-7BMK demonstrates the wingroot installation of the NR-30 cannon, as well as the suction relief doors round the nose section (seen partly open on the aircraft in the foreground). Note also the position of the pitot boom, which was moved around to the '10 o'clock' position early on in the 'Fitter's' history.

Right: These Polish Su-7BM 'Fitter-As' appear to have been updated to Su-7BMK standard with the enlarged fairing – obscured here by the technicians who appear to be repacking the 'chutes – for the twin brake 'chutes of this variant. All single-seat Su-7s were designated 'Fitter-A' by ASCC/NATO, while the two-seat Su-7UM was known as 'Moujik'. Experimental Su-7s included the 100LDU testbed of 1968, derived from an Su-7UM, and used as a remotely piloted aircraft to investigate flight stability for the T-4 bomber.

Sukhoi Su-9/11

Following the restoration of the Sukhoi OKB in 1953, work was initiated on projects for both tactical fighters and interceptors.

The PVO's Su-9 'Fishpot-B' regiments were maintained on alert status along the northern border of the Soviet Union during the height of the Cold War. Production at Novosibirsk ran between 1957-62 and resulted in 888 aircraft being built. A further batch of 126 aircraft was completed at Moscow between 1959-61.

Development of the latter resulted in the T-3 (NATO/ASCC 'Fishpot-A') delta-winged supersonic interceptor, powered by a Lyul'ka AL-7F turbojet and equipped with an *Almaz* radar mounted above a supersonic nose air intake. The T-3 was the first of several prototypes intended to investigate the integration of supersonic intakes and radar. The T-3 carried an *Almaz* radar, with twin antennas – the ranging antenna was housed inside the intake, with the search scanner placed at the 12 o'clock position, within a conical radome. The second prototype was built around the Toropov K-7L or Grushin K-6V missiles systems, reflecting the intention that the T-3 would form the basis of a front-line interceptor. On 26 May 1956 the T-3 recorded its first flight – the aircraft later attained speeds of 1,305 mph (2100 km/h) and displayed a service ceiling of 59,055 ft (18000 m). Following the construction of further prototype aircraft, including the PT-7 with area-ruled fuselage and reconfigured twin conical radomes housing an improved *Almaz*-7 radar set, four PT-8 pre-production aircraft were built in autumn 1957, each with a circular nose intake compatible with a single large radar antenna in the centrebody, full combat avionics and dogtooth wing leading edge. Before production could begin in earnest, the problematic *Almaz* radar and K-7L and K-6V missiles (unsuccessful competitors to the K-8/R-8 series) were abandoned in June 1958.

Revised weaponry

Instead, a similar weapons fit comprising a basic RP-9U *Sapfir* radar and four RS-2US command-guided missiles was chosen for the production aircraft. In this form, the Su-9 ('Fishpot-B)' entered production immediately after the completion of a small batch of PT-8s. The aircraft was powered by a single AL-7F-100 turbojet, developing 21,164 lb (9600 kg) of thrust with afterburning. By 1962 a total of 1,014 aircraft had been built, together with 50 two-seat combat trainers. Experimental derivatives included the T-405 and T-431 for engine development and record-breaking, the Su-9UL for automatic and semi-automatic interception guidance and ground-level ejection testing, and the 100L of 1967, rebuilt with a new wing scaled from the projected Sukhoi T-4 Mach-3 strike aircraft. On their withdrawal between 1963-66, many examples were converted to become Su-9RM radio-controlled targets.

Above: Design of the Su-9U 'Maiden' two-seat operational trainer began in 1959. The aircraft was regarded as a combat trainer, and as such included a TsD-30T radar with twin displays, and a Lazur *automatic guidance system. Limited production was initiated in 1961.*

Above: The T-47 served as the prototype for the Su-11. An enlarged and lengthened nose section contained the new Oryol-D *radar. Flight tests began in July 1958.*

Right: Su-11 production began at Novosibirsk in 1961, immediately after the Su-9 was phased out of production. The Su-11 featured new onboard equipment including the Vozdukh-1 *automatic guidance system. The R-8 AAMs had considerably greater range and altitude compared to the Su-9's RS-2US (AA-1 'Alkali') weapons.*

An unarmed Su-9 departs for a training mission. During its service life the interceptor was steadily upgraded. Modifications to the 'Fishpot-A' included the addition of forward fuselage anti-surge doors, a more powerful AL-7F1-100 turbojet in place of the original AL-7F-1, further fuel carriage within the unused gun bays, nosewheel braking, a new integral fuel tank within a reworked central fuselage section, and improved KS-2 and KS-3 ejection seats.

Above: In 1959 the first Su-9 interceptors entered service with PVO combat units, initially replacing the MiG-17PF/PFM in the Moscow and Baku regions. On 1 May 1960, I. Mentyukov happened to be on a stop-over at an airbase at Sverdlov, while ferrying an early production Su-9 from Novosibirsk. Mentyukov scrambled his unarmed aircraft to intercept a U-2 reconnaissance aircraft. The invader, flown by Francis Gary Powers, evaded Mentyukov's aircraft but was ultimately shot down by a surface-to-air missile.

The principal drawback of the Su-9 was the limited performance of its weapons system, and this was addressed by the Su-11 with the *Uragan*-5B interception complex comprising the RP-11 *Oryol* radar (carried in the enlarged radome originally intended to house the *Almaz*) and R-8M (later R-98) 'Anab' missiles. The latter were carried in both infra-red and semi-active radar guided versions. The 22,266-lb (10100-kg) AL-7F-2 turbojet was the chosen powerplant, offering increased power, and overall fuel capacity was increased. Avionics improvements included the introduction of an AP-39 autopilot and *Sirena*-3 radar warning system. A maiden flight of the new aircraft was made on 6 January 1958, and interception systems tests were completed in June 1961. Commissioned in January 1962, the Su-11 was hampered by poor handling as a result of its heavy nose which disrupted its balance. The 'Fishpot-C' production run was halted after the completion of only 112 aircraft. But, the Su-11 remained a capable interceptor: its maxi-mum speed of 1,454 mph (2340 km/h) at 36,089 ft (11000 m) remained unrivalled in the USSR until the advent of the MiG-25 'Foxbat'.

In addition to its enlarged forward fuselage, two upper fuselage fairings, containing electrical wiring, distinguished the Su-11 from its forebearer, the Su-9. The Su-11 was recommended for service on account of its increased combat radius, high altitude capability and increased target detection and locking range.

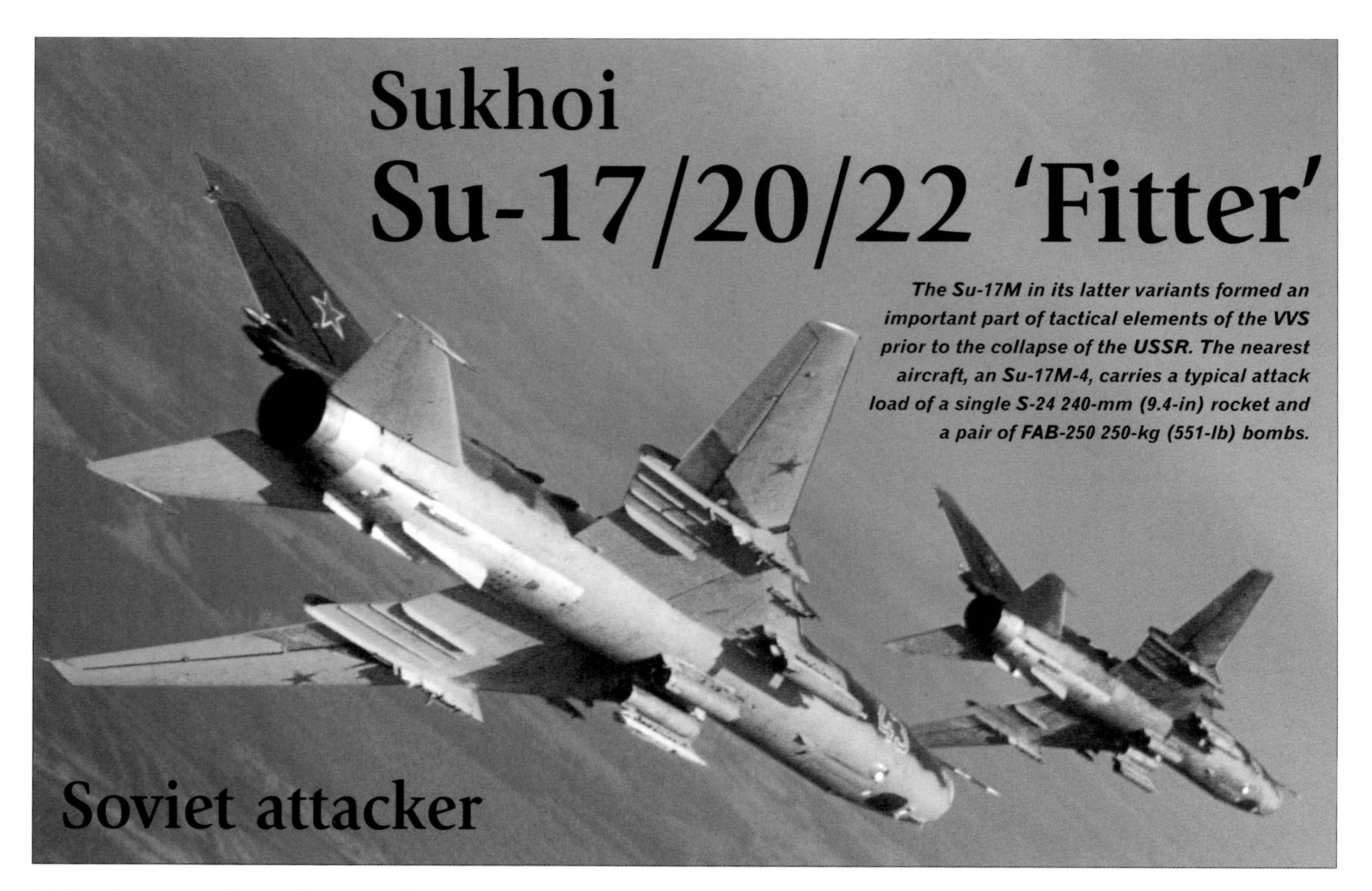

Sukhoi Su-17/20/22 'Fitter'

Soviet attacker

The Su-17M in its latter variants formed an important part of tactical elements of the VVS prior to the collapse of the USSR. The nearest aircraft, an Su-17M-4, carries a typical attack load of a single S-24 240-mm (9.4-in) rocket and a pair of FAB-250 250-kg (551-lb) bombs.

Maintaining much similarity with its Su-7 forebear, the combat-proven Su-17 'Fitter' is capable of carrying double the bombload, from an airstrip half as long as that of its predecessor. After over 30 years of service, it remains in the inventory of a number of air arms.

During the mid-1960s, following the introduction of the Su-7B into service, and with design work on the improved Su-7BKL and Su-7BMK variants underway, Sukhoi confronted the task of improving the take-off and landing performance of its fighter-bombers. The Su-7BKL had been equipped with RATO gear and braking parachutes, but more radical approaches were to be considered for future warplanes.

The S-22I experimental variable-geometry fighter-bomber was based on a Su-7BM airframe, but introduced variable sweep on the outer wing section alone, with the pivot outboard of the landing gear. This method minimised structural redesign, and reduced the effect of the shift in centre of aerodynamic pressure and centre of gravity created by the variable wing sweep. The S-22I, the Soviet Union's first variable geometry aircraft, made its first flight on 2 August 1966.

Su-17 into production

In comparison to the Su-7, the S-22I displayed greatly improved take-off and landing performance; meanwhile, range and endurance at low wing sweep angles were also improved, despite a reduction in fuel load, and an increase in weight over the Su-7BM. In November 1967, series production was approved.

The production version of the S-22I was known as the Su-17 (or S-32 to the Design Bureau). The Su-17 designation had been used previously for the Type 'R' swept-wing experimental fighter of 1949. Despite the new wing, the Su-17 maintained basic commonality with the Su-7BKL/BMK, incorporating the spine fairing of the Su-7U for additional equipment. Two additional stores pylons were added on the fixed wing section, making a total of six hardpoints. Hydraulic and fuel systems and electronic equipment and avionics fit was essentially duplicated from the Su-7BKL. Tactical capability was improved through the introduction of the Kh-23 (AS-7 'Kerry') ASM, and provision for up to four drop tanks. The wing-root NR-30 30-mm cannon of the Su-7B were retained. The maximum combat load of the initial Su-17 was 6,612 lb (3,000 kg).

The Su-17 represented a great advance in tactical capability over its predecessors, but weight increases on the production aircraft meant that in terms of performance, only the take-off and landing characteristics were actually improved over those of the Su-7BKL. Nevertheless, Su-17 series production began in 1969, initially in parallel with manufacture of the Su-7B, before the latter was phased out in 1971.

The first major series-produced version was the Su-17M, which introduced the AL-21F-3 powerplant, increased fuel capacity and improved equipment. The new-generation AL-21F-3 turbojet developed greater thrust, but had smaller dimensions, allowing for an increased fuel load. A new hydraulic system, and cruciform brake 'chute were added, together with a modernised bombsight. Additional underfuselage pylons increased the number of hardpoints to nine. The Su-17M was delivered to Far East elements of the Soviet air arm from 1972, and was also exported as the Su-20. Differing only minimally from the Su-17M (including the introduction of the R-3S/AA-2 'Atoll' AAM), the Su-20 served with the air forces of Poland, Egypt, Syria and Iraq.

The Su-17M was followed in 1975 by the Su-17M-2, with improved ordnance delivery systems. The key to the Su-17M-2's advance in capability was the *Fon* laser rangefinder,

***Right:** The Su-17M of 1971 was the first quantity-produced Su-17 version. This example is armed with 80-mm B-8M1 and 57-mm UB-32M/57 rockets pods, and UPK-23/250 23-mm cannon pods.*

***Below:** The Su-17UM, represented here in prototype form, was the first of the 'Fitter' family to introduce the characteristic revised cockpit and forward fuselage profile, improving the pilot's view.*

combined with an optical sight, combination bomb/gunsight and integrated navigation system. The latter could automatically fly the aircraft to a predetermined target. The characteristic feature of the Su-17M-2 and its Su-22 export equivalent, however, was the Doppler fairing under the nose. The Su-17M-2 could carry Kh-25 (AS-10 'Karen') and Kh-29L (AS-14 'Kedge') ASMs, as well as R-60 (AA-8 'Aphid') AAMs. Surprisingly, the export relative of the Su-17M-2, the Su-22, was equipped with the R-29B-300 engine of the MiG-23BN/MiG-27 series, within an increased-width rear fuselage. The Su-22, lacking the advanced weapons introduced on the Soviets' Su-17M-2, was delivered to Angola, Libya and Peru, all of which took it into combat.

Sukhoi next addressed the cockpit layout of the Su-17 family, in order to provide the pilot with an improved view. A redesign was necessary and this first appeared on the Su-17UM tandem two-seat trainer, which featured an all-new forward fuselage angled down by six degrees and an enlarged dorsal fairing. Although single- and two-seat aircraft were requested in 1974, the two-seat Su-17UM was afforded higher priority, and first flew in 1975.

Slovakia's Su-22M-4R fleet was tasked with tactical reconnaissance duties, for which the aircraft mounted the KKR combined IR/photographic/TV pod. The aircraft were formerly operated by 47 PZLP, the Czechoslovakian tactical reconnaissance regiment.

A radical redesign

In concert with the Su-17UM, Sukhoi developed the Su-17M-3 fighter-bomber. The first new-generation single-seater, the Su-17M-3 retained the redesigned forward fuselage design of the Su-17UM, with the instructor's position replaced with an additional fuel tank. Two additional underwing hardpoints, for carriage of the R-60 AAM, were added, and the *Klyen*-PS laser station replaced the earlier *Fon*. Series production of the Su-17UM and Su-17M-3 began in 1975/76, both incorporating increased vertical tail area to combat low speed instability.

Export versions of the Su-17UM and Su-17M-3 were designated Su-22M and Su-22U, respectively, both powered by the R-29 turbojet. The down-graded Su-22M was followed by the Su-22M-3 from 1982, with the complete equipment package of the Su-17M-3.

In order to unify training, the Su-17UM with its reduced combat load was superseded by the Su-17UM-3, with the sight and other equipment of the Su-17M-3. Production began in 1978, and ultimately all Su-17UMs were brought up to definitive UM-3 standard. The Su-17UM-3 was in turn exported as the Su-22UM-3. A few of these were delivered with R-29 engines, before export versions were fitted with the AL-21F-3 as standard from 1983.

The final production version of the Su-17 was the definitive Su-17M-4 (completed for export as the Su-22M-4). Entering production in 1980, this variant is distinguished by its dorsal fairing air intake. However, the major advance over earlier models is the introduction of an integrated navigation and sight system, incorporating a computer, laser rangefinder, new navigation and sighting equipment, illumination radar and TV display.

***Below:** Angola's Su-22s (export versions of the undernose Doppler-equipped Su-17M-2) saw some operational use. Examples were based at Menongue during the main 1986 offensive against UNITA.*

Variants

Su-7IG (S-22I)

The S-22I was an experimental variable-geometry derivative of the Su-7BM, incorporating minimum structural change. The wing pivot was located aft of the landing gear, creating a movable outer wing section with leading edge sweep varying from 30° to 63°. The single prototype was first flown by V. I. Ilyushin on 2 August 1966. On 9 July 1967, the S-22I was flown by I. K. Kukushev at the Domodedovo air display. After the addition of the new variable-sweep, high-lift wing, empty weight was increased to 20,900 lb (9480 kg), compared to 18,447 lb (8370 kg) for the Su-7BM.

Su-17 (S-32) 'Fitter-B Mod'

Known to the Sukhoi Design Bureau as the S-32, the pre-series aircraft received the customer designation Su-17. The production go-ahead for the aircraft, which served with a single evaluation regiment, was given in 1967, and production began in 1969. The Su-17 had a spine fairing similar to that of the Su-7U, and two prominent cable ducts on the side of the fuselage, inherited from the Su-7BKL/BMK. Two additional pylons were added to the fixed wing section to complete a total of six. The strengthened main landing gear could be fitted with skis for operations from snow-covered airstrips. Compared to the Su-7BKL, the weight of the Su-17 was increased by around 2,204 lb (1000 kg). The Su-17 cockpit was updated with a K-36 ejection seat.

Su-17M (S-32M) 'Fitter-C' and Su-20 (S-32MK) 'Fitter-C'

The first series production aircraft was the Su-17M which flew in 1971, and which introduced the new-generation AL-21F-3 engine in place of the Su-17's AL-7F-1. The Su-17M (an example is pictured at the Irkutsk test facility) carried additional fuel, and the cable ducts were removed. The height of the tail fin was increased, and the forward fuselage lengthened by 8 in (0.23 m). A new cylindrical rear fuselage section was added in conjunction with the smaller AL-21F-3 powerplant, a rear-view mirror was added to the canopy, and a single cruciform brake chute was added. The total number of pylons was increased to nine, with forward fuselage and outboard wing pylons capable of carrying drop tanks. The export version of the Su-17M was the Su-20, first flown in 1972, and delivered to Poland, Egypt, Syria and Iraq.

Su-17R and Su-20R 'Fitter-C'/Recce conversions

The Su-17R and its Su-20R export equivalent featured few internal changes, but incorporated wiring and plumbing for a choice of three Sukhoi-designed KKR multi-sensor reconnaissance pods on the centreline. One pod carried forward radar and Elint receivers; one a forward camera, SLAR and Elint modules; and one carried four cameras, IRLS and a photoflash cartridge battery. Pictured (right) is a Polish Su-20R of 7 PLB-R (Air Bomber-Reconnaissance Regiment) seen at Powidz in 1991. Examples of the Su-22 have also been modified to carry KKR recce packages under the designation Su-22R. More recent tactical reconnaissance versions are the Su-17M-3R (S-52R) and Su-17M-4R (S-54R). These were exported as the Su-22M-3R and Su-22M-4R respectively. While the Su-17M-3R was modified to carry the centreline KKR pod during production, the Su-17M-4R was so equipped from the beginning of its production run.

Su-17M-2 (S-32M2) 'Fitter-D' & Su-22 (S-32M2K) 'Fitter-F'

First flown in 1973, the Su-17M-2 (a former Soviet example from the Tambov Pilot School pictured below right) was developed in order to improve ordnance delivery with the introduction of the *Fon* laser rangefinder and other equipment, including a distinctive undernose Doppler fairing. Series production took place from 1975 to 1977, and the export version was the Su-22 (Peruvian examples from Escuadron de Caza 11 'Los Tigres' pictured below left) with R-29BS-300 engine. The Su-22, also delivered to Angola and Libya, was produced between 1976 and 1980, with a downgraded avionics fit.

Su-17UM (S-52U) 'Fitter-E' & Su-22U (S-52UK) 'Fitter-G'

Introducing a redesigned forward fuselage and cockpit in order to improve pilot view, the Su-17UM two-seat combat trainer was the first of the 'second generation' Su-17s. The Su-17UM (and its Su-22U export equivalent with R-29BS-300 engine) also introduced a new, larger, dorsal fairing, and both were produced between 1976 and 1981. The 'hump-back' fuselage was inherited by the Su-17M-3.

Su-17UM-3 (S-52UM3) 'Fitter-G' and Su-22UM-3 (S-52UM3K) 'Fitter-G'

The Su-17UM-3 unified Soviet pilot training by bringing the basic Su-17UM combat trainer to Su-17M-3 standard (a Soviet example is pictured above, with the instructor's periscope deployed). The Su-17UM-3 was produced from 1978, with the equipment of the Su-17M-3. Su-17UMs were eventually upgraded to Su-17UM-3 standard during 1979/80. The export version of the Su-17UM-3 was the Su-22UM-3. Powered by the R-29BS-300. Production of the Su-22UM-3 began in 1982. From 1983, however, all export versions were fitted with AL-21F-3 turbojets, resulting in the Su-22UM-3K (a Polish example of which is pictured above, with rear fuselage ECM dispensers).

Su-17M-4 (S-54) 'Fitter-K' and Su-22M-4 (S-54K) 'Fitter-K'

The definitive single-seat 'Fitter' was the Su-17M-4, and its Su-22M-4 export equivalent (pictured right in East German service). The 'Fitter-K' carries an integrated navigation and weapons system, reducing pilot workload, and enhancing tactical capability. This system includes a sighting system consisting of a computer, laser rangefinder, radar and TV display. While improving the capabilities of the new variant, the system also causes some reduction in fuel capacity, since the new avionics occupy space behind the cockpit that was previously used for fuel. The M-4 can be differentiated from the M-3 by virtue of a new air intake in the dorsal fairing. Su-17M-4 production began in 1980, and the aircraft (together with Su-17UM-3s) were upgraded in 1987 following Soviet experience in Afghanistan. Both the Su-17M-4 and Su-22M-4 (series production of which began in 1984) are powered by the AL-21F-3.

Su-17M-3 (S-52) 'Fitter-H' & Su-22M (S-52K) 'Fitter-J'

The Su-17M-3 was developed in conjunction, and built in parallel with, the Su-17UM to fulfil a government requirement (a Soviet example is pictured below left, with an S-25 heavyweight rocket underwing) for a new fighter-bomber version. The forward cockpit structure was inherited from the Su-17UM, with the instructor's position now used to house additional fuel. Two additional pylons for R-60 self-defence AAMs were added underwing, and the weapons system was updated with the *Klyen*-PS laser targeting system. The export version was the R-29BS-300-powered Su-22M (built 1979–81), a Libyan example of which is pictured (below), armed with R-3S AAMs, as intercepted by a US Navy aircraft over the Mediterranean in 1981.

This Su-17M-4 was operated by the 20 Aviatsionnaya Polk Istrebeitelei-Bombardirovchikov (20th Fighter-Bomber Regiment), based at Gross-Dölln (Templin) in the former East Germany. '27 Yellow' is armed with UB-32-57 57-mm (2.24-in) rocket pods and R-60 self-defence missiles underwing, with Kh-25MP (AS-12 'Kegler') anti-radiation missiles under the fuselage.

Only a handful of Su-24s were built for export, with the bulk of production going to the Soviets. When the Soviet Union disintegrated in the early 1990s, the fleet was largely divided between Russia and the Ukraine. The Ukrainian fleet received the majority of the Su-24MP 'Fencer-F' electronic warfare platforms.

Sukhoi Su-24 'Fencer'

Sukhoi's 'suitcase'

Designed to offer the Soviet Union the same capabilities the US enjoyed with the F-111, the Su-24 offers brute force coupled with a wide-ranging payload. Even after 30 years of service, the 'Fencer' is still a vital aspect of the Russian air force.

In the 1950s the tactical arm of the Soviet air force, the FA (*Frontovaya Aviahtsiya*, or Frontal Aviation), took delivery of its first Sukhoi Su-7B 'Fitter-A' fighter-bombers. No replacement was forthcoming for the elderly Il-28 bombers until the arrival of the Yak-28 'Brewer' early in the next decade. The Yak-28 proved disappointing because it suffered from a short range, a small warload, and severe restrictions in the firing of its guns and in the accurate delivery of its bombs.

By the mid-1960s, two important factors had become evident. The first was the superiority of equivalent USAF designs, such as the F-111. These aircraft could outperform any current Soviet type, carry a wider range of weapons and they possessed outstandingly superior avionics.

The second factor made it imperative to challenge the rapid developments in surface-to-air missile capability: active radar-homing missiles were now capable of destroying any aircraft at the altitudes at which Soviet aircraft could currently attack. Ways had to be found of flying safely at supersonic speed underneath the radar screen and of locating and destroying the target from this altitude.

Long-range bomber

To meet this challenge, Sukhoi began work on a new aircraft. Sukhoi had already started work on the Su-17 but decided to press ahead on a longer range interdiction bomber. Their goal was to emulate the performance of the F-111, but the concept of a variable-geometry aircraft was initially disregarded in favour of a fixed swept wing aircraft. The resultant S6 had a two-man tandem cockpit with side-by-side engines. Tests soon proved that the S6 was inadequate for the task it was designed to do and it was scrapped. A new design called the T6 was started, which had a double-delta wing, similar to that of the Su-15TM, side-by-side seating and two Tumanskii R-27F2-300 turbojets. But during testing, the air force modified their demands for the new aircraft and the current configuration for the T6-1 proved inefficient. Once again, attention turned to the variable-geometry concept. The wings were added to the old fuselage and the new aircraft was designated T6-2I. First flight was achieved on 17 January 1970.

From above the T6-1 clearly displays its aerodynamic origins in the Su-15TM 'Flagon'. Buried in the fuselage were four RD36-35 lift engines, fed with air via intakes in the upper fuselage. Barely visible are the doors that opened to act as intakes for the vertical engines.

Armament was carried on six hardpoints with the exception of an internal GSh-6-23 cannon beneath the fuselage side.

Test flying of the T6-2I continued from 1970 to 1976; it performed about 300 flights during this time. At first the T6-2I was used for performance and stability tests, in particular for examining controllability at different wing sweep angles. Later, the automatic flight controls, essential to reduce pilot fatigue on high-speed operations

Su-24s based in Europe, such as these 'Fencer-Bs' (background) and 'Fencer-Cs' (foreground) at Osla in Poland, represented the powerhouse of the Soviet forces in Europe.

of long duration, were put through a rigorous test programme by flying sorties at very low altitude.

At the end of 1970 the T6-2I was joined in the performance test programme by the second variable-sweep prototype: aircraft T6-3I. Ninety flights were undertaken on this aircraft in 1971, which together with the test flights of the T6-2I, imposed a heavy schedule that year for the test team. The T6-3I also completed its test programme in 1976, the final year being predominantly occupied by determining its ability to take off and land from a large variety of unpaved runways. Like the T6-2I, it made about 300 flights.

Test pilot Vladimir Ilyushin conducted the first flight of the T6-3I and the third swing-wing prototype: the T6-4I on 16 June 1971. Unfortunately, the T6-4I crashed in 1973 after completing only 120 test flights.

'Brewer' replacement

Confident in the design, and undoubtedly influenced by the T6-2I's vastly superior capabilities when compared with the Yak-28s in service, the Soviet air force did not wait for the test programme to be completed before ordering the T6-2I into production as the Su-24. Preparations for series production of the Su-24 had begun at Novosibirsk. In December 1971 the first production aircraft – the seventh swing-wing airframe – was taken for its maiden flight by factory test pilot Vladimir Vylomov. The aircraft was assigned the construction number 0115301: Batch 01 built by factory No. 153.

The Su-24 was constantly modified during early production, as lessons learnt by the hastily deployed service units were relayed back to the OKB (*Opytno Konstruktorskoye Byuro*), or design bureau. Many were retrofitted with later features. Pressure from the VVS to increase range was responded to at the beginning of the eighth production batch when the capacity of the number one tank was increased to 220 Imp gal (1000 litres). From the 15th batch of aircraft the rear fuselage was redesigned to reduce drag.

Into service

When news of the introduction of the Sukhoi Su-24 into VVS service was given by Admiral Moorer, USN, in 1974, very little was known about it in the West; even the designation, quoted as 'Su-19', was incorrect and this error was not rectified until 1981. On entering service with Frontal Aviation regiments that had previously operated such types as the Yak-28 and MiG-27, the Su-24 proved to be much more demanding in maintenance and service. Considering the complexity of its systems, this was hardly surprising.
Extra headaches were caused by the fact that this was the VVS's first experience with systems controlled by an onboard computer.

Alternatively, one cause for satisfaction was the aircraft's ability to withstand bird strikes; a collision with a large eagle and another with 17 sparrows resulted in no serious damage – at least not to the aircraft. Despite these difficulties, and no doubt remembering the idiosyncrasies of their previous mounts, the air crews liked the Su-24 and it was they who christened it *Chemodahn* (suitcase), a reference to the slab-sided shape of its fuselage. They appreciated the good field of view, the well-planned cockpit and even the automatic flight systems, especially on low-level operations. Flight handling was reasonably easy, even though the Su-24 could be less forgiving in certain circumstances.

Although most Su-24s were supplied to the VVS, a regiment was transferred in 1989 to the AVMF (Naval Aviation), to support the Baltic Fleet. The 4 GvOMShAP is still operational with the Su-24M, for which training is undertaken by the 240 GvIISAP, at Ostrov.

'Fencer' matures

Lacking any defensive weaponry other than R-60 AAMs, the Su-24MR is a highly effective reconnaissance aircraft. Its varied surveillance systems are datalinked to ground stations, ensuring the speedy transferral of information.

Deficiencies in the early 'Fencers' led to the advanced Su-24M, with increased weapons capability. From this variant came specialised reconnaissance and electronic warfare versions that, almost 30 years later, still play an integral role in Russian air force operations.

Production of the Su-24 proceeded at Novosibirsk, with improvements constantly being incorporated. Recognition of the individual production batches is complicated by many of the modifications being retrofitted to aircraft built previously. None of these alterations resulted in a new designation and it was not until 1978 that sufficient changes took place on the production lines to justify the change to Su-24M (signifying 'modified').

Major changes were made to the avionics, the most fundamental being the installation of a new weapons control system now known as the *Tigr*-NS. To accommodate the updated equipment the forward fuselage was extended by 29.9 in (76 cm), while still retaining the nose radome.

Less obvious, but equally innovative, was the replacement of the electro-optical sighting system by the *Kayra*-24M day/night low-light-level TV system/laser designator. This device enabled the aircraft to carry laser- and TV-guided missiles such as the Kh-25ML, Kh-29L and Kh-29T, dispensing with the previously necessary external designator pod.

Not only were better weapons now an option, but also the number that could be carried was increased by the addition of a ninth hardpoint. These amendments offered the Su-24M numerous extra selections from a formidable array of weaponry. A new defence system known as *Karpaty* was introduced, with the small hemispherical *Mak* infra-red sensor situated amidships on the fuselage roof. Combat capability was greatly improved by the addition to all Su-24Ms of an inflight refuelling system.

Export Su-24MK

For many years Su-24s were manufactured exclusively for the Soviet air force, but in the mid-1980s permission was granted to export them to Arab states. In the late 1980s Sukhoi designed a version of the Su-24M for the newly opened and potentially lucrative export market. It was a specially modified version designated Su-24MK (*kommercheskiy* meaning 'commercial', i.e., export version). There were very few differences between the Su-24M and the Su-24MK and those differences were mainly in the avionics, particularly the IFF equipment and weapons options; for example, the Su-24MK could carry more bombs – 38 FAB-100s compared with 34 on the Su-24M, and four rather than two air-to-air missiles. A different computer, designated TsVM-24, was also installed. Any country now prepared to purchase this type could, no doubt, have its particular requirements met.

For Soviet units operating the 'Fencer', the new mount proved vastly more demanding than their previous MiG-27s and Yak-28s. There were initial teething problems with the avionics and new systems but despite these difficulties, the air crews liked the Su-24.

A Ukrainian 'Fencer' crew boards its Su-24M for a training sortie. The aircraft's sturdy undercarriage was designed for use on various unprepared surfaces but, in practice, the Su-24 has operated almost exclusively from hard runways.

The Ukrainian air force inherited around 180 'Fencers' arranged in two divisions. The 32nd BAD had 'Fencer-B/Cs' while the 289th BAD had Su-24M 'Fencer-Ds' (illustrated). Both units also had a small number of recce Su-24MRs assigned.

Export sales of the Su-24MK were made to Iraq (24 aircraft), Libya (15), Syria (12), Iran (nine) and Algeria (10).

Reconnaissance variant

By the mid-1970s it had become clear that existing reconnaissance aircraft in the VVS were inadequate. Aircraft suffered from limited range and outdated equipment. Sukhoi modified two airframes, T6M-26 and T6M-34, to become T6MR-26 and T6MR-34 (R for reconnaissance) respectively. The variant was known as Su-24MR to the VVS, and the first flight took place in September 1980.

Most of the ground-attack equipment was removed from the Su-24MR, but the basic structure and layout remained unchanged. A smaller nose radome was complemented by a large SLAR panel and two smaller dielectric panels. These covered reconnaissance equipment and were located on each side of the nose. Three underfuselage hardpoints were removed and the built-in cannon omitted.

In addition, a comprehensive reconnaissance suite, known as BKR-1 *Shtyk*, was developed. It afforded both visual and electronic reconnaissance by day or by night and could function efficiently in all weather conditions. Its constituent parts were a thermal imaging unit, a television camera and a panoramic camera which had a lens of 3.6-in (90.5-mm) diameter. It had a *Shtyk* MR-1 synthetic aperture SLAR, radiation monitor, radio-monitoring pod and a laser pod. The laser scanned an area four times the height of the aircraft and gave an image of almost photographic quality.

Defence suppression

Design work on the Su-24MP electronic countermeasures (ECM) aircraft began in 1976. Construction of these prototypes entailed the modification of two Su-24M airframes, the T6M-25 and the T6M-35, which were then redesignated T6MP-25 and T6MP-35 respectively; the P indicating that it was an ECM platform. The first flight of the Su-24MP took place in December 1979.

Very little technical information relating to this variant has been released, but it is known to have a sophisticated and extensive network of systems for detecting, locating, analysing, identifying, classifying, storing and, if required, jamming all known electromagnetic emissions. Up to four R-60 or R-60M air-to-air missiles can be carried, but no air-to-ground missiles. The internal cannon is retained. It has been stated that only about 20 of this variant were built and their mission is electronic reconnaissance, intelligence-gathering and performing the invaluable service of escorting attack aircraft to their targets and neutralising hostile radars.

The 'Fencer' made its operational debut in 1984 during the Afghan war. Its precision bombing capability and superior weapons load made it a valuable addition to the Soviet forces in-theatre.

It is now more than 30 years since the first 'Fencer' entered Soviet service. Despite many improvements, the basic aircraft does not incorporate much in the way of modern developments and lacks any 'stealthy' aspects. As a result, Russia is pursuing an upgrade of the Su-24 in order to preserve its still formidable capability in the coming years, and pending the arrival in numbers of the Su-34.

Above: Russian sources state that nine Su-24MKs were delivered to Iran following the acquisition of 24 ex-Iraqi aircraft during the 1991 Gulf War. By contrast, Iranian sources state that 14 were bought from Russia before 16 to 18 ex-Iraqi aircraft were acquired.

Left: Of note in this view of an Su-24M in maximum sweep configuration is the small hemispherical* Mak *missile approach warning sensor mounted on the spine behind the cockpit, and the retractable refuelling probe ahead of the windscreen.

Sukhoi Su-25 'Frogfoot'

***Above:** Far removed from its single-seat attack cousin, the Su-25UTG was intended to train Soviet pilots in basic carrier operations and as such is fully equipped for carrier operations.*

Red Army supporter

Built in relatively small numbers, and equipping only a handful of Frontal Aviation regiments, the Su-25 is an effective and popular close air support aircraft, which saw extensive action in Afghanistan. In recent years a host of new variants has emerged, although few have entered large-scale production.

In the early 1960s, project discussions on the need for a new Soviet ground-attack aircraft were held. The reasons behind these talks were the emergence of new data from southeast Asia and other localised conflicts, the Warsaw Pact Dniepr '67 exercise, analyses of the new USAF A-X attack aircraft project (resulting in the development of the A-10 Thunderbolt II), and the requirement for better damage resistance and survivability.

General I. P. Pavlovskiy, Commander of Army, was the leading person in these discussions, and he managed to persuade the highest authorities about the necessity for new ground-attack aircraft. The Ministry of Air Industry issued the official proposals in March 1969 and four construction bureaux – Mikoyan, Yakovlev, Ilyushin and Sukhoi OKB – took part in the competition.

Unorthodox proposal

The latter submitted its T8 project as a private venture by a group of designers. Its design did not comply with the thinking of the period, which had produced aircraft such as the MiG-23/27 'Flogger'. However, the design proved successful enough to win the competition, although continued development of the T8 would be needed before the aircraft could enter front-line units.

As it catches the wire aboard the carrier Admiral Kuznetsov, *one of the small fleet of Su-25UTGs is brought to a halt. Following the collapse of the USSR, five examples were given to the Ukraine.*

Sukhoi was keen to test its new aircraft under combat conditions and two T8 prototypes took part in Operation Romb-1, which involved gun and weapon trials in Afghanistan in April/March 1980. The state acceptance trials were finished by another member of the early T8 prototype batch. With final trials protocol coming to an end, recommendation to put the new aircraft into production – under the designation of Su-25 – was agreed in March 1981. The new aircraft had been initially detected in the West by a US satellite in 1977, whereupon it was designated 'Frogfoot'.

Many in the West were puzzled that Sukhoi had adopted a thirsty turbojet instead of an economical turbofan, but designers argued

Repainted and fully restored, one of the early developmental T8s is seen at a Russian air base. Clearly illustrated are the more slender nose profile and smaller intakes of the early models. During development, at least two T8s were lost.

that the higher thrust available with the Tumanskii R-95s offered better agility at lower altitudes. Coupled with this was the fact that the project had begun as a private venture and the development of an entirely new powerplant would have resulted in a huge increase in the cost of the programme.

The achievement of economy and simplicity in the design was the first major goal, and so systems from existing aircraft were utilised wherever possible. Manoeuvrability was the second goal, the third being that the aircraft should be able to operate fully laden from semi-prepared airstrips close to the front line where maintenance facilities would be limited. Finally, the 'Frogfoot' had to be able to survive battle damage. To this end, the pilot sat in a 1-in (2.5-cm) thick titanium bathtub, shielded by armoured glass. Vital systems in the aircraft were protected by armour and the fuel tanks were filled with reticulated foam and surrounded by inert gas to minimise the chance of explosions.

Su-25s quickly began rolling off the production line at Tbilisi, and the VVS wasted no time in sending the vastly improved and more capable aircraft into the skies over Afghanistan again, eventually equipping the 200th Guards Independent Fighter Bomber Regiment at Bagram. Twenty-three Su-25s were lost to enemy action during the war, one falling to a Pakistani F-16. Despite the losses, the 'Frogfoot' achieved a highly respectable combat record, although many were to return to their bases with considerable damaged inflicted by shoulder-launched SAMs.

Equipped with a revised canopy and 'hump-back', 'Blue 09' was the second Su-25T developed to improve the ground-attack capability of the 'Frogfoot'.

Post-war service

The Su-25 has enjoyed some export success, the first customer being Czechoslovakia in 1984 which received 36 examples. Bulgaria followed in 1985 with an order for 36. The first non-Warsaw Pact operator was Iraq, which obtained 30, although some sources quote 45 examples. These were active during the Gulf War, but their performance was less than impressive, with 30 examples being shot down or destroyed in their hangars by Coalition forces. The first African user was Angola, with 14 examples being delivered between 1988 and 1989; these saw extensive action in the numerous bush-wars to plague this continent.

The two-seat Su-25UB 'Frogfoots' retain the full combat capability of the single-seat Su-25. The Ukraine inherited around 60 Su-25s on the collapse of the USSR, including five navalised two-seat examples which served with the 299th ShAP naval unit at Saki.

Following the introduction of the single-seat Su-25 'Frogfoot-A' and its tandem two-seat operational trainer derivative, Su-25UB 'Frogfoot-B', Sukhoi has proposed a number of variations of these baseline models. Following the development of the Russian aircraft-carrier programme, Sukhoi developed the Su-25UTG. This utilises the two-seat fuselage of the trainer variant and is equipped with arrester gear.

By far the most capable variant yet developed utilising the Su-25 airframe is the Su-25T, which makes use of the two-seat fuselage, but is fitted for single-pilot configuration only. The rear space is used for extra avionics, the nose of the aircraft houses improved Shkval avionics, and a larger fuselage-mounted cannon is installed.

The greatest improvement is seen in the cockpit, which is equipped with MFDs; the Su-25T is thus able to deliver the latest air-to-ground weapons. A further improvement of this variant is the Su-25TM (Su-39), of which eight were delivered for state acceptance trials, before Russia elected in 1999 to adopt the Su-25SM, a more modest upgrade of existing aircraft using some Su-25TM avionics. The two-seat equivalent of the Su-25SM upgrade is known as the Su-25UBM.

Below: In response to the NATO/ASCC designation of 'Frogfoot', a single Czech Su-25K received a highly elaborate colour scheme for performances at Western air shows. Painted on the tail was the design of a large frog crushing a tank with a mallet.

Development

Above: Among the latest developments of the 'Frogfoot' is the Su-25TM (Su-39). Utilising the two-seat fuselage of the Su-25UB, the TM dispenses with the rear seat to allow for the accommodation of extra avionics to undertake missions in all weathers. Though far more capable than the Su-25 'Frogfoot-A', only a handful of TMs have entered service, with focus now on upgrade of existing airframes.

Left: In the search for a suitable ground-attack aircraft, both Sukhoi and Ilyushin submitted design studies. Sukhoi's winning design adopted a highly conventional layout, with the engines widely separated so that no single AAA hit could disable both.

The Sukhoi Su-25 'Frogfoot' utilises proven systems incorporated into a heavily armoured airframe. Originally developed purely as a battlefield day-attack aircraft, the latest variants of the Su-25 are able to undertake missions in all weathers, 24 hours a day.

The development of the 'Frogfoot' can be traced back to the late 1960s. Having observed with great interest the progress of the USAF's AX programme, which resulted in the development of the A-10 Thunderbolt II, the USSR reviewed its own existing fighter-bombers. To everyone's surprise, the elderly MiG-17s and MiG-15s proved to be more effective than the faster, but less agile, MiG-21s and Su-7s. In addition, during the Six-Day War the devastating effectiveness of 30-mm cannon-equipped Israeli fighters (including obsolete Ouragans and Mystères) against ground targets (including tanks) prompted General I. P. Pavlovskii, commander of the Red Army, to call for the development of a new ground-attack aircraft.

Sukhoi's 'Shturmovik' was designed by a group of senior personnel, including Oleg Samolovich, D. N. Gorbachev, Y. V. Ivashetchkin, V. M. Lebedyev and A. Monachev, who based the design on a configuration produced by I. V. Savchenko, commander of the air force academy. The aircraft design, known as the SPB project, was designed around a pair of 3,865-lb st (17.2-kN) Ivchenko/Lotarev AI-25T engines. It was estimated that the machine would have a maximum speed of between 310 mph and 500 mph (500 and 800 km/h) and a range of 465 miles (750 km). Sukhoi stressed the key words of 'closer, lower and quieter', rather than the contemporary VVS slogan of 'higher, faster, further'. The programme goals were the design of an aircraft with high battle damage resistance and tolerance, which would be simple and economic to produce, operate and maintain, which would have unmatched performance and agility at very low level and which could operate fully laden from a semi-prepared 390-ft (120-m) airstrip.

Official request

Officialdom caught up with the Sukhoi bureau in March 1969, when an official request for the 'Shturmovik' aircraft was launched. Mikhail Simonov was appointed head of the design team, with the Sukhoi design now known as the T8.

The T8 mock-up was presented to the authorities at Khodinka, near Moscow. Although an official order for the prototype had not been placed, two prototypes (T8-1 and T8-2) were, in fact, already under construction, Sukhoi having authorised commencement of the work on 6 June 1972. The official order for the two prototypes (plus T8-0, a static test airframe) was finally issued on 6 May 1974. T8-1 undertook its first high-speed taxi trials on 25 December 1975. However, two days before the maiden flight (planned for 22 February 1975), one of the RD-9 powerplants suffered turbine failure, causing major damage. This, allied with many other problems, resulted in the decision to rebuild the entire aircraft and, after a two-year lay-up, the revised design was revealed on 26 April 1978. Designated as the T8-D, this aircraft was the first prototype to resemble the final Su-25, with long-span wings and a taller tailfin.

Prior to this, in March 1976, the aircraft had been re-engined with R95Sh engines to become the T8-2D. The navigation and attack suite of the Su-17M-2 had been replaced with that of the Su-17M-3. This equipment was subsequently fitted to the T8-3 and the following developmental models, which numbered 15,

Above: Apart from the pylons furthest outboard, all of the underwing hardpoints fitted to the Su-25 are of the heavy-duty universal type. The centre pylons on each side are wired to allow the carriage of ECM jammer pods. Adaptor rails allow for the fitting of air-to-air missiles, primarily the R-60/R-60M family.

Positioned between each powerplant is a welded titanium keel. This serves to protect the opposite engine from fire damage in the event of the other being hit.

including two-seat variants.

During the aircraft's development, at least two T8s undertook combat testing in Afghanistan, where the aircraft acquired a highly distinguished combat record.

The first production Su-25 rolled off the production line at Tbilisi, Georgia, in April 1981. Despite the Su-25's tremendous weapons and operational capability, export success was not forthcoming, with relatively few Warsaw Pact nations acquiring the aircraft. However, the Russian air force has been impressed with the Su-25's capability and has decided to upgrade the 'Frogfoot'.

Su-25 'Frogfoot'

This 'Frogfoot', 'Red 29', was one of those based at Bagram, Afghanistan during the late 1980s (it is seen here in the markings it wore in 1988). It was during this period that Soviet operations in Afghanistan were at their peak, a fact reflected by the number of incursions made by VVS combat aircraft over the Pakistani border.

Warload
This aircraft is seen carrying a load of four FAB-250-270 250-kg (551-lb) bombs and four UV-32M rocket pods. FAB (*fugasnaya avia bomba*, aerial demolition bomb)-series bombs have been in production since the 1950s and are unsophisticated high-drag weapons, filled with high explosive. The Su-25 can carry a maximum load of eight FAB-250s – the outermost pylons on each wing are not stressed to carry the weight of bombs, and are often fitted with rockets.

Grach
It was in Afghanistan that the *grach* (rook) marking, which has become synonymous with the Su-25 in Soviet (and Russian) service, first appeared. The origins of the cartoon bird are unclear, but the marking soon appeared as nose-art on virtually all the aircraft that served in Afghanistan.

Wingtip airbrakes
Early-production Su-25s had a straightforward two-section, clamshell airbrake. It was subsequently modified and two smaller 'petals' added, resulting in an enlarged four-section, staggered articulated airbrake.

Undercarriage
The nose gear of the Su-25 is offset to port, and fitted with a mudguard to reduce the risk of debris ingestion to the engines. The main undercarriage uses levered suspension legs, an oleo-pneumatic shock absorber and low-pressure tyres to enhance rough-field performance.

Armoured cockpit
The Su-25 pilot sits on a K-36L ejection seat, surrounded by 0.94 in (24 mm) of welded titanium, under an armoured canopy which opens to starboard. Above the canopy is a small mirror to compensate for the pronounced lack of rearward visibility. The canopy transparency is curved, apart from the reinforced (flat) front panel.

Brake 'chute
All Su-25s (except the naval Su-25UTG) have a pair of brake 'chutes housed in the extended tail fairing, hidden behind a neat 'flip-up' cover. The 'chutes themselves are of the cruciform PTK-25 type, each with an area of 270 sq ft (25 m²), and are deployed on landing, using springs and smaller drogue 'chutes.

Su-27 'Flanker'
Sukhoi's superfighter

Above: The Su-27M (Su-35) was developed as an advanced multi-role derivative of the Su-27. In the 1990s it entered many international fighter competitions without success.

Sukhoi's Su-27 'Flanker' represents the jewel in the crown of the Russian aerospace industry. The basic variant is without peer as a long-range interceptor, while advanced derivatives look set to dominate Russian military aviation into the 21st century.

Massive, and with sufficient internal fuel capacity to enjoy an unmatched radius of action, the Su-27 'Flanker' was originally designed to meet the challenging requirements of the Soviet air defence air arm, the IA-PVO. In addition to long range, the Su-27 also has an effective multi-spectral suite of sensors, with radar, infra-red, and laser rangefinding. In certain circumstances, the Su-27 can actually detect, locate and identify its targets without using radar, and thus without betraying its presence to enemy radar warning receivers. The Su-27 enjoys great 'combat persistence' with up to 12 hardpoints for a range of sophisticated air-to-air missiles, including up to eight beyond-visual-range missiles. But the basic 'Flanker' is much more than just a long-range bomber destroyer.

Air show audiences have watched transfixed as Su-27s have performed manoeuvres which no Western front-line jet of its generation can duplicate, demonstrating predictable and

The basic Su-27 design has spawned major advanced derivatives, the most fundamentally changed of which is the Su-27IB (OKB Su-34) long-range strike aircraft. This marries the Su-27's fuselage with a new forward section featuring side-by-side seating and a 'platypus' nose. The Su-27IB and related naval Su-32FN have been offered to supplant the heavier bombers of Long Range Aviation, albeit while serving with Frontal Aviation regiments.

Left: The Cope India exercise of 2004 pitted the Indian Air Force's Su-30K 'Flankers' in simulated combat missions against USAF F-15 Eagles. The results were widely seen as a considerable success for the Indians and their Russian-supplied fighter equipment.

Below: One of the Su-27M prototypes, 'Bort 709', is seen during a tour of Africa and the Middle East, for which the aircraft wore an unusual desert camouflage. Intensive efforts were made to sell the aircraft to the UAE which, at the time, was seeking a new fighter.

safe handling characteristics in the extreme corners of the envelope. This gives the Su-27 pilot unparalleled agility in a low-speed fight, and allows him or her to 'point' the nose far away from the direction of flight to aim the weapons in an off-axis 'snapshot'.

Original design flaws

Like any fighter, the Su-27 has its weaknesses. Its radar is powerful, but onboard computer processing capacity is inadequate, and the system cannot always prioritise all targets. The pilot can become swamped with information, and to maintain situational awareness must rely on ground control or an AWACS platform. Similarly, the cockpit is a generation behind contemporary Western fighter cockpits, increasing pilot workload. Much of the Su-27's extraordinary agility is available only at low all-up weights, and when fully laden with fuel and weapons its limitations are more restrictive.

Sukhoi's political pre-eminence has secured the future of the 'Flanker'. Rivals claim (with some justification) that when a Sukhoi and a non-Sukhoi design have competed for Russian state funding, the Sukhoi aircraft has inevitably 'won', even when it has been inferior, or less suitable for the particular requirement. This is exemplified by the Su-27K (Su-33) naval variant, which won in the face of competition from the arguably more capable Mikoyan MiG-29K.

Sukhoi overcame many obstacles in getting the Su-27 into service. The original T10 design was seriously flawed and had to undergo a fundamental redesign before it was suitable for operational use in even its original, rather narrow role. Since then, Sukhoi has improved and refined the aircraft to fulfil a variety of roles. The OKB has been cushioned from the worst effects of the cutbacks by its political pre-eminence. Thus, while its rivals languish in the doldrums, Sukhoi is kept relatively busy developing and marketing advanced derivatives of the original Su-27, most recently the Su-30MK export versions.This has also ensured that the Russian air force is becoming increasingly based around variants of the Su-27.

The development of the advanced single-seat Su-27M has apparently ended, with only a small batch having been delivered to the Russian air force's test establishment. The advanced Su-27M was formally redesignated Su-35 during 1993, in a bid to gain foreign orders. The first two prototypes were followed by a batch of between five and nine aircraft built at Komsomolsk. The first prototype made its maiden flight on 28 June 1988, more than two years before the basic Su-27 'Flanker-B' was in large-scale squadron service. Another commercial dead-end, the ultra-agile Su-37 derivative of the Su-35, equipped with AL-37FU thrust-vectoring (TV) engine nozzles, has at least informed thrust-vectoring versions of the two-seat Su-30MK, as adopted by India.

Once used primarily as a long-range air defence interceptor, the Su-27 and its close relatives increasingly dominate Frontal Aviation, while a small quantity of Su-27K (Su-33) interceptors form the sole fighter equipment of Russia's carrier air arm. Indeed, such is the prominence of the family that the 'Flanker' may well finally represent the single future fighter for the Russian air forces.

Su-27 'Flanker-B'

The impressive Sukhoi Su-27 'Flanker-B' displayed to the public at air shows is a far cry from the original Sukhoi T10 'Flanker-A' prototype. This 'Flanker-B' displays to advantage the revised wing shape, reprofiled rear fuselage with ventral fins, new radome shape, repositioned nosegear and single dorsal airbrake.

The Su-27 'Flanker' represents one of the jewels in the crown of the Russian aerospace industry. Available for export on the world market, the capable and agile 'Flanker-B' emerged after a major redesign of the less than successful prototype T10 'Flanker-A'.

After the dramatic failure of the original T10 'Flanker-A' to live up to expectations, two partially complete airframes were finished to a revised design, under the new designation T10S.

Major changes

The wings had a reduced leading-edge sweep, lost their fences, had increased area and were given square-cut tips mounting missile launch rails. The trailing-edge flaps and separate outboard ailerons were replaced by single-section flaperons extending out from the root to about 60 per cent span.

The tailfins were increased in size and moved outboard to slender booms beside the engine nacelles and were returned to the vertical. Ventral strakes were fitted below the same tailbooms to enhance directional stability and increase spin resistance.

The tailplanes were also increased in size and gained distinctive cropped tips. The flat, shallow, beaver tail between the engine nozzles was replaced by a lengthened cylindrical tail sting, tipped by a conical fairing, providing a housing for twin braking parachutes and providing space for chaff/flare dispensers. The fuselage cross-sections were reduced and the wing fillets were of reduced radius.

The nose was lengthened and refined in shape, while the nosewheel was moved aft. The oleos of the main undercarriage units were altered to slope forward, allowing them to retract better into the wing/fuselage centre-section. The undercarriage doors were also redesigned, with a large dorsal airbrake replacing the forward doors, which had functioned as speed brakes. Even the cockpit canopy was redesigned, being given a longer, flatter, more streamlined profile. The definitive AL-31F engines were housed in redesigned nacelles. Gridded intake screens were added in the main intakes, to reduce the danger of FOD ingestion during take-off and landing. The aircraft initially lacked the extended tailcone of the production Su-27.

The first T10S made its maiden flight on 20 April 1981, but was lost in September 1981, due to fuel system problems.

The second T10S was lost in December 1981 due to uncommanded pitch-ups after the separation of the automatic flaps.

These accidents aside, the Su-27 had clearly been transformed, and its pilots raved about its handling and performance characteristics. A decision to produce the type was taken in 1982, and the first production aircraft was rolled out in November of that year.

Four Su-27 'Flanker-Bs' formate on a Beriev A-50 'Mainstay' AEW&C aircraft in a pose symbolic of the air defence role. In reality, the A-50 is more used to controlling MiG-31 interceptors than 'Flankers'.

With its upgraded radar, the two-seat Su-30MK has been developed as a multi-role strike fighter. It carries an impressive array of air-to-air and air-to-surface weapons, including precision-guided missiles. The Su-30MKI has been exported to India, which has retrofitted some earlier (Su-30K and Su-30MK-1) aircraft with canard foreplanes and thrust-vectoring engine nozzles.

The first MKI flew on 1 July 1997 and was equipped with AL-31FP thrust-vectoring nozzles, giving it superb manoeuvrability. A second prototype flew in 1998. However, India had already received eight Su-30MK-1 long-range interceptors, without canards and thrust vectoring, as a stop-gap measure. These entered service with No. 24 'Hunting Hawks' Squadron at Pune in June 1997. A batch of 10 Su-30Ks was subsequently received in October 1999 from a cancelled Indonesian order, these adding a limited PGM capability. The next 10 deliveries were the first of the canard-equipped, thrust-vectoring Su-30MKIs, these entering service with No. 20 'Lightnings' Squadron in September 2002. These have since been joined by two further batches of 12 and 10 Su-30MKIs, delivered in 2004 and 2005 respectively, and providing a total of 50 aircraft. The second Su-30MKIs operator is No. 30 'Rhinos' Squadron. The earlier Su-30MK-1s and Su-30Ks are intended to be brought up to the 'definitive' Su-30MKI standard by HAL. Meanwhile, licence production of the Su-30MKI by the same company is now likely to extend beyond the planned 140, the first locally built aircraft being delivered to the IAF by HAL in November 2004.

Su-30MKK

The Su-30MKK is a multi-role twin-seat fighter developed for China as a follow-on to the first-generation Su-27SK/Su-27UBK and locally built Shenyang J-11, and is equipped to perform a range of air superiority and strike missions. In contrast to India's Su-30MKI, the MKK lacks both canards and thrust-vectoring engines and is equipped with mainly Russian avionics. The overall aerodynamic and structural design owes much to the single-seat Su-27SK and Su-27M, production of which is also handled by KnAAPO at Komsomolsk-on-Amur.

The first MKK flew on 19 May 1999 and, following the completion of tests, the first Chinese order for 38 aircraft was placed in August 1999; these began to be delivered to the 3rd Air Division at Wuhu in December 2000. In July 2001 China placed a follow-up order for a similar number of aircraft that were delivered between 2000 and 2003. A third batch of 24 Su-30MKK2 variants was then contracted in January 2003 and the last examples were handed over in August 2004. The more advanced MKK2 version is optimised for the anti-shipping mission and is operated by the People's Liberation Army Naval Air Force (PLANAF). New weapons options include the Kh-31A (AS-17 'Krypton') supersonic anti-ship missile.

Additional customers

The Irkutsk-built Su-30MKM variant for Malaysia is based on the MKI and therefore has canards, thrust-vectoring engines and Bars multi-mode radar.

Another southeast Asian 'Flanker' customer is Vietnam, which ordered four KnAAPO-built Su-30MK2s (plus eight options) in December 2003. These join 12 first-generation Su-27SK/UBKs that have been in use since the mid-1990s.

Indonesia, which had cancelled an earlier 'Flanker' order, signed for a pair of KnAAPO-built Su-30MKs (and two single-seat Su-27SKs) in April 2003, the two multi-role fighters aircraft arriving in Java in September. Further acquisitions have since been delayed by economic problems.

Appearing at the MAKS'99 air show was the Su-30 ('302'), which on one day was liberally armed with dumb bombs, while on another, flew with R-73s, R-77s and Kh-31s, thus reflecting the aircraft's true multi-role capability. Unpainted, the Su-30 flew alongside the Test Pilots Su-27PD team.

Su-27IB, Su-32FN and Su-34

Strike 'Flankers'

The side-by-side seating Su-27 variants are radical developments of the original 'Flanker' interceptor, and their evolution has been shrouded in confusion and not a little mystery. What is clear is that they promise a deadly combination of long-range 'reach' and powerful attack 'punch'.

Although Sukhoi's Su-27 has always had a secondary ground-attack capability, Sukhoi chose to develop a dedicated two-seat attack version. This radically rebuilt aircraft was dubbed the Su-27IB (*Istrebitel Bombardirovschik*, meaning fighter-bomber).

The prototype, which first flew on 13 April 1990, was converted from an Su-27UB trainer, with a new side-by-side cockpit section (including the nose gear) grafted onto the existing fuselage. The Su-27IB has a distinctive long, flattened 'platypus' nose. The aircraft is also fitted with small canards on the chines running back to the wing leading edge.

Western perception of the Su-27IB was muddied when a photograph was released of the prototype apparently landing on the carrier *Tiblisi*. It was announced that this aircraft was the 'Su-27KU', a carrier training version – though it had no arrestor hook! Photographs of the Su-27IB, this time carrying a heavy warload, were released after the aircraft was presented to commanders at Minsk-Maschulische in 1992.

Production variants

The designation Su-34 was applied, by Sukhoi, to the production version of the Su-27IB, for the Russian air force. The first pre-production Su-34 was rolled out from Sukhoi's Novosibirsk plant in 1993, making a maiden flight on 18 December.

The full-standard Su-34 is fitted with 12 hardpoints and can carry up to 17,640 lb (8000 kg) of weapons. It is cleared to carry virtually the full range of Russian air-to-surface ordnance. This could include bombs, cluster bomb dispensers, a variety of unguided or laser-guided rockets, or a number of precision-guided weapons, including as the KAB-500 or the KAB-1500 LGBs.

The cockpit of the aircraft uses a mix of conventional instruments and multi-function CRT displays (in the central console, shared by the two crew). The large forward cabin gives the pilots room in which to

Above: This photograph of the Su-27IB prototype, labelled as the 'Su-27KU', caused great confusion for many years, with even Sukhoi denying that the Su-27IB designation existed.

Top: Wearing show number 343, Su-32FN '44' takes-off at the 1997 Paris Air Show. The naval strike variant of the Su-27IB, the Su-32FN was proposed by Sukhoi as a shore-based, long-range all-weather attack aircraft. It was also to have a limited ASW capability.

The Su-27IB/Su-34 series has a large tail 'sting' which may be capable of housing a targetting and guidance radar for a rear-firing defensive missile system.

This is the first pre-production Su-34 (Sukhoi Bureau designation T10V-2) which is the Russian air force version of the Su-27IB. For many years, the air force continued to use the original Su-27IB designation.

move around on long-duration missions. There is also a small food heater and even a toilet.

Maritime mission

Although the Su-34 was envisaged as a replacement for the air force's Su-24s in the tactical strike role, Sukhoi first presented the Su-34 at the 1995 Paris Air Show using the surprise designation Su-32FN. The aircraft was described as an all-weather, 24-hour maritime strike aircraft, equipped with the Sea Snake sea-search and attack radar.

The Su-27IB/Su-34 was originally earmarked to replace all of Russia's tactical strike aircraft by 2004, but this goal was clearly far too optimistic, and only eight aircraft were available by the end of 2003. Meanwhile, the Su-32FN project for the Russian navy seems to have been put on hold. The Russian air force has ordered an initial batch of 18 Su-34 production aircraft, from an eventual requirement of up to 200. The first two production aircraft were handed over to the air force in December 2006, and the type is due to enter operational service in 2010.

Su-27IB

The Su-27IB (known to the Bureau as the T10V-1) was unveiled in the early 1990s under the guise of a side-by-side two-seat trainer, for carrier operations. It was given the spurious designation 'Su-27KU'. Sukhoi repeatedly denied the Su-27IB designation, as that pointed to the aircraft's true combat role, and made strenuous efforts to conceal all documentation that referred to the 'Su-27IB'. For example, at the 1992 Minsk-Maschulische, a display board describing the aircraft as the Su-27IB was covered before photographers could reach it. Subsequently, Sukhoi was more open about the aircraft's role and attempted to split the Su-27IB into dedicated land attack (Su-34) and maritime attack (Su-32FN) variants. The aircraft seen here, 'Blue 42', was the Su-27IB prototype which first flew on 13 April 1990 – the first of a new breed of larger attack 'Flankers'.

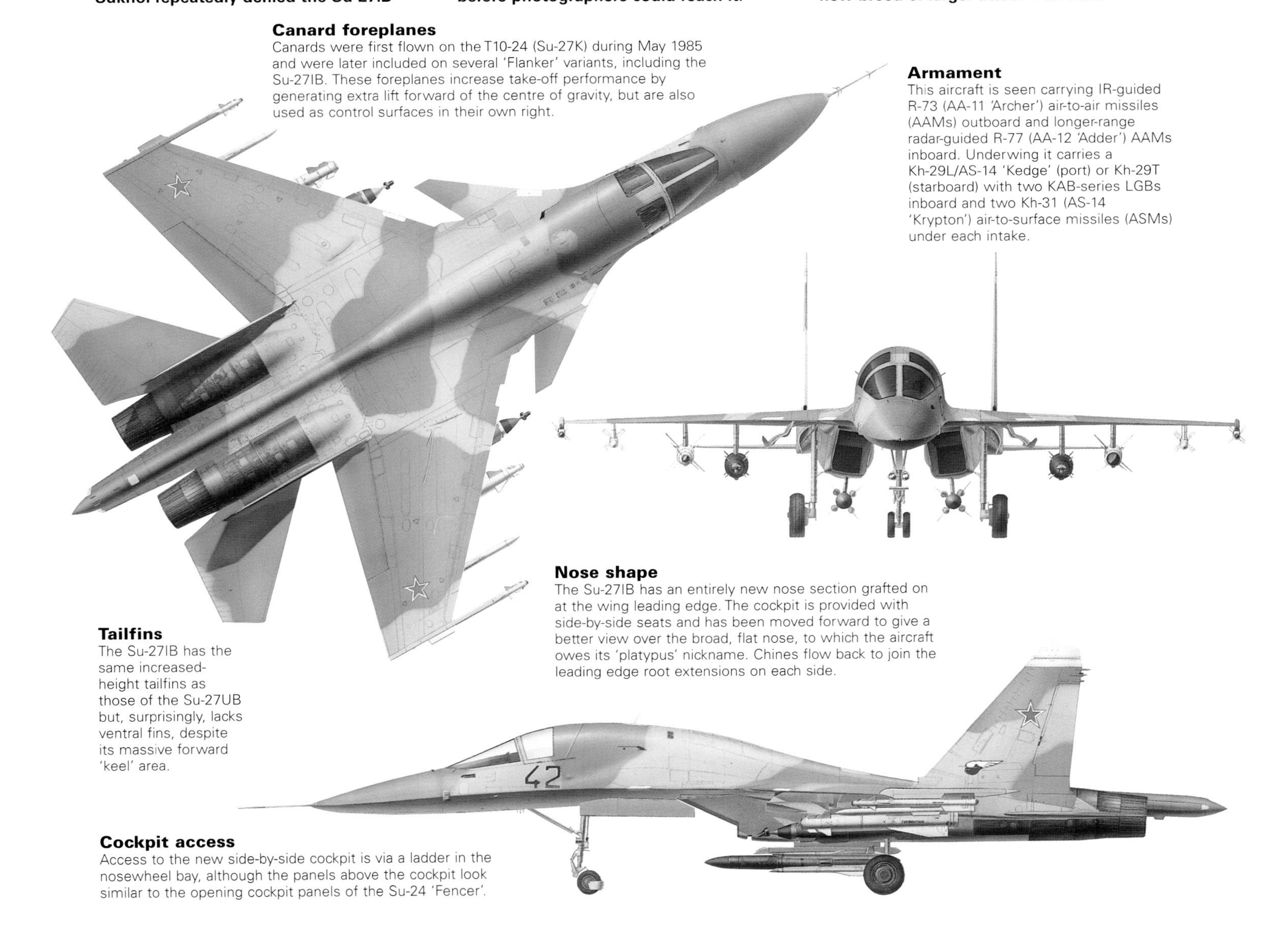

Canard foreplanes
Canards were first flown on the T10-24 (Su-27K) during May 1985 and were later included on several 'Flanker' variants, including the Su-27IB. These foreplanes increase take-off performance by generating extra lift forward of the centre of gravity, but are also used as control surfaces in their own right.

Armament
This aircraft is seen carrying IR-guided R-73 (AA-11 'Archer') air-to-air missiles (AAMs) outboard and longer-range radar-guided R-77 (AA-12 'Adder') AAMs inboard. Underwing it carries a Kh-29L/AS-14 'Kedge' (port) or Kh-29T (starboard) with two KAB-series LGBs inboard and two Kh-31 (AS-14 'Krypton') air-to-surface missiles (ASMs) under each intake.

Nose shape
The Su-27IB has an entirely new nose section grafted on at the wing leading edge. The cockpit is provided with side-by-side seats and has been moved forward to give a better view over the broad, flat nose, to which the aircraft owes its 'platypus' nickname. Chines flow back to join the leading edge root extensions on each side.

Tailfins
The Su-27IB has the same increased-height tailfins as those of the Su-27UB but, surprisingly, lacks ventral fins, despite its massive forward 'keel' area.

Cockpit access
Access to the new side-by-side cockpit is via a ladder in the nosewheel bay, although the panels above the cockpit look similar to the opening cockpit panels of the Su-24 'Fencer'.

'Flanker' operators

While Russia remains the principal Su-27 operator, Belarus, Kazahkstan, Ukraine and Uzbekistan all fly 'Flankers' in the air defence role, while the Su-30MK series in particular has won valuable export orders.

Kazahkstan

Among the CIS states Kazahkstan has one of the less-impoverished air forces. Some 20 Su-27s and Su-27UBs are in service, the last four of which were delivered early in 2000. The rest were acquired from Russia in exchange for 'Bear' bombers. A number are now stored.

Uzbekistan

The 62 IAP of the Uzbek air force, based at Andizhan, has 25 'Flanker-Bs' and 6 'Flanker-Cs' on strength. It is unlikely that all of these aircraft remain airworthy, however.

Belarus

For its air defence needs Belarus relies on the MiG-29 'Fulcrum' and Su-27 'Flanker'. Belarus began the 21st century with some 21 Su-27 'Flanker-B' interceptors (pictured) in service, with conversion and continuation training for the type being handled by four Su-27UB 'Flanker-C' aircraft. The aircraft serve with 61 IAB at Baranovichi.

Russia

The Russian air force remains the major Su-27 operator. About 200 'Flanker-Bs' (above) fly alongside 300 MiG-31s as the teeth of the air defences, while the Su-34 – a type which the air force would like to purchase as a replacement for its Su-24s – is slowly entering service. A tiny number of Su-30s and Su-35s are also in service. Naval Aviation flies around 24 Su-33s (top), which are flown from the carrier *Admiral Kuznetsov*. The navalised 'Flanker' was previously known as the Su-27K, before the navy adopted the Su-33 designation. In order to provide pilot training for the small Su-33 fleet – and possibly a carrier-based strike capability – Sukhoi has developed the side-by-side seating Su-33UB (Su-27KUB) derivative, which first flew in 1999.

Ukraine

Ukraine inherited its Su-27 fleet after the break-up of the USSR and is planning to upgrade the survivors to extend their service life. In 2007, two brigades were operational: the 831st Fighter Aviation Brigade, with its 12-strong 'Flanker-B' fleet (and a number of Su-27UB 'Flanker-C' two-seat trainers) based at Myrgorod; and the 9th Brigade at Zhitomyr.

Venezuela

The most recent export success for the Su-30MK concerns Venezuela, which selected the type as a replacement for the F-16. In June 2006 it was confirmed that the Hugo Chavez regime had secured a deal for 24 Su-30MK2s. Deliveries began in November 2006 and are due to continue until 2008. Venezuela's aircraft are to the Su-30MK2 standard, similar to the Indian Su-30MKI. They are equipped with N-001VEP radar, air-to-ground optimised fire control system and a redesigned cockpit with four MFDs and a new HUD.

Malaysia and Indonesia

As part of significant defence modernisation plans, Malaysia placed a $900 million order for 18 examples of the Su-30MKM in August 2003, with deliveries to the Royal Malaysian Air Force planned to begin in 2007. Indonesia, meanwhile, ordered two Su-30MKKs (and two single-seat Su-27SKs) in April 2003, entering service in 2004.

African operators

In 1998/99 Eritrea purchased 10 MiG-29s. Probably acquired from Moldova, these machines were most likely maintained by Ukrainian pilots and were seen to pose a significant threat to Ethiopia during the two countries ongoing border dispute. In response, Ethiopia received six single- and a pair of two-seat first-generation 'Flanker-B/Cs', taken from Russian air force stocks, in the same timescale. Of this original batch, one machine was lost during an air display, but was replaced. The Sukhois were flown in combat by Russian and probably Ukrainian mercenary pilots and accounted for four of Eritrea's 'Fulcrums' in air-to-air combat, plus a fifth that was damaged so badly by a near-miss with an Ethiopian AAM, that it was grounded. Three of the MiG kills were scored with R-73 AAMs, the fourth with the Su-27's internal gun. In response to Ethiopian Su-27 success, Eritrea in turn purchased eight Su-27s and two Su-27UBs in 2003. Previously, in mid-2000, another African customer emerged, Angola obtaining eight 'Flanker-B/Cs' from Russia, these also being flown by Ukrainian pilots. At least one example has been lost to a UNITA shoulder-launched missile.

China

China received the first of its 78 first-generation 'Flankers', in 1992. Of these aircraft, as many as 28 are two-seat Su-27UBKs, while the remainder are single-seat Su-27SKs. In Chinese service the aircraft is designated as the J-11 and licenced production by Shenyang began in 1998, with the aim of producing some 200 aircraft. In 1999 China also ordered 38 two-seat multi-role Su-30MKK aircraft, built at Irkutsk, with deliveries beginning in 2000. In 2001 China announced an order for a further 38 Su-30MKKs, while 24 examples of the more advanced Su-30MKK2 variant were purchased in 2003.

India

India had a long-standing requirement for the Su-30MKI. This multi-role tandem two-seat version of the 'Flanker-C' represents possibly the most advanced variant of the 'Flanker' family and certainly the most advanced offered for export. It is equipped with both canards and thrust-vectoring exhaust nozzles. Orders for the first 50 were placed with Sukhoi in 1996, the first eight aircraft having been delivered in 1997, while a further 10 that had been built for Indonesia and subsequently cancelled, were delivered in 1999. To Su-30K standard, the latter machines will be upgraded to full MKI standard. Further MKI deliveries were put on hold while the air force deliberated over the final avionics fit before resuming in 2002. Current plans foresee HAL building at least a further 140 MKIs under licence.

Vietnam

Vietnam purchased 12 'Flankers' as the first stage in its long-needed air force re-equipment programme. The first batch of six machines was delivered in 1994, with a second following three years later. A mix of 'Flanker-Bs' (illustrated) and 'Flanker-Cs' was purchased. These were followed in 2003 with a US$100 million order for four two-seat Su-30MK2s, with options on a further eight aircraft.

In the 1950s, some Tu-16s were converted into tankers, a role in which they survived in service into the 1990s (left). The early tankers used a novel 'wingtip-to-wingtip' transfer technique, seen below, as a Tu-16 'Badger-G' refuels from a Tu-16N 'Badger-A'. The Tu-16N was fitted with a modernised version of the refuelling system first tested by the Tu-2 'Bat' and Tu-4 'Bull'. Inflight refuelling trials were first carried out by the Tu-16Z in 1955. From 1963, Tu-16Ns fitted with a more conventional probe and drogue unit in the bomb bay were used primarily to provide fuel for bomber regiments equipped with the Tu-22 and Tu-22M Blinder.

Tupolev Tu-16 'Badger'

Bombers, tankers and missile-carriers

Ordered in 1948 to produce a bomber combining the speed offered by turbojets with the range and bombload of the Superfortress-derived Tu-4 'Bull', Tupolev's resulting design was the classic 'Badger'.

The Tupolev 'Badger' was developed as a twin-jet medium bomber to complement the strategic Myasishchev M-4 and Tupolev Tu-95. The bomb-bay was sized to accommodate the USSR's largest bomb, the 9000-kg (19,840-lb) FAB-9000; this allowed the use of a fuselage shortened from, but closely based on, that of the Tu-85 (itself derived from the Tu-4). The basic requirement was, however, to carry a load of 11,020 lb (5000 kg) over 3,100 miles (5000 km). The central part of the fuselage was waisted rather than circular, minimising the cross-sectional area where the engines joined the fuselage (the powerplant location was formulated by the legendary Tupolev himself), reducing drag considerably. The swept wing incorporated huge integral fuel tanks. The wing proved too thin to accommodate the bogie undercarriage, which retracted into streamlined pods projecting from the trailing edge. Such pods subsequently became a trademark of Tupolev products.

Maiden flight

The Tu-88 prototype made its maiden flight in April 1952, powered by AM-3A engines, while the second AM-3M-engined prototype flew later the same year. Evaluation against Ilyushin's conservative Il-46 only served to underline the larger Tu-88's incredible performance, and it was ordered into production as the Tu-16. Limited production with the RD-3 engine began in late 1953. Nine aircraft were available for the 1954 May Day flypast over Red Square, while 54 were in the 1955 Aviation Day flypast 15 months later. About 1,520 of all variants were built before production ceased, excluding production in China, where the aircraft is designated Xian H-6, and remains in front-line service in various forms.

The production RD-3M-powered Tu-16A nuclear bomber dispensed with the pressurised

Left: Development of the Tu-16, seen here in prototype 'Aircraft 88' form, was reliant upon that of the Mikulin M-209 engine (later AM-3 and RD-3). The AM-3 was first air-tested under a Tu-4LL bomber testbed. The Tu-88 first flew on 27 April 1952, with a crew led by N. S. Rybko.

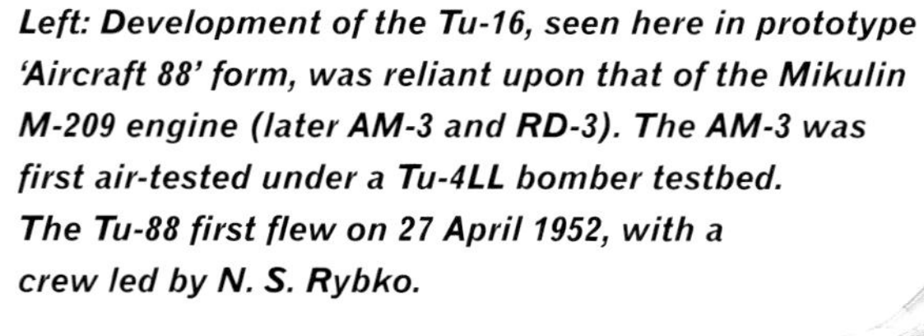

Right: The Tu-16K-10-26 could carry a mixed load of one centreline K-10 and two underwing K-26 missiles, although a single asymmetric K-26 was a more normal load.

The first major production version, built from late 1954, the Tu-16A 'Badger-A' was equipped with the PV-23 fire control system, linked to the PRS-1* Argon *tail radar under the rudder. The port-side nose gun installation, with a single AM-23 23-mm cannon with 100 rounds, was aimed by one of the pilots by reflector sight.

tunnel between cockpit and rear gunner's compartment, necessitating the provision of separate rear-fuselage entry hatches. The undernose radome for the *Rubin* nav/bombing radar was deepened slightly and overwing fences lengthened. A glazed nose station housed the navigator/bombardier, behind the side-by-side pilots sat the radar operator, while the dorsal gunner managed electrical systems and signals. In the tail was a ventral gunner, provided with lateral optical blisters, and a tail gunner in the rear turret.

Most Tu-16As were rebuilt for other purposes after 1960, although Egypt received 20 of the approximately 700 built, most of which were destroyed on the ground in the 1967 Six-Day War.

The Tu-16N conversion was developed as a tanker for other Tu-16s. The tanker could be recognised externally by a wingtip extension, outboard of a pipe-like tube which projected aft from the trailing edge. The Tu-16N had a total transferable fuel load of 42,000 lb (19000 kg).

In addition to the Tu-16N, further 'Badger-As' were converted as tankers for the probe-equipped Tu-22 'Blinder' from 1963. These aircraft had a hose/drogue unit installed in the former bomb bay. The probe-and-drogue tankers had a transferable fuel load of 33,000 lb (15000 kg), because the HDU took up room in the bomb bay that was usually occupied by fuel tanks.

Missile-carrier conversions

Many redundant 'Badger-As' were also converted to serve as missile carriers, the first anti-shipping missile-carrying variant of the 'Badger' being the Tu-16KS. This was given the NATO designation 'Badger-B' and was a minimum-change adaption of the basic bomber, fitted with a radar altimeter and a missile-control radar in a retractable radome which was housed in the weapons bay. Principal weapon was the KS-1 Komet, known to NATO as the AS-1 'Kennel', one of which could be carried under each wing. Twenty-five Komet-armed 'Badger-Bs' were exported to Indonesia, survivors being stored in the 1970s.

First seen at the 1961 Aviation Day display, the Tu-16K-10 was the second anti-shipping variant, and was given the designation 'Badger-C' by NATO. The major external difference from earlier Tu-16s was the addition of a large flat radome for a new 'Puff Ball' surface surveillance, target acquisition and designation radar. It was designed to operate with the K-10 (AS-2 'Kipper') supersonic anti-ship missile.

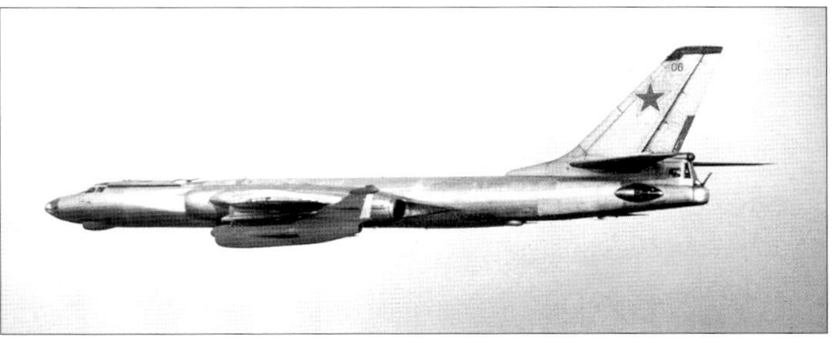

The large KS-1 Komet missile of the Tu-16KS was a relatively unsophisticated beam-rider, with a maximum range of around 50 miles (80 km). It became operational in the late 1950s.

Known to NATO as 'Badger-G', the Tu-16K-11-16 was a rebuilt 'Badger-B' equipped to carry two KSR-5/KSR-11 (AS-5 'Kelt') missiles. The supersonic 'Kelt' weighed three tonnes and had a range of over 186 miles (300 km). It had a pre-programmable autopilot, with active terminal guidance. The 'Badger-G' replaced the retractable radar of the 'B' with a new chin radar, leaving the bomb bay free for the carriage of conventional weaponry. 'Badger-Gs' saw action with both Egypt and Iraq.

'Badger-Cs' were subsequently modified to carry the supersonic Kh-26 (AS-6 'Kingfish'). The Mach-3 Kh-26 had a range in excess of 311 miles (500 km).

'Badger-Gs' were also modified to carry the 'Kingfish' anti-ship missile. The prototype and early conversions used their existing avionics fit, but later models were equipped with a new guidance radar mounted in a large belly radome in front of the bomb bay.

Reconnaissance 'Badgers'

The pioneering Tu-16 jet bomber became most familiar to NATO as a maritime reconnaissance aircraft. This 'Badger-D' is keeping a very close eye on HMS Ark Royal.

For nearly three decades variants of the Tupolev Tu-16, known as the 'Badger' to NATO, were one of the most important Soviet maritime reconnaissance and electronic intelligence platforms.

The first dedicated reconnaissance Tu-16 identified by NATO was the Tu-16Ye 'Badger-D'. This was a conversion based on redundant 'Badger-C' missile-carrying airframes which was designed to gather electronic intelligence. The 'Badger-D' retained its predecessor's distinctive broad, flattened nose radome, though the chin radome was replaced by a slightly larger item. Three passive antenna blisters were added along the centreline, one large and two small. Crew complement was increased to eight or nine by equipment operators.

Bomber conversions

The Tu-16R 'Badger-E' was produced by converting redundant 'Badger-A' bombers. A dedicated reconnaissance aircraft with provision for a camera/sensor pallet inside the former bomb bay, it could also perform EW missions, and carried two widely spaced passive receiver antennas under the fuselage.

The Tu-16P 'Badger-F' was similar in appearance, but carried large equipment pods on its underwing pylons and sometimes had prominent blade antennas above and below the fuselage. Dedicated maritime Elint platforms, 'Badger-Fs' were seen with a wide variety of aerial and antenna configurations. The Elint-tasked Tu-16P 'Badger-K' could be identified by its less widely spaced underfuselage teardrop fairings, which were also of equal size. The rearmost antenna was located just inside the area of the former bomb bay, leaving a long gap between it and the ventral gun turret. The aircraft had a row of tiny protuberances in the former bomb doors, and usually had a camera window ahead of the port intake.

The Tu-16P 'Badger-L' reporting name was reserved for an updated maritime Elint or EW platform of similar configuration to the 'Badger-F.' It, too, had

Above: A Tu-16Ye 'Badger-D' is photographed at very close range by a US Navy fighter. The 'Badger-D' was the first electronic reconnaissance variant of the 'Badger'.

Above: The Tu-16P 'Badger-K' had two equally sized underfuselage radomes, one of which was mounted on the bomb-bay doors. It was probably designed for precision ELINT collection in a dense signal environment.

***Above:* The wedge-shaped intakes easily distinguish the Tu-22M3 'Backfire-C' from previous models. They allowed the aircraft's dash speed to be raised above Mach 2.**

***Left:* Despite being difficult to fly, and extremely unpopular, the Tu-22 enjoyed a lengthy career, notably in the reconnaissance and electronic warfare roles.**

minefield as a relatively low-risk fallback option to the Mach 3-capable Sukhoi T-4 bomber, which in the event only reached prototype status. Although it was essentially a completely different aircraft, the 'Backfire' used the Tu-22M (M for 'modified') designation to ease its political progress through the Soviet system.

Tupolev designed the aircraft with variable-geometry wings, permitting a considerable increase in fuel load. Unlike the revolutionary T-4, the Tu-22M was based on a development of the Tu-22's weapon system, and retained the Kh-22 missile as its prime armament. Most missions would employ just one missile carried in a recessed centreline bay, although wing pylons could mount a further two missiles on short-range missions. Conventional free-fall bombing capability was retained.

After a small run of Tu-22M0 and Tu-22M1 aircraft, the main production version – the Tu-22M2 'Backfire-B' – was introduced. Its range performance sparked immediate controversy as US agencies simply could not believe that it was an intermediate-range aircraft. The USAF and Defense Intelligence Agency calculated a combat radius of around 3,500 miles (5630 km), which put the aircraft firmly into the 'strategic' camp, while the CIA was quoting a 2,100-mile (3380-km) radius. This confusion was exploited considerably by the Soviets, who steadfastly refused to reveal any data about the aircraft. Eventually, the Soviets removed the inflight refuelling probes from Tu-22M.

When range data finally became available, the lower estimates of the CIA were shown to be nearer the mark. Indeed, the Tu-22M was intended for exactly the same European/Asian land targets and US Navy carrier targets as its predecessor, the Tu-22 'Blinder'.

'Backfire' development

Tu-22M2s entered service in 1976 and immediately proved to be far better than the 'Blinders'. Continued development produced the Tu-22M3, which had a reprofiled nose and wedge-shaped intakes, among other improvements, which raised dash speed to Mach 2.05 and improved range by around one-third. New weapons were also introduced, including the Kh-15 (AS-16 'Kickback') high-speed missile with nuclear or high-explosive warhead.

'Backfires' saw brief action during the fighting in Afghanistan, and were used in 1995 over Chechnya.

The Tu-22M 'Backfire' is still Russia's premier bomber, with around 200 believed to be in service with both air force (with a total of between 50 and 70 aircraft) and navy regiments. Ukraine also operated numbers of Tu-22M2s and Tu-22M3s, although these had all either been scrapped or demoted to museum exhibits by early 2006.

With the break-up of the Soviet Union, Tupolev was permitted to undertake a limited sales campaign for the 'Backfire', based on the Tu-22M3. Iran and China have been linked to the type, but only India came close to a purchase.

Tu-22/22M variants

Although developed primarily as a low-level attack aircraft for Long-Range Aviation, the Tu-22M3 is best known as a medium-range maritime strike platform through its exploits with the Soviet, and now Russian, naval fleets.

Tu-22 'Blinder'

The Tu-22 was originally designed to be a free-fall bomber, but the increase in the sophistication of SAMs and the threat of interceptor aircraft led bomber designers in the 1960s to look at ways of producing a stand-off capability. Thus, only 15 Tu-22B 'Blinder-Bs' were built as such and were used mainly for training within the Soviet services. The only export customers, Iraq and Libya, did receive Tu-22B aircraft, but they were late-build Tu-22R aircraft modified to the free-fall bomber standard.

The second version produced, the Tu-22R 'Blinder-C', was equipped with camera equipment in the nose and weapons bay. The aircraft was oriented towards traditional military reconnaissance, especially naval, but retained a bombing capability. A total of 127 Tu-22Rs was built, making it the most common 'Blinder' model manufactured. Aircraft fitted with inflight refuelling equipment were redesignated as Tu-22RDs (left, above). Adding improved ELINT reconnaissance gear to the aircraft produced the Tu-22RK, or Tu-22RKD if equipped with a refuelling probe. Another upgrade of the reconnaissance equipment on the Tu-22RD in the early 1980s produced the Tu-22RDM.

The 'Blinder' was a difficult aircraft to fly, and a dedicated trainer version was required because the aircraft only had a single cockpit. To overcome this problem, the Tu-22U ('Blinder-D') was produced, with a second raised cockpit above the first. The prototype was completed in 1960 and a total of 46 of the aircraft was produced.

In order for the Tu-22 to survive, the aircraft needed to have the ability to carry stand-off attack missiles. The type was re-designed to carry the Kh-22 cruise missile. Taking to the air for the first time in early 1961, a total of just 76 Tu-22K missile carriers (also given the ASCC codename 'Blinder-B') was built at Kazan. These included the improved Tu-22KD with upgraded engines. Although intended to replace the Tu-16 in both air force and navy service, insufficient numbers were built to replace the air force 'Badgers'. Only a handful of Tu-22K missile carriers were delivered to the Soviet navy for trials. Tu-22Ks built to use an anti-radar version of the Kh-22 missile were designated Tu-22KPs, distinguished by having a 'pitchfork' aerial on the right side of the nose. Anti-radar missile carriers with a refuelling probe were called Tu-22KPDs.

An electronic warfare version, the Tu-22P 'Blinder-E', was built in the early 1960s. It also was used in the electronic jamming role. A total of 47 Tu-22P-1s and Tu-22P-2s was built, the two versions varying in the precise configuration of their electronics package. As was the case with the other Tu-22 variants, the aircraft were upgraded with the RD-7M-2 engines and refuelling probe from 1965, and redesignated the Tu-22PD (left, below). Eventually, the EW package was improved, leading to the Tu-22P-4, P-6 and P-7 variants. The Tu-22PD was usually issued on the basis of one squadron per regiment of Tu-22K missile carriers, to provide EW support.

Tu-22P 'Blinder-E'

The Tu-22P was the final production version of the 'Blinder' and was intended to serve chiefly alongside the Tu-22K as an escort jammer. One squadron of 'Blinder-Es' was generally allocated to each Tu-22K regiment. The Tu-22P played a small but important role during the final years of its front-line career in the Soviet Union, when it escorted Tu-22M2 'Backfires' on bombing missions over Afghanistan.

Handling qualities

The Tu-22 did not have a reputation as a 'pilot's aircraft' and could be very difficult and dangerous to fly. The aircraft could not be allowed to slow down to less than 180 mph (290 km/h) on approach, as this risked an uncontrollable pitch-up and stall.

Tu-22M 'Backfire'

Promoted by Tupolev as an upgrade of the Tu-22 'Blinder', the Tu-22M was an entirely new aircraft. The first prototype, Tu-22M0, was delivered to the Flight Test Institute (LII) at Zhukhovskii in the summer of 1969, just two years after the project had been given the go-ahead over Sukhoi's delta-winged T-4. The Tu-22M0 completed its first test flight on 30 August 1969, and a pre-production run of 10 aircraft was planned. Nine pre-series Tu-22M0s were built at Kazan between 1969 and 1971. However, the Kuznetsov NK-144-22 engines were inefficient, limiting the Tu-22M0's range to 2,573 miles (4140 km), well below expectations. The final Tu-22M0 introduced several production features, including the rear defensive gun position in place of the aircraft's previous large ECM fairing. The distinctive wing-mounted undercarriage fairings of the Tu-22M0 were abandoned on later aircraft. A single Tu-22M0 (left, below) is preserved at Monino, east of Moscow. The Tu-22M1 first series production aircraft incorporated new Kuznetsov NK-22 engines, offering 10 per cent more thrust.

Following the completion of Tu-22 production, Tu-22M1 manufacture was scheduled to begin at Kazan in 1971. The Tu-22M1 introduced revised wingroot landing gear, and increased wingspan, although problems persisted. Only nine Tu-22M1s were built from 1971 to 1972, and operational trials were conducted by the 185th Guards Heavy Bomber Aviation Regiment, Poltava, Ukraine. Other airframes were perhaps used in trials carried out by naval regiments, but the problematic Tu-22M1 never reached quantity production.

The Tu-22M2 'Backfire-B' (left, above) was the definitive production variant. Production lasted from 1972 to 1983, and a total of 211 airframes were completed. Initially fitted with a refuelling probe on the nose, this was later deleted under SALT (Strategic Arms Limitation Treaty), removing intercontinental range. Other recognisable Tu-22M2 features include the conventional splitter-plate intakes and twin tail guns. In addition to service with the Long-Range Aviation branch of the air force, the Tu-22M2 was delivered to the Northern and Black Sea Fleets.

Introducing new NK-25 engines, an improved and strengthened wing and revised forward-raked air intakes, the Tu-22M3 succeeded the Tu-22M2 on the Kazan production line, and was accepted for service in 1983. Optimised for low-level operations, the first aircraft were deployed to the 185th Guards Heavy Bomber Aviation Regiment, and 268 Tu-22M3s were built before production was halted in 1993. The Kh-22 remained a principal weapon; however, the Tu-22M3 introduced a new weapon to the 'Backfire' inventory, with up to six Kh-15 (AS-16 'Kickback') ASMs carried on an internal rotary launcher. The Tu-22M3 also carries a new Ural ECM system. In the late 1980s, work on the Tu-22MP (a Tu-22M3 variant) began, but this dedicated EW-escort jammer had not yet entered service by the time 'Backfire' production came to an end. A further Tu-22M3 sub-variant is the Tu-22M3(R) quick-reaction strategic reconnaissance aircraft, the first being accepted for navy use following conversion in 1984. Twelve more Tu-22M3(R)s were later accepted for service, and their equipment includes a large bomb-bay sensor package.

Tu-22M3 'Backfire-C'

Prior to the dissolution of the Soviet AV-MF (Aviatsiya Voyenno-Morskoyo Flota), the Tu-22M3 was operated by subordinated regiments (MRAPs) of missile-carrying bombers (also including Tu-16Ks and Tu-22M2s) within naval aviation divisions (MRADs). Subsequently, the Tu-22M3 fleet was divided between two divisions of two regiments each, comprising the Russian navy's Northern Fleet (regiments at Lakhta and Olenya) and Pacific Fleet (two regiments at Alekseyevka), as well as a small number with the Naval High Command, based at the Ostrov Naval Aviation training base.

Carrier group strike

Attacks against NATO carrier battle groups were the most high-profile missions likely to be encountered by Soviet AV-MF 'Backfire' crews. AV-MF 'Backfire' tactics ensured that at least seven aircraft from each strike package would have a chance of scoring a direct hit on the targeted aircraft-carrier. For greater efficiency, the Tu-22M3 could work in concert with Tu-95RTs 'Bear-D' ELINT/over-the-horizon (OTH) target designator aircraft.

Crew training

AV-MF Tu-22M crews are trained in the Tu-134UBL, seating 12 trainees and carrying Tu-22M instrument panels. The older Tu-134Sh-1 is a dedicated navigator trainer with 13 trainee stations and practice bomb MERs. The single Tu-134UBK was developed exclusively for AV-MF Tu-22M crews, and carries PNA radar, a bombsight and a Kh-22 acquisition round.

Bomb bay

Within the Tu-22M3's internal weapons bay, the MKU-6-1 rotary launcher can carry six Kh-15 (AS-16 'Kickback') tactical cruise missiles. A further four weapons can be carried externally on the outer wing stations. The conventional Kh-15A carries an active radar seeker; the Kh-15P has a passive anti-radar seeker.

The Raduga Kh-22 (NATO AS-4 'Kitchen') ASM is the primary anti-shipping weapon of the Tu-22M3 – up to three examples can be carried.

Kh-22 attack profile

Following a Mach 2.5 steep terminal phase dive, a single example of the Kh-22 anti-shipping weapon can tear a 215-sq ft (20-m²) hole in the side of a ship, before burning its way 39 ft (12 m) into the vessel, ensuring the destruction of the internal bulkheads. The standard Kh-22 carries a 2,205-lb (1000-kg) high-explosive warhead (Kh-22P/N variants carried a 3.5-kT nuclear warhead) and possesses a range of 340 miles (550 km) when launched at high altitude.

Tail armament

Tu-22M3 defensive armament is provided by a single twin-barrelled GSh-23 cannon in the tail barbette. Ammunition supply is 1,200 rounds of PIKS infra-red decoy and PRLS chaff ammunition. The gun is aimed using the PRS-4 'Krypton' radar or supplementary TP-1 TV sight.

Tupolev Tu-160 'Blackjack'

Soviet superbomber

Conceived as a counterpart to the B-1, to which it is externally similar, there are some notable differences in that the Tu-160 has 79 per cent more engine power and, although appreciably larger, reportedly has a smaller radar cross-section.

As part of the Soviet Union's nuclear triad, the Tu-160 'Blackjack' offered an intercontinental bombing ability together with 'stealthy' design and fearsome firepower. However, following the demise of the Soviet Union, the Tu-160 has, like so many other ventures, proven too costly and difficult to maintain, and only a small number remain in service.

The Tu-160 'Blackjack' is the largest-ever Soviet bomber, dwarfing the similar-looking American B-1B, and is the heaviest combat aircraft ever built. The Soviet bomber was heavily influenced by the original B-1A, which first flew in 1974, but which was cancelled in 1977. Originally designated Product 70, the Tu-160 made its maiden flight on 19 December 1981. Spotted by a prowling US spy satellite three weeks before this, the new aircraft received the reporting name 'Ram-P' before being re-designated 'Blackjack'. The aircraft revealed many features in common with the B-1, although the Soviet aircraft was clearly very much bigger.

When the B-1A project was reborn as the cheaper, less complex B-1B, all thoughts of high-level penetration had been abandoned, and the less sophisticated aircraft was expected to use low-level flight (where it was limited to subsonic speeds) and reduced radar cross-section to penetrate enemy defences. In the USSR, there was no such cost-cutting exercise, and the Tu-160 remained committed to both low-level penetration (at transonic speeds), and high-level penetration at speeds of about Mach 1.9.

The variable-geometry wings, with their full-span leading-edge slats and trailing-edge double-slotted flaps, confer a useful combination of benign low-speed handling and high supersonic speed. Wing sweep is manually selected, with three settings: 20° for take-off and landing, 35° for cruise, and 65° for high-speed flight. The trailing edge of the inboard section of the flaps (immobilised when the wings are swept back) has no fuselage slot to retract into when the wing is swept. Instead, therefore, it folds upwards to be aligned with the aircraft centreline, thereby acting as a fence. Some aircraft have a 'double-jointed' folding section which can fold up to be a fence at either 35° or 65°.

The purpose of the long, straight fairings on the sides of the rear fuselage is unknown. They may house a digital databus, which would require a long, unbroken area, and are similar to fairings seen on various sub-types of the 'Bear' turboprop bomber.

Crew accommodation

The Tu-160 has a crew of four, sitting in side-by-side pairs on K-36D ejection seats. The crew enter the cockpit via a ladder in the rear part of the nose gear bay. The pilot and co-pilot are provided with fighter-type control columns, and although the aircraft has a fly-by-wire control system, all cockpit

Although Russia's 'Blackjack' fleet is small in number, the type remains a very useful long-range strike asset, and the latest upgrades have added precision-guided weapons capability and conventional cruise missiles.

Like the B-1B or Su-24, the Tu-160 uses a variable-geometry wing to reconcile the conflicting demands of supersonic flight and low-speed handling. Wing sweep is conducted manually with settings of 20° for take-off and landing, 35° for cruising flight and 65° for a high-speed supersonic dash.

displays are conventional analogue instruments. In front of the cockpit is the long, pointed radome for the terrain-following and attack radar, with a fairing below it for the forward-looking TV camera used for visual weapon aiming. Intercontinental range is assured by the provision of a fully retractable inflight refuelling probe.

The Tu-160's offensive warload is carried in two tandem weapons bays in the belly. These are each normally equipped with a rotary carousel which can carry either six Kh-55 (AS-15 'Kent') cruise missiles or 12 Kh-15 (AS-16 'Kickback') 'SRAMskis'. The Kh-55 has a range in excess of 1,864 miles (3000 km) and a 200-kT nuclear warhead.

The development programme of the Tu-160 was extremely protracted, and at least one prototype is believed to have been lost. Series production was at Kazan and continued until January 1992. Even after the aircraft entered service, problems continued to severely restrict operations, with a shortage of basic flying equipment and problems with the ejection seats, while reliability of the aircraft, its engines and systems bordered on the unacceptable. Operations were supported by teams from the Kazan factory and Tupolev, who continued to deliver aircraft before a common standard and configuration were agreed upon. Thus, wingspans, equipment fit, and intake configuration differ from aircraft to aircraft.

'Blackjack' today

Nineteen completed Tu-160s were delivered to the two squadrons of the 184th Heavy Bomber Regiment at Priluki in the Ukraine from May 1987. These were left at the base under Ukrainian command after the disintegration of the USSR. Eight of these aircraft were transferred to Russia in 1999. Under the Strategic Arms Reduction Treaty (START) I treaty, the remaining Ukrainian aircraft were scrapped.

Russia currently operates 15 Tu-160s, which are in the process of an upgrade, adding, among other features, a conventional cruise missile capability.

Tu-160 'Blackjack-A'

Wearing a white scheme, presumably as protection against nuclear flash (like Britain's V-bomber force of the 1960s), this Tu-160 was part of the 184th Heavy Bomber Regiment, based at Priluki in the Ukraine. The current operator is the 121st Heavy Bomber Regiment at Engels, Russia.

'Blackjack' crew

The 'Blackjack' is flown by a crew of four, comprising two pilots sitting side-by-side, and two navigators behind. One of the latter is known as a 'navigator-operator' and is responsible for aiming the weapons, while the other navigator is responsible for en route navigation. All crew members sit on K-36 upward-firing ejection seats.

Powerplant

Located in two nacelles under the inner wing section, the four engines of the Tu-160 are Kuznetsov-designed NK-32 turbofans (Type R). Developed for the Tu-22M 'Backfire', each delivers 55,055 lb (245 kN) of thrust in full afterburner.

Missile load

Each rotary launcher can carry six Kh-55 cruise missiles, or alternatively 12 Kh-15 defence suppression missiles. A typical load would include both missile types.

Defensive systems

Mounted under the tail of the Tu-160 are a battery of 72 chaff/flare dispensers. Built into the fuselage is a defensive avionics suite, with receiver antennas and jammers located in the tail bullet fairing, tailcone and under flush dielectric panels in the leading edge of the wing glove section.

Fin

The large fin incorporates a long dorsal fin for structural integrity and additional keel area. At approximately third-span is a fairing which houses the actuators and spindle joints for the tailerons and which extends beyond the trailing edge for housing ECM equipment. Above this fairing is a one-piece, all-moving rudder. All control is handled by a fly-by-wire system.

Fuel

Most of the aircraft's fuel is housed in the large wing centre-section, and is sufficient to provide a range of about 8,700 miles (14000 km). Mission endurance is further extended by inflight refuelling, a probe for which is located in the nose ahead of the cockpit. This is retractable, covered by long double doors when not in use.

Undercarriage

Each main undercarriage strut holds a six-wheel (arranged in three pairs) bogie. These retract backwards to lie in the wing centre-section between the fuselage and engine nacelles. Each wheel measures 4 ft 1½ in (1.26 m) in diameter and 1 ft 4½ in (0.419 m) in thickness. The wheel track is narrow at 17 ft 8½ in (5.4 m).

Vickers Valiant

V-bomber pioneer

Above: Identified by its 'letterbox' intakes and finished in highly polished metal, WB210 was the first prototype. The very vision of a schoolboy fantasy when it appeared in 1951, the Valiant's Mach 0.84 performance more than matched its sleek, futuristic looks.

Top: WB215 was the second prototype, seen here testing the underwing tanks. The No. 2 aircraft introduced enlarged intakes with a single divider.

As the first of the V-bombers to enter service, it fell to the Valiant to pioneer virtually every aspect and role for the new force: strategic bomber at both high and low levels, tanker, ECM platform and reconnaissance aircraft, while seeing action during the Suez campaign. Most importantly, it was the only British aircraft to drop live nuclear weapons.

When Britain made the decision to develop its own atomic weapon (which materialised as the Blue Danube), it followed that it needed a new jet bomber to carry it. Specification B.35/46 was issued, resulting in a 1947 order for the Avro Vulcan and Handley Page Victor. A year later, following considerable pressure from Vickers, a third bomber was ordered, the Type 660, for which Specification B.9/48 was written.

This third bomber, which became the Vickers Valiant, was less ambitious in its range, load and altitude characteristics, but could be in service much earlier than the other two, more closely matching the timetable for the production of operational bombs.

Two prototypes of the Type 660 were ordered in April 1948. The Type 660 featured an extremely sleek cigar-shaped fuselage, with only a bombing cupola and bulged flight deck to spoil its lines. A large bomb bay, indeed the whole aircraft, was designed around the dimensions of the Blue Danube.

The high-mounted wing featured moderate sweep, giving a limiting Mach number of 0.84. The engines were buried in the wingroots and were, in the interests of sleekness, of the axial-flow design. The Rolls-Royce Avon was the specified engine, although the Sapphire was chosen as a back-up, and would have powered the second prototype if the Avon had not matured sufficiently during its development. A novel feature of the Type 660 was that almost every system was controlled and actuated electrically, thereby saving many hundreds of pounds in pipes, pumps and other equipment associated with hydraulic systems.

Serialled WB210, the first prototype was moved to Wisley airfield for its first flight, which was made on 18 May 1951. The aircraft was lost on 12 January 1952 when it caught fire during engine relight trials.

Production Valiant B.Mk 1s were built at Weybridge. They were ordered in a succession of small batches while the RAF awaited the Vulcan and Victor to enter production. The first seven were used for trials work, followed by 29 for delivery to the RAF. They were followed by 11 new-build and one conversion B(PR).Mk 1s for dual bomber/reconnaissance duties, 13 B(PR)K.Mk 1s which also had provision for inflight-refuelling, and 44 B(K).Mk 1s dual bomber/tankers.

Into service

On 8 February 1955, Valiant WP206 was delivered to newly formed No. 138 Squadron at Gaydon. Later that month, No. 232 OCU was formed to handle training for the new bomber.

No. 138's 'A' Flight moved to its operational base at Wittering in

Above: Valiants were built with provision for two de Havilland Super Sprite jettisonable rockets for assisted take-offs, although they were not employed operationally. The ability is demonstrated here by the second prototype.

Left: WP204 was typical of early production Valiants (it was the sixth). Compared to the prototypes they had lengthened jetpipes, and carried NBS radar from the outset.

The last of 106 Valiants departs the factory airfield at Wisley in September 1957. The later aircraft of the final batch (44 built as B(K).Mk 1s) had Avon 205 engines with water/methanol boosting, and a lengthened tailcone housing rear-warning radar.

July 1955. As Blue Danube bombs were already in place, this date marks the beginning of Britain's nuclear deterrent capability, although it would be some time before this could be declared fully operational. No. 543 Squadron, the reconnaissance unit, formed next, taking its aircraft from Gaydon to Wyton in November. Valiants were delivered with rapidity during 1956, allowing five more units to form: Nos 148, 207 and 214 at Marham, No. 7 at Honington and No. 49 at Wittering. The latter unit was a dedicated trials unit, formed especially for live weapon trials from 'C' Flight, No. 138 Squadron. In early 1957 No. 90 Squadron formed at Honington, to complete the Valiant fleet of six bomber squadrons, one recce unit and one trials squadron, all within No. 3 Group, Bomber Command.

Life on the V-force

Most of the V-force operating procedures were forged using the Valiant, and from an early date long-distance deployments were undertaken. In the autumn of 1955 two No. 138 Sqn Valiants trekked to Australia, testing the ability of the aircraft to navigate over long distances. Force dispersal was regularly practised, as were detachments to the Mediterranean. Valiants also went to the US in 1957 to participate in a SAC bombing competition.

It was not until 1957 that Vulcans entered full service, by which time the Valiant had held the strategic deterrent mission for two years, armed with Blue Danube. From 1958 the Valiant squadrons at Marham could be armed with US-owned Mk 5 bombs, while in the last years of the Valiant's existence it could also carry the Red Beard tactical bomb.

In the early 1960s, the continuing delivery of Vulcans and Victors released Valiants from the nuclear bomber role for use in other tasks. Withdrawal of the type from the Main Bomber Force began on the first day of 1960, when one Marham unit was reassigned to SACEUR. Marham's other two bomber units followed, the role being continued until the Valiant's demise in early 1965. No. 214 Squadron had been involved in tanking since mid-1958, followed by No. 90 Squadron from 1961. Both retained a bombing tasking, although this was given up in April 1962.

Despite the fact that the Valiant had been fully replaced in the bombing role, only two of the seven bomber squadrons disbanded, No. 138 being the first to go, in April 1962, and No. 7 in September the same year. It was some testament to the versatility of the design that seven Valiant squadrons continued in service in other roles.

Operation Musketeer – Valiants go to war

Operation Musketeer was the codename covering the Suez operation, conducted in conjunction with French and Israeli forces. Twenty-four Valiants were deployed to RAF Luqa, Malta, to fly conventional bombing missions (codenamed Albert) during the campaign which lasted from 31 October to 6 November 1956. A related operation, called Goldflake, covered the deployment of Valiants to deter an attack by Egyptian forces on Cyprus. No. 138 Squadron was completely deployed (eight aircraft), while other contributing units were No. 148 (six aircraft), No. 207 (six) and No. 214 (four). The Valiants operated alongside Canberras deployed to both Luqa and Akrotiri (Cyprus). Canberra B.Mk 6s from No. 139 Squadron provided target-marking for some Valiant strikes. The targets were mainly Egyptian airfields, the first to be hit being Almaza, which was visited by five Valiants from No. 148 Sqn and one from No. 214. Abu Sueir, Cairo West, Fayid, Kabrit, Kasfareet and Luxor airfields were also hit, as were barracks, marshalling yards and a submarine repair depot. During attacks on airfields the Valiants aimed for runway intersections, and crews were briefed to avoid camp areas to keep casualties on the ground to a minimum. Valiant sorties were virtually unopposed, although they met with only mixed success as many of the assembled aircraft had not been fitted with NBS bombing radar or T.2 visual bombsights.

A Valiant B.Mk 1 rests in its dispersal at Luqa between Suez bombing missions. In the background at least four other Valiants and eight Canberras can be seen. A Hastings transport is visible under the nose. Shackletons transported much of the ground support for the Valiant units.

Although the RAF's VC10 fleet is coming to the end of its useful service life, the type is still a vitally important element in the UK's front-line. The VC10s served with distinction during Desert Storm and were then active over the Balkans, before returning to the Gulf in 2003. The hemp scheme seen here has since been superseded by a grey low infra-red paint scheme.

Vickers VC10

Military VC10s

Having entered RAF service as a transport in 1966, the VC10, in various marks, remains a key RAF tanker/transport asset in the early 21st century.

Modification of the Vickers VC10 airliner into a transport gave the RAF useful passenger and cargo-carrying capacity at lower cost compared to the development of a new aircraft. Meeting specification C.239 of 1960 for a strategic long-range transport for what was then Transport Command, the first military VC10s were similar to the civil Standard VC10 but had uprated Rolls-Royce Conway engines and the additional fin fuel cell of the Super VC10. Rearward-facing seats were fitted, as was a side-loading freight door and refuelling probe on the nose centreline forward of the cockpit windows. In addition, a Bristol Siddeley Artouste auxiliary power unit was located in the tailcone.

The first RAF VC10 C.Mk 1 made its maiden flight on 26 November 1965 with initial deliveries to No. 10 Squadron at Fairford in July 1966. No. 10 Sqn was the sole operator of the transport version and undertook the first overseas training flight to Hong Kong in August 1966, regular route flights beginning in April 1967. The later squadron increased its VC10 flights to 27 a month to the Far East via the Persian Gulf, No. 10 relocating to share the main RAF transport

Above: Freight and trooping flights are the C.Mk 1(K)s primary tasks. This machine was photographed at Sarajevo airport while flying in support of UN operations.

The RAF's tanker force regularly operates with other air forces. This mixed formation includes a VC10 K.Mk 4, Tornados and French Mirage 2000s.

***Above:* Early in 1992 a decision was made to modify all 13 remaining C.Mk 1s to tanker/transport standard. Retaining full passenger and freight capability, the C.Mk 1(K) has only the two underwing pods and lacks both the centreline Mk 17 and any additional tanks. Work also included general rectification and the embodiment of regular modifications as well as the installation of the tanker-related 'plumbing' and closed-circuit TV.**

***Left:* The K.Mk 2s and K.Mk 3s accommodated an extra 3,500 Imp gal (15910 litres) of fuel in five equal-sized cells in the former passenger cabin. The tanks were installed via the freight doors of the 'Supers' before they were sealed, but the K.Mk 2s had to be cut in half during conversion. The six standard wing tanks in all VC10s hold a total of 17,925 Imp gal (81480 litres), in addition to the optional fin tank and some 20 Imp gal (91 litres) in each of the refuelling units' reservoirs.**

base at Brize Norton with the Belfasts of No. 53 Sqn. Despite clipping 4 hours 30 minutes off the flight time of the Comet and 12 hours off that of the Britannia, the VC10's Far East destinations meant a long haul of just over 19 hours to Singapore and 22 hours to Hong Kong. Carrying less than half its full payload, the VC10 had a range exceeding 5,000 miles (8047 km).

Foreseeing retirement of the Victor K.Mk 2 tanker force, Air Staff Requirement 406 was made public in 1978, calling for a replacement type, to which a VC10 conversion was tendered. BAe secured the contract, then worth some £40 million, in May 1979, for the 1982/83 delivery of nine aircraft. These comprised five VC10 K.Mk 2s produced from ex-Gulf Air (originally BOAC) Series V1101 early-production VC10s and four K.Mk 3s, the last of the type built, which were Series V1154 Super VC10s once of East African Airways.

The first K.Mk 2 made its maiden flight on 22 June 1982, but not until 1 May 1984 was a specific operating unit formed when No. 101 Sqn was established at Brize Norton. The type's missions included support of Phantom and Lightning (later Tornado F.Mk 3) interceptions of Soviet aircraft around the UK coast and overseas flights with combat aircraft deployed for exercises and training. Refuelled by another VC10 and a TriStar, ZA147 established a non-stop flight record of 16 hours 1 minute 30 seconds between the UK (Brize) and Perth, Australia, on 2 April 1987.

British Airways flew its last scheduled Super VC10 service on 29 March 1981 and 14 of its Supers, plus 23 extra Conways, were bought by the RAF for spare parts reclamation.
In March 1989, the Ministry of Defence requested tenders to meet two needs: Air Staff Requirement 415 for conversion of five of the British Airways Super VC10s to K.Mk 4 standard and ASR416 covering upgrading of eight No. 101 Squadron aircraft to C.Mk 1(K) standard. The first of the resulting VC10 K.Mk 4s entered service with No. 101 Sqn in 1993 and these aircraft, along with the K.Mk 3s and the last of the C.Mk 1(K) fleet, continue to bear the brunt of the RAF's inflight refuelling effort in 2007, pending replacement by the Future Strategic Tanker Aircraft (FSTA), based on the Airbus A330.

As well as supporting regular RAF training flights and deployments, the VC10s have to undertake the bulk of inflight refuelling test missions with new aircraft and equipment. This VC10 K.Mk 2 was photographed while refuelling a Strike/Attack Operational Evaluation Unit Harrier GR.Mk 7 in 1997.

Aside from successful operations with the US Navy and USAF, the A-7 Corsair II found three foreign operators, Greece, Portugal (pictured), and, more recently, Thailand.

Vought A-7 Corsair II

Hard-hitting 'SLUF'

The A-7 Corsair II flew its last combat mission in Operation Desert Storm, after which it was put out to pasture to make space for a new generation of hi-tech warplanes. Having acquired a superb reputation in a number of conflicts, it is, today, missed by many.

The Corsair II no longer flies in American colours. But for 30 years the distinctive A-7 fought in every conflict that came its way, and established a dominant position as a superb subsonic attack aircraft.

Pilots called it the SLUF (Short Little Ugly F*****) and loved it with a passion. Ground combat commanders liked the A-7 because it offered a new standard of accuracy when it unleashed bombs on a target, the bombs often being aimed only a short distance from 'friendlies'.

The Corsair II's economical turbofan engine also gave it the 'legs' to rove in enemy territory and strike at will. When the A-7 replaced the A-4 Skyhawk in the Gulf of Tonkin in 1967, pilots suddenly discovered that they had enough fuel to roam freely over North Vietnam. No target was too far away, nor was any target too small to be struck, now, with pinpoint accuracy. By the standards of the mid-1960s, the A-7 Corsair II was a 'smart' bomb-carrying warplane before the world's air forces began developing 'smart bombs'.

The A-7 was a straightforward, shoulder-wing aircraft with swept flight surfaces, provision for inflight refuelling, and narrow-track tricycle landing gear. Despite its somewhat awkward appearance, it was a very conventional design except for its continuous-solution NWDS (navigation and weapon delivery system), the most advanced such system of its era.

YA-7A BuNo. 152580 was the first prototype and was rolled out of the LTV hangars at NAS Dallas on 13 August 1965. Its first flight was on 27 September of the same year. It was named Corsair II in honour of the Chance Vought F4U Corsair of World War II fame.

Right: Developed for combat-crew training, the A-7K was a two-seater based on the A-7D. The aircraft, 31 of which were built, only equipped ANG units and this example (the prototype A-7K, 73-1008) was part of the 152nd Tactical Fighter Training Squadron, Arizona ANG.

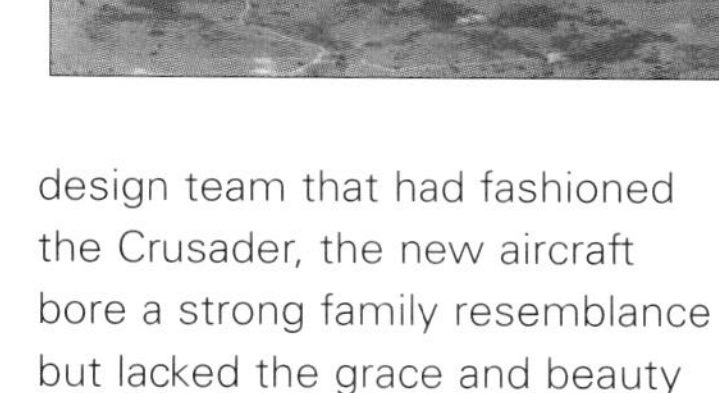

Below: Sidewinders and bombs arm this A-7E as it heads across the Arabian peninsula on the way to attack Iraqi targets. Only two US Navy light attack units, based on the USS John F. Kennedy**, used A-7s in the 1991 Gulf War.**

The pilot sat very far forward, at the very tip of the nose, ahead of the nose wheel. He – or she, since the A-7 was the first combat aircraft to be flown by female aviators, first inducted into the USN in 1974 – could not even see the swept wings from the cockpit. Visibility was good, and the 'SLUF' was easy to handle when taxiing on the ground and when flying in the 'pattern' around an airfield or aircraft-carrier.

It would have been a brilliant design, except that the A-7 Corsair II lacked sufficient power to go along with a fine airframe, weapons-hauling capability, accuracy and range. Even later versions with improved engines never provided enough thrust to give the pilot a comfortable margin of flexibility.

It was in 1964 that the US Navy chose Vought to build a new attack aircraft based upon its much-admired F-8 Crusader supersonic fighter. Created on the drawing board by the same design team that had fashioned the Crusader, the new aircraft bore a strong family resemblance but lacked the grace and beauty of its predecessor.

The first pre-production Corsair II completed its maiden flight on 27 September 1965, almost exactly a decade after that of its Crusader forebear. By then, the US was deeply committed to a build-up in Vietnam. Early A-7s were in the combat zone within two years of that first flight.

In 1967, the navigation and weapons delivery system of the A-7 was the most advanced in the world. Pilots were delighted that they could actually 'pickle' a bomb on a specific building, or on the centre of a bridge, even if the target was in a congested area. The development of laser-guided and other PGMs was occurring at the same time that the A-7 was appearing on carrier decks, and over time the Corsair II gained the ability to carry 'smart' bombs.

On a typical mission, a Corsair II carried up to 15,000 lb (6804 kg) of weapons on six wing and two fuselage pylons.

Although Vought had not previously had the Air Force as a customer, the USAF adopted the A-7 (although not the Corsair II name). In Vietnam, USAF 'SLUFs' excelled in the 'Sandy' mission, escorting that rescue helicopters that picked up downed airmen in enemy terrain.

Final flurry

The A-7 became a staple aircraft of the ANG, and with Greece and Portugal. Thailand later acquired ex-USN aircraft.

Very late in the career of the Corsair II, just a year before Operation Desert Storm in which the US Navy flew the type in combat for the last time, Vought built and flew two prototypes of an extensively redesigned, much more advanced, version with afterburning engines and new avionics systems. Flight tests revealed great promise, but the second-generation Corsair II never went into production.

Above: Engulfed in steam from a catapult track, this A-7E is prepared for launch from USS John F. Kennedy**. The aircraft's outer stores stations are fitted with triple ejection racks carrying cluster bombs, while defensive AIM-9s are mounted on fuselage rails.**

Right: It was during Vietnam that the Corsair II first saw combat and it was in this conflict, due to its superb performance, that its reputation was forged.

An A-7E of VA-192 'Golden Dragons', a CAG bird, hauls bombs into harm's way. A-7s replaced A-4 Skyhawks in light attack squadrons. Now pilots had the fuel to rove anywhere in North Vietnam and strike at will.

US Navy service

Despite launching problems, once it was aloft, the A-7A could roam anywhere in Vietnam. It was ugly and underpowered, but it could go further and carry more than its predecessor, the A-4 Skyhawk.

The US Navy A-7A entered the fray in southeast Asia on 4 December 1967 with attack squadron VA-147 'Argonauts', flying from USS *Ranger*. On 17 December, A-7As joined A-4 Skyhawks and A-6 Intruders in an assault on the Hai Duong rail and highway bridge between Haiphong and Hanoi.

For the rest of the war, the shipborne A-7 gave naval aviators a platform that could roam North Vietnam at leisure, striking when targets of opportunity presented themselves. The Corsair II not only had a roomy cockpit and a huge ordnance load, it had almost double the endurance of the Skyhawk, giving its pilots much longer 'reach' and greater flexibility. The NWDS of the Corsair II also introduced a new standard of precision accuracy.

A typical bombload consisted of 12 500-lb (227-kg) Mk 82 iron bombs fitted on MERs (multiple ejector racks). Lt Benjamin Short of VA-82 'Marauders' was carrying this load on a 1968 mission when he located a concrete bridge on North Vietnam's Route One, spanning about 400 ft (120 m). He made his run-in and cut across the bridge at a slight angle, putting eight or nine of the bombs on the bridge.

As he pulled off, he rolled up on a wingtip after bringing his nose up well above the horizon. From this perch, he examined the results. There was plenty of smoke and fire, but little damage to the bridge. Despite the accuracy the A-7 assured, bridges remained exceedingly difficult targets throughout the war.

The USN continued to improve the Corsair II and to introduce new capabilities. Even the A-7E model, however, which began flying with the 'Argonauts' and the 'Diamonds' of VA-146 from USS *America* in May 1970 was still – like all warplanes in this series – underpowered. American fliers greatly admired the bombload, range, endurance and flexibility, but wished that the Corsair II had just a little more power, especially when needing to move quickly in and out of a target area. In May 1972, USN Corsairs supported the mining of Haiphong harbour as the US began its final massive campaign near the end of the war.

Both USAF and US Navy A-7s remained in the Vietnam fight until the end. With the A-7A passing out of squadron service in the mid- to late-1970s, the A-7E became the US Navy's primary light attack platform. The A-7E entered first-line service with VA-174 in 1969 and the variant saw extensive service over Vietnam.

Return to war

September 1983 saw the A-7E back in combat. A flotilla of US ships, tasked with supporting a multinational peacekeeping force in Beirut was fired upon by shore-based Syrian artillery. A TARPS-pod equipped F-14A was launched, with a pair of VA-12 Corsairs from USS *Dwight D. Eisenhower* flying SEAD support. In the event, no ordnance was expended, but the A-7s would remain on station until the end of the year, with shots fired on many occasions.

On 3 December, a brace of F-14As was fired upon by Syrian

VA-27 'Royal Maces' was one of the earliest A-7A units to be introduced into combat in southeast Asia. An example can be seen here, 'bombed up' and waiting to take off.

Left: ***The Texas Instruments AN/AAR-4S FLIR pod was introduced to the A-7E community from 1977. Weighing 720 lb (327 kg), the pod occupied the inner starboard wing pylon and was fully integrated with the aircraft's systems to allow low-level navigation and attacks to be carried out at night.***

Below: ***These Naval Air Warfare Center A-7Es were photographed dropping inert 500-lb (227-kg) retarded bombs on a flight from their China Lake base.***

forces, leading to full-scale strikes by A-6s and A-7Es. The strikes seemed generally successful, although the loss of both a Corsair and an Intruder cast a shadow over the entire operation. Rather more conclusive was the involvement of A-7Es from *Independence* in the 1983 action against Grenada.

As part of its complement, 'Indy' included two squadrons, VA-15 and VA-87, with the A-7E. Urgent Fury, the US invasion of Grenada, got under way on 23 October. Corsairs were called in during the morning to support US Army Rangers. Later, a group of US Navy SEALs, pinned down by fire, called on A-7s for relief. The Corsairs attacked enemy positions, but one turned out to be in use as a psychiatric hospital. Later, the A-7's involvement in the campaign would score the type another black mark, when an A-7E attacked a misidentified target on 27 October, injuring 16 US troops. Nevertheless, overall, the ability of the Corsair to provide close support and, in the majority of cases, to hit targets accurately, was an important factor in the operation's success.

As the 1980s wore on, the A-7 became a key element in all but two of the Navy's air wings. Eleven out of 13 operational carriers boasted A-7Es, all embarking two squadrons of the type. The writing was on the wall however, as the F/A-18A approached its service debut.

Libya and back to Iran

In 1986 a large naval presence was established off Libya, including VA-81 and VA-83 with their A-7Es aboard *Saratoga*. A number of minor exchanges saw A-7s launching HARMs against Libyan SAM sites, but on 5 April a discotheque in Berlin, crammed with US military personnel, was blown up.

The US response was swift, Operation El Dorado Canyon seeing USAF F-111s and USN A-6E Intruders attacking ground targets in Libya. *America*, which had replaced *Saratoga*, dispatched the A-7Es of VA-46 and VA-72 against SAM sites with great success.

By 1988, the Hornet had entered service in strength, but the 'SLUF' could still deliver the goods when required. The A-7Es of VA-22 and VA-94 got the chance to demonstrate this ability on 14 April in the Persian Gulf. When USS *Samuel B. Roberts* hit a mine, the Corsairs were called in to make retaliatory strikes against Iranian oil platforms and shipping.

As the Navy's last two A-7 units, VA-46 and VA-72 were part way through their transition to the F/A-18 when the A-7's final call to war came. Flying from *John F. Kennedy*, A-7s of the two squadrons expended around 2,000,000 lb (206116 kg) of ordnance and fired in excess of 140 HARMs, during the course of 745 Desert Storm missions. On 16 May 1991, almost immediately upon returning from the Gulf, the Corsair II was formally retired.

A-7E Corsair II

A-7E BuNo. 158842 ('AC/402') was assigned to Commander John Leenhouts, VA-72's executive officer and a leading exponent of naval Corsair operations. VA-72 flew from USS *John F. Kennedy* (CV-67), alongside VA-46, as part of CVW-3 for the duration of Operation Desert Storm.

AGM-88 HARM
Expended in huge numbers by a wide range of warplane types, the High-Speed Anti-Radiation missile gave the A-7E a formidable lethal SEAD capability. An interesting tactic developed during the war was to 'lob' a number of missiles ahead of an advancing strike package, the presence of such a threat being more than enough to force the Iraqi air SAM/AAA search radar operators to shut their systems down.

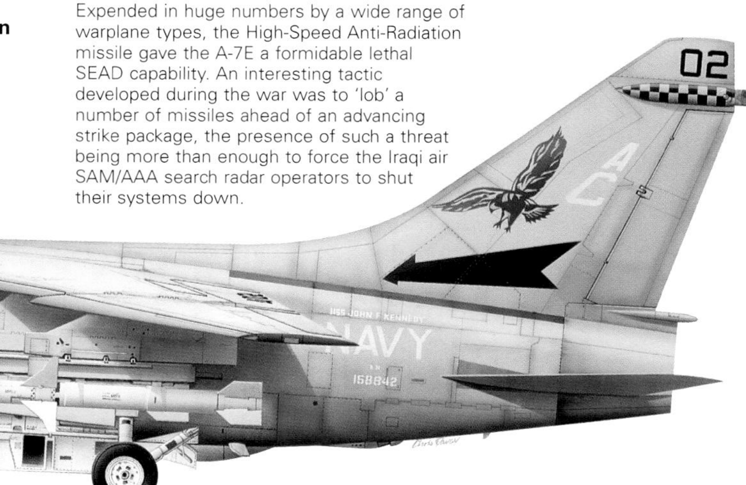

In ANG service the A-7D wore four different camouflage schemes. The initial SEA three-tone scheme gave way to this wrap-around scheme. It was followed by 'lizard', and finally two-tone grey.

USAF service

Having seen brief but intense action in southeast Asia, the A-7D became the backbone of the Air National Guard's attack force until replaced in the early 1990s by the more modern F-16.

Although it was introduced to combat by the USAF late in the Vietnam War, the 'SLUF' acquitted itself well, notably in the 'Sandy' rescue support role, and during the *Mayaguez* incident in May 1975.

Not until October 1972 did the USAF begin to deploy the A-7D aircraft on combat missions in Vietnam. The A-7D quickly emerged as a replacement for the A-1 Skyraider in the 'Sandy' CSAR mission. Again, although this warplane was underpowered, its enormous range and flexibility were a great asset to commanders seeking to cover a rescue mission.

Vietnam units

Most of the USAF's A-7Ds were operated by the 354th Tactical Fighter Wing, deployed from Myrtle Beach AFB, South Carolina. Others were flown by the independent 3rd Tactical Fighter Squadron. The latter was commanded by Lt Col Edward R. 'Moose' Skowron who enjoyed a reputation for 'derring-do'. On one rescue mission, he criss-crossed the pick-up site, drawing fire from North Vietnamese guns, in order to pinpoint the enemy to enable a rescue chopper to make a successful 'grab'. Although Skowron was not hit on that mission, the A-7 established a reputation for being able to absorb battle damage, yet whisk its pilot safely home.

The capability of the A-7D was vindicated during a spectacular mission in November 1972 when Cpt. Colin A. 'Arnie' Clarke flew perhaps the longest fighter sortie of the war. Seeking to engineer a rescue of a two-man F-105G Wild Weasel crew shot down near Vinh, Clarke spent a marathon 12 hours in his A-7D cockpit with four refuellings from KC-135s. He fought poor weather, faulty communications, and heavy ground fire to guide two HH-53 'Super Jolly' helicopters to the rescue. This was the last F-105 crew downed in the Vietnam War, and Clarke's extraordinary effort resulted in its extraction from enemy territory. Clarke was awarded the Air Force Cross for his actions.

In the active-duty US Air Force the A-7D was an interim type, bridging the gap between the F-100/F-4 and the A-10A in the interdiction role. Only three major CONUS-based units were equipped with the 'SLUF' (which was never officially known as Corsair II in USAF parlance): the 23rd, 354th and 355th TFWs. The latter was based at Davis-Monthan (hence the 'DM' tailcode) and handled all A-7 training during the type's brief active-duty career. This is the aircraft of Colonel Fred Haeffner, who was wing commander between August 1972 and July 1974. The machine was chosen for its appropriate serial number and is marked with the fin-stripe colours of the constituent squadrons. The two stars below the cockpit rail represent Haeffner's kills from the Vietnam War, gained while flying F-4Cs.

Above: Many deployments were made to Europe. Here 157th TFS aircraft are seen at Wittering in 1978 during **Coronet Teal.**

Right: **Scrappy** *served with the 162nd FS, the last A-7 unit. The undernose fairing housed the Pave Penny laser target seeker.*

Not long after the return of A-7s from the warzone, the first active-duty unit, the 333rd TFTS of the 355th TFW at Davis-Monthan AFB, Arizona, began its transition to the A-10A in 1976. The final active-duty A-7 wing, the 23rd TFW at England AFB, Louisiana, began conversion to the A-10 in September 1980.

As a result of this front-line re-equipment, large numbers of A-7Ds were released to join those already serving with the Air National Guard. The first A-7Ds for the Guard had been delivered to the 188th TFS, New Mexico ANG, in October 1973, and in the following year a further three units re-equipped. In the remaining years of the 1970s, a further 10 squadrons adopted the 'SLUF', and by 1982 the total force stood at 15 squadrons, the A-7 forming the backbone of the ANG attack force.

Training for the ANG squadrons was first handled by the Arizona ANG at Tucson, although in 1984 this task was handed over to the newly formed 195th TFTS at the same base. By this time, the ANG had received 30 new-build A-7K two-seaters, this variant having first flown in January 1981, the prototype being a conversion of an A-7D.

Two A-7 units transitioned to the F-16 in the mid-1980s. For the remainder of the decade the ANG force stabilised at 13 squadrons plus the RTU (Replacement Training Unit).

A-7 improvements

Several modifications were applied to the fleet. The first was the adoption from 1977 of Automatic Maneuver Flaps which improved handling at high angles of attack and countered a tendency to depart at nose-high attitudes. The Pave Penny marked target seeker was also added to 383 A-7D/Ks.

Finally, in 1987/88 a total of 78 A-7D/Ks were given the LANA (Low Altitude Night Attack) system, which consisted of FLIR, wide-angle HUD, AN/APQ-126 radar and automatic flight control system. LANA A-7s were issued to three squadrons.

ANG A-7s made many overseas deployments. During one of these, to Howard AFB, Panama, in late 1989, the Guard was called to action. Six aircraft of the 112th TFS/Ohio ANG flew 22 close support sorties during Operation Just Cause, the invasion of Panama.

From 1990 the ANG began retiring its A-7 fleet, most squadrons converting to F-16s. Three squadrons converted in 1991, seven in 1992 and the final three in 1993. The last squadron was the 162nd Fighter Squadron, Ohio ANG.

Tucson's fine weather made it a natural choice to be the A-7 training base. The 195th TFTS was established in 1984 as the Replacement Training Unit, a role which it completed in July 1991 as the need for new A-7 pilots had evaporated. This is one of the squadron's A-7Ks.

Left: The last camouflage scheme used by the A-7 was this two-tone grey pattern, first applied in 1987 to the three Ohio ANG squadrons. This pair is from Iowa's 124th TFS, which operated LANA aircraft.

Above: The 3rd TFS was formed to give PACAF its own A-7D unit in the combat theatre. 3rd TFS aircraft took part in the evacuation of Saigon in April 1975 and the rescue of the merchant vessel **Mayaguez.**

Vought F8U/F-8 Crusader

The last gunfighter

Vought's Crusader did not suffer the performance penalties often associated with aircraft designed for the rigours of operations at sea. The 'MiG-Master', or 'the last gunfighter' as it became known after its exploits in Vietnam, easily outperformed USAF fighters of the day and became a jet fighter classic.

While aircraft like the USAF's 'Century Series' fighters had made supersonic flight an everyday occurrence in the early 1950s, carrierborne aircraft lagged behind in the performance stakes, encumbered as they were by the stronger airframes, extra equipment and extra fuel made necessary by operations from aircraft-carriers.

With a view to rectifying this situation, the US Navy issued a call for an advanced carrier fighter in September 1952, eight manufacturers receiving requests for design proposals.

Guns and missiles

As well as the usual features of a carrier aircraft, the successful design was to carry machine-guns or cannon as well as missiles, and was to be highly manoeuvrable.

One of the companies approached was Chance Vought, the highly experienced builder of naval aircraft. It was Vought's Model V-383, powered by an afterburning Pratt & Whitney J57 turbojet, that was declared the winner in May 1953 and the designation XF8U-1 assigned to the two prototypes.

Several features helped the F8U to meet the USN's performance requirements. Lightweight metals were included in the aircraft's construction, the aerodynamics of which incorporated the recently developed area-ruled fuselage which reduced drag. An innovation unique to the Crusader was its variable-incidence wing, which could be

Above: Two F8U prototypes were built, the first taking to the air for the first time on 25 March 1955. The design required no major alterations, entering production soon after the first flight.

Top: 'Flaming mouth' intake markings were a feature of the F8U-2s (F-8Cs) of VF-84 'Vagabonds' (later 'Jolly Rogers'), which received examples of the variant in 1961 and flew them for three years before transitioning to the F-4B Phantom II.

Inflight refuelling capability was a feature of the Crusader from the outset. Here, an early production F8U-1 maintains a tail-down attitude to stay in contact with a North American AJ-2 Savage tanker.

***Above:* The F8U-2N (later F-8D) was perhaps the ultimate fighter model of the Crusader. Fitted with a more powerful J57 engine than the F-8C and devoid of air-to-ground equipment, the D-model was considered by many pilots to be the fastest Crusader and the most enjoyable variant to fly.**

***Below:* The 'Two-sader', XF8U-1T (BuNo. 143710), remained a 'one-off'. Offered to, but rejected by, the USN as a conversion trainer, the two-seat, dual-control aircraft served with Vought as a demonstrator, and later with the USN Test Pilots' School and NASA.**

raised by 7° for take-off and landing, allowing the fuselage to remain 'straight and level' during these regimes and thus improving forward visibility.

Maiden flight

Twenty-two months later, in March 1955, the first Crusader made its maiden flight, at Edwards AFB. With no major design flaws requiring rectification, the F8U-1 entered production almost straight away and the initial examples were delivered in September 1955. The USMC accepted its first production Crusader in January 1956, as the first 13 USN pilots, from VF-32 and VF(AW)-3, were beginning Crusader training.

Initial F8U carrier qualifications were scheduled for April 1956 and the third pre-production aircraft was loaded aboard USS *Forrestal*. On 4 April the aircraft made six touch-and-goes on the ship's deck, followed by the first arrested landing and first catapult take-off. Further trials reinforced the basic correctness of the design and the aircraft was set for fleet service.

Meanwhile, in order to show off its new fighter, the US Navy determined to surpass USAF speed records. Actually, the US Navy did not want the F8U to achieve its top speed because it did not want to disclose the full capabilities of the new aircraft. In two speed runs on 21 August 1956, the 12th production F8U-1 hit an average of 1,015 mph (1633 km/h), a little slower than the British mark established by the Fairey FD2, but nearly 200 mph (322 km/h) faster than the USAF's record.

VX-3's ship-to-ship dash

A visit to the new 'Forrestal'-class carrier *Saratoga* by President Eisenhower afforded the Navy its next opportunity to parade the F8U-1. VX-3 made a two-aircraft cross-country dash. Launching on 6 June 1957 from USS *Bon Homme Richard* off the California coast, the two F8U-1s flew towards Dallas. The pair refuelled from AJ-2 tankers, then blasted back up to their 45,000-ft (13716-m) cruising altitude and their cruise speed of Mach 0.96.

Finally, as they approached the East Coast, the aircraft descended towards the *Saratoga*. A fast fly-by was made at 600 kt (689 mph; 1106 km/h), barely 75 ft (23 m) above the water, before coming in to land. It was an impressive display, and the elapsed time from launch to trap was three hours and 28 minutes, an unofficial record.

Another transcontinental dash took place on 16 July 1958. Marine Major John H. Glenn planned a west-to-east transcontinental dash known as Project Bullet. The flight would be made at supersonic speed and, in the course of it, the entire US would be photographed. Glenn would fly from Los Angeles in the third F8U-1P, escorted by an F8U-1, with AJ-1 Savages flying as inflight tankers.

The F8U-1 was forced to abort the flight when its inflight refuelling probe was damaged during the first refuelling. Glenn pressed on alone and, three hours and 23 minutes later, touched down at New York's Floyd Bennett Field. The average speed was 725.55 mph (1167.63 km/h), Mach 1.1.

Fleet deployments

While the early Crusaders garnered public recognition, the F8U-1 was entering the fleet. VX-3 received the initial production F8U-1s in December 1956, but VF-32 was the first fleet squadron to re-equip at NAS Cecil Field in March 1957, followed by West Coast squadrons VF-154 and VF(AW)-3. February 1958 saw the first Crusader deployment, in USS *Hancock* with VF-194 in the Pacific, and VF-32 in *Saratoga* for the first Atlantic deployment.

Events in Lebanon brought US intervention in summer 1958 when Eisenhower ordered amphibious landings by the Marines. VF-32 flew its new F8U-2s from *Saratoga* during the crisis, patrolling the beaches during the landings. It was the first time the Crusader had entered a hostile area.

Development of a dedicated photo-reconnaissance platform began using the 32nd F8U-1. The fighter's cannon were deleted and to accommodate the cameras, the fuselage belly was flattened and the inflight refuelling probe was completely enclosed. The horizontal tail was reduced to increase the aircraft's speed, which would be the F8U-1P's only defence.

The F8U-1P first flew on 17 December 1956, and eventually matured as the RF-8G which joined the fleet in October 1965. The photo-Crusader faced its first real test during the Cuban Missile Crisis of 1962. Both VFP-62 and VMCJ-2 were placed on standby, but in the event four Marine pilots were temporarily assigned to VFP-62 for the operations.

The ultimate USN Crusader variant was the F8U-2NE (F-8E), which boasted a larger radar and a full air-to-ground capability. This aircraft, seen during carrier trials, carries a Mk 84 2,000-lb (907-kg) bomb and eight Zuni rockets.

Crusader in service

Above: VF-124 was the Pacific coast F-8 training unit and was responsible for training many of the pilots who flew the type in Vietnam.

As the first carrier-borne aircraft capable of speeds in excess of 1,000 mph (1600 km/h), the Crusader enjoyed a long and illustrious career with the US Navy, US Marine Corps and the French navy.

The F8U-1E (F-8B) with AN/APS-67 radar for limited all-weather capability first flew in September 1958, but the first true fleet Crusader fighter was the 'Charlie', which flew in August 1957 as the F8U-2. It used the 17,500-lb (77.85-kN) afterburning thrust J57-P-16 engine.

A characteristic feature of the Crusader line appeared on the C model: the fuselage ventral strakes which were designed to increase directional stability at high altitudes. The F-8C also gained two additional AIM-9s.

A development of the F8U-2 was the -2N, eventually redesignated F-8D. Many pilots considered the D model, with its powerful J57-P-20 engine delivering 18,000 lb (80.07 kN) of thrust in afterburner, to be the fastest Crusader. Although it equipped several fleet squadrons by 1965, and saw heavy action (albeit with only two Navy squadrons in the initial phases of direct US involvement in Vietnam), it was quickly superseded by the definitive 'E'.

With the introduction of the F8U-2NE (F-8E), the Crusader had matured as a multi-role warplane. It was essentially an improvement on the F-8D, featuring improved radar and engine plus avionics to fire the Bullpup ASM, and a pair of underwing pylons. Some F-8Es were later modified as F-8Js with boundary layer control for improved low-speed handling, while F-8Cs and F-8Bs were upgraded as F-8Ks and F-8Ls respectively.

Retirement process

After a long and eventful career, which included a deep involvement in combat over Vietnam, the fighter Crusader began to fade from front-line Navy service. The last Navy fighter F-8 retired on 19 May 1976, the last USMC fighter F-8 retiring in the same year.

However, VFP-63 continued to provide RF-8G detachments for the Navy's carriers throughout the late 1970s, while the retirement of the RA-5C Vigilante in 1979 and the scarcity of the USMCs RF-4Bs, led to the RF-8G being even more busy than usual. Indeed, the RF-8Gs were given J57-P-420 engines in 1977, giving nearly one-third more power and just in time for the

Above: VF-32 was the first Fleet squadron to receive the Crusader, taking delivery of its F8U-1s in March 1957. The Crusader marked a massive leap in performance and combat capability over its predecessors, the McDonnell F3H Demon (seen here, rear left) and the Douglas F4D Skyray. The 'Swordsmen' traded in their Crusaders for F-4B Phantoms in 1965.

RF-8 Crusaders provided critical reconnaissance for over 20 years. For most of the 1960s VFP-62 provided the photo-reconnaissance detachments to the Atlantic fleet carriers, and played an important role during the 1962 Cuban missile crisis. The squadron traded its RF-8As (shown) for RF-8Gs in 1965.

1979 Iranian hostage crisis. VFP-63's Det 5 provided vital reconnaissance during the operation, which was the photo-Crusader's last combat cruise.

The RF-8s last cruise, to the Indian Ocean, finished on 22 March 1982 and on 28 May the last fleet Crusader flew into retirement. Yet still the F-8 refused to go away. The photo-Crusader continuing to fly with the Naval Air Reserve, with VFP-206 destined to be the very last US Navy Crusader squadron. In October 1986, VFP-206 flew carrier qualifications on the USS *America* and on 18 October an RF-8G flew the Crusader's last carrier launch.On 29 March 1987 the last Crusader squadron retired, along with the last RF-8.

French service

The Crusader's career was as long with France's Aéronavale as it was with the US Navy, and the Crusader's success is all the more remarkable since only 42 F-8s entered French service.

The French wanted a replacement for the ageing first-generation jets that flew from their two new carriers, *Foch* and *Clemenceau*, but the Crusader's high approach speed gave cause for concern in operating from smaller decks. Vought extensively reworked the F-8's wing and incorporated boundary layer control, which blew hot engine air over the wing-control surfaces, creating more lift and thus reducing the approach and stall speeds. The horizontal tail was also enlarged for better stability. An F-8D was used for the test airframe and flew in February 1964, and the first production F-8E(FN) flew that June. The production run was completed in January 1965.

In May 1965, the first qualifications on board a French carrier were conducted. Although the F-8E(FN) retained the US armament of four 20-mm cannon, the external missile load was altered to accommodate the MATRA R.530 and R.550 AAMs.

A quartet of F-8Es from VMF(AW)-312 passes over the San Bernadino mountains close to the unit's home at MCAS El Toro in California. The ground-attack capability of the F-8E was to be greatly appreciated by the Corps when it took the type to war in Vietnam. The 'Checkerboards' received its first F8U-1s in 1959 and only had a short combat tour with F-8Es at Da Nang in 1965.

Two Flottilles de Chasse were equipped with the F-8, 12F and 14F being recommissioned in October 1964 and March 1965, respectively. 14F transitioned to the Super Etendard in May 1979.

The only combat service the F-8(FN)s saw was during September 1983. *Foch* arrived off Lebanon on 6 September, and on 22 September F-8E(FN)s flew CAP for a Super Etendard strike that hit rebel positions in Lebanon. The air group transferred to *Clemenceau* when that ship relieved *Foch* in early October. Several reconnaissance missions were then flown.

In late 1977, the Philippine government purchased 35 F-8Hs, 25 of which were to be completely refurbished by Vought and the remaining 10 to serve as replacement aircraft. These went to the 7th Tactical Fighter Squadron at Basa, Luzon.

In March 1984, Vought sent a contingent to help the Philippine air force refurbish its 19 remaining F-8Hs. The Crusaders had begun to show deterioration in the humid Philippine environment. Finally, only 12 F-8s remained, with only eight airframes being fully mission-capable at any one time. By 1991, those that remained were retired.

After a major rework, including strengthening the wings, France's refurbished F-8E(FN)s were redesignated F-8Ps. These 17 aircraft remained in service until 12F finally disbanded in December 1999.

F-8E Crusader

This well-worn F-8E belongs to US Marine Corps all-weather fighter squadron VMF(AW)-235 and is depicted as it would have appeared during the time of the siege of Khe Sanh in 1968. The unit's 'Bozo Noses' nickname was derived from the red star-studded star markings applied to the nose, ventral fins and tail.

Zuni rockets
The 5-in (127-mm) Zuni rocket was the most widely used of the F-8's attack weapons. The aircraft could not carry the standard four-round LAU-10 launcher on the fuselage pylons, and so specialised two-round launchers were developed. The rockets had various warheads in the 43- to 56-lb (19.5- to 25.5-kg) class, including HE frag, general purpose, anti-personnel, incendiary, smoke and flare.

VMF(AW)-235
The 'Death Angels' rapidly became one of the best-known units flying in Vietnam. The squadron's two deployments to Vietnam ran from February 1966 to November 1966 and from May 1967 to the end of 1968. The unit flew 9,140 operational missions.

The Yak-25RV high-altitude reconnaissance aircraft was evolved from the Yak-25 during 1957/58 in response to the U-2. All-new straight wings were added to ensure high-altitude performance.

Yakovlev Yak-25/26/27/28

Tactical twinjets

In 1951 Yakovlev began development of a new two-seat all-weather interceptor to patrol the northern expanses of the USSR. The Yak-25 was in turn developed into the long-span 'Mandrake' spyplane.

Soviet PVO units stationed in the extreme north of the USSR were the first to re-equip with the new Yak-25M. These units were scattered over a vast territory, often hundreds of miles apart. Quite often the Yak-25Ms had to ward off NATO spyplanes and escort the B-52s which habitually patrolled the northern borders of the USSR.

Two fighter units with the Group of Soviet Forces in Germany also operated the Yak-25M, between 1956 and 1965.

Despite the fact that the Yak-25M differed considerably from the MiG-17 in design philosophy (it had two engines, a bicycle landing gear, and dual controls), conversion from the 'Fresco' to the 'Flashlight-A' presented no problems. Many pilots transitioning to the Yak-25M were pleased with its spacious cockpit, which was an improvement over the cramped workstation of the MiG-17.

The Yak-25M equipped with the RP-6 radar was the first Soviet all-weather interceptor with limited 'lookdown' capability and able to destroy targets flying below 3,280 ft (1000 m). The Yak-25M was phased out in 1969. Fifteen years is not much of a service term for a warplane, but this is no reflection on its qualities; indeed, the Yak-25M 'Flashlight' earned the affection and trust of its crews.

Reconnaissance platform

The Yak-25RV reconnaissance development also stayed in service for about 15 years until superseded by the new MiG-25R and MiG-25RB. Surprisingly, despite being stationed in East Germany the Yak-25RV was never noted over Western Europe. However, it was noted over China, India and Pakistan.

Development of the Yak-123 light tactical bomber was completed in 1955, and the aircraft received the service

The Yak-120 was the first prototype for the Yak-25 patrol interceptor, with RP-6 Sokol *radar, and two 37-mm cannon on the centre fuselage sides. The aircraft was first flown by V. M. Volkov on 19 June 1952, and was ordered in late 1953.*

***Left:** The Yak-25M introduced the definitive **RP-6** radar in place of the interim **RP-1** Izumrud carried by the initial production 'Flashlight-A'. A total of 406 aircraft were completed.*

***Below:** The Yak-26 bomber, seen here in modified form, could carry eight 100-kg (220-lb) **FAB-100 HE** bombs, four 250-kg (551-lb) **FAB-250 HE** bombs or two 500-kg (1,102-lb) **FAB-500** weapons as an alternative to a nuclear store.*

designation Yak-26. The aircraft was primarily intended to carry one nuclear 'special store'. The RD-9AK afterburning turbojet specified for the first prototype was a version of the RD-9B powering most MiG-19 versions.

Even with interim RD-9AK engines the Yak-123 was markedly superior in speed and service ceiling to the Il-28 which made up the backbone of the Soviet tactical bomber force; in fact, it was the Soviet Union's first supersonic tactical bomber.

By the end of 1956 a pre-production batch of Yak-26s had been completed. Given the satisfactory results of trials, the next logical thing to do would be to launch production of the upgraded Yak-26, since by mid-1957 the Soviet air force still had no supersonic bombers on strength. However, Yakovlev was already working on a much more capable tactical bomber whose development had been initiated in March 1956. Designated Yak-129, this aircraft would be powered by more powerful Tumanskii R-11-300 afterburning turbojets and a bomb load of 6,613 lb (3000 kg). Thus the VVS preferred the as-yet unflown Yak-129 (the future Yak-28) – a decision later proven wise.

Designated Yak-122, the Soviet Union's first supersonic reconnaissance aircraft was developed in parallel with the Yak-123. The Yak-122 shared the fate of the Yak-123 bomber – for much the same reasons; being a parallel development, it shared the bomber's design flaws and was surpassed by more capable types before the aircraft had a chance to mature.

Nevertheless, Yakovlev sought ways of improving the Yak-122. The aircraft was subsequently converted into the first prototype of the Yak-27R tactical reconnaissance aircraft which did enter production.

The Yak-121 was effectively the first prototype of a new interceptor which received the service designation Yak-27. Being very familiar with the basic 'Flashlight-A', the Saratov aircraft factory had no major problems gearing up for Yak-27 production, which began in 1956, incorporating various changes based on the Yak-121's test results and a revised air force requirement issued in 1955. The Yak-27 was built in two versions, with cannons or AAMs.

In the event, the cannon-armed 'Flashlight-C' was not proceeded with. The chosen missile for the Yak-27 was the K-8; consequently, the 'missilised' Flashlight-C received the designation Yak-27K. Production Yak-27Ks underwent manufacturer's flight tests throughout 1958. Generally the Yak-27K earned positive comments from the pilots who flew it. Yet the aircraft was destined never to enter service.

Success at last

The OKB's efforts with the Yak-27 were not in vain, as one version finally did enter production after all. In 1958 the Yak-122 reconnaissance prototype underwent a major conversion, becoming the prototype of the Yak-27R 'Mangrove' tactical reconnaissance aircraft. The navigator/RSO's station was reworked and the result was a cross-breed between the Yak-26 bomber prototype and the original Yak-122. The aircraft was powered by RD-9Fs. All in all the Saratov aircraft factory produced 180 Yak-27Rs which saw service with the tactical arm of the VVS for the next 20 years.

*Yak-27Rs were stationed in East Germany and Poland as well as within the **USSR**, the 16th Air Army operating the type between 1966 and 1971. In East Germany the aircraft was operated by the 11th **ORAP** at Neu-Welzow and the 931st **GvORAP** at Stendal, which later moved to Werneuchen.*

'Brewer' and 'Firebar'

The second Yak-28 prototype was used to test the performance of the R-11AF-300 production engine.

In March 1958, Yakovlev was instructed to initiate development of a new two-seat supersonic tactical bomber, a further refinement of the prolific Yak-25 series. The powerplants for the aircraft were to be 11,864-lb (51.96-kN) thrust afterburning versions of the Tumanskii R-11, effectively the engine used by the Yak-25RV reconnaissance platform.

The resulting Yak-129 prototype represented a hybrid of the Yak-26 and Yak-27R, but incorporated several new features, notably the R-11A-300 engines, based on the R-11-300 units employed by MiG-21 prototypes. The Yak-129's wing structure was similar to that of the Yak-27R, but introduced increased chord, while the fuselage was like that of the Yak-26 but with an extra bay inserted. The undercarriage was also based on that of the Yak-26, although it could 'kneel' to increase AoA during take-off.

First prototype

The first prototype Yak-129 completed its flight test programme during May-October 1958, proving to be perhaps the most impressive of Yakovlev's twin-jets, and in particular displaying excellent take-off and landing characteristics. This aircraft was followed by two additional prototypes, which carried the production standard R-11AF-300 engine, its output of 13,338 lb (59.31 kN) representing a threefold increase in thrust compared to the original Yak-120.

Following the completion of testing in early 1960, by which time the aircraft had gained a fully powered tailplane, series production was ordered. The initial production Yak-28B (ASCC 'Brewer-A') was identical to the second prototype, but incorporated operational equipment including the RBP-3 navigation and blind-bombing radar, installed aft of the forward undercarriage unit. The OBP-115 optical bombsight was installed in the underside of the glazed nose, while jettisonable fuel tanks were added underwing.

Following completion of the 37th aircraft, production switched to the definitive Yak-28I ('Brewer-C') version in 1962, and both types entered front-line Frontal Aviation service, replacing the Il-28. In order to enhance take-off and general performance in icy conditions, twin underfuselage rocket bottles and anti-skid nosewheels were both standard on later Yak-28s.

The Yak-28L ('Brewer-B') was closely related to the Yak-28I, and was developed in order to overcome bomb-loading difficulties encountered with the earlier machines. The obstructive underfuselage radome was removed, and the radar replaced with the DBS-2S *Lotos* navigation system. Although it was easier to arm and refuel the Yak-28L, decreasing turnaround time, the aircraft was now dependent on signals received from ground stations, reducing operational radius, and prohibiting low-level attacks. Completing tests in late 1962, the Yak-28L was re-engined with uprated R-11AF2-300 engines and new anti-surge air intakes

Replacing the Yak-28B in production, the Yak-28I 'Brewer-C' became the most important bomber version, and also introduced a new OPB-16 optical sight within the reconfigured nose.

Typical missile armament for the Yak-28P were the Bisnovat R-8M1 (IR-guided) and R-8M2 (radar-guided) AAMs (NATO AA-3 'Anab'). This Yak-28MP, however, also carries R-3S (AA-2 'Atoll') short-range IR-guided AAMs on the inner wing hardpoints.

and fully controllable exhaust nozzles. From 1962, 111 Yak-28Ls were delivered, its absence of radar making it one of the fastest bomber versions.

Meanwhile, the improved Yak-28I had entered production, and became the principal bomber type, with 223 delivered, all with R-11AF2-300 engines and definitive nacelles. The aircraft's designation was taken from the new *Initsiativa*-2 navigation and blind-bombing radar, occupying an extra fuselage bay, and operating in conjunction with an AP-28K autopilot to increase bombing accuracy. The new systems enabled the Yak-28I crew to search for and engage targets over land and sea, remaining independent of any other form of guidance.

Interceptor development

The basis of the Yak-28P ('Firebar') interceptor was the K-8M complex, comprising the *Oryol*-D radar, electronic links and cockpit displays, and the R-8M family of AAMs with 5 to 7.60 mile (8–12 km) range. Development was swift, as much of the armament system had been tested by the Su-11. The bomb bay was given over to fuel, guns were deleted, the airframe structure restressed and the radar was carried in a new pointed radome. The navigator/WSO was seated behind the pilot under a tandem pressurised canopy. A *Lazur* beam/beacon receiver provided guidance in adverse weather conditions. First flown in 1960, the R-11AF2-300-engined Yak-28P had an active career with the VVS, operating in particular from the shorter runways of the Arctic regions. A total of 435 aircraft was produced from 1962 to 1967, with the final aircraft delivered to Yak-28MP standard, with R-3S capability, *Oryol*-DP radar in a reconfigured radome and uprated R-13F-300 engines, providing blistering performance: a maximum speed of 1,491 mph (2400 km/h), and a service ceiling of 55,774 ft (17000 m) with four underwing air-to-air missiles.

Recce and EW

In 1961, Yakovlev began development of an improved reconnaissance aircraft, based on the Yak-28 airframe, in order to replace the Yak-27R. Design was based on the Yak-28I, with a modified, fully glazed navigator's station, raised pilot's canopy, increased fuel load and a deleted bomb bay enabling the installation of new sensors.

A modified *Initsiativa*-2R radar was carried, and three sensor compartments between this installation and the rear undercarriage unit could mount any of five payloads configured for low-altitude day, continuous image, IR linescan and high-altitude topography or night photography work. The fifth unit was an Elint system. After intensive evaluation, a total of 183 Yak-28R ('Brewer-D') aircraft was built until 1970.

In order to fulfil the defence-suppression role, the Yak-28R-derived Yak-28PP ('Brewer-E') was developed in 1970. Gun and reconnaissance equipment were replaced by a radio-electronic warfare complex, the main active jammer stations being served by two blade antennas under the engine nacelles. A chaff-dispensing system was also added. The Yak-28PP had a Doppler radar, linked to a computer to assist accurate navigation. The Yak-28PP had the longest term of service of any 'Brewer' variant, remaining in use into the 1990s.

The first dedicated dual-control trainer for the Yakovlev twin-jet series was the Yak-28U, the prototype of which was completed in 1962. Based on the original short-type fuselage, the Yak-28U ('Maestro') featured a redesigned nose, with the navigator's station replaced by a simple housing for the instructor's cockpit. All armament was deleted. After completion of evaluation in 1964, a total of 183 such trainers was built.

Above: The Yak-28R prototype was unveiled in early 1963, and undertook testing at Akhtubinsk until August. Many 'Brewer-Ds' were modified to other versions during or after production, and the type enjoyed a long career.

Right: The Yak-28U, represented by this pre-production example, had a 297-Imp gal (1350-litre) bomb bay fuel tank, and the original R-11AF-300 engines with their short oval inlets.

Glossary of Abbreviations

AAA Anti-Aircraft Artillery
A&AEE Aeroplane & Armament Experimental Establishment
AAM Air-to-Air Aissile
AB Air Base
ACC Air Combat Command
ACCS Airborne Command and Control Squadron
ACM Air Combat Manoeuvering
ACW Air Control Wing
ADC Air Defense Command
AEW Airborne Early Warning
AEW&C Airborne Early Warning and Control
AFB Air Force Base
AFRes Air Force Reserve
AFSC Air Force Systems Command
ALCM Air-Launched Cruise Missile
AMARC Aerospace Maintenance and Regeneration Center
AMI Aeronautica Militare Italiana (Italian air force)
AMP Avionics Modernisation Program
ANG Air National Guard
APU Auxiliary Power Unit
ARM Anti-Radar Missile
ARS Air Refueling Squadron
ARW Air Refueling Wing
ASM Air-to-Surface Missile
AWACS Airborne Warning and Control System

BVR Beyond Visual Range
BW Bomb Wing

CALCM Conventional Air-Launched Cruise Missile
CAP Combat Air Patrol
CAS Close Air Support
CBU Cluster Bomb Unit
CCTS Combat Crew Training Squadron
CEAM Centre d'Experimentations Aériennes Militaires
CFE Conventional Forces in Europe
CFT Conformal Fuel Tank
CinCLANT Commander in Chief, Atlantic Fleet
CinCPAC Commander in Chief, Pacific Fleet
COD Carrier Onboard Delivery
COIN Counter-Insurgency
CRT Cathode Ray Tube
CSAR Combat Search and Rescue
CTOL Conventional Take-Off and Landing

EC Escadron de Chasse
ECCM Electronic Counter-Countermeasures
ECM Electronic Countermeasures
ECS Electronic Combat Squadron
ECT Escadron de chasse et de transformation
ECW Electronic Combat Wing
EDCA Escadron de Détection et de Contrôle Aéroportés
Elint Electronic Intelligence
EO Electro-Optical
ERV Escadron de Ravitaillement en Vol
ESM Electronic Support Measures

FAA Fleet Air Arm
FAC Forward Air Control/Controller
FADEC Full Authority Digital Engine Control
FEAF Far East Air Force (UK)
FEAF Far East Air Forces (US)
FIS Fighter Interceptor Squadron
FLIR Forward-Looking Infra-Red
FMF Fleet Marine Force
FRADU Fleet Requirements Air Direction Unit
FRS Fleet Replacement Squadron
FS Fighter Squadron
FSD Full Scale Development
FTS Flying Training School
FW Fighter Wing
FWS Fighter Weapons Squadron

GE Groupement Ecole

HARM High Speed Anti-Radiation Missile
HDD Head-Down Display
HOTAS Hands On Throttle and Stick
HUD head-up display
HVAR High-Velocity Aircraft Rocket

ICBM Intercontinental Ballistic Missile
IDF/AF Israeli Defence Force/Air Force
IFF Identification Friend of Foe
IFIS Integrated Flight Information System
IFTU Intensive Flying Trials Unit
INAS Indian Naval Air Squadron
INS Internal Navigation System
IOC Initial Operational Capability
IR Infra-Red
IRLS Infra-Red Linescan
JASDF Japanese Air Self-Defence Force
JDAM Joint Direct Attack Munition
J-STARS Joint Surveillance Target Attack Radar System
JTIDS Joint Tactical Information Distribution System

LABS Low-Altitude Bombing System
LANTIRN Low-Altitude Navigation and Targeting Infra-Red for Night
LGB Laser-Guided Bomb
LIFT Lead-In Fighter Trainer
LLLTV Low-Light-Level Television

MAC Military Airlift Command
MAD Magnetic-Anomaly Detector
MATS Military Air Transport Service
MAW Military Airlift Wing
MEAF Middle East Air Force
MFD Multi-Function Display
MSIP Multi-Stage Improvement Program
MTI Moving Target Indication

NACA National Advisory Committee for Aeronautics
NAS Naval Air Squadron (UK)
NAS Naval Air Station (US)
NASA National Aeronautics and Space Administration
NASARR North American Search And Ranging Radar
NEAF Near East Air Force
NVG Night Vision Goggles

OCU Operational Conversion Unit

PACAF Pacific Air Forces
PGM Precision-Guided Munition

QRA Quick Reaction Alert
RAAF Royal Australian Air Force
RAF Royal Air Force
RAG
RATO Rocket-Assisted Take-off
RCAF Royal Canadian Air Force
RHAWS Radar Homing And Warning System
RNZAF Royal New Zealand Air Force
RoCAF Republic of China Air Force
RTU Replacement Training Unit
RWR Radar Warning Receiver

SAC Strategic Air Command
SACEUR Supreme Allied Commander Europe
SACLANT Supreme Allied Commander Atlantic
SAR Search and Rescue
SAR Synthetic-Aperture Radar
SEAD Suppression of Enemy Air Defences
Sigint Signals Intelligence
SLAM Standoff Land Attack Missile
SLAR Side-Looking Airborne Radar
SLEP Service Life Extension Program
SRAM Short-Range Attack Missile
SRW Strategic Reconnaissance Wing
STOVL Short Take-off and Vertical Landing

TAC Tactical Air Command
TACAMO Take Charge And Move Out
TACAN Tactical Aid to Navigation
TAF Tactical Air Force
TAW Tactical Airlift Wing
TFR Terrain-Following Radar
TFS Tactical Fighter Squadron
TFTS Tactical Fighter Training Squadron
TFW Tactical Fighter Wing
TISEO
TNI-AU Tentara Nasional Indonesia – Angkatan Udara (Indonesian air force)
TRG Tactical Reconnaissance Group
TRW Tactical Reconnaissance Wing
TTW Tactical Training Wing
TWU Tactical Weapons Unit

USAAF United States Army Air Force
USAF United States Air Force
USAFE United States Air Forces in Europe
USMC United States Marine Corps
USN United States Navy

VOR VHF omni-directional radio range
V/STOL vertical and/or short take-off and landing
VTOL vertical take-off and landing

Index